Mathematics for Quantum Chemistry

Mathematics

for

Quantum

Chemistry

JAY MARTIN ANDERSON
Bryn Mawr College

W. A. Benjamin, Inc.

NEW YORK   AMSTERDAM

1966

Mathematics for Quantum Chemistry

Library of Congress Catalog Card Number: 66–13997
Manufactured in the United States of America

*The manuscript was put into production on July 23, 1965;
this volume was published on January 3, 1966*

W. A. BENJAMIN, INC.
New York, New York 10016

With the fondest of memories, to my first class:

BARBARA, CANDY, ELLEN, LYNNE, MARCIA, ROBERTA, AND ROWENA

Preface

Recent trends in chemical education force students of chemistry into contact with the applications of quantum mechanics at an earlier and earlier point in their development. This direction of undergraduate chemistry curricula is important for several reasons: the wealth of physico-chemical information which is gleaned from molecular spectroscopy and other techniques which are based on quantum mechanics; the trend of descriptive chemistry to rely on concepts taken from quantum mechanics; the growing concern in theoretical chemistry to adequately explain molecular phenomena by means of quantum mechanics.

The rush to introduce the student to these bold and exciting studies often leaves him uncomfortable in the mathematical formalism in which these studies are couched, unsure of the connection between the conventional Newtonian world to which he is accustomed and the world of molecular phenomena, and unable to apply his new-found theoretical knowledge to problems of molecular structure and motion.

In the present work I shall attempt to present only two main topics from mathematics, and two from physics. These are the calculus of orthogonal functions and the algebra of vector spaces from mathematics, and the Lagrangian and Hamiltonian formulation of classical mechanics and its applications to molecular motion from physics. I have selected these four topics because of their relevance to modern quantum chemistry, especially in the application of quantum mechanics to molecular spectroscopy. This emphasis on molecular spectroscopy betrays my personal interest and excitement in this growing and popular field of endeavor; it also eliminates from the pages of this brief book a consideration of other topics which may be equally stimulating to my colleagues and to their students. Relativity, electricity, magnetism, and radiation physics were eliminated because they are generally better treated elsewhere and in greater depth than this work allows; similarly, group theory and differential equations, including approximate methods of solution, are left to other treatises.

This book attempts to lay down a central core of physical and mathematical background for quantum chemistry in general, but for molecular spectroscopy in particular. It assumes a knowledge of calculus through partial derivatives and multiple integration (usually about one and one-half years), a year of physics, and chemistry through a year of physical chemistry. This material has been used as the basis of a one-semester course at Bryn Mawr College entitled "Applied Mathematics for Chemists" for students with approximately the indicated background; this course immediately precedes the first course in quantum mechanics.

The author is indebted to Addison-Wesley Publishing Co. for permission to quote from their publications, and W. A. Benjamin, Inc. for their continued help and encouragement.

JAY MARTIN ANDERSON

Bryn Mawr, Pennsylvania
October 1965

Contents

Preface, vii

1 Introduction, 1

2 Orthogonal Functions, 6

3   *Linear Algebra, 48*

4   *Classical Mechanics, 105*

5   *Conclusion, 136*

Appendix   Mathematical Background and Bibliography, 143

Answers to Problems, 147

Index, 151

1

Introduction

1–1 EIGENVALUE PROBLEMS IN QUANTUM MECHANICS

The mathematics and physics that are relevant to quantum chemistry are, almost without exception, oriented toward the solution of a particular kind of problem, the calculation of properties of a molecular system from the fundamental properties (charge, mass) of the particles composing the system. A good example of this is the calculation of the *energy* of the electrons in a molecule, using only the charge of the electron, Planck's constant, and so forth. The reader is probably already aware of the nature of the answer to this problem. There are a number of discrete values for the energy which the electrons in the molecule can assume up to a point, but higher values for the electronic energy occur in a continuous range. These energy values are shown qualitatively in Fig. 1–1. Quantum mechanics does provide the result that some physical quantities may take on only *some* values, not *all* values, as experiments indicated. The allowed values for a physical quantity are called *eigenvalues*, from the German for *characteristic values*. A particular physical quantity may assume an eigenvalue from a continuum, or perhaps from a finite or infinite discrete set of eigenvalues. The energy of an atom, for instance, may take on one of an

1

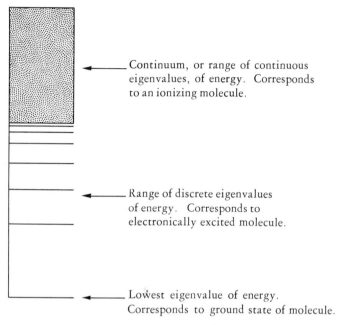

Continuum, or range of continuous
eigenvalues, of energy. Corresponds
to an ionizing molecule.

Range of discrete eigenvalues
of energy. Corresponds to
electronically excited molecule.

Lowest eigenvalue of energy.
Corresponds to ground state of molecule.

Figure 1–1   Eigenvalues of the energy of a molecule.

infinite number of discrete values, as well as values from a higher-
lying range of continuous eigenvalues, called the *continuum*. More
often than not, chemistry is concerned with the discrete eigenvalues
of a quantity, rather than its continuum of eigenvalues.

The mathematical problem of finding the eigenvalues of a quantity
is called an *eigenvalue problem;* it is usually cast in the form of an
equation called an *eigenvalue equation*. An eigenvalue equation for a
physical quantity Q has the deceptively simple appearance

$$Qf = qf \tag{1–1}$$

In this equation, f is a function, called the *eigenfunction* for the quantity Q, with the eigenvalue q. The element Q is called an *operator*,
and the statement Qf tells us to change the function f into a new
function, according to a set of instructions implicit in the definition
of the operator Q. The eigenvalue equation, Eq. 1–1, then informs

us that, by applying these "instructions" of the operator $\mathbb{Q}$ to f, we get merely a multiple, q, of the function f. The function $\mathbb{Q}f$ differs from the function f by a multiplicative constant q. It may very well be the case that several eigenfunctions have the same eigenvalue; that is, $\mathbb{Q}f_1 = qf_1$, $\mathbb{Q}f_2 = qf_2$, and so forth. If this is the case, the eigenvalue q is said to be *degenerate*, and the number of eigenfunctions that have the same eigenvalue is called the *degree of degeneracy*.

Operators may simply be numbers or functions; for example, the operator $\mathfrak{X}$ may be defined by the instruction "multiply the operand function by x"; thus, $\mathfrak{X} x^2 = x^3$. On the other hand, operators may be more complex than just numbers or functions. For example, the student has already used the operator (although probably not by that name) Δ, which means, or is defined by the instructions, "evaluate the change in." For example, if we operate Δ on the thermodynamic function H, the enthalpy, we get a new function ΔH, the change in the enthalpy, $\Delta H = H_2 - H_1$. Another operator that is familiar is d/dx, meaning, "evaluate the derivative with respect to x."

It is the job of quantum mechanics to tell us how to form operators corresponding to the physical quantities which we wish to measure. Our task for the moment will be to learn how to solve the eigenvalue equations for such operators, and especially the vocabulary and concepts that are used to discuss the solutions. Quantum mechanics itself, however, grew up from two different points of view, which represent two analogous mathematical formulations of eigenvalue problems.

The first of these points of view is the *wave mechanics* of Schrödinger In wave mechanics, operators are differential expressions, such as the operator d/dx referred to above, and the eigenvalue equation then takes the form of a differential equation, and relies on the calculus for its solution. The second formulation is the *matrix mechanics* of Heisenberg, in which operators are represented by algebraic entities called *matrices;* instead of a function in the eigenvalue equation, the matrix operator operates on a *vector* ξ to transform ξ into a vector parallel to ξ, but q times as long:

$$\mathbb{Q}\xi = q\xi \qquad (1-2)$$

Equation 1–2 is the matrix-mechanical formulation of the eigenvalue problem. Matrices and vectors are defined and discussed in detail in Chapter 3. As in Eq. 1–1, q is the eigenvalue of the quantity Q, ξ is the *eigenvector*, and Q is the operator represented as a matrix. The solution of this form of the eigenvalue problem relies on algebra.

These apparently different mathematical and physical approaches to quantum mechanical problems are really deeply interrelated; the work of Dirac shows the underlying equivalence of the two points of view, as well as of the corresponding mathematical techniques.

1–2 EIGENVALUE PROBLEMS IN CLASSICAL MECHANICS

We have briefly discussed the role of eigenvalue equations in quantum mechanics. But a number of problems of classical mechanics may also be expressed in a simple and meaningful way as eigenvalue problems. Among these are the problems of the vibrations and rotations of a mechanical system, such as a molecule. These physical problems are of importance to the chemist concerned with molecular motion and spectroscopy. In vibrations, the normal modes and frequencies of oscillation appear as eigenvectors and eigenvalues; in rotations, the principal axes and moments of inertia emerge from an eigenvalue problem. It should be noted, however, that a correct description of these systems on the molecular level nearly always requires quantum mechanics, not classical mechanics.

1–3 SCOPE OF THIS BOOK

With our course thus determined by the kinds of problems we wish to be able to set up, solve, and understand, we shall proceed first to a study of a certain class of functions germane to eigenfunction problems, then to a number of aspects of vector algebra and matrix algebra, finally to a synthesis of the two points of view of eigenvalue problems. We shall conclude with a study of classical mechanics to see how the vibrations of a mechanical system, such as a molecule, may be formulated as an eigenvalue problem. We shall also attempt to formulate Newtonian mechanics in such a way that the connection to quantum mechanics is clear.

Along the way, we shall learn some methods of solving eigenvalue problems, and take up applications of interest in chemistry. Our emphasis throughout will be primarily on concepts, secondarily on methods, and only lastly on the detailed proofs of the mathematical theorems. At the end of each chapter, a set of problems is given. Answers and hints for solution for many of the problems are found at the back of the book.

Problem

1. Find the eigenfunctions of the operator d/dx.

2

Orthogonal Functions

Two properties are, almost without exception, possessed by the eigenfunctions of operators corresponding to important physical quantities: *orthogonality* and *normality*. The purpose of this chapter is to develop these concepts in detail and to illustrate a number of their applications. Of primary usefulness is the idea of an *expansion in orthogonal functions*. As an example of this technique, we shall examine the *Fourier series* in some detail. We shall also learn how to construct orthogonal functions by the *Schmidt orthogonalization procedure*, and how orthogonal functions arise from the solution of particular differential equations. To illustrate the latter concepts, we shall investigate the properties of the *Legendre polynomials*, and briefly mention other of the important "special functions" which arise in quantum chemistry. A brief discussion of some of the elements of the calculus and of complex variables are given in the Appendix. The reader would be wise to check his familiarity with this material before advancing into the present chapter.

2-1 INTRODUCTORY CONCEPTS:
ORTHOGONALITY AND NORMALIZATION

We may best begin our discussion of orthogonal functions by reviewing the concept of *function*. The concept of function has three essential ingredients. We agree first to define a function on a particu-

6

lar region of the number scale, say, from *a* to *b*. Second, we agree that there exists a variable (say, *x*) that can independently assume values in the region from *a* to *b*. Third, we agree by some prescribed rule that for any value of *x* there exists a *definite* value of *y*. Then we say that *y* is a function of *x* on the range $a \leq x \leq b$. This definition may be modified in a number of ways—so as to include more than one independent variable—but these three essential ingredients persist: an independent variable; a range on which the independent variable assumes its values; a dependent variable related to the independent variable by a prescribed rule.

The simplest way of notating the statement "*y* is a function of *x*" is to write $y = y(x)$. This notation is compact, yet may be misleading. The left side of the equation is simply the name of a variable—we do not know it is the dependent variable until we see the right side of the equation. The right side uses the letter *y* again, but here the symbol $y(\ )$ means something different than just the name of the variable. The meaning of $y(\ )$ is that *y* is a dependent variable whose value may be found by some prescribed rule from the quantity inside the parentheses. Left out of the notation $y = y(x)$ is the interval, or range, of the independent variable *x* for which the functional relationship is defined. This is not always of importance in elementary considerations of the idea of function, but it is of supreme importance to the notion of expansion of a function. Hence, we introduce a definition.

Definition *Expansion interval* (or, simply, *interval*). The expansion interval is the range of the independent variable assumed by the functions under consideration. This does not imply that the function may not be defined for other values of the independent variable; we just decline to consider those other values.

The expansion interval is usually notated [*a*, *b*], meaning that the independent variable *x* is allowed values on the range $a \leq x \leq b$. We proceed now to four definitions in rapid succession.

Definition *Inner product.* The inner product of the two (in general, complex-valued) functions *f* and *g* of a continuous variable on their expansion interval [*a*, *b*] is

$$\langle f \mid g \rangle = \int_a^b f(x)^* g(x)\, dx \ . \tag{2-1}$$

The inner product of two functions is defined *on their expansion interval*. The inner product is notated by some authors (f, g), but this can easily be confused with the notation for two-dimensional coordinates or for an open interval. We shall use the notation $\langle f \mid g \rangle$. The order is quite important:

$$\langle g \mid f \rangle = \int g(x)^* f(x)\, dx = \left(\int f(x)^* g(x)\, dx \right)^*$$
$$= \langle f \mid g \rangle^* \qquad (2\text{-}2)$$

For real-valued functions, the order is not important. Equation 2–2 illustrates an important feature of the inner product that arises again and again: "turning around," or *transposing an inner product gives the complex conjugate of that inner product*. Constants may be removed at will from the inner product symbol: if b and c are (complex) numbers, $\langle bf \mid cg \rangle = b^* c \langle f \mid g \rangle$.

The inner product is a concept of no small significance. It has a geometrical analog, that of the *dot product* or *scalar product* of vectors that may already be familiar, which we shall discuss in Chapter 3.

In analogy to the geometrical property of perpendicularity of vectors, both functions and vectors afford the sweeping and general concept of *orthogonality*.

Definition   Two functions, $f(x)$ and $g(x)$, are said to be *orthogonal* on the interval $[a, b]$ if their inner product on $[a, b]$ is zero:

$$\langle f \mid g \rangle = \int_a^b f^* g = 0 = \int_a^b g^* f = \langle g \mid f \rangle \qquad (2\text{-}3)$$

If the inner product is to be zero, it does not matter which function "comes first" in the inner product, so the orthogonality of f and g may be expressed by either $\langle f \mid g \rangle = 0$ or $\langle g \mid f \rangle = 0$. The perpendicularity of two vectors is related to this definition of orthogonality: two vectors are perpendicular if their dot product is zero.

Definition   The *norm* of a function on the interval $[a, b]$ is the inner product of the function with itself, and may be symbolized by N:

$$N(f) = \langle f \mid f \rangle = \int_a^b f^* f \qquad (2\text{-}4)$$

The norm of a function is a real, positive quantity; it is analogous to the square of the length of a vector. That the norm is real and positive may be easily demonstrated by

$$f^*f = (\operatorname{Re} f - i \operatorname{Im} f)(\operatorname{Re} f + i \operatorname{Im} f) = (\operatorname{Re} f)^2 + (\operatorname{Im} f)^2 \quad (2\text{-}5)$$

which is positive definite. Then the integral of f^*f, which gives the norm of f, is also positive definite. The positiveness of the norm is of use to us at once.

> **Definition** A function is said to be *normalized*[1] if its norm is one; that is, if $\langle f \mid f \rangle = 1$.

Since the norm of a function on a particular interval is always simply a positive real number, we can always form a multiple of a given function which is normalized. Suppose f has a norm N. Then the function $f/N^{1/2}$ will have a norm of one, since

$$\left\langle \frac{f}{N^{1/2}} \,\middle|\, \frac{f}{N^{1/2}} \right\rangle = \frac{1}{N}\langle f \mid f \rangle = \frac{N}{N} = 1 \quad (2\text{-}6)$$

The process of dividing a function by the square root of its norm is called *normalizing the function*, or, sometimes, normalizing the function to unity.

Let us use the five definitions we have introduced thus far in some examples. Suppose we consider functions defined on the interval $[-1, 1]$. As an example of the computation of an inner product, let us evaluate $\langle x \mid x^2 \rangle$.

$$\langle x \mid x^2 \rangle = \int_{-1}^{+1} x^* x^2 \, dx = \int_{-1}^{+1} x^3 \, dx = \left. \frac{x^4}{4} \right|_{-1}^{+1} = 0 \quad (2\text{-}7)$$

The computation of this simple inner product gives zero. We therefore may state that, on $[-1, 1]$, x and x^2 are orthogonal functions. Notice the importance of specifying the interval: on the interval $[0, 1]$, the inner product $\langle x \mid x^2 \rangle$ is

$$\langle x \mid x^2 \rangle = \int_{0}^{1} x^3 = \left. \frac{x^4}{4} \right|_{0}^{1} = \frac{1}{4} \quad (2\text{-}8)$$

---

[1] Normalization to unity is not the only possible normalization, but it is the most common, and will be used throughout this book.

and the functions are not orthogonal. The expansion interval must be specified before a statement about orthogonality can be made. The same is true for normality. On $[-1, 1]$, the function x has the norm

$$N(x) = \langle x \mid x \rangle = \int_{-1}^{+1} x^2 = \tfrac{2}{3} \qquad (2\text{-}9)$$

but on the interval $[0, 1]$, the norm

$$N(x) = \langle x \mid x \rangle = \int_{0}^{1} x^2 = \tfrac{1}{3} \qquad (2\text{-}10)$$

One very useful property of functions may be introduced at this point. Very often, the integrals which form inner products may be simplified by using symmetry properties of the functions. This symmetry may be expressed by two definitions.

Definition   An *even function* is a function for which $f(x) = f(-x)$; an *odd function* is a function for which $f(x) = -f(-x)$.

Evenness or oddness is easily pictured. Figure 2–1a shows a graph of the function $f(x) = x^2$, which is even, since $(x)^2 = (-x)^2$. Graphically speaking, the plot of $f(x)$ is symmetrical about the ordinate axis. Figure 2–1b shows the function $f(x) = x^3$, which is odd, since $(x)^3 = -(-x)^3$. The plot to the right is the negative of the plot to the left of the ordinate axis. The integrals of even or odd functions are especially simple *if the interval is symmetric*. The following theorem results.

Theorem   The integral of an even function on a symmetric interval is twice the integral on the half-interval; the integral of an odd function on a symmetric interval is zero.

This theorem is illustrated graphically in Fig. 2–2. It may be proven by dividing the full symmetric interval into two half-intervals:

$$\int_{-a}^{a} (\text{even}) = \int_{-a}^{0} (\text{even}) + \int_{0}^{a} (\text{even}) \qquad (2\text{-}11)$$

But, since an even function of x is the same as the even function of $-x$, we may replace the integral over the negative half-interval

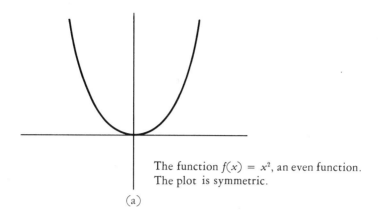

The function $f(x) = x^2$, an even function.
The plot is symmetric.

(a)

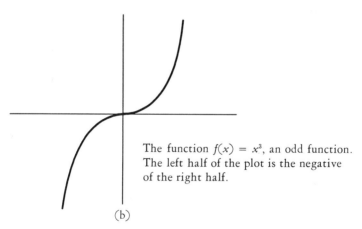

The function $f(x) = x^3$, an odd function.
The left half of the plot is the negative
of the right half.

(b)

Figure 2–1   Even and odd functions.

$[-a, 0]$ by the integral over the positive half-interval $[0, a]$ without
changing the function:

$$\int_{-a}^{a} (\text{even}) = \int_{0}^{a} (\text{even}) + \int_{0}^{a} (\text{even}) = 2\int_{0}^{a} (\text{even}) \quad (2\text{–}12)$$

which proves the first part of the theorem.   The second part is as
simple:

$$\int_{-a}^{a} (\text{odd}) = \int_{-a}^{0} (\text{odd}) + \int_{0}^{a} (\text{odd})$$

$$= - \int_{0}^{a} (\text{odd}) + \int_{0}^{a} (\text{odd}) = 0 \qquad (2\text{-}13)$$

For odd functions, the integral over the negative half-interval may be replaced by an integral over the positive half-interval if the sign of the function is changed. Equation 2–13 gives the second part of the theorem.

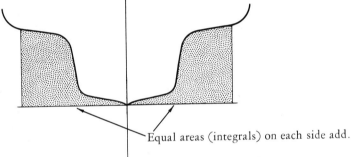

Equal areas (integrals) on each side add.

(a) The integral of an even function on a symmetric interval is twice the integral on the half-interval.

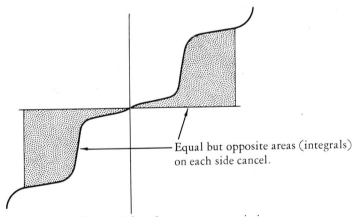

Equal but opposite areas (integrals) on each side cancel.

(b) The integral of an odd function on a symmetric interval is zero.

Figure 2–2   Integrals of even and odd functions.

Application of this theorem to the calculation of inner products on symmetric intervals gives another result.

> **Theorem** On the symmetric interval $[-a, a]$, the inner product of an odd function with an odd function, or of an even function with an even function, is not zero, and may be calculated by twice the inner product over either half-interval $[-a, 0]$ or $[0, a]$; the inner product of an even function with an odd function is zero, no matter what the form of the function.

In the foregoing five definitions, we have considered only two arbitrary functions. However, the power and usefulness of the definitions established above really become apparent when we consider *sets of functions*. A set of functions is a collection of functions of the *same variable*, defined on the *same interval*, and *characterized by a rule* for figuring out all the functions in the set. For example, all the powers of x constitute a set of functions. We write this set, using braces, as $\{x^n\}$, indicating all these functions of x: $x^0 = 1$, $x^1 = x$, x^2, x^3, x^4, and so on. The general exponent n indicates the rule for figuring out each member of the set of functions. To be complete, we must specify the interval under consideration, and the values that n, often called the *index*, may take on, like this: "the set of functions $\{x^n\}$, on $[-1, 1]$, for $n = 0$ and all positive integers."

To round out our description of sets of functions which are useful in quantum chemistry, we introduce three new definitions.

> **Definition** A *complete set of functions*, $\{F_i\}$, is a set of functions such that any other function f may be expressed as a linear combination of members of the set $\{F_i\}$ on a prescribed expansion interval to whatever precision may be desired.[2]

If the set $\{F_i\}$ is complete, then we may expand f in terms of the functions F_i like this:

$$f(x) = a_1 F_1(x) + a_2 F_2(x) + \cdots + a_n F_n(x) + \cdots$$
$$= \sum_{n=1}^{\infty} a_n F_n(x) \tag{2-14}$$

---

[2] The uniform continuity of the functions of the set $\{F_i\}$ and of the function f is tacitly assumed here, and throughout; this definition could be made more rigorous if such concepts were used, but this is not of importance in quantum chemistry.

Generally speaking, proving that a set of functions is complete is quite difficult, and for our purposes we shall consider only such sets of functions which are known to be complete, and not consider completeness proofs per se.

> **Definition**   An *orthogonal set of functions*, or a *set of orthogonal functions*, is a set of functions each of which is orthogonal on a prescribed interval to all other members of the set.

That is, the set $\{F_i\}$ is an orthogonal set if every member is orthogonal to every other member:

$$\langle F_j \mid F_k \rangle = 0 \tag{2-15}$$

for all j and k such that $j \neq k$. Such a set of functions, which we shall consider in the third section of this chapter, is the set $\{\sin nx, \cos nx\}$, on $[-\pi, \pi]$, for n zero or positive integers. The proof of the orthogonality of these functions is one of the problems at the end of this chapter; notice that it involves three separate proofs:

$$\langle \sin nx \mid \sin mx \rangle = 0 \qquad n \neq m \tag{2-16a}$$

$$\langle \cos nx \mid \cos mx \rangle = 0 \qquad n \neq m \tag{2-16b}$$

$$\langle \sin nx \mid \cos nx \rangle = 0 \qquad \text{for all } n \tag{2-16c}$$

Finally, we combine the definitions of orthogonality and normalization.

> **Definition**   An *orthonormal set of functions* is an orthogonal set of functions, each of which is normalized.

That is, the set $\{F_i\}$ is orthonormal if

$$\langle F_j \mid F_k \rangle = 0 \qquad \text{for all } j \neq k \tag{2-17a}$$

and

$$\langle F_j \mid F_j \rangle = 1 \qquad \text{for all } j \tag{2-17b}$$

The pair of equations 2–17a and 2–17b occurs so often in discussing orthonormal functions that a special symbol has been introduced to combine Eqs. 2–17a and 2–17b. The *Kronecker delta symbol*, or *Kronecker delta*, or *delta symbol* δ_{ij} has the meaning $\delta_{ij} = 0$ for $i \neq j$, $\delta_{ij} = 1$ for $i = j$. If we use the Kronecker delta symbol, the condition for orthonormality, Eqs. 2–17a and 2–17b may be simply expressed as

$$\langle F_j \mid F_k \rangle = \delta_{jk} \qquad \text{for all } j \text{ and } k \qquad (2\text{–}18)$$

In this chapter, orthonormal sets will be indicated by lower case Greek letters, such as $\{\phi_i\}$.

In this section we have defined a number of terms of importance, inner product, orthogonality, norm and normalization, completeness, and orthogonal and orthonormal sets of functions; we have also used the property of evenness or oddness of functions to simplify integrals over symmetric intervals.

2–2 EXPANSION IN TERMS OF ORTHONORMAL FUNCTIONS

In this section we shall learn how to expand a given function, on a prescribed interval, in terms of a set of orthonormal functions. Since the operations that occur in the calculation which follows occur often in discussions of orthonormal functions and later in discussions of orthonormal vectors, the calculation is set aside from the text.

$$f(x) = \sum_i a_i \phi_i(x) \qquad (2\text{–}19)$$

$$\phi_j(x)^* f(x) = \sum_i a_i \phi_j(x)^* \phi_i(x) \qquad (2\text{–}20)$$

$$\int \phi_j(x)^* f(x)\, dx = \sum_i a_i \int \phi_j(x)^* \phi_i(x)\, dx \qquad (2\text{–}21)$$

$$\langle \phi_j \mid f \rangle = \sum_i a_i \langle \phi_j \mid \phi_i \rangle \qquad (2\text{–}22)$$

$$\langle \phi_j \mid f \rangle = \sum_i a_i \delta_{ji} \qquad (2\text{–}23)$$

$$\langle \phi_j \mid f \rangle = a_j \qquad (2\text{–}24)$$

Equation 2–19 shows the expansion that we desire to use to express $f(x)$ on a particular expansion interval (not specified here) as a linear combination of the members of the set of orthonormal functions $\{\phi_i\}$.

Equation 2–20 gives the result of multiplying each side of the equation by $\phi_j(x)^*$, the complex conjugate of some member of the set $\{\phi_i\}$. Equation 2–21 gives the result of integrating both sides of Eq. 2–20 over the expansion interval. However, the result of Eqs. 2–20 and 2–21 is simply the formation of the inner product of ϕ_j (on the left) with Eq. 2–19 (on the right).

The definition of orthonormality is used in Eq. 2–23 to replace $\langle \phi_j \mid \phi_i \rangle$ with the Kronecker delta δ_{ji}.

Lastly, the sum over i on the right side of Eq. 2–23 is evaluated. If this sum were written out, it would look like this:

$$\sum_i a_i \delta_{ji} = a_1 \delta_{j1} + a_2 \delta_{j2} + \cdots + a_j \delta_{jj} + \cdots + a_n \delta_{jn} + \cdots$$

$$(2\text{–}25)$$

All the delta symbols but one are identically zero. The only one that is not zero is $\delta_{jj} = 1$. However, then the sum gives

$$\sum_i a_i \delta_{ji} = a_j \delta_{jj} = a_j \cdot 1 = a_j \qquad (2\text{–}26)$$

The use of the delta symbols, which in turn stems from the property of orthonormality, is the key to a simple evaluation of the coefficients a_i for the expansion in orthonormal functions. The evaluation of the sum in Eq. 2–23 follows a simple rule: *A sum involving the products of a Kronecker delta with other quantities "picks out" that term for which the subscripts of the Kronecker delta are identical; or only that term survives for which the subscripts are identical.*

Finally, Eq. 2–24 is a formula for calculating the expansion coefficients in an expansion of a function of a given interval in members of an orthonormal set, $a_j = \langle \phi_j \mid f \rangle$. The expansion coefficients may be complex numbers. The use of a letter subscript should not obscure the issue: if we needed a_1, we would evaluate $\langle \phi_1 \mid f \rangle$; if a_2, $\langle \phi_2 \mid f \rangle$; if a_{309}, $\langle \phi_{309} \mid f \rangle$, and so on. We shall work an example in depth in the following section.

We turn next to a question of practical importance. If an expansion in orthonormal functions is curtailed after a finite number of terms, what error is incurred? The answer to this question reveals a new property of the expansion coefficients: these coefficients minimize the error of a curtailed expansion. Denote the error after taking n terms by M_n. This error is evaluated[3] by

$$M_n = \int |f(x) - \sum_{j=1}^{n} b_j \phi_j|^2 \, dx \qquad (2\text{-}27)$$

that is, by the area under a plot of the square of the absolute value of the residual as a function of x. The integral is taken over the expansion interval. The meaning of M_n is illustrated graphically in Fig. 2-3. Since $c^*c = |c|^2$, we may write

$$M_n = \int \left[f^* - \sum_{j=1}^{n} b_j^* \phi_j^* \right] \left[f - \sum_{i=1}^{n} b_i \phi_i \right]$$

$$= \langle f \mid f \rangle - \sum_{j=1}^{n} b_j^* \langle \phi_j \mid f \rangle - \sum_{i=1}^{n} b_i \langle f \mid \phi_i \rangle$$

$$+ \sum_{i,\,j=1}^{n} b_j^* b_i \langle \phi_j \mid \phi_i \rangle \qquad (2\text{-}28)$$

Notice that a different summation index is used in each factor in Eq. 2-28. Summation indices are often referred to as *dummy indices*, since their *name alone* confers no special meaning. However, they must often be distinguished *by name* with care. For example,

$$\left(\sum_i c_i \phi_i \right) \left(\sum_i c_i \phi_i \right)$$

might casually be written

$$\sum_i c_i^2 \phi_i^2,$$

but this is not what the product connotes. If the sums are written out, $(c_1 \phi_1 + c_2 \phi_2 + \cdots)(c_1 \phi_1 + c_2 \phi_2 + \cdots)$ is equal to $c_1^2 \phi_1^2 + c_1 c_2 \phi_1 \phi_2 + c_2 c_1 \phi_2 \phi_1 + c_2^2 \phi_2^2 + \cdots$, which is quite different from

---

[3] This is the "least-squares" criterion for error. Others are also applicable. It should also be noted that the curtailed expansion will not be normalized if the total function is.

$$\sum_i c_i^2 \phi_i^2 = c_1^2 \phi_1^2 + c_2^2 \phi_2^2 + \cdots .$$

To ensure that the proper answer—the one with the cross terms—is

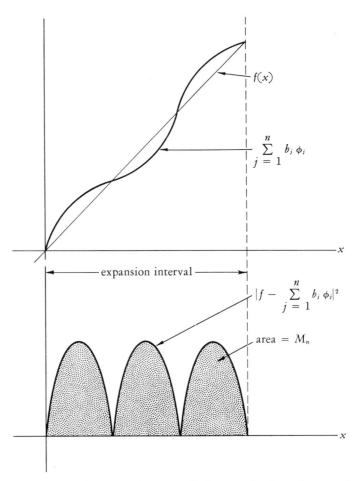

Figure 2-3 The error in a curtailed expansion in orthonormal functions is $M_n = \int |f - \sum_{j=1}^{n} b_j \phi_j|^2.$

written, we use the notation

$$\left(\sum_i c_i \phi_i\right)\left(\sum_j c_j \phi_j\right) = \sum_{i,j} c_i c_j \phi_i \phi_j.$$

In the last term of Eq. 2–28 we may substitute the Kronecker delta, because the set $\{\phi_i\}$ is orthonormal:

$$M_n = \langle f \mid f \rangle - \sum_{j=1}^{n} b_j^* \langle \phi_j \mid f \rangle - \sum_{i=1}^{n} b_i \langle f \mid \phi_i \rangle + \sum_{i,\,j=1}^{n} b_j^* b_i \delta_{ji}$$

$$= \langle f \mid f \rangle - \sum_{j=1}^{n} [b_j \langle f \mid \phi_j \rangle + b_j^* \langle \phi_j \mid f \rangle - b_j^* b_j] \qquad (2\text{–}29)$$

The sum over i involving only the delta symbol leaves just the sum over j, with the terms surviving for which $i = j$, and, since the name of the summation index is unimportant, each of the three terms has been expressed in the index j, and combined.

We would find the "best" set of coefficients for the expansion by minimizing the error M_n with respect to these coefficients, b_j. This involves two steps since the b_j have both a real and an imaginary part. This double-minimum problem may be expressed by requiring $\partial M_n/\partial b_j = \partial M_n/\partial(b_j^*) = 0$ for all j. Taking derivatives of Eq. 2–29, we obtain

$$\frac{\partial M_n}{\partial b_j} = 0 = -\langle f \mid \phi_j \rangle + b_j^* \qquad (2\text{–}30a)$$

$$\frac{\partial M_n}{\partial(b_j^*)} = 0 = -\langle \phi_j \mid f \rangle + b_j \qquad (2\text{–}30b)$$

These equations are complex conjugates of one another, and the "best" coefficients for the expansion, in the sense of minimizing the error, are given by

$$b_j = \langle \phi_j \mid f \rangle \qquad (2\text{–}31)$$

The coefficients given by Eq. 2–31 are, in fact, the coefficients that *must* be used in an expansion in orthonormal functions. Hence, $a_j = b_j = \langle \phi_j \mid f \rangle$ are not only the "right" coefficients (Eq. 2–24), but also the "best" (Eq. 2–31).

After substituting $a_j = b_j = \langle \phi_j \mid f \rangle$ into Eq. 2–29, we calculate the error to be

$$M_n = \langle f \mid f \rangle - \sum_{j=1}^{n} a_j a_j^* + a_j^* a_j - a_j^* a_j$$

$$= \langle f \mid f \rangle - \sum_{j=1}^{n} |a_j|^2 \qquad (2\text{--}32)$$

We conclude this section with an important relation concerning inner products, called the *expansion theorem*.

Theorem   The inner product $\langle f \mid g \rangle$ may be expanded in terms of an orthonormal set $\{\phi_i\}$ as

$$\langle f \mid g \rangle = \sum_i \langle f \mid \phi_i \rangle \langle \phi_i \mid g \rangle \qquad (2\text{--}33)$$

To prove this theorem, expand f as $f = \sum_i a_i \phi_i$, and g as $g = \sum_j b_j \phi_j$. Then,

$$\langle f \mid g \rangle = \int f^* g = \sum_i \sum_j \int a_i^* \phi_i^* b_j \phi_j$$

$$= \sum_{ij} a_i^* b_j \langle \phi_i \mid \phi_j \rangle = \sum_{ij} a_i^* b_j \delta_{ij}.$$

However, $a_i^* = \langle \phi_i \mid f \rangle^* = \langle f \mid \phi_i \rangle$, and $b_i = \langle \phi_i \mid g \rangle$.   Hence,

$$\langle f \mid g \rangle = \sum_i \langle f \mid \phi_i \rangle \langle \phi_i \mid g \rangle.$$

The structure $\mid \phi_i \rangle \langle \phi_i \mid$ which occurs in the expansion theorem will come to have more meaning later on in the book.   For the time being, we may notice that in the expansion theorem we have but inserted $\mid \phi_i \rangle \langle \phi_i \mid$ between $\langle f \mid$ and $\mid g \rangle$ and summed over i.   Such is indeed the case; this operation may be called "inserting a complete set of states."   The content of the expansion theorem may be written $\sum_i \mid \phi_i \rangle \langle \phi_i \mid = 1$. The structure $\mid \phi_i \rangle \langle \phi_i \mid$ is not an inner product as defined in Eq. 2–1; it is an element that has not heretofore entered our discussions. Actually, it is an operator. The sense in which it is an operator will become apparent later.

In this section, we have derived the formula for the coefficients in an expansion in terms of orthonormal functions; we have demonstrated that these coefficients minimize the error in a curtailed expansion, and we have derived a formula for the error that is incurred by curtailing an expansion. Finally, we have derived the expansion theorem for the inner product.

2–3   THE FOURIER SERIES

The Fourier series is an expansion of a function in the orthonormal functions which are proportional to $\{\sin mx, \cos mx\}$. We mentioned in the first section that these functions are orthogonal, but we derive now their norm on the interval $[-\pi, \pi]$.

$$N(\sin mx) = \langle \sin mx \mid \sin mx \rangle = \int_{-\pi}^{\pi} \sin^2 mx \, dx$$

$$= \frac{1}{m} \int_{-m\pi}^{m\pi} \sin^2 y \, dy = \pi \tag{2–34}$$

Similarly,

$$N(\cos mx) = \langle \cos mx \mid \cos mx \rangle = \frac{1}{m} \int_{-m\pi}^{m\pi} \cos^2 y \, dy = \pi \tag{2–35}$$

Equations 2–34 and 2–35 are valid for all values of m, except for $m = 0$, where each result yields the ambiguous $N = 0/0$. To clarify the $m = 0$ case, we must separately evaluate

$$N(\sin 0x) = \langle \sin 0x \mid \sin 0x \rangle = \int_{-\pi}^{\pi} 0 \, dx = 0 \tag{2–36}$$

and

$$N(\cos 0x) = \langle \cos 0x \mid \cos 0x \rangle = \int_{-\pi}^{\pi} 1 \, dx = 2\pi \tag{2–37}$$

All these results may be expressed by

$$
\begin{aligned}
N(\sin mx) &= \pi && \text{for } m \neq 0 \\
&= 0 && \text{for } m = 0 \\
N(\cos mx) &= \pi && \text{for } m \neq 0 \\
&= 2\pi && \text{for } m = 0
\end{aligned}
\qquad (2\text{-}38a)
$$

or, using the Kronecker delta, by

$$
\begin{aligned}
N(\sin mx) &= \pi - \pi\delta_{m0} \\
N(\cos mx) &= \pi + \pi\delta_{m0}
\end{aligned}
\qquad (2\text{-}38b)
$$

Together with the orthogonality relations, we may then write all possible inner products of $\{\sin mx, \cos mx\}$ by

$$
\begin{aligned}
\langle \sin mx \mid \cos mx \rangle &= 0 \\
\langle \sin mx \mid \sin nx \rangle &= (1 - \delta_{m0})\pi\delta_{mn} \\
\langle \cos mx \mid \cos nx \rangle &= (1 + \delta_{m0})\pi\delta_{mn}
\end{aligned}
\qquad (2\text{-}39)
$$

for all m, n = any positive integer or zero. Since we shall be using our previous formula, Eq. 2–24, for calculating the expansion coefficients for an expansion in orthonormal functions, we must use, instead of the set of functions $\{\sin mx, \cos mx\}$, the set of functions $\{(2\pi)^{-1/2}, \pi^{-1/2}\sin mx, \pi^{-1/2}\cos mx\}$, for $m = 1, 2, \ldots$, for expansion on the interval $[-\pi, \pi]$.

For these orthonormal functions, the expansion coefficients will be

$$
\begin{aligned}
a_0 &= \langle (2\pi)^{-1/2} \mid f \rangle \\
a_m &= \langle \pi^{-1/2}\cos mx \mid f \rangle \\
b_m &= \langle \pi^{-1/2}\sin mx \mid f \rangle
\end{aligned}
\qquad (2\text{-}40)
$$

where the expansion is

$$
f(x) = a_0(2\pi)^{-1/2} + \sum_{m=1}^{\infty} a_m(\pi^{-1/2}\cos mx) + \sum_{m=1}^{\infty} b_m(\pi^{-1/2}\sin mx)
$$
$$
(2\text{-}41)
$$

This is not the usual form of the Fourier series, but this is an example of an expansion in orthonormal functions. Usually, the constants are removed from the terms by explicitly writing out the expansion coefficients:

$$f(x) = \frac{1}{2\pi}\langle 1 \mid f \rangle + \frac{1}{\pi}\sum_{m=1}^{\infty}[\langle\cos mx \mid f\rangle\cos mx + \langle\sin mx \mid f\rangle\sin mx]$$

$$(2\text{-}42)$$

This gives the final result

$$f(x) = \frac{c_0}{2} + \sum_{m=1}^{\infty} c_m \cos mx + \sum_{m=1}^{\infty} d_m \sin mx \qquad (2\text{-}43)$$

$$c_m = \frac{1}{\pi}\langle\cos mx \mid f\rangle \qquad (2\text{-}44a)$$

$$d_m = \frac{1}{\pi}\langle\sin mx \mid f\rangle \qquad (2\text{-}44b)$$

on the interval $[-\pi, \pi]$. This is the form in which the Fourier series is usually written. Notice that the lead term is divided by two. This is because the norm of $\cos 0x$ is 2π, whereas for all other values of m, the norm of $\cos mx$ is π.

We can make two simple extensions of the Fourier series at once by using the property of evenness and oddness of functions. The sine function is odd; $\sin x = -\sin(-x)$. The cosine function is even; $\cos x = \cos(-x)$. This being the case, we may formulate these two rules.

(1) *The Fourier expansion on $[-\pi, \pi]$ of an odd function is made up only of sine terms:* $f(x) = \sum_{m=1}^{\infty} d_m \sin mx.$ (2) *The Fourier expansion on $[-\pi, \pi]$ of an even function is made up only of cosine terms:* $f(x) = c_0/2 + \sum_{m=1}^{\infty} c_m \cos mx.$ For, if f is odd, all inner products $\langle\cos mx \mid f\rangle \equiv 0$; and, if f is even, all inner products $\langle\sin mx \mid f\rangle \equiv 0$.

EXAMPLE

The expansion of $f(x) = x$ on $[-\pi, \pi]$. Since $f(x) = x$ is odd, only sine terms occur, and we may write

$$x = \sum_{m=1}^{\infty} d_m \sin mx \qquad m = 1, 2, \ldots \text{ on } [-\pi, \pi]$$

where

$$d_m = \frac{1}{\pi} \langle \sin mx \mid x \rangle$$

$$= \frac{1}{\pi} \int_{-\pi}^{\pi} x \sin mx \, dx = \frac{1}{m^2\pi} \int_{-m\pi}^{m\pi} y \sin y \, dy$$

$$= \frac{1}{m^2\pi} (-y \cos y + \sin y) \Big|_{-m\pi}^{m\pi}$$

$$= \frac{-m\pi \cos m\pi - m\pi \cos m\pi}{m^2\pi} - \frac{2(-1)^{m+1}}{m}$$

and the Fourier series is

$$x = \sum_{m=1}^{\infty} \frac{2(-1)^{m+1}}{m} \sin mx$$

$$= 2 \sin x - \sin 2x + \tfrac{2}{3} \sin 3x - \cdots$$

The comparison of the Fourier series curtailed after three terms with the function itself is shown in Fig. 2–4. The mean-square error after taking three terms can be found using Eq. 2–32 as follows:

$$M_3 = \langle x \mid x \rangle - \sum_{j=1}^{3} |a_j|^2 \qquad (2\text{--}45)$$

According to Eqs. 2–40 and 2–44a, $a_j = \pi^{1/2}c_j$, so that

$$M_3 = \int_{-\pi}^{\pi} x_2 \, dx - 4\pi - 1\pi - \frac{4}{9}\pi = \frac{2\pi^3}{3} - \frac{49\pi}{9} \simeq 6.8;$$

the square root of this, 2.6, may be compared with the area under the function $\pi^2 = 9.9$. Therefore, after three terms, a relative error of about 26% persists.

The use of Fourier series to describe functions has an important electronic analog. It is usually the case that one can generate sine and cosine functions electronically with ease. The generation of other functions can then be done by an electronic Fourier synthesis. Such a synthesis could be used to generate the so-called "sawtooth" wave shown in Fig. 2–5a. The sawtooth pattern is an endless series of plots of $f(x) = x$ vs. x on $[-\pi, \pi]$, which has the Fourier components derived in the example. Figure 2–5b shows a three-term approximation to the sawtooth wave. Such waveforms are used for sweeps, as in oscilloscopes and television.

The functions {sin mx} and {cos mx} are individually complete on either half-interval $[-\pi, 0]$ or $[0, \pi]$. These functions are also orthogonal on either half-interval, and all have the norm $\pi/2$, except cos $0x$, whose norm is π. Therefore, we can construct two distinct "half Fourier series":

$$f(x) = \frac{c_0}{2} + \sum_{m=1}^{\infty} c_m \cos mx \qquad (2\text{–}46a)$$

$$c_m = \frac{2}{\pi} \langle \cos mx \mid f \rangle \qquad (2\text{–}46b)$$

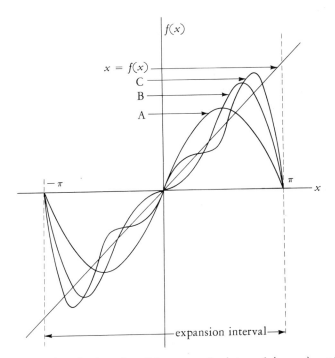

Figure 2–4 The function $f(x) = x$ on the interval $(-\pi, \pi)$, and the Fourier series for $f(x)$ after **(A)** one term, **(B)** two terms, and **(C)** three terms.

$$f(x) = \sum_{m=1}^{\infty} d_m \sin mx \qquad (2\text{-}47a)$$

$$d_m = \frac{2}{\pi} \langle \sin mx \mid f \rangle \qquad (2\text{-}47b)$$

each on either interval $[-\pi, 0]$ or $[0, \pi]$. Likewise, either the full or half Fourier series may be extended to any symmetric interval $[-a, a]$ or half of a symmetric interval $[-a, 0]$ or $[0, a]$ by a scale expansion, such as

$$f(x) = \frac{c_0}{2} + \sum_{m=1}^{\infty} \left(c_m \cos \frac{m\pi x}{a} + d_m \sin \frac{m\pi x}{a} \right) \qquad (2\text{-}48)$$

with $c_m = (1/a)\langle \cos(m\pi x/a) \mid f \rangle$, $d_m = (1/a)\langle \sin(m\pi x/a) \mid f \rangle$. A very important revision of the Fourier series for quantum mechanics is the formulation

$$f(x) = \sum_{m=-\infty}^{\infty} a_m e^{imx} \qquad \text{on } [-\pi, \pi] \qquad (2\text{-}49)$$

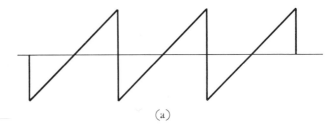

(a)

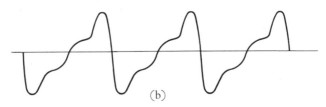

(b)

Figure 2–5 (a) The "sawtooth" wave, and (b) a three-term Fourier synthesis of the sawtooth wave.

For, if {cos *mx*, sin *mx*} is complete for all positive values of *m* and zero, then {$e^{imx} = \cos mx + i \sin mx$} is complete for all integral values—positive, negative, and zero—of *m*. To put it another way, including the complex conjugate of the functions {e^{imx}} completes the set. These modifications of the basic Fourier series are subjects of a number of the problems at the end of the chapter.

In this section, we have exhibited a very useful expansion in orthonormal functions, the Fourier series (expansion in sines and cosines), and have commented on its usefulness and extension.

2–4 CONSTRUCTION OF ORTHONORMAL FUNCTIONS

Thus far, we have discussed in general the properties of ortho-normal functions, their use in series expansions, and the particular example of the Fourier series. We have pointed out that a suffi-ciently precise expansion can be achieved only if the set of functions, orthonormal or not, is complete. In this section, we shall show how an orthonormal complete set of functions may be formed from a set of complete functions. Before we take up the actual formation, we must introduce one aspect of completeness which plays an important rôle in this discussion and also in the work that follows. We begin with a definition.

> **Definition** A set of functions is said to be *linearly independent* if none of the functions can be expressed as a linear combination of the rest. Similarly, a set of functions is said to be *linearly dependent* if at least one of the functions may be related to one or more of the other functions by a linear equation.

This definition may be expressed mathematically by saying that a set of functions {F_i} is linearly independent if the identity

$$\sum_i c_i F_i = c_1 F_1 + c_2 F_2 + \cdots = 0 \qquad (2\text{-}50)$$

can be solved only with all the $c_i = 0$; the set {F_i} is linearly de-pendent if this equation can be solved with at least one of the $c_i \neq 0$.

Take, for example, these two sets of functions:

$$
\begin{aligned}
F_1 &= 1 & G_1 &= 1 \\
F_2 &= x & G_2 &= x \\
F_3 &= 7x + 4 & G_3 &= x^2 \\
F_4 &= x^3 & G_4 &= x^3
\end{aligned}
$$

The set $\{G_i\}$ is linearly independent. It is not possible for any linear combination of those functions to add to zero, as in Eq. 2–50. To put it another way, there is no linear relation connecting those four functions: the function $G_3 = x^2$ is not a linear combination of 1, x, and x^3. The set $\{F_i\}$ is linearly dependent. Function F_3 is a linear combination of F_1, F_2, and F_4; $F_3 = 7F_2 + 4F_1$. That is, Eq. 2–50 can be solved with some of the $c_i \neq 0$; $-4F_1 - 7F_2 + 1F_3 + 0F_4 = 0$.

A set of complete functions will always contain a linearly independent subset. This is an important statement that is offered without proof; it is the first step in generating a complete set of orthonormal functions.

As an example, consider the powers of x on the interval $[-1, 1]$. Taylor's theorem essentially guarantees that the set $\{x^n\}$, $n = 0$, 1, 2, $\cdots$ is complete. We have just seen that these functions are also linearly independent. Consider the sets of functions below. The set $\{F_i'\}$ is complete; the linearly independent set $\{F_i\}$ was formed by removing the linearly dependent member of $\{F_i'\}$. The set $\{G_i\}$ is also linearly independent and complete; it differs from $\{F_i\}$ only in the order of arrangement.

$\{F_i'\}$	$\{F_i\}$	$\{G_i\}$
1	1	1
x	x	x^2
$2x$	$\cdots$	x^4
x^2	x^2	$\cdots$
x^3	x^3	x
x^4	x^4	x^3
$\cdots$	$\cdots$	$\cdots$

Construction of a complete set of orthonormal functions can always be accomplished from a complete, linearly independent set of functions. The procedure for this construction is known as the *Schmidt orthogonalization procedure*. Rather than give a complete account of procedure, we shall illustrate the idea, state the general conclusion, and then work an illustrative example. Suppose we have a complete, linearly independent set of functions $\{f_i\}$, defined on a prescribed interval. We wish to form an orthonormal set $\{\phi_i\}$ from the $\{f_i\}$.

Step 1. Let ϕ_0 be f_0 normalized. That is, let the first ϕ function be simply proportional to the first f function. The norm of f_0 is $N_0 = \langle f_0 \mid f_0 \rangle$, so that $\phi_0 = f_0/N_0^{1/2}$.

Step 2. Let ϕ_1 be a linear combination of ϕ_0 and f_1 which is orthogonal to ϕ_0, and normalized. This can be done in general since the set $\{f_i\}$ is linearly independent. That is,

$$\phi_1 = N_1^{-1/2}(c\phi_0 + f_1) \qquad (2\text{-}51)$$

where

$$\langle \phi_0 \mid \phi_1 \rangle = 0 \qquad (2\text{-}52)$$

The orthogonality condition gives

$$c\langle \phi_0 \mid \phi_0 \rangle + \langle \phi_0 \mid f_1 \rangle = 0 \qquad (2\text{-}53a)$$
$$c = -\langle \phi_0 \mid f_1 \rangle \qquad (2\text{-}53b)$$

Then,

$$\phi_1 = N_1^{-1/2}(f_1 - \langle \phi_0 \mid f_1 \rangle \phi_0) \qquad (2\text{-}54)$$

and

$$\begin{aligned} N_1 &= \langle f_1 \mid f_1 \rangle - \langle \phi_0 \mid f_1 \rangle \langle f_1 \mid \phi_0 \rangle - \langle \phi_0 \mid f_1 \rangle \langle \phi_0 \mid f_1 \rangle + \langle \phi_0 \mid f_1 \rangle^2 \\ &= \langle f_1 \mid f_1 \rangle - |\langle \phi_0 \mid f_1 \rangle|^2 \end{aligned} \qquad (2\text{-}55)$$

This process is then continued until the complete, orthonormal set is generated. The general term is

$$\phi_k = N_k^{-1/2}\left(f_k - \sum_{j=0}^{k-1} \langle \phi_j \mid f_k \rangle \phi_j\right) \qquad (2\text{-}56)$$

with

$$N_k = \langle f_k \mid f_k \rangle - \sum_{j=0}^{k-1} |\langle \phi_j \mid f_k \rangle|^2 \qquad (2\text{-}57)$$

It should be clear from this discussion that functions will not be normalizable if their norm is not finite. Not all functions on all intervals are normalizable: the set $\{x^n\}$ on $(-\infty, \infty)$ is not, for example. The quantum mechanics of molecular structure is concerned almost exclusively with normalizable, or *square-integrable* functions.

As an example of the Schmidt process, we shall consider the functions $\{\exp[-x^2/2]x^n\}$ on the full line, $(-\infty, \infty)$. We begin by showing that these functions are normalizable.

$$\langle f_n \mid f_n \rangle = \int_{-\infty}^{\infty} \exp\left[\frac{-x^2}{2}\right] x^n \exp\left[\frac{-x^2}{2}\right] x^n \, dx$$

$$= \int_{-\infty}^{\infty} \exp[-x^2] x^{2n} \, dx \qquad (2\text{-}58)$$

Since the integrand is an even function, we may simplify the integral to

$$\langle f_n \mid f_n \rangle = 2 \int_{0}^{\infty} \exp[-x^2] x^{2n} \, dx = \int_{0}^{\infty} e^{-y} y^{(n-1/2)} \, dy \quad (2\text{-}59)$$

which may successively be integrated by parts to give

$$\langle f_n \mid f_n \rangle = (n - \tfrac{1}{2})(n - \tfrac{3}{2}) \cdots (\tfrac{1}{2}) \int_{0}^{\infty} e^{-y} y^{-1/2} \, dy$$

$$= 2(n - \tfrac{1}{2})(n - \tfrac{3}{2}) \cdots (\tfrac{1}{2}) \int_{0}^{\infty} e^{-x^2} \, dx$$

$$= (2n - 1)(2n - 3) \cdots (3)(1)\pi^{1/2}/2^n \qquad (2\text{-}60)$$

where the known integral $\int_{0}^{\infty} e^{-x^2} \, dx = \dfrac{\pi^{1/2}}{2}$ has been substituted.

The norm N_n is finite for any n, so all functions in the set $\{\exp[-x^2/2]x^n\}$ are normalizable. It is the presence of the decaying exponential $\exp[-x^2/2]$ that renders the integral finite and the functions square integrable.

To construct an orthonormal set, we begin by normalizing $f_0 = \exp[-x^2/2]x^0 = \exp[-x^2/2]$. The norm is $\pi^{1/2}$, so we have $\phi_0 = \pi^{-1/4} \exp[-x^2/2]$.

The next function is found from Eqs. 2–54 and 2–55, which are specific cases of Eqs. 2–56 and 2–57, respectively. In order to use these equations, we must first evaluate $\langle \phi_0 \mid f_1 \rangle$ and $\langle f_1 \mid f_1 \rangle$:

$$\langle \phi_0 \mid f_1 \rangle = \int_{-\infty}^{\infty} \exp\left[\frac{-x^2}{2}\right] \pi^{-1/4} \exp\left[\frac{-x^2}{2}\right] x \, dx = 0 \quad (2\text{–}61)$$

because the integrand is odd, and

$$\langle f_1 \mid f_1 \rangle = \pi^{1/2}/2 \quad (2\text{–}62)$$

from Eq. 2–60. Then

$$N_1 = \langle f_1 \mid f_1 \rangle - |\langle \phi_0 \mid f_1 \rangle|^2 = \pi^{1/2}/2 \quad (2\text{–}63)$$

and

$$\phi_1 = N_1^{-1/2}(f_1 - \langle \phi_0 \mid f_1 \rangle \phi_0) = 2^{1/2}\pi^{-1/4} \exp\left[\frac{-x^2}{2}\right] x \quad (2\text{–}64)$$

The reader should notice that all integrals of the form $\langle \phi_i \mid f_j \rangle$ where i is even and j odd, or vice versa, are zero for these sets of functions because the integrand is odd. This greatly simplifies the calculation.

The next function will be calculated according to Eqs. 2–56 and 2–57, as follows:

$$\begin{aligned} \phi_2 &= N_2^{-1/2}(f_2 - \langle \phi_0 \mid f_2 \rangle \phi_0 - \langle \phi_1 \mid f_2 \rangle \phi_1) \\ &= N_2^{-1/2}(f_2 - \langle \phi_0 \mid f_2 \rangle \phi_0) \end{aligned} \quad (2\text{–}65)$$

and

$$\begin{aligned} N_2 &= \langle f_2 \mid f_2 \rangle - |\langle \phi_0 \mid f_2 \rangle|^2 - |\langle \phi_1 \mid f_2 \rangle|^2 \\ &= \langle f_2 \mid f_2 \rangle - |\langle \phi_0 \mid f_2 \rangle|^2 \end{aligned} \quad (2\text{–}66)$$

We need to evaluate $\langle f_2 \mid f_2 \rangle$ and $\langle \phi_0 \mid f_2 \rangle$. From Eq. 2–60,

$$\langle f_2 \mid f_2 \rangle = \tfrac{3}{4}\pi^{1/2} \quad (2\text{–}67)$$

and

$$\begin{aligned} \langle \phi_0 \mid f_2 \rangle &= \int_{-\infty}^{\infty} \pi^{-1/4} \exp\left[\frac{-x^2}{2}\right] \exp\left[\frac{-x^2}{2}\right] x^2 \, dx \\ &= \pi^{-1/4} \int_{-\infty}^{\infty} x^2 \exp[-x^2] \, dx = \pi^{-1/4} \frac{\pi^{1/2}}{2} \\ &= \frac{\pi^{1/4}}{2} \end{aligned} \quad (2\text{–}68)$$

Finally,

$$N_2 = \frac{3}{4}\pi^{1/2} - \frac{1}{4}\pi^{1/2} = \frac{\pi^{1/2}}{2} \tag{2-69}$$

$$\phi_2 = (\sqrt{2}\pi^{-1/4})\left\{\exp\left[\frac{-x^2}{2}\right]x^2 - \frac{\pi^{1/4}}{2}\pi^{-1/4}\exp\left[\frac{-x^2}{2}\right]\right\}$$

$$= \pi^{-1/4}\exp\left[\frac{-x^2}{2}\right]\frac{(2x^2 - 1)}{\sqrt{2}} \tag{2-70}$$

The set of orthonormal functions that would be generated in this way are all of the form $\pi^{-1/4}\exp[-x^2/2]H_n(x)$, where $H_n(x)$ represents one of the polynomials

$$H_0(x) = 1$$
$$H_1(x) = \sqrt{2}x \tag{2-71}$$
$$H_2(x) = 2x^2 - 1$$
$$\cdots$$

The even-numbered polynomials contain even powers of x only, and the odd-numbered polynomials contain odd powers of x only. These polynomials are proportional to the famous *Hermite polynomials*. The functions that we have constructed to be orthonormal on $(-\infty, \infty)$ from the set $\{\exp[-x^2/2]x^n\}$ are the solutions for the wave function of a quantum-mechanical harmonic oscillator. We have, of course, carried out our construction with no attention to any particular physical problem. That we accidentally—by this route—come across the solution to a physical problem emphasizes the significance and simplicity of the harmonic oscillator in quantum mechanics.

Thus, in this section, we have further developed the properties of functions with the concepts of linear independence and normalizability, and we have shown how a complete orthonormal set of functions can be constructed from a complete, linearly independent set. Lastly, we have begun crudely to relate the properties of orthonormal functions to the wave functions describing physical situations.

2-5   THE LEGENDRE POLYNOMIALS AND OTHER SPECIAL FUNCTIONS

In this section we examine a number of sets of orthonormal functions on various intervals. This could be a mammoth undertaking.

The relations among such functions are tabulated in larger treatises, and the proofs of these relations are seldom of importance in quantum chemistry. Therefore, this section is devoted to a detailed examination of one of the special functions, the Legendre polynomials, and a cursory tabulation of others, including Laguerre and Hermite functions.

The Legendre polynomials are of importance in a number of quantum-chemical problems. They are the basis for the wave functions for angular momentum, and therefore occur in problems involving spherical motion, such as that of the electron in a hydrogen atom or the rotations of a molecule. In this context, the Legendre polynomials are important in describing the angular dependence of one-electron atomic orbitals; this dependence, in turn, forms the basis of the geometry of chemical compounds.

There are a number of ways of forming these polynomials, three of which are quite general.

(a) Schmidt orthogonalization of a linearly independent complete set.

(b) Solution of a differential equation.

(c) Use of a generating function.

In addition, we shall describe a formula for the Legendre polynomials. We begin with the orthogonalization procedure.

Legendre polynomials by Schmidt orthogonalization. The Legendre polynomials result from applying the Schmidt procedure to the set $\{x^n\}$ on the interval $[-1, 1]$. The choice of the interval $[-1, 1]$ is specific to the Legendre polynomials. We begin by letting ϕ_0 be proportional to $x^0 = 1$, and normalized on the interval:

$$N_0 = \int_{-1}^{1} 1 \, dx = 2 \tag{2-72}$$

$$\phi_0 = \left(\tfrac{1}{2}\right)^{1/2} \tag{2-73}$$

Then, using Eqs. 2–56 and 2–57,

$$N_1 = \langle f_1 \mid f_1 \rangle - |\langle \phi_0 \mid f_1 \rangle|^2 = \langle f_1 \mid f_1 \rangle = \int_{-1}^{1} x^2 \, dx = \tfrac{2}{3} \tag{2-74}$$

$$\phi_1 = N_1^{-1/2} \left(f_1 - \langle \phi_0 \mid f_1 \rangle \phi_0 \right) = \left(\tfrac{3}{2}\right)^{1/2} x \tag{2-75}$$

Here, by realizing the oddness of the integrand, we have set $\langle \phi_0 \mid f_1 \rangle = 0$; and similarly, for all inner products where the sum of the indices is odd. This behavior was also noticed for the Hermite polynomials in the previous section.

Proceeding, we find

$$N_2 = \langle f_2 \mid f_2 \rangle - |\langle \phi_0 \mid f_2 \rangle|^2 \tag{2-76}$$

$$\phi_2 = N_2^{-1/2}(f_2 - \langle \phi_0 \mid f_2 \rangle \phi_0) \tag{2-77}$$

so we need to calculate

$$\langle f_2 \mid f_2 \rangle = \int_{-1}^{1} x^4 \, dx = \tfrac{2}{5} \tag{2-78}$$

$$\langle \phi_0 \mid f_2 \rangle = \int_{-1}^{1} (\tfrac{1}{2})^{1/2} x^2 \, dx = (\tfrac{1}{2})^{1/2} \tfrac{2}{3} \tag{2-79}$$

whence

$$N_2 = \tfrac{2}{5} - \tfrac{1}{2} \cdot \tfrac{4}{9} = \tfrac{8}{45} \tag{2-80}$$

$$\phi_2 = (\tfrac{45}{8})^{1/2}(x^2 - \tfrac{1}{3}) = (\tfrac{5}{2})^{1/2}(\tfrac{3}{2}x^2 - \tfrac{1}{2}) \tag{2-81}$$

The functions that are appearing are

$$\phi_0 = (\tfrac{1}{2})^{1/2} \cdot 1$$
$$\phi_1 = (\tfrac{3}{2})^{1/2} \cdot x$$
$$\phi_2 = (\tfrac{5}{2})^{1/2} \cdot (\tfrac{3}{2}x^2 - \tfrac{1}{2})$$
$$\phi_3 = (\tfrac{7}{2})^{1/2} \cdot (\tfrac{5}{2}x^3 - \tfrac{3}{2}x) \tag{2-82}$$

The polynomials at the right are the Legendre polynomials; the whole orthonormal set of functions is $\{[(2n + 1)/2]^{1/2} P_n(x)\}$, where $P_n(x)$ signifies the *Legendre polynomial of rank n*.

Solution of Legendre's differential equation. The Legendre polynomials are the solutions of the differential equation

$$\frac{d}{dx}\left[(1 - x^2)\frac{df}{dx}\right] + l(l + 1)f = 0 \tag{2-83}$$

where l is a positive integer or zero. That the polynomials that have been generated by orthogonalization of $\{x^n\}$ on $[-1, 1]$ are solutions of Eq. 2–83 can be verified by direct substitution. However, we may derive this result directly using a method that is a prototype for the solution of many differential equations.

We attempt a power series solution for f, $f = \sum_n a_n x^n$. Substituting this trial solution (often called *Ansatz*, from the German) into Eq. 2–83, we obtain

$$\frac{d}{dx}\left[(1-x^2)\sum_n na_nx^{n-1}\right] + \left[l(l+1)\sum_n a_nx^n\right] = 0$$

$$\frac{d}{dx}\left[\sum_n na_nx^{n-1} - \sum_n na_nx^{n+1}\right] + \sum_n l(l+1)a_nx^n = 0$$

$$\sum_n n(n-1)a_nx^{n-2} - \sum_n n(n+1)a_nx^n + \sum_n l(l+1)a_nx^n = 0$$

$$(2\text{–}84)$$

If we collect all similar powers of x, we obtain

$$\sum_n x^n[(n+2)(n+1)a_{n+2} - n(n+1)a_n + l(l+1)a_n] = 0$$

$$(2\text{–}85)$$

but, for the series to be identically zero, each term must be identically zero, since the functions $\{x^n\}$ are linearly independent. This gives the *recursion relation* for the expansion coefficients,

$$a_{n+2} = \frac{[n(n+1) - l(l+1)]a_n}{(n+2)(n+1)} \qquad (2\text{–}86)$$

Equation 2–86 gives a rule for finding every other coefficient starting with the first. That is, if $a_0 = 1$, then Eq. 2–86 gives $a_2 = -l(l+1)/2$, $a_4 = [6 - l(l+1)]/12 \cdot [-l(l+1)/2]$, and so forth. The coefficients depend on the value of l. Suppose we continue on, finding all the even coefficients. If the *rank* of the equation, l, is even, eventually n will equal l for some term, $n(n+1)$ will equal $l(l+1)$, and the following coefficient, a_{n+2}, will equal zero. Then all following coefficients will also equal zero. In other words, if l is even, the even terms of the power series cut off at $n = l$. The odd terms, of course, keep on going. This infinite series of odd powers diverges at $x = \pm 1$, and is not of physical interest; the finite series of even powers gives

$$l = 0 \qquad a_0 = 1 \qquad f_0 = 1$$
$$l = 2 \qquad a_0 = 1$$
$$\qquad\qquad a_2 = -3 \qquad f_2 = -3x^2 + 1$$

and so forth, which are proportional to the Legendre polynomials derived by orthogonalization. It has become customary to choose a_0 such that the polynomial $f_n = 1$ at $x = +1$. Then

$$
\begin{array}{lll}
l = 0 & a_0 = 1 & P_0 = 1 \\
l = 2 & a_0 = -\tfrac{1}{2} & \\
 & a_2 = \tfrac{3}{2} & P_2 = \tfrac{3}{2}x^2 - \tfrac{1}{2}
\end{array}
$$

and so on.

Similarly, if l is odd, the series in odd powers terminates at $n = l$, and the series in even powers is an infinite series, divergent at $x = \pm 1$. Again, we choose a_0 such that $f_n(+1) = 1$. Then

$$
\begin{array}{lll}
l = 1 & a_1 = 1 & P_1 = x \\
l = 3 & a_1 = -\tfrac{3}{2} & \\
 & a_3 = \tfrac{5}{2} & P_3 = \tfrac{5}{2}x^3 - \tfrac{3}{2}x
\end{array}
$$

and so forth. The method of power series substitution is very powerful. The usual result is a recursion relation which may be interpreted, within the context of the problem, as we have done here.

The generating function for Legendre polynomials. A generating function for a set of functions is some function of two variables such that when this function is expanded as a power series in one of the variables, the coefficients are the set of functions in the other variable. The generating function for Legendre polynomials is

$$
F(x, t) = (1 - 2xt + t^2)^{-1/2} = \sum_n P_n(x)t^n \qquad (2\text{-}87)
$$

If the generating function is written as $[1 - (2xt - t^2)]^{-1/2}$, it may be expanded in the binomial series

$$
F(x, t) = 1 + \frac{1}{2} \cdot \frac{1}{1!}(2xt - t^2) + \frac{1}{2} \cdot \frac{3}{2} \cdot \frac{1}{2!}(2xt - t^2)^2
$$
$$
+ \frac{1}{2} \cdot \frac{3}{2} \cdot \frac{5}{2} \cdot \frac{1}{3!}(2xt - t^2)^3 + \cdots \qquad (2\text{-}88)
$$

and then rearranged in powers of t:

$$
F(x, t) = 1 + (x)(t) + \left(\frac{-1}{2} + \frac{3}{2}x^2\right)(t^2)
$$

$$+ \left(\frac{-3}{2}x + \frac{5}{2}x^3 \right)(t^3) + \cdots$$

$$= \sum_n P_n(x)t^n \tag{2-89}$$

Often many useful relations may be derived from a generating function; however, there are no general methods for constructing a generating function.

Rodrigues' formula for the Legendre polynomials. As a final example Of a formula for finding Legendre polynomials, we derive Rodrigues' formula,

$$P_l(x) = \frac{1}{2^l l!} \frac{d^l}{dx^l}(x^2 - 1)^l \tag{2-90}$$

Consider the differential equation

$$(1 - x^2)\frac{dy}{dx} + 2lxy = 0 \tag{2-91}$$

which can be solved by the elementary "separation of variables" technique, giving

$$\frac{dy}{y} = \frac{-2lx\,dx}{1 - x^2} \tag{2-92}$$

whose integral is

$$y = (1 - x^2)^l \tag{2-93}$$

If the original differential equation, Eq. 2-91, is now differentiated $(n + 1)$ times,[4] the result is

$$(1 - x^2)\frac{d^{l+2}y}{dx^{l+2}} + (l + 1)(-2x)\frac{d^{l+1}y}{dx^{l+1}}$$
$$+ \frac{l(l + 1)}{2}(-2)\frac{d^l y}{dx^l} + 2xn\frac{d^{l+1}y}{dx^{l+1}}$$
$$+ 2n(n + 1)\frac{d^l y}{dx^l} = 0 \tag{2-94}$$

---

[4] In this derivation, use has been made of the expansion of the nth derivative of a product: $d^n/dx^n(uv) = (d^nu/dx^n)v + n(d^{n-1}u/dx^{n-1})(dv/dx) + \cdots$, a series with binomial coefficients.

If we now substitute into this equation $f = d^l y/dx^l$, we find that f is a solution of Legendre's differential equation:

$$(1 - x^2)\frac{d^2 f}{dx^2} - 2x\frac{df}{dx} + l(l + 1)f = 0$$

$$\frac{d}{dx}\left[(1 - x^2)^l\frac{df}{dx}\right] + l(l + 1)f = 0 \qquad (2\text{--}95)$$

Therefore, $f = d^l y/dx^l = d^l/dx^l(1 - x^2)^l$ is a solution of Legendre's equation. However, the solutions of Legendre's equation are the Legendre polynomials. We have only to insure $f(+1) = 1$, as we required, to establish the relation desired. If the formula is expanded as a derivative of a product,[4] we obtain

$$f = \frac{d^l}{dx^l}[(x + 1)^l(x - 1)^l]$$

$$= [(x - 1)^l]\left[\frac{d^l}{dx^l}(x + 1)^l\right]$$

$$+ l\left[\frac{d}{dx}(x - 1)^l\right]\left[\frac{d^{l-1}}{dx^{l-1}}(x + 1)^l\right] + \cdots$$

$$+ l\left[\frac{d^{l-1}}{dx^{l-1}}(x - 1)^l\right]\left[\frac{d}{dx}(x + 1)^l\right]$$

$$+ \left[\frac{d^l}{dx^l}(x - 1)^l\right][(x + 1)^l] \qquad (2\text{--}96)$$

Evaluated at $x = 1$, all the terms but the last are zero, since each will contain powers of $(x - 1)$. The last term, however, does not contain powers of $(x - 1)$: $(d^l/dx^l)(x - 1)^l = l!$ and $(x + 1)^l = 2^l$. Therefore, $f(1) = 2^l l!$; to make $f(1) = 1$, and agree with the Legendre polynomials, we divide by the factor

$$P_l(x) = \frac{1}{2^l l!}\frac{d^l}{dx^l}(1 - x^2)^l \qquad (2\text{--}97)$$

Having described four different methods for finding Legendre polynomials (and there are others, too), we shall now use these formulas to derive some of the salient properties of the polynomials.

Evaluation of $P_l(x)$ at $x = -1$, $x = 0$. We have restricted our definition of the polynomials by the boundary condition $P_l(+1) =$

$+1$, but it is also useful to know the values of $P_l(x)$ at the other boundary, $P_l(-1)$, and in the middle of the interval, $P_l(0)$. Rodrigues' formula is useful for obtaining $P_l(-1)$. From an expansion of $P_l(x) = (1/2^l l!)(d^l/dx^l)(1 - x^2)^l$ similar to that given in Eq. 2-96, it is clear that only the first term will be nonzero at $x = -1$, since all other terms involve powers of $(x + 1)$. That first term at $x = -1$ is $(-2)^l l!$. Then,

$$P_l(-1) = \frac{1}{2^l l!}(-2)^l l! = (-1)^l \qquad (2\text{-}98)$$

That is, $P_l(-1)$ is $+1$ or -1 as l is even or odd.

We may also use Rodrigues' formula to evaluate $P_l(0)$. The binomial expansion of $(x^2 - 1)^l$ gives

$$(x^2 - 1)^n = x^{2n} + \frac{n(-1)}{1!}x^{2n-2} + \cdots$$

$$+ \frac{(-1)^k n(n-1)(n-2)\cdots(n-k+1)}{k!}x^{2n-2k}$$

$$+ \cdots + n(-1)^{n-1}x^2 + (-1)^n \qquad (2\text{-}99)$$

For the polynomial P_n, we require the nth derivative of Eq. 2-99. All terms in the binomial expansion afford zero for the result of taking n derivatives and evaluating at $x = 0$, except a possible term in x^n. If there is a term in x^n, the nth derivative, at $x = 0$, will give $n!$. There will be a term in x^n only if n is even, so that there can be some value of k in Eq. 2-99 for which $2n - 2k = n$, namely $k = n/2$. From these considerations, we conclude

$$\frac{d^n}{dx^n}(x^2 - 1)^n\Big|_{x=0} = 0 \qquad (2\text{-}100a)$$

if n is odd, and

$$\frac{d^n}{dx^n}(x^2 - 1)^n\Big|_{x=0} = (-1)^{n/2}\frac{n(n-1)\cdots\left(n - \frac{n}{2} + 1\right)n!}{(n/2)!} \qquad (2\text{-}100b)$$

if n is even.

The nonzero result can be simplified. Let $2l = n$, and then

$$P_{2l}(0) = \left(\frac{1}{2^2(2l)!}\right)(-1)^l\frac{(2l)(2l+1)\cdots(l+2)(l+1)(2l)!}{l!}$$

$$= \left(\frac{1}{2^{2l}}\right)(-1)^l$$

$$\times \frac{(2l)(2l-1)\cdots(l+2)(l+1)(l)(l-1)\cdots(2)(1)}{l!l!}$$

$$= \left(\frac{1}{2^{2l}}\right)(-1)^l \frac{(2l-1)(2l-3)\cdots(3)(1)(2^l)}{l!}$$

$$= (-1)^l \frac{(2l-1)!!}{2^l l!} \qquad\qquad (2\text{-}101)$$

where the symbol $(2l-1)!!$, read "$2l-1$ double factorial," indicates a product of every other integer, $n!! = n(n-2)(n-4)\cdots$. This result may also be derived using the generating function for the Legendre polynomials. For, setting $x = 0$ in $F(x, t) = [1 - 2xt + t^2]^{-1/2}$, we obtain

$$F(0, t) = \sum_n P_n(0)t^n = (1 + t^2)^{-1/2}$$

$$= 1 - \frac{1}{1!}\cdot\frac{1}{2}t^2 + \frac{1}{2!}\cdot\frac{1}{2}\cdot\frac{3}{2}t^4 - \cdots$$

$$= \sum_{n \text{ even}} \frac{(n-1)!!(-1)^{n/2}}{(2^{n/2})}\left(\frac{n}{2}\right)!t^n$$

$$= \sum_l \frac{(2l-1)!!(-1)^l}{2^l l! t^{2l}} \qquad\qquad (2\text{-}102)$$

A plot of the first four Legendre polynomials is shown in Fig. 2–6. The values of $P_l(\pm 1)$ and $P_l(0)$ are apparent.

Recursion relations among Legendre polynomials. As a further example of the use of the generating function, we derive two recursion relations interrelating the Legendre polynomials. By differentiating Eq. 2–87 with respect to t, we obtain

$$\frac{\partial F(x, t)}{\partial t} = (x - t)(1 - 2xt + t^2)^{-3/2} = \sum_n nt^{n-1}P_n(x) \qquad\qquad (2\text{-}103)$$

which may be rearranged to give

$$(x - t)(1 - 2xt + t^2)^{-1/2} = (1 - 2xt + t^2)\sum_n nt^{n-1}P_n(x)$$

$$(2\text{-}104)$$

$$(x - t) \sum_n t^n P_n(x) = (1 - 2xt + t^2) \sum_n nt^{n-1}P_n(x)$$

Since the powers of t are linearly independent, we can equate coefficients of t^n:

$$xP_n - P_{n-1} = (n + 1)P_{n+1} - 2nxP_n + (n - 1)P_{n-1}$$

or

$$(n + 1)P_{n+1} - (2n + 1)xP_n + nP_{n-1} = 0 \qquad (2\text{--}105)$$

which interrelates the various Legendre polynomials. For instance,
given P_1 and P_2, we may find P_3 by using $n = 2$ in Eq. 2–105:

$$
\begin{aligned}
P_3 &= \frac{(2 \cdot 2 + 1)xP_2 - 2P_1}{2 + 1} = \frac{3P_2 - 2P_1}{3} \\
&= \frac{5x(\frac{3}{2}x^2 - \frac{1}{2}) - 2x}{3} = \frac{5}{2}x^2 - \frac{5}{6}x - \frac{2}{3}x \\
&= \frac{5}{2}x^3 - \frac{3}{2}x \qquad (2\text{--}106)
\end{aligned}
$$

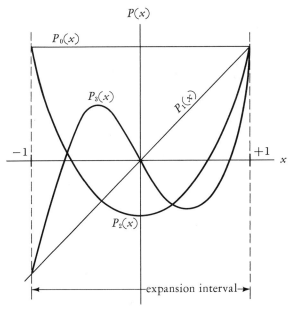

Figure 2–6   Legendre polynomials $P_n(x)$ for $n = 0, 1, 2, 3$.

This recursion relation can be used to generate higher Legendre polynomials.

Another relation, obtained by differentiating Eq. 2–87 with respect to x, is

$$\frac{\partial F(x, t)}{\partial x} = t(1 - 2xt + t^2)^{-3/2} = \sum_n P'_n(x)t^n \qquad (2\text{–}107)$$

which yields

$$t \sum_n P_n t^n = (1 - 2xt + t^2)P'_n t^n \qquad (2\text{–}108)$$

or, for t^n,

$$P_{n-1} = P'_n - 2xP'_{n-1} + P'_{n-2} \qquad (2\text{–}109)$$

This recursion relation relates the Legendre polynomials to their first derivatives. Many other useful relations may be derived by analogous manipulations of the generating function.

Spherical harmonics: an orthonormal set in two variables. Legendre's differential equation, Eq. 2–83, is a special case of the equation

$$\frac{d}{dx}\left[(1 - x^2)\frac{df}{dx}\right] + \left[l(l + 1) - \frac{m^2}{1 - x^2}\right]f = 0 \qquad (2\text{–}110)$$

where m is an integer. If $m = 0$, Eq. 2–110 is identical to Eq. 2–83. The solutions to this equation are known as the associated Legendre functions, $P_l{}^m(x) = (-1)^m(1 - x^2)^{m/2} d^m P_l(x)/dx^m$. The associated Legendre functions are marked by two indices, m and l. The associated Legendre functions are also orthogonal on the interval $[-1, 1]$ in the sense $\langle P_{l'}{}^m \mid P_l{}^m \rangle = 0$. The inner product of two associated Legendre functions for different l but the same m is zero. The norm of the associated Legendre functions is

$$N(P_l{}^m) = (2)(l + m)!/(2l + 1)(l - m)!$$

The set of functions

$$\left\{\frac{(2l + 1)(l - m)!}{2(l + m)!} P_l{}^m(x)\right\}$$

defined on $[-1, 1]$, for a fixed value of m and $l = m, m + 1, \ldots$ are complete and orthonormal. The Legendre polynomials themselves are an example of this set, for, if $m = 0$, this set is identical to the set formed by Schmidt orthogonalization.

The associated Legendre functions may be rewritten as functions of an angle variable θ, on $0 \leq \theta \leq \pi$, by replacing x by $\cos \theta$. The functions $\{P_l^m(\theta)\}$ are therefore a complete orthogonal set of functions on the interval $[0, \pi]$ in the variable θ. However, we saw in Section 2–3 that the set $\{(2\pi)^{-1/2} e^{im\phi}\}$ is a complete orthonormal set of the interval $[0, 2\pi]$ in the variable ϕ. By multiplying each of the functions $[(2l + 1)(l - m)!/2(l + m)!]^{1/2} P_l^m (\cos \theta)$ by the members of this other complete, orthonormal set, $\{(2\pi)^{-1/2} e^{im\phi}\}$, we obtain a set of functions, complete and orthonormal in two variables, called the *spherical harmonics:*

$$Y_{l,m}(\theta, \phi) = \left[\frac{(2l + 1)(l - m)!}{4\pi(l + m)!} \right]^{1/2} P_l^{|m|} (\cos \theta) e^{im\phi} \qquad (2\text{--}111)$$

with

$$Y_{l,-m}(\theta, \phi) = (-1)^m Y_{l,m}^* \qquad (2\text{--}112)$$

The index m is usually called the *order*, and the index l the *rank* of the spherical harmonics. The rank assumes the values $l = 0, 1, 2, \ldots$; the order m, the values $-l, (-l + 1), \ldots, 0, \ldots, (l - 1), l$.

We have now spent some time discussing the ins and outs of Legendre polynomials and the associated Legendre functions. Lest the student miss the forest for the trees, we now recapitulate the salient points of our discussion.

1. A set of polynomials can be formed by Schmidt orthogonalization from the complete set $\{x^n\}$ on $[-1, 1]$. Except for a normalization factor, these are the Legendre polynomials.

2. These same polynomials are solutions of the differential equation $(d/dx)[(1 - x^2) \, df/dx] + l(l + 1)f = 0$.

3. These same polynomials are the coefficients in a series expansion in powers of t of $F(x, t) = (1 - 2xt + t^2)^{-1/2}$.

4. These same polynomials are given by $(1/2^l l!)(d^l/dx^l)(1 - x^2)^l$.

5. A number of relations may be derived from points 3 and 4.

6. Functions $P_l{}^m(x) = (-1)^m (1 - x^2)^{m/2} (d^m P_l/dx^m)$, called the associated Legendre functions, are solutions of the differential equation $(d/dx)[(1 - x^2)(df/dx)] + [l(l + 1) - (m^2/(1 - x^2))]f = 0$. These functions are orthogonal for different l and the same m.

7. The functions of two variables (the angles θ and ϕ), $Y_{l,m}(\theta, \phi)$, formed by multiplying the normalized associated Legendre functions by the harmonic functions $e^{im\phi}/(2\pi)^{-1/2}$, are orthonormal and complete on the intervals $0 \le \theta \le \pi$ and $0 \le \phi \le 2\pi$.

This section has attempted to present the two following ideas.

1. An illustration of the ways of forming the important special functions of mathematical physics: orthogonalization, power series solution of a differential equation, and generating function.

2. A record for the student's use—but by no means his memorization—of some of the important properties of a number of functions which occur in chemistry. The behavior of these functions, even in a qualitative way, gives useful information about chemical systems. For example, since $P_{2l+1}(0) = 0$, the p and f atomic orbitals have no electron density perpendicular to their axes. The student should endeavor to become as familiar with the Legendre (and other) functions as he is with sines and cosines, so that he may easily picture the behavior of chemical systems which these functions describe.

For the most part, these and other facts can be found elsewhere. Some students, hopefully, will come to enjoy the mathematical manipulations—investigating the properties of integrals and derivatives—but this is not usually the most important part of attacking a physical problem.

This section concludes with a summary of the occurrence of the special functions of use in quantum chemistry.

Special functions of quantum chemistry

Harmonic, $\{e^{imx}\}$.

 Differential equation: $(d^2f/dx^2) + m^2f = 0$.
 Orthogonalization: on $[0, 2\pi]$.
 Normalization: multiply by $(2\pi)^{-1/2}$.
 Occurrence: translational motion.

Legendre, $\{P_l(x)\}$.

      Differential equation: $(1 - x^2)(d^2f/dx^2) - 2x\, df/dx + l(l + 1)f = 0$.

      Orthogonalization: on $[-1, 1]$ from $\{x^n\}$.

      Normalization: $[(2l + 1)/2]^{1/2}$.

      Generating function: $(1 - 2xt + t^2)^{-1/2} = \sum_n P_n(x)t^n$.

      Occurrence: angular motion.

Associated Legendre, $\{P_l^m(x)\}$.

      Differential equation: $(1 - x^2)(d^2f/dx^2) - 2x(df/dx) + [l(l + 1) - m^2/(1 - x^2)]f = 0$.

      Orthogonalization: for same m, different l, on $[-1, 1]$.

      Normalization: $[(2l + 1)(l - m)!/2(l + m)!]^{1/2}$.

      Occurrence: angular motion.

Laguerre, $\{L_n(x)\}$.

      Differential equation:
$$x(d^2f/dx^2) + (df/dx) - (\tfrac{1}{2} + x/4 + n)f = 0.$$

      Orthogonalization: on $[0, \infty)$, from $\{e^{-x/2}x^n\}$.

      Normalization: $1/n!$.

      Generating function: $\exp[-xt/(1 - t)]/(1 - t) = \sum_n L_n(x)t^n$.

      Occurrence: radial motion.

Hermite, $\{H_n(x)\}$.

      Differential equation: $(d^2f/dx^2) - 2x(df/dx) + 2nf = 0$.

      Orthogonalization: on $(-\infty, \infty)$, from $\{\exp[-x^2/2]x^n\}$.

      Normalization: $[1/2^n n! \pi^{1/2}]^{1/2}$.

      Generating function: $\exp[2tx - t^2] = \sum_n H_n(x)t^n/n!$.

      Occurrence: harmonic oscillator.

Problems

1. Show that the set of functions $\{\sin mx, \cos nx\}$, for positive, integral values of m and n, are orthogonal on the interval $[-\pi, \pi]$.

2. Classify the following functions as even, odd, or neither even nor odd. If the function is neither even nor odd, decompose the function into the sum of an even function and an odd function. (a) x^2; (b) x^3; (c) $x \sin x$; (d) $x^3 \cos nx$ (n integral); (e) x^4; (f) $\log[(1 + x)/(1 - x)]$; (g) e^x; (h) e^{ix}.

3. Show that the sets of functions $\{\sin mx\}$, $\{\cos mx\}$ are orthogonal on

the interval $[0, \pi]$. Find, on this interval, the norms of these functions. Calculate the expansion coefficients for an expansion in these sets of functions.

4. Expand the function $x - x^2$ on the interval $[-\pi, \pi]$; on the interval $[0, \pi]$ in sines; on the interval $[0, \pi]$ in cosines. Which expansion converges most rapidly on $[0, \pi]$?

5. Expand the function $\sin^2 x$ in a sine series and a cosine series on $[0, \pi]$. Which expansion converges most rapidly? Compare the situation with that of Problem 4.

6. Using the information and results of Problems 4 and 5 and the expansion theorem, calculate the inner product $\langle \sin x \mid x - x^2 \rangle$ on $[0, \pi]$.

7. Show that the functions $\{e^{imx}\}$ are orthogonal on the interval $[0, 2\pi]$. Find the norm of these functions. Calculate the expansion coefficients for an expansion in these functions. Compare these coefficients with the usual expansion coefficients in a Fourier series.

8. A *square wave* is defined by $f(x) = a$ for $0 < x < \pi$, $f(x) = -a$ for $-\pi < x < 0$. Carry out a Fourier series expansion for the square wave.

9. A *triangular wave* is defined by $f(x) = x + \pi$ on $-\pi \leq x \leq 0$, $f(x) = \pi - x$ on $0 \leq x \leq \pi$. Carry out a Fourier series expansion for the triangular wave.

10. Show that the functions $\{\exp[2ni\pi x/(b - a)]\}$ are orthogonal on the interval $[a, b]$.

11. A Taylor series about zero is an expansion in powers of x. Is the Taylor series an expansion in orthogonal functions? Show how different sets of orthonormal functions may be constructed from the powers of x used in the Taylor series.

12. The functions $\{\sin^n x\}$, for $n = 0, 1, 2, \ldots$ are not an orthonormal set. Show that the orthonormal set which can be constructed from this set on the interval $[-\pi, \pi]$ are just the functions of Problem 1.

13. Use the differential equation, Eq. 2–110, to prove that the associated Legendre functions are, in fact, orthogonal as stated.

14. Verify the orthogonalization of the Laguerre polynomials as stated in the list of special functions; verify their normalization.

15. Verify the normalization of the Hermite polynomials as stated in the list of special functions.

16. Expand the function e^x in Legendre, Hermite, and Laguerre polynomials, and compare the results. Notice that the expansion intervals are quite different.

17. The discussion of the Schmidt procedure was somewhat arbitrary in the choice of the expansion interval. With a number of trial examples, show

what effect changing the expansion interval has on the orthogonal functions.

18. In spectroscopy, *selection rules* govern what transitions between energy levels are allowed. For so-called *electric dipole transitions*, the intensity of a spectroscopic absorption is proportional to $|\langle \psi_1 | x\psi_2 \rangle|^2$, which is called the *transition dipole moment*. Calculate the transition dipole moment for the following transitions of the harmonic oscillator, where $\psi_n(x) = \exp[-x^2/2]H_n(x)$.

$$\psi_1 \rightarrow \psi_2 \qquad \psi_2 \rightarrow \psi_3$$
$$\psi_1 \rightarrow \psi_3 \qquad \psi_3 \rightarrow \psi_4$$
$$\psi_1 \rightarrow \psi_4$$

Do you see a pattern emerging? Can you formulate and prove the general selection rules for the harmonic oscillator?

3

Linear Algebra

We mentioned briefly in Chapter 1 that quantum mechanics may be looked upon from two points of view. The first, Schrödinger's wave mechanics, casts eigenvalue equations in the form of differential equations of functions of one or more variables. With this in mind, we studied in depth the concept of orthogonal functions in Chapter 2 in order to establish the kind of language needed to discuss the Schrödinger wave functions. We concluded by solving one such differential equation, Legendre's differential equation, and related the solution to the established concepts and behavior of orthonormal functions.

The second point of view from which quantum mechanics can be studied is Heisenberg's matrix mechanics. In this chapter we shall be concerned with building up the vocabulary of algebra that is used in studying matrix mechanics. We shall also introduce in a more complete fashion the entities called operators, which were mentioned in Chapter 1, and derive some traditional results of interest and importance in quantum chemistry.

3–1 INTRODUCTION

With no further ado, we begin with a barrage of definitions.

Definition An n-dimensional *vector* α is an n-tuple, or list of n numbers: $\alpha = (\alpha_1, \alpha_2, \ldots, \alpha_n)$. The n numbers $\alpha_1, \alpha_2, \ldots, \alpha_n$ are called the *components* of the vector; they are arranged in a prespecified order; they may be real or complex.

We shall denote vectors by Greek letters. An example is a conventional physical vector in three-dimensional space represented by three numbers that denote the $x, y,$ and z components, respectively.

Definition A *vector space* is a set of vectors with two properties:
(a) A unique, commutative sum is defined by $\alpha^1 + \alpha^2 = \alpha^2 + \alpha^1 = (\alpha_1^1 + \alpha_1^2, \alpha_2^1 + \alpha_2^2, \ldots, \alpha_n^1 + \alpha_n^2)$.
(b) Any vector α and any scalar c define a unique product $c\alpha = (c\alpha_1, c\alpha_2, \ldots, c\alpha_n)$ which is both distributive [i.e., $c(\alpha + \beta) = c\alpha + c\beta$] and associative [i.e., $(c_1 c_2)\alpha = c_1(c_2\alpha)$].

The student should realize that these properties are familiar in the case of three-dimensional physical vectors. We denote members of a *set* of vectors with a superscript, $\{\alpha^i\}$, but components of a single vector with a subscript.

Definition A *Euclidean vector space* is a vector space for which the components of the vectors are real, and such that with any two vectors we may associate a real *inner product* $\langle \alpha \mid \beta \rangle = \alpha_1\beta_1 + \alpha_2\beta_2 + \cdots + \alpha_n\beta_n$, that is symmetric [$\langle \alpha \mid \beta \rangle = \langle \beta \mid \alpha \rangle$], bilinear [$\langle \alpha + \beta \mid \gamma \rangle = \langle \alpha \mid \gamma \rangle + \langle \beta \mid \gamma \rangle$], and positive [$\langle \alpha \mid \alpha \rangle \geq 0$].

This definition of inner product uses the same symbol, $\langle \mid \rangle$, that was used for inner products of functions.

A slightly different, and more general, definition of inner product is involved in the definition of a slightly different, and more general, vector space.

Definition A *Hermitian vector space* is a vector space for which the components of the vectors may be complex, and such that with any two vectors α and β, we may associate a complex inner product $\langle \alpha \mid \beta \rangle = \alpha_1^*\beta_1 + \alpha_2^*\beta_2 + \cdots + \alpha_n^*\beta_n$, which is Hermitian [$\langle \alpha \mid \beta \rangle = \langle \beta \mid \alpha \rangle^*$], bilinear [$\langle \alpha + \beta \mid \gamma \rangle = \langle \alpha \mid \gamma \rangle + \langle \beta \mid \gamma \rangle$], and positive [$\langle \alpha \mid \alpha \rangle \geq 0$].

Two comparisons should be made. First, compare the definition of inner product that appears here

$$\langle \alpha \mid \beta \rangle = \sum_i \alpha_i^*\beta_i \qquad (3\text{--}1)$$

with that of Chapter 2 (Eq. 2–1)

$$\langle f \mid g \rangle = \int f(x)^* g(x) \, dx$$

The difference is that the vector inner product is defined by a sum over a discrete index, whereas the function inner product is defined by an integral over a continuous variable. This difference—the exchange of a discrete index for a continuous variable—is much of what distinguishes the Heisenberg from the Schrödinger picture.

Again, notice the difference between Euclidean and Hermitian vector spaces: the inner product in a Euclidean vector space is real and symmetric; in a Hermitian vector space the inner product is complex and Hermitian. This property of inner products in Hermitian vector spaces should recall the analogous property of the inner product of two functions: *Transposing an inner product gives the complex conjugate of that inner product.*

Definition   Two vectors are said to be *orthogonal* if their inner product is zero.

This definition is strictly parallel to the definition of orthogonality of functions; it makes the concept of orthogonality one of sweeping generality, and establishes a connection to the familiar property of perpendicular vectors.

Definition   Again, by analogy with the material on functions which has gone before, we define the *norm* of a vector by $N(\alpha) = \langle \alpha \mid \alpha \rangle = |\alpha|^2$.

The norm corresponds to the length of a vector in physical three-dimensional space. Two final definitions continue the parallel structure of the algebra of vector spaces with the calculus of functions.

Definition   A vector is said to be *normalized* if its norm is one.

Definition   An *orthonormal set of vectors* is a set of vectors, each of which is normalized, and each of which is orthogonal to every other vector in the set.

As an illustration of these definitions, we prove Schwarz's inequality.

Theorem   *Schwarz's inequality:* $|\langle \alpha \mid \beta \rangle| \leq |\alpha| \cdot |\beta|$.

If either α or β is zero, the equality sign obtains, and the theorem is trivial. If neither α nor β is zero, we construct the theorem with the aid of two arbitrary scalars, c and d. By the positiveness property of inner products,

$$0 \leq \langle c\alpha + d\beta \mid c\alpha + d\beta \rangle \tag{3-2}$$

and, by bilinearity,

$$0 \leq c^* \langle \alpha \mid c\alpha + d\beta \rangle + d^* \langle \beta \mid c\alpha + d\beta \rangle$$
$$\leq c^* c \langle \alpha \mid \alpha \rangle + c^* d \langle \alpha \mid \beta \rangle + d^* c \langle \beta \mid \alpha \rangle + d^* d \langle \beta \mid \beta \rangle \tag{3-3}$$

This equation is true for any value of c and d; therefore, it must be true for the particular values $c = - \langle \alpha \mid \beta \rangle$, and $d = \langle \alpha \mid \alpha \rangle$. With this, Eq. 3-3 yields

$$0 \leq c^* cd - c^* dc - d^* cc^* + d^* d \langle \beta \mid \beta \rangle$$
$$\leq d[-c^* c + d^* \langle \beta \mid \beta \rangle] \tag{3-4}$$

so that

$$0 \leq - \mid \langle \alpha \mid \beta \rangle \mid^2 + \langle \alpha \mid \alpha \rangle \langle \beta \mid \beta \rangle \tag{3-5}$$

or

$$\mid \langle \alpha \mid \beta \rangle \mid^2 \leq \mid \alpha \mid^2 \mid \beta \mid^2 \tag{3-6}$$
$$\mid \langle \alpha \mid \beta \rangle \mid \leq \mid \alpha \mid \mid \beta \mid \tag{3-7}$$

Having established definitions of inner product and norm which apply to both functions and vectors, we may apply to vectors results which were studied in detail for functions. We proceed to a consideration of sets of vectors; our results will, to a large extent, parallel the results obtained in our earlier study of sets of functions.

The concept of completeness of a set of functions has an analog in terms of vector spaces.

Definition A vector space is *spanned* by a set of vectors $\{\alpha^i\}$ if any vector in the vector space can be expressed as a linear combination of the set $\{\alpha^i\}$.

This definition should be easily pictured in terms of the usual three-dimensional Euclidean vector space (which we shall call 3D space hereafter). As an example, the vectors $(1, 0, 0)$, $(0, 1, 0)$, $(0, 0, 1)$ *span* 3D space. These are just the unit vectors in the three coordinate directions, and it is a familiar fact that any vector may be expressed as a linear combination of the three unit vectors. This definition prompts a more rigorous interpretation of the idea of dimension.

> **Definition** The *dimension* of a vector space is the minimum number of vectors required to span the vector space.

In the example given above, no two vectors are sufficient to span 3D space, but four vectors, say, $(1, 0, 0)$, $(0, 1, 0)$, $(0, 0, 1)$, and $(1, 1, 1)$ are redundant. Any one of them could be omitted and the remaining three would span 3D space. Of course, not all sets of three vectors span 3D space. The vectors $(1, 0, 0)$, $(0, 1, 0)$, $(1, 1, 0)$, although three (the dimension) in number, do not span 3D space. Hopefully, the reader can see why. These vectors are linearly dependent, and so one is redundant. The concept of linear independence thus makes an appearance again in our consideration of vector spaces.

> **Definition** A set of vectors α^1, α^2, . . . , α^n is *linearly independent* if the equation
>
> $$c_1\alpha^1 + c_2\alpha^2 + \cdots + c_n\alpha^n = \sum_i c_i\alpha^i = 0 \qquad (3\text{-}8)$$
>
> requires all $c_i = 0$. The set $\{\alpha_i\}$ is *linearly dependent* if Eq. 3-8 can be solved with some $c_i \neq 0$.

These properties of vector spaces allow the convenient concept of a basis.

> **Definition** A *basis* of (or for) a vector space is *some* linearly independent set of vectors that spans the vector space; an *orthonormal basis* of a vector space is some orthonormal set which spans the space.

These definitions should recall the process used to form an orthonormal set of functions from a linearly independent set, the Schmidt orthogonalization procedure. This procedure may be used for vectors with no modification. If the linearly independent set is notated $\{\alpha^i\}$ and the orthonormal set $\{\phi^i\}$, the pertinent formulas are

$$\phi^k = N_k^{-1/2}(\alpha^k - \sum_{j=0}^{k-1} \langle \phi^j \mid \alpha^k \rangle \phi^j) \qquad (3\text{-}9)$$

$$N_k = \langle \alpha^k \mid \alpha^k \rangle - \sum_{j=0}^{k-1} |\langle \phi^j \mid \alpha^k \rangle|^2 \qquad (3\text{-}10)$$

With this background, in almost all respects parallel to that of orthonormal functions, it should be clear that all the algebraic "machinery" is now available for the expansion of vectors in terms of an orthonormal set of vectors. Precisely the same derivation that was set aside from the text in Chapter 2, Eqs. 2–19 through 2–24, applies to the vector problem. We have, therefore, the expansion of an arbitrary vector ξ in the set $\{\phi^i\}$, according to

$$\xi = \sum_i c_i \phi^i \qquad (3\text{-}11)$$

with the expansion coefficients (perhaps complex)

$$c_i = \langle \phi^i \mid \xi \rangle \qquad (3\text{-}12)$$

We may also borrow from Chapter 2 the expansion theorem for inner products,

$$\langle \xi \mid \eta \rangle = \sum_i \langle \xi \mid \phi^i \rangle \langle \phi^i \mid \eta \rangle \qquad (3\text{-}13)$$

where the set $\{\phi^i\}$ is orthonormal.

One departure—a useful one—from the parallel study of vector spaces and functions is that for finite-dimensional vector spaces we may carry out straightforward tests to determine whether or not a set of vectors is linearly independent. The reader may recall that this question was generally bypassed offhand in talking about sets of functions, and we relied there more on intuition than on thorough reasoning.

For sets of vectors, however, we may carefully make an analysis to determine if the set (finite) is linearly independent. This analysis makes a fitting conclusion to this section and an introduction to the next, since the mathematical element called a *matrix* appears.

In considering linear independence, we want to try to find some c_i's, not zero, that satisfy Eq. 3–8. In order to make this search something better than trial and error, a simple procedure has been developed.

Line up the vectors in rows. Suppose there are three vectors α, β, γ, each of which has four components. Our lineup looks like this:

$$
\begin{array}{cccc}
\alpha_1 & \alpha_2 & \alpha_3 & \alpha_4 \\
\beta_1 & \beta_2 & \beta_3 & \beta_4 \\
\gamma_1 & \gamma_2 & \gamma_3 & \gamma_4
\end{array}
$$

Begin with the bottom row. We can surely find some multiple of α_1, which, when added to γ_1, gives 0. In fact, that multiple is $-\gamma_1/\alpha_1$. Multiply all the α_i's (the first row) by this constant, and add to the bottom row. Our lineup now looks like this:

$$
\begin{array}{cccc}
\alpha_1 & \alpha_2 & \alpha_3 & \alpha_4 \\
\beta_1 & \beta_2 & \beta_3 & \beta_4 \\
0 & \gamma_2 - \dfrac{\gamma_1\alpha_2}{\alpha_1} & \gamma_3 - \dfrac{\gamma_1\alpha_3}{\alpha_1} & \gamma_4 - \dfrac{\gamma_1\alpha_4}{\alpha_1}
\end{array}
$$

In the same way, we can "annihilate" β_1 by finding a multiple of α_1 that when added to β_1 gives 0. By continuing this process (next annihilating γ_2), we tend toward a lineup that looks like this:

$$
\begin{array}{cccc}
\times & \times & \times & \times \\
0 & \times & \times & \times \\
0 & 0 & \times & \times
\end{array}
$$

A lineup like this, with no row all zeros when the lower left corner is all zeros, indicates that no linear combination of the α, β, γ vectors adds to zero, and the vectors are linearly independent. If, however, the lineup were to come out

$$
\begin{array}{cccc}
\times & \times & \times & \times \\
0 & \times & \times & \times \\
0 & 0 & 0 & 0
\end{array}
$$

then there was some linear combination of the α, β, and γ vectors which added to zero (final last row), and the vectors would be linearly dependent.

This idea can now be expressed in formal terms.

Definition A rectangular array of scalars (real or complex) is called a *matrix*. The scalar located in the *i*th row and *j*th column is called the *i, j element* of the matrix. A matrix with *n* rows and *m* columns is designated an $n \times m$ matrix.

Definition The *elementary row operations* which may be performed on a matrix are

1. Multiplying a row by a constant.
2. Adding two rows together.
3. Exchanging two rows.

Definition The *diagonal* (or, *principal diagonal*) of a matrix *A* consists of the elements $\{a_{ii}\}$, that is, $a_{11}, a_{22}, a_{33}, \cdots$, and so forth. These elements are called the *diagonal elements*.

Definition A matrix, all of whose elements below and to the left of the diagonal are zero, is called a *triangular matrix*.

Definition Matrices which may be formed from one another by elementary row operations are said to be *row equivalent*.

Theorem A set of vectors is said to be linearly independent if the components of these vectors may be made the rows of a matrix which is row equivalent to a triangular matrix containing no all-zero rows.

This theorem expresses the method that we have outlined for testing for linear independence. The theorem and the method will be clearer with two examples.

EXAMPLE 1

Are the vectors $(1, -1, 3)$, $(2, -4, 1)$, $(0, 3, 2)$ linearly independent? We form the matrix (contained in parentheses) and perform elementary row operations on this matrix.

$$\begin{pmatrix} 1 & -1 & 3 \\ 2 & -4 & 1 \\ 0 & 3 & 2 \end{pmatrix}$$

The 3, 1 element is already zero. Force the 2, 1 element to be zero by adding to the second row -2 times the first row.

$$\frac{[\text{2nd row}]}{-2 \times [\text{1st row}]} \rightarrow \begin{pmatrix} 1 & -1 & 3 \\ 0 & -2 & -5 \\ 0 & 3 & 2 \end{pmatrix}$$

For simplicity, multiply the second row by $-\frac{1}{2}$.

$$—[2\text{nd row}] \times (-\tfrac{1}{2}) \to \begin{pmatrix} 1 & -1 & 3 \\ 0 & 1 & \tfrac{5}{2} \\ 0 & 3 & 2 \end{pmatrix}$$

Force the 3, 2 element to be zero by multiplying the second row by -3 and adding to the third row.

$$\frac{[3\text{rd row}]}{-3 \times [2\text{nd row}]} \to \begin{pmatrix} 1 & -1 & 3 \\ 0 & 1 & \tfrac{5}{2} \\ 0 & 0 & -\tfrac{11}{2} \end{pmatrix}$$

The matrix is now in triangular form. All rows contain at least one non-zero element; therefore, the vectors are linearly independent.

EXAMPLE 2

Are the vectors $(1, 2i, 1 + i)$, $(4, 6 - i, 7)$, and $(-2, -6 + 5i, -5 + 2i)$ linearly independent? We again form the matrix and systematically perform elementary row operations.

$$\begin{pmatrix} 1 & 2i & 1 + i \\ 4 & 6 - i & 7 \\ -2 & -6 + 5i & -5 + 2i \end{pmatrix}$$

$$—[3\text{rd}] + 2 \times [1\text{st}] \to \begin{pmatrix} 1 & 2i & 1 + i \\ 4 & 6 - i & 7 \\ 0 & -6 + 9i & -3 + 4i \end{pmatrix}$$

$$—[2\text{nd}] - 4 \times [1\text{st}] \to \begin{pmatrix} 1 & 2i & 1 + i \\ 0 & 6 - 9i & 3 - 4i \\ 0 & -6 + 9i & -3 + 4i \end{pmatrix}$$

$$—[3\text{rd}] + [2\text{nd}] \to \begin{pmatrix} 1 & 2i & 1 + i \\ 0 & 6 - 9i & 3 - 4i \\ 0 & 0 & 0 \end{pmatrix}$$

The matrix is now in triangular form. One row is all zeros; therefore, the vectors are linearly dependent. We can go back and find the constants that satisfy Eq. 3–8:

$$2\alpha^1 + \alpha^3 + (-4\alpha^1 + \alpha^2) = 0$$
$$-2\alpha^1 + \alpha^2 + \alpha^3 = 0$$

In this section we have developed the properties of vectors in a way parallel to those developed for functions. The Schmidt orthogonalization procedure, expansion in an orthonormal basis set, and the expansion theorem are results which may be borrowed from Chapter 2. A simple test for linear independence has been demonstrated. This test introduces algebraic elements called matrices, and some of their properties and parts, such as elements, diagonals, rows and columns, and row equivalence.

3-2 MATRICES, DETERMINANTS, AND LINEAR EQUATIONS

Matrices. The definition of a matrix was introduced in the previous section as a formal aid to the test for linear independence of vectors. However, matrices have more applications than to serve as aids in this one kind of problem. From the point of view of quantum mechanics, matrices will be used to represent operators, as was hinted at in Chapter 1. This use of matrices will be studied in detail in Section 4 of this chapter, and prompts our consideration of more of the properties of matrices at this time.

> **Definition** Two matrices may be added if they have the same dimensions. The *sum* of an $n \times m$ matrix A and an $n \times m$ matrix B is an $n \times m$ matrix C whose elements are given by the formula

$$c_{ij} = a_{ij} + b_{ij} \tag{3-14}$$

That is, matrices are added by adding their elements. We shall notate matrices by capital letters, and their elements by lower case letters.

EXAMPLE

$$\begin{pmatrix} 1 & 3 & 2 & 5 \\ 0 & 7 & 9 & 4 \\ 6 & -2 & 5 & 1 \end{pmatrix} + \begin{pmatrix} 4 & -3 & 1 & -6 \\ 0 & 0 & -2 & 1 \\ 1 & -1 & 1 & -1 \end{pmatrix} = \begin{pmatrix} 5 & 0 & 3 & -1 \\ 0 & 7 & 7 & 5 \\ 7 & -3 & 6 & 0 \end{pmatrix}$$

The definition of addition is not one which surprises students. The definition of multiplication, however, does not resemble the usual idea of multiplying two numbers.

> **Definition** Two matrices may be multiplied if the multiplier has the same number of columns as the multiplicand has rows. The *product* of an $n \times m$ matrix A and an $m \times p$ matrix B is an $n \times p$ matrix C whose elements are given by the formula

$$c_{ij} = \sum_{k=1}^{m} a_{ik} b_{kj} \tag{3-15}$$

Notice the rule which restricts the matrices which can be multiplied.

$$\left(n \times m \right) \cdot \left(m \times p \right) = \left(n \times p \right)$$

In particular, square matrices of the same dimension may always be multiplied.

$$\left(n \times n \right) \cdot \left(n \times n \right) = \left(n \times n \right)$$

Since we shall be representing operators by square matrices, their properties are of particular importance to us.

Compare the way in which a product of two matrices is formed to the way in which a sum is formed. Matrices are added by adding their elements, but matrices are not multiplied simply by multiplying their elements. Although we shall have many occasions to use Eq. 3–15 per se, nevertheless, it is useful to see what that equation means in terms of the actual operations. Suppose we wish to compute the product of a 2 × 3 and a 3 × 4 matrix. The result is a 2 × 4 matrix. The 2, 3 element would be given by

$$c_{23} = \sum_{k=1}^{3} a_{2k}b_{k3} = a_{21}b_{13} + a_{22}b_{23} + a_{23}b_{33} \qquad (3\text{–}16)$$

A diagram might help visualize what elements these are.

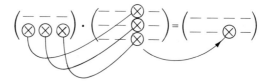

Often people (even professionals) will multiply matrices by running their left forefinger across the row of the multiplier (left) matrix, and their right forefinger down the column of the multiplicand (right) matrix.

EXAMPLE 1

As an example, find the product shown below·

$$\begin{pmatrix} 3 & 1 & 2 \\ 1 & 2 & 3 \end{pmatrix}\begin{pmatrix} 1 & 0 & 1 & 0 \\ 0 & 1 & 0 & 1 \\ 1 & 0 & 1 & 0 \end{pmatrix} = \begin{pmatrix} c_{11} & c_{12} & c_{13} & c_{14} \\ c_{21} & c_{22} & c_{23} & c_{24} \end{pmatrix}$$

By Eq. 3–15 we compute the eight matrix elements:

$$c_{11} = 3{\cdot}1 + 1{\cdot}0 + 2{\cdot}1 = 5 \qquad c_{21} = 1{\cdot}1 + 2{\cdot}0 + 3{\cdot}1 = 4$$
$$c_{12} = 3{\cdot}0 + 1{\cdot}1 + 2{\cdot}0 = 1 \qquad c_{22} = 1{\cdot}0 + 2{\cdot}1 + 3{\cdot}0 = 2$$
$$c_{13} = 3{\cdot}1 + 1{\cdot}0 + 2{\cdot}1 = 5 \qquad c_{23} = 1{\cdot}1 + 2{\cdot}0 + 3{\cdot}1 = 4$$
$$c_{14} = 3{\cdot}0 + 1{\cdot}1 + 2{\cdot}0 = 1 \qquad c_{24} = 1{\cdot}0 + 2{\cdot}1 + 3{\cdot}0 = 2$$

The product is

$$\begin{pmatrix} 5 & 1 & 5 & 1 \\ 4 & 2 & 4 & 2 \end{pmatrix}$$

The student should verify these elements, and also confirm the "forefinger method" for multiplying the two matrices shown.

EXAMPLE 2

Work out the product of two square matrices shown below.

$$\begin{pmatrix} 1 & 2 \\ 3 & 4 \end{pmatrix}\begin{pmatrix} 4 & 3 \\ 2 & 1 \end{pmatrix} = \begin{pmatrix} 8 & 5 \\ 20 & 13 \end{pmatrix}$$

Another peculiar property of matrix multiplication is that it is noncommutative. The multiplication of scalars, and the addition of scalars and matrices are all commutative operations: $ab = ba$, $a + b = b + a$, $A + B = B + A$. Matrix multiplication is, in general, not commutative: $AB \neq BA$. We can be concerned with commutation only for square matrices, since nonsquare matrices cannot be multiplied in both directions. In Example 2 above,

$$\begin{pmatrix} 1 & 2 \\ 3 & 4 \end{pmatrix}\begin{pmatrix} 4 & 3 \\ 2 & 1 \end{pmatrix} = \begin{pmatrix} 8 & 5 \\ 20 & 13 \end{pmatrix} \neq \begin{pmatrix} 13 & 20 \\ 5 & 8 \end{pmatrix} = \begin{pmatrix} 4 & 3 \\ 2 & 1 \end{pmatrix}\begin{pmatrix} 1 & 2 \\ 3 & 4 \end{pmatrix}$$

We continue our discussion of the elementary arithmetic of matrices by mentioning two matrices which are the analogs of the numbers zero and one. The *zero*, or *null matrix*, 0, is a matrix, all of whose elements are zero. Analogous to the number zero, the zero matrix is the matrix that, when added to any matrix (of the same dimensions), gives the same matrix for the sum:

$$A + 0 = A \qquad (3\text{-}17)$$

The *identity, or unit matrix,* E (denoted by some I or 1), is the (square) matrix whose diagonal elements are all ones, and whose off-diagonal elements are all zeros. This definition may be made very concise by the use of the Kronecker delta. We define

$$e_{ii} = 1 \qquad (3\text{-}18a)$$

for all i and

$$e_{ij} = 0 \qquad (3\text{-}18b)$$

for all $i \neq j$. This is equivalent to defining

$$e_{ij} = \delta_{ij} \qquad (3\text{-}18c)$$

The identity matrix, defined only for square matrices, has a property analogous to the number one, namely, the product of E with any matrix (square and of the same dimension as E) gives that matrix as product: $EA = A$.

For practice in using the general formula, Eq. 3–15, we prove that E commutes with all matrices (of the same dimension). The i, j element of the product EA is

$$(EA)_{ij} = \sum_k e_{ik} a_{kj} = \sum_k \delta_{ik} a_{kj} = a_{ij} \qquad (3\text{-}19)$$

but

$$(AE)_{ij} = \sum_k a_{ik} e_{kj} = \sum_k a_{ik} \delta_{kj} = a_{ij} = (EA)_{ij} \qquad (3\text{-}20)$$

That there is a matrix with properties analogous to the number one prompts us to ask whether there is an analog to the reciprocal (and therefore to division) for matrices.

Definition   The *inverse* of a square matrix A, denoted A^{-1}, is that matrix for which $A^{-1}A = AA^{-1} = E$. *Inverse* is defined only for square matrices.

We shall discuss two ways of finding the inverse of a matrix. The first of these is quite similar to the test for linear independence introduced in the previous section. The second is defined in terms of determinants, and will be discussed somewhat later. The idea of row equivalence is the clue to the first method.

> **Theorem** A square matrix A has an inverse if and only if its rows are linearly independent. The inverse may be found by the following procedure. Perform elementary row operations on A to form E. Then, perform these same row operations in the same order on E to form A^{-1}.

Notice that a matrix, even a nonzero matrix, need not have an inverse.

As the theorem in the previous section implied, A is row equivalent to E only if the rows of A are linearly independent. The proof of this theorem is left to the interested reader to find in one of the many excellent texts on algebra. We shall illustrate the theorem by an example.

EXAMPLE
To find the inverse of

$$A = \begin{pmatrix} 1 & 2 \\ 3 & 4 \end{pmatrix}$$

we begin by performing elementary row operations on A to form E:

$$\begin{pmatrix} 1 & 2 \\ 3 & 4 \end{pmatrix} \xrightarrow[3 \times [\text{1st}]]{[\text{2nd}] -} \begin{pmatrix} 1 & 2 \\ 0 & -2 \end{pmatrix} \xrightarrow{[\text{2nd}] \div \atop -2} \begin{pmatrix} 1 & 2 \\ 0 & 1 \end{pmatrix} \xrightarrow[2 \times [\text{2nd}]]{[\text{1st}] -} \begin{pmatrix} 1 & 0 \\ 0 & 1 \end{pmatrix} = E$$

We then perform these same operations on E:

$$\begin{pmatrix} 1 & 0 \\ 0 & 1 \end{pmatrix} \xrightarrow[3 \times [\text{1st}]]{[\text{2nd}] -} \begin{pmatrix} 1 & 0 \\ -3 & 1 \end{pmatrix} \xrightarrow{[\text{2nd}] \atop \div -2}$$

$$\begin{pmatrix} 1 & 0 \\ \frac{3}{2} & -\frac{1}{2} \end{pmatrix} \xrightarrow[2 \times [\text{2nd}]]{[\text{1st}] -} \begin{pmatrix} -2 & 1 \\ \frac{3}{2} & -\frac{1}{2} \end{pmatrix} = A^{-1}$$

As a check, multiply the answer by A:

$$\begin{pmatrix} -2 & 1 \\ \frac{3}{2} & -\frac{1}{2} \end{pmatrix}\begin{pmatrix} 1 & 2 \\ 3 & 4 \end{pmatrix} = \begin{pmatrix} 1 & 0 \\ 0 & 1 \end{pmatrix}$$

This technique is cumbersome and prone to error; the student will find the technique using determinants to be somewhat safer. We conclude our discussion of matrix algebra with one further definition.

> **Definition** The *transpose* of a square matrix A, denoted A', has elements $a'_{ij} = a_{ji}$. It can be visualized by flipping the matrix A about its diagonal.

The transpose of a matrix plays an important role in quantum mechanics. Multiplication of transposes follows a simple rule,

$$(AB)' = B'A' \qquad (3\text{-}21)$$

which is also followed by inverses when they exist,

$$(AB)^{-1} = B^{-1}A^{-1} \qquad (3\text{-}22)$$

Determinants. The formal definition of a determinant is sufficiently complicated that we begin with a practical example of the use of determinants. One of the important applications of determinants is in the solution of simultaneous linear equations. As an example, consider this set of equations:

$$\begin{aligned} a_{11}x_1 + a_{12}x_2 &= b_1 \\ a_{21}x_1 + a_{22}x_2 &= b_2 \end{aligned} \qquad (3\text{-}23)$$

Writing the equations in this form does, of course, prejudice us toward a matrix point of view which we shall develop later. For the present, we solve Eqs. 3–23 by substitution. We find from the second equation that $x_2 = (b_2 - a_{21}x_1)/a_{22}$, and, substituting this result into the first equation, we obtain the solution

$$x_1 = \frac{a_{22}b_1 - a_{12}b_2}{a_{11}a_{22} - a_{12}a_{21}} \qquad (3\text{-}24)$$

The denominator of this expression contains all four of the coefficients in the simultaneous equations 3–23. In fact, this denominator is the *determinant* of a matrix which we shall call the *coefficient matrix*.

$$A = \begin{pmatrix} a_{11} & a_{12} \\ a_{21} & a_{22} \end{pmatrix} \qquad (3\text{-}25a)$$

$$\begin{vmatrix} a_{11} & a_{12} \\ a_{21} & a_{22} \end{vmatrix} \equiv a_{11}a_{22} - a_{12}a_{21} \qquad (3\text{-}25b)$$

The numerator of Eq. 3–24 may also be written as a determinant, so that the results are

$$x_1 = \frac{\begin{vmatrix} b_1 & a_{12} \\ b_2 & a_{22} \end{vmatrix}}{\begin{vmatrix} a_{11} & a_{12} \\ a_{21} & a_{22} \end{vmatrix}} \qquad x_2 = \frac{\begin{vmatrix} a_{11} & b_1 \\ a_{12} & b_2 \end{vmatrix}}{\begin{vmatrix} a_{11} & a_{12} \\ a_{21} & a_{22} \end{vmatrix}} \qquad (3\text{-}26)$$

This result is a special case of a theorem that we shall discuss later called *Cramer's rule*. The 2 × 2 determinant has the simple definition given in Eq. 3–25b. Determinants corresponding to large square matrices have a definition that is more complex, and not immediately generalizable from Eq. 3–25b.

Definition A *permutation of n integers*, P, is a way of ordering the *n* integers; there are *n*! such permutations. The *sign of a permutation*, sign P, is positive if an even number of interchanges of two indices achieves the permutation, and negative if an odd number of interchanges achieves the permutation.

EXAMPLE

For the integers (1, 2, 3), an odd permutation would be (2, 1, 3); an even permutation would be (2, 3, 1).

Definition The *determinant* of a square matrix A, denoted $|A|$ or det A, is a number, real or complex, such that

$$|A| = \sum_{\text{all perm. } P}^{n!} (\text{sign } P) a_{1,P1} a_{2,P2} \cdots a_{n,Pn} \qquad (3\text{-}27)$$

EXAMPLE

As an example of this formula for finding determinants, consider a 3 × 3 example. There are 3! = 6 terms. Evaluate

$$\begin{vmatrix} a_{11} & a_{12} & a_{13} \\ a_{21} & a_{22} & a_{23} \\ a_{31} & a_{32} & a_{33} \end{vmatrix}$$

Term	Permutation			Interchanges	Sign P
$a_{11}a_{22}a_{33}$	1	2	3	0	+
$a_{11}a_{23}a_{32}$	1	3	2	1	−
$a_{12}a_{21}a_{33}$	2	1	3	1	−
$a_{12}a_{23}a_{31}$	2	3	1	2	+
$a_{13}a_{22}a_{31}$	3	2	1	1	−
$a_{13}a_{21}a_{32}$	3	1	2	2	+

Putting these terms together, with the correct signs, we get

$$|A| = a_{11}a_{22}a_{33} + a_{12}a_{23}a_{31} + a_{13}a_{21}a_{32} - a_{11}a_{23}a_{32}$$
$$- a_{12}a_{21}a_{33} - a_{13}a_{22}a_{31} \qquad (3\text{--}28)$$

This is a cumbersome procedure at best, and there is a simpler way. We may get a clue to this simpler way by grouping together all the terms which contain a_{11}, a_{12}, and a_{13}, respectively.

$$|A| = a_{11}(a_{22}a_{33} - a_{23}a_{32}) + a_{12}(a_{23}a_{31} - a_{21}a_{33})$$
$$+ a_{13}(a_{21}a_{32} - a_{22}a_{31}) \qquad (3\text{--}29a)$$

$$= a_{11}\begin{vmatrix} a_{22} & a_{23} \\ a_{32} & a_{33} \end{vmatrix} - a_{12}\begin{vmatrix} a_{21} & a_{23} \\ a_{31} & a_{33} \end{vmatrix} + a_{13}\begin{vmatrix} a_{21} & a_{22} \\ a_{31} & a_{32} \end{vmatrix} \qquad (3\text{--}29b)$$

Eq. 3–29a illustrates the *expansion of a determinant in cofactors;* Eq. 3–29b, the *expansion of a determinant in minors*.

Definition The *cofactor*, A_{ij}, of an element a_{ij} in an $n \times n$ square matrix A is a number that can be represented by an $(n - 1) \times (n - 1)$ determinant, such that the determinant of A is given by

$$|A| = \sum_j a_{ij}A_{ij}$$

for any and all i. The *minor*, M_{ij}, of an element a_{ij} in an $n \times n$ square matrix A is a number, represented by an $(n - 1) \times (n - 1)$ determinant found by striking the ith row and jth column from A. The minor and the cofactor are related by at most a change of sign: $A_{ij} = M_{ij}(-1)^{i+j}$.

EXAMPLE

As an example, consider the 2, 3 minor and cofactor for this 4×4 matrix:

$$A = \begin{pmatrix} a_{11} & a_{12} & a_{13} & a_{14} \\ a_{21} & a_{22} & a_{23} & a_{24} \\ a_{31} & a_{32} & a_{33} & a_{34} \\ a_{41} & a_{42} & a_{43} & a_{44} \end{pmatrix} \text{----strike out 2nd row----}$$

strike out 3rd column

$$M_{23} = \begin{vmatrix} a_{11} & a_{12} & a_{14} \\ a_{31} & a_{32} & a_{34} \\ a_{41} & a_{42} & a_{44} \end{vmatrix}$$

$$A_{23} = -\begin{vmatrix} a_{11} & a_{12} & a_{14} \\ a_{31} & a_{32} & a_{34} \\ a_{41} & a_{42} & a_{44} \end{vmatrix} = (-1)^{2+3}M_{23}$$

Theorem The determinant of an $n \times n$ matrix A may be expanded in cofactors or minors:

$$\det A = \sum_j a_{ij} A_{ij} = \sum_j a_{ij} (-1)^{i+j} M_{ij} \qquad (3\text{-}30)$$

for any i.

EXAMPLE

Evaluate the 3×3 determinant shown below by expansion in minors and by direct use of Eq. 3-28.

$$\begin{vmatrix} 1 & 0 & 2 \\ 3 & 4 & -1 \\ -2 & 1 & 1 \end{vmatrix} = 1 \begin{vmatrix} 4 & -1 \\ 1 & 1 \end{vmatrix} - 0 \begin{vmatrix} 3 & -1 \\ -2 & 1 \end{vmatrix} + 2 \begin{vmatrix} 3 & 4 \\ -2 & 1 \end{vmatrix} = 5 - 0 + 22 = 27$$

$$= -3 \begin{vmatrix} 0 & 2 \\ 1 & 1 \end{vmatrix} + 4 \begin{vmatrix} 1 & 2 \\ -2 & 1 \end{vmatrix} - (-1) \begin{vmatrix} 1 & 0 \\ -2 & 1 \end{vmatrix} = 6 + 20 \\ + 1 = 27$$

$$= -2 \begin{vmatrix} 0 & 2 \\ 4 & -1 \end{vmatrix} - 1 \begin{vmatrix} 1 & 2 \\ 3 & -1 \end{vmatrix} + 1 \begin{vmatrix} 1 & 0 \\ 3 & 4 \end{vmatrix} = 16 + 7 + 4 = 27$$

$$= (1)(4)(1) + (0)(-1)(-2) + (2)(3)(1) - (1)(-1)(1) \\ - (0)(3)(1) - (2)(4)(-2) = 4 + 0 + 6 + 1 - 0 \\ + 16 = 27$$

The first equation in the example is an expansion in minors of the first row; the second, of the second row; the third, of the third row. The last equation is a direct evaluation, using Eq. 3-28, the special case of Eq. 3-27.

Expansion by minors is especially helpful if there are zeros in the determinant, as in the first equation of the previous example.

The elementary row operations that we have used to test for linear independence in vectors may also be used to aid in the evaluation of determinants.

Theorem Multiplying a row of a square matrix by a constant multiplies the determinant of that matrix by that constant.

If we expand A in cofactors of the row in question,

$$|A| = \sum_j a_{ij} A_{ij} \qquad (3\text{-}31)$$

Multiplying the ith row by a constant c gives a new matrix B, whose determinant is

$$|B| = \sum_j b_{ij}B_{ij} = \sum_j ca_{ij}A_{ij} = c\sum_j a_{ij}A_{ij} = c|A| \quad (3\text{-}32)$$

Theorem   The exchange of two rows of a matrix changes the sign of the determinant of that matrix.

This result can be proved by relying on the general definition of a determinant. Without going into details, all the terms in the expansion are the same for the original matrix and the matrix with the exchanged rows. The signs of the terms will be different throughout because one additional exchange of indices has been made. This theorem has an immediate corollary.

Corollary   A square matrix with two identical rows has a zero determinant.

This is so because exchanging the identical rows gives a determinant of opposite sign, but exchanging the identical rows must also give the same determinant. Hence $|A| = -|A|$, which is true only if $|A| = 0$. Finally, the result of performing the last elementary row operation is obtained.

Theorem   The addition of two rows of a square matrix leaves the determinant unchanged.

We may prove this by expanding the determinant of B, where the sum of the ith and kth rows of A forms the ith row of B. Use cofactors of the ith row of B.

$$|B| = \sum_j b_{ij}B_{ij} = \sum_j (a_{ij} + a_{kj})A_{ij} = \sum_j a_{ij}A_{ij} + \sum_j a_{kj}A_{ij}$$

$$(3\text{-}33)$$

The first term is the expansion of $|A|$ in cofactors of the ith row of A. The second term looks like an expansion in cofactors—it would be, if the matrix A had identical ith and kth rows. Hence the second term represents a cofactor expansion of a determinant with two identical rows; that determinant is zero. Therefore, $|B| = |A|$.

By way of recapitulation, the accompanying table gives the results of the elementary row operations on the value of a determinant.

Elementary row operation	Effect on value of determinant
1. Multiply row by constant.	Multiply determinant by constant.
2. Exchange rows.	Change sign or determinant.
3. Add rows.	No change.

We conclude this discussion of elementary properties of determinants with two further results of importance.

Theorem The determinant of the product of two square matrices is the product of their determinants: $|AB| = |A| \cdot |B|$.

Theorem The determinant of a square matrix is equal to the determinant of the transpose of that matrix: $|A| = |A'|$.

The proof of the latter theorem relies on an examination of the general definition of a determinant. All the terms are alike, and all the signs match as well. This theorem allows us to rephrase all our results about matrices in a column language rather than a row language. These statements are given in the following list, which also serves to sum up our knowledge of determinants.

Row-language statements	Analogous column-language statements
1. Expansion of a determinant by row cofactors or minors: $$|A| = \sum_i a_{ij}A_{ij}$$ $$= \sum_i a_{ij}M_{ij}(-1)^{i+j}.$$	Expansion of a determinant by column cofactors or minors: $$|A| = \sum_j a_{ij}A_{ij}$$ $$= \sum_j a_{ij}M_{ij}(-1)^{i+j}.$$
2. Multiply row by constant, multiply determinant by constant.	Multiply column by constant, multiply determinant by constant.
3. Interchange rows, change sign of determinant.	Interchange columns, change sign of determinant.
4. Matrix with two identical rows has zero determinant.	Matrix with two identical columns has zero determinant.
5. Adding two rows together leaves determinant unchanged.	Adding two columns together leaves determinant unchanged.

With this background in the properties of determinants, we may approach two problems in a simpler way. Both the problem of testing for linear independence of vectors (as rows of a matrix) and the problem of matrix inversion have been solved using row equivalence. Each of these procedures is cumbersome, especially for large matrices. A straightforward application of the properties of determinants affords a more compact solution to both of these problems.

> **Theorem** A square matrix A has an inverse if $|A| \neq 0$; the i, j element of the inverse matrix A^{-1} is

$$(A^{-1})_{ij} = \frac{A'_{ij}}{|A|} = \frac{A_{ji}}{|A|} \tag{3-34}$$

Expanding $|A|$ in cofactors, we have

$$a_{i1}A_{i1} + a_{i2}A_{i2} + \cdots + a_{in}A_{in} = |A| = \sum_j a_{ij}A_{ij} \tag{3-35}$$

but, using the same principle as we did in Eq. 3-33 to set the second term equal to zero, we have also

$$\sum_j a_{kj}A_{ij} = 0 \tag{3-36}$$

for $i \neq k$. These may be combined as

$$\sum_j a_{kj}\frac{A_{ij}}{|A|} = \delta_{ki} \tag{3-37}$$

where δ_{ik} is an element of the unit matrix E. The left side of Eq. 3-37 looks almost like a matrix product. We may make it be such by writing, for the cofactor A_{ij}, the cofactor A'_{ji} from the transposed matrix. Then the element $A'_{ji}/|A| = a_{ji}^{-1}$, since

$$\sum_j a_{kj}a_{ji}^{-1} = \delta_{ki}.$$

Notice that these elements exist only for nonzero $|A|$. Here, the symbol a_{ij}^{-1} is not used to represent $1/a_{ij}$, but to represent the i, j element of the matrix A^{-1}. This affords a more straightforward path to matrix inversion. As an example, let us do the previous example again.

EXAMPLE

Find the inverse of

$$\begin{pmatrix} 1 & 2 \\ 3 & 4 \end{pmatrix}$$

By the formula given above,

$$a_{11}^{-1} = \frac{A_{11}'}{|A|} = \frac{4}{-2} = -2$$

$$a_{12}^{-1} = \frac{A_{12}'}{|A|} = \frac{-2}{-2} = 1$$

$$a_{21}^{-1} = \frac{A_{21}'}{|A|} = \frac{-3}{-2} = \frac{3}{2}$$

$$a_{22}^{-1} = \frac{A_{22}'}{|A|} = \frac{1}{-2} = \frac{-1}{2}$$

hence

$$A^{-1} = \begin{pmatrix} -2 & 1 \\ \frac{3}{2} & -\frac{1}{2} \end{pmatrix}$$

as was found previously.

Finally, we may combine our result on linear independence and matrix inversion (derived by row-equivalence arguments) with our result on nonzero determinants and matrix inversion to yield the following result relating linear independence to nonzero determinants.

Theorem The rows of a square matrix are linearly independent if and only if the determinant of the matrix is nonzero.

Simultaneous Linear Equations. The methods of matrix and determinant algebra may be applied with force to the solution of simultaneous linear equations. The results will be stated without proof, and a number of examples will illustrate the methods.

By way of introduction to this problem, note that the general set of simultaneous linear equations may be represented as a single matrix equation. A set of m equations in n unknowns may be represented either by

$$\begin{aligned} a_{11}x_1 + a_{12}x_2 + \cdots + a_{1n}x_n &= b_1 \\ a_{21}x_1 + a_{22}x_2 + \cdots + a_{2n}x_n &= b_2 \\ \vdots \quad\quad \vdots \quad\quad\quad\quad \vdots \quad\quad \vdots \\ a_{m1}x_1 + a_{m2}x_2 + \cdots + a_{mn}x_n &= b_m \end{aligned} \qquad (3\text{-}38)$$

or by the matrix equation

$$AX = B \qquad (3\text{-}39)$$

where A is an $m \times n$ matrix of coefficients, X an $n \times 1$ matrix of unknowns, and B an $m \times 1$ matrix of constants:

$$\begin{pmatrix} a_{11} & a_{12} & \cdots & a_{1n} \\ a_{21} & a_{22} & \cdots & a_{2n} \\ \vdots & \vdots & & \vdots \\ a_{m1} & a_{m2} & \cdots & a_{mn} \end{pmatrix} \begin{pmatrix} x_1 \\ x_2 \\ \vdots \\ x_n \end{pmatrix} = \begin{pmatrix} b_1 \\ b_2 \\ \vdots \\ b_m \end{pmatrix} \qquad (3\text{-}40)$$

We shall define at the outset two concepts.

> **Definition** The *augmented matrix* for a set of m simultaneous linear equations in n unknowns is an $m \times (n + 1)$ matrix formed by appending the $m \times 1$ matrix of constants on the right of the $n \times m$ matrix of coefficients. If, for example, A and B are the matrices in Eq. 3-40, then the augmented matrix $*A$ is
>
> $$*A = \begin{pmatrix} a_{11} & a_{12} & \cdots & a_{1n} & b_1 \\ a_{21} & a_{22} & \cdots & a_{2n} & b_2 \\ \vdots & \vdots & & \vdots & \vdots \\ a_{m1} & a_{m2} & \cdots & a_{mn} & b_m \end{pmatrix} \qquad (3\text{-}41)$$
>
> **Definition** A set of simultaneous linear equations is called *homogeneous* if the matrix B is zero.

The results, offered almost entirely without proof, are expressed in the following theorems.

> **Theorem** A set of n simultaneous linear equations in n unknowns has a solution if the coefficient determinant is not zero. The solution may be constructed by matrix inversion, or by *Cramer's rule*.

If $AX = B$, then $A^{-1}AX = A^{-1}B$. So the entire set of solutions X may be generated if A^{-1} is known. However, A^{-1} exists only if $|A| \neq 0$. The result is

$$X = A^{-1}B \qquad (3\text{-}42)$$

In particular,

$$x_i = \sum_j (A^{-1})_{ij} b_j$$

$$= \sum_j \frac{A_{ji}}{|A|} b_j = \sum_j \frac{b_j A_{ji}}{|A|} \qquad (3\text{-}43)$$

Equation 3–43 involves a sum,

$$\sum_j b_j A_{ji}$$

which is the column cofactor expansion of a determinant whose ith column is the constant matrix B. However, this is Cramer's rule in its familiar form:

$$x_i = \frac{\begin{vmatrix} a_{11} \cdots b_1 \cdots a_{1n} \\ a_{21} \cdots b_2 \cdots a_{2n} \\ \vdots \quad \vdots \quad \vdots \\ a_{n1} \cdots b_n \cdots a_{nn} \end{vmatrix}}{|A|} \qquad (3\text{-}44)$$

Theorem A set of m simultaneous linear equations in n unknowns, $AX = B$, has a solution if the number of linearly independent rows, r, in A is the same as the number of linearly independent rows in *A. If such is the case, r of the unknowns may be expressed in terms of the remaining $n - r$, which may be given arbitrary values.

Theorem A set of m simultaneous, linear, homogeneous equations in n unknowns always has the trivial solution $X = 0$. There will be a nonzero (nontrivial) solution if the coefficient matrix A has fewer linearly independent rows than there are unknowns. Again, r of the unknowns may be expressed in terms of the remaining $n - r$, which may be assigned arbitrary values.

We conclude this section with a number of examples of these theorems.

EXAMPLE 1

Two linear equations in two unknowns.

$$4x + 4y = 2$$
$$8x - 2y = 4$$

The Cramer's rule solution is

$$x = \frac{\begin{vmatrix} 2 & 4 \\ 4 & -2 \end{vmatrix}}{\begin{vmatrix} 4 & 4 \\ 8 & -2 \end{vmatrix}} = \frac{-20}{-40} = \frac{1}{2}$$

$$y = \frac{\begin{vmatrix} 4 & 2 \\ 8 & -4 \end{vmatrix}}{\begin{vmatrix} 4 & 4 \\ 8 & -2 \end{vmatrix}} = \frac{0}{-40} = 0$$

The matrix solution can be found from the rule that, if $AX = C$, $X = A^{-1}C$. The inverse of the coefficient matrix is the matrix

$$\begin{pmatrix} \frac{1}{20} & \frac{1}{10} \\ \frac{1}{5} & -\frac{1}{10} \end{pmatrix}$$

Then the solution to the set of equations is

$$\begin{pmatrix} x \\ y \end{pmatrix} = \begin{pmatrix} \frac{1}{20} & \frac{1}{10} \\ \frac{1}{5} & -\frac{1}{10} \end{pmatrix} \begin{pmatrix} 2 \\ 4 \end{pmatrix} = \begin{pmatrix} \frac{2}{20} + \frac{4}{10} \\ \frac{2}{5} - \frac{4}{10} \end{pmatrix} = \begin{pmatrix} \frac{1}{2} \\ 0 \end{pmatrix}$$

This matrix equation says $x = \frac{1}{2}$, $y = 0$.

EXAMPLE 2
   Three equations in two unknowns.

$$4x + 4y = 2$$
$$8x - 2y = 4$$
$$x + y = 1$$

The matrix of coefficients,

$$\begin{pmatrix} 4 & 4 \\ 8 & -2 \\ 1 & 1 \end{pmatrix}$$

is row equivalent to

$$\begin{pmatrix} 1 & 1 \\ 0 & 10 \\ 0 & 0 \end{pmatrix}$$

and has two linearly independent rows. The augmented matrix,

$$\begin{pmatrix} 4 & 4 & 2 \\ 8 & -2 & 4 \\ 1 & 1 & 1 \end{pmatrix}$$

is row equivalent to

$$\begin{pmatrix} 1 & 1 & \frac{1}{2} \\ 0 & 1 & 0 \\ 0 & 0 & 1 \end{pmatrix}$$

and has three linearly independent rows. There is, therefore, no solution to this set of equations.

EXAMPLE 3

Three equations in two unknowns.

$$4x + 4y = 2$$
$$8x - 2y = 4$$
$$3x + \frac{y}{2} = \frac{3}{2}$$

The matrix of coefficients,

$$\begin{pmatrix} 4 & 4 \\ 8 & -2 \\ 3 & \frac{1}{2} \end{pmatrix}$$

is row equivalent to

$$\begin{pmatrix} 1 & 1 \\ 0 & 1 \\ 0 & 0 \end{pmatrix}$$

and has two linearly independent rows. The augmented matrix

$$\begin{pmatrix} 4 & 4 & 2 \\ 8 & -2 & 4 \\ 3 & \frac{1}{2} & \frac{3}{2} \end{pmatrix}$$

is row equivalent to

$$\begin{pmatrix} 1 & 1 & \frac{1}{2} \\ 0 & 1 & 0 \\ 0 & 0 & 0 \end{pmatrix}$$

and also has two linearly independent rows. This set of equations does have a solution. The solution can be obtained from any matrix row equivalent to the augmented matrix. Using this last matrix as a guide, write the *equivalent* matrix equation

$$\begin{pmatrix} 1 & 1 \\ 0 & 1 \end{pmatrix}\begin{pmatrix} x \\ y \end{pmatrix} = \begin{pmatrix} \frac{1}{2} \\ 0 \end{pmatrix}$$

The solution to this equation can be found by the usual technique (see Example 1), and is $x = \frac{1}{2}, y = 0$, which is the same as the solution to Example 1. This could also be expressed by saying that, since the equations of this example are linearly dependent, and since two of these equations are identical to the equations of Example 1, the solution to this set must also be identical to the solution to Example 1.

EXAMPLE 4

Two equations in three unknowns.

$$x + y + z = 2$$
$$x - y - z = 1$$

The coefficient matrix,

$$\begin{pmatrix} 1 & 1 & 1 \\ 1 & -1 & -1 \end{pmatrix}$$

has two linearly independent rows, since it is row equivalent to the matrix

$$\begin{pmatrix} 1 & 1 & 1 \\ 0 & -2 & -2 \end{pmatrix}$$

The augmented matrix,

$$\begin{pmatrix} 1 & 1 & 1 & 2 \\ 1 & -1 & -1 & 1 \end{pmatrix}$$

which is row equivalent to

$$\begin{pmatrix} 1 & 1 & 1 & 2 \\ 0 & -2 & -2 & -1 \end{pmatrix}$$

also has two linearly independent rows; therefore, this set of equations has a solution. As in the previous example, this set of equations can be solved by appealing to a matrix which is row equivalent to the augmented matrix, and writing

$$\begin{pmatrix} 1 & 1 & 1 \\ 0 & -2 & -2 \end{pmatrix}\begin{pmatrix} x \\ y \\ z \end{pmatrix} = \begin{pmatrix} x + y + z \\ -2y - 2z \end{pmatrix} = \begin{pmatrix} 2 \\ -1 \end{pmatrix}$$

whence, $x = 2 - y - z$ and $y + z = \frac{1}{2}$. The solution can be expressed $x = \frac{3}{2}, z = \frac{1}{2} - y$. There are an infinite number of solutions. That is, there is one solution for every possible value of y. The general solution can be checked by substitution into the equations themselves, which gives an identity in each case. One solution might be $x = \frac{3}{2}$, $y = 0$, $z = \frac{1}{2}$; another might be $x = \frac{3}{2}$, $y = 1$, $z = -\frac{1}{2}$, and so forth.

EXAMPLE 5

Two equations in three unknowns.

$$x + y + z = 2$$
$$x + y + z = 1$$

This set of equations has no solutions, which is obvious by inspection. The result can be proved by examining the coefficient matrix,

$$\begin{pmatrix} 1 & 1 & 1 \\ 1 & 1 & 1 \end{pmatrix}$$

which is row equivalent to

$$\begin{pmatrix} 1 & 1 & 1 \\ 0 & 0 & 0 \end{pmatrix}$$

and therefore has one linearly independent row. On the other hand, the augmented matrix,

$$\begin{pmatrix} 1 & 1 & 1 & 2 \\ 1 & 1 & 1 & 1 \end{pmatrix}$$

is row equivalent to

$$\begin{pmatrix} 1 & 1 & 1 & 2 \\ 0 & 0 & 0 & -1 \end{pmatrix}$$

and therefore has two linearly independent rows. Since the coefficient matrix and the augmented matrix have different numbers of linearly independent rows, there is no solution to this set of equations.

EXAMPLE 6

Three homogeneous equations in three unknowns.

$$3x + 4y + z = 0$$
$$2x + 6y + 4z = 0$$
$$x - y + z = 0$$

The coefficient matrix,

$$\begin{pmatrix} 3 & 4 & 1 \\ 2 & 6 & 4 \\ 1 & -1 & 1 \end{pmatrix}$$

has a determinant equal to 30, and three linearly independent rows, and therefore there is no solution to this set of homogeneous equations, except the trivial solution $x = y = z = 0$.

EXAMPLE 7

Three homogeneous equations in three unknowns.

$$x + y + z = 0$$
$$x - y - z = 0$$
$$x + 3y + 3z = 0$$

The coefficient matrix has a determinant

$$\begin{vmatrix} 1 & 1 & 1 \\ 1 & -1 & -1 \\ 1 & 3 & 3 \end{vmatrix} = 0$$

and there is a solution to this set of equations. To find the solution, rely again on a matrix which is row equivalent to the augmented matrix. The augmented matrix is

$$\begin{pmatrix} 1 & 1 & 1 & 0 \\ 1 & -1 & -1 & 0 \\ 1 & 3 & 3 & 0 \end{pmatrix}$$

which is row eqiuvalent to

$$\begin{pmatrix} 1 & 1 & 1 & 0 \\ 0 & 1 & 1 & 0 \\ 0 & 0 & 0 & 0 \end{pmatrix}$$

and has only two linearly independent rows. The solution of a matrix equation written from this augmented matrix is $x + y + z = 0$, and $y + z = 0$. That is to say, a general solution is $x = 0$, $y = -z$. There are any number of particular solutions, as before. One is the ever present trivial solution $x = y = z = 0$; another might be $x = 0, y = 1, z = -1$.

3–3   LINEAR TRANSFORMATIONS

In defining a function in Chapter 2, we emphasized the single value that the function delivered if presented with a single value of the independent variable on some specified interval. A transformation is a generalization of this concept.

Definition Let there exist n independent variables x_i ($i = 1$, $2, \ldots, n$), each defined on a specified interval, such as $a_1 \leq x_1 \leq b_1$, $a_2 \leq x_2 \leq b_2$, and so forth. If there then exist m dependent variables, y_i, each of which is a single-valued function of the n independent variables x_i, we say that there exists a *transformation* which carries a region in n-dimensional space (or n space) into m-dimensional space (or m space). We write $y_i = T(x_i)$, and refer to the set of values y_i as the *image* of the set of values x_i under T. We shall represent transformations with capital letters.

To continue the algebraic theme established in the first sections of this chapter, we restrict the discussion at once to linear transformations.

Definition A transformation A is linear if
1. $A(x_i + x_j) = A(x_i) + A(x_j)$
2. $A(cx_i) = cA(x_i)$
where c is a scalar.

This definition contains two aspects of linearity which should be familiar in retrospect. These two aspects necessarily imply that a linear transformation has the form

$$
\begin{aligned}
a_{11}x_1 + a_{12}x_2 + \cdots + a_{1n}x_n &= y_1 \\
\vdots \qquad \vdots \qquad\quad \vdots \\
a_{m1}x_1 + a_{m2}x_2 + \cdots + a_{mn}x_n &= y_m
\end{aligned} \tag{3-45}
$$

which, expressed in matrix language, is

$$
AX = Y \tag{3-46}
$$

where A is an $m \times n$ matrix, X an $n \times 1$ matrix, and Y an $m \times 1$ matrix. Having discovered that matrices may be used to represent linear transformations, we may call upon our past development of matrix algebra to help understand the properties of these transformations. The introduction of the term *rank* will simplify the discussion.

Definition The *rank of a matrix* is the largest number of linearly independent rows in the matrix; alternatively, the rank of a matrix is the dimension of the largest nonzero determinant which can be formed from the matrix elements. The *rank of a linear transformation* is equal to the rank of the matrix which represents the linear transformation.

The relationship between nonzero determinants and linear independence establishes the alternative definition of rank. We shall now present a general result and then illustrate it with a specific example.

> **Theorem** Suppose a linear transformation of n space into m space has rank r. The image in m space will be an r-dimensional subregion which is described by a linear equation in the m coordinates of m space. In particular, the transformation will map n space into all of m space if the transformation has rank $r = m$.

By way of proof, consider the $m \times n$ matrix which represents a linear transformation. If only r of the rows of this matrix are linearly independent, then $m - r$ of the rows are dependent. This implies that $m - r$ of the coordinates in m space are linearly dependent. As a consequence, the image of n space in m space is on an r-dimensional subregion whose equation is linear in the m coordinates.

EXAMPLE

Consider the transformation

$$\left.\begin{aligned} x + y + z = u \\ x + y + z = v \end{aligned}\right\} T$$

The rank of T is the rank of the matrix

$$\begin{pmatrix} 1 & 1 & 1 \\ 1 & 1 & 1 \end{pmatrix}$$

which has one linearly independent row; the rank is therefore one. In fact, since the rows of the matrix are the same, $u = v$. Hence the image of XYZ space on UV space is the line $u = v$, a one-dimensional subregion in UV space.

In quantum mechanics, where, as the student will learn, a premium is placed on the properties of orthogonality and normality of functions or vectors, particular attention is paid to the kinds of transformations which retain these properties. In a Euclidean vector space, this kind of transformation is called *orthogonal;* in a Hermitian vector space, the analogous transformation is called *unitary.*

Definition An *orthogonal transformation* preserves the length (normalization) and orthogonality of vectors in a Euclidean vector space; a *unitary transformation* preserves orthogonality and normalization of vectors in a Hermitian vector space.

This definition is basic, but rather sterile unless we interpret it in terms of the structure of the transformation—the relations between the matrix elements of the matrix representing the transformation. We may examine this structure by using this very definition. Suppose there is a complete, orthonormal set of vectors $\{\phi^i\}$. We have already established that an arbitrary vector α may be expanded in terms of the vectors $\{\phi^i\}$ according to

$$\alpha = \sum_i a_i \phi^i \qquad (3\text{-}47)$$

as described in Eq. 3–11 and the discussion there. Now suppose we require that the expansion of α in terms of the ϕ^i's preserve length and orthogonality. That is, suppose α is a member of a second complete orthonormal set $\{\psi^i\}$, $\alpha = \psi^j$, say. Then

$$\psi^j = \sum_i a_{ji} \phi^i \qquad (3\text{-}48)$$

The coefficient a_i in Eq. 3–47 has now been modified with a second index j indicating which of the vectors in the set $\{\psi^j\}$ is being considered. The inverse expansion is also possible (this is to be proved in one of the problems), so that

$$\phi^i = \sum_k b_{ik} \psi^k \qquad (3\text{-}49)$$

Combining these equations, we find

$$\psi^j = \sum_i a_{ji} \phi^i = \sum_i a_{ji} \sum_k b_{ik} \psi^k = \sum_k \left(\sum_i a_{ji} b_{ik} \right) \psi^k \qquad (3\text{-}50)$$

The only way for Eq. 3–50 to be true, since the ψ^i's are linearly independent, is for $\sum_i a_{ji} b_{ik} = 1$ for $j = k$, and $\sum_i a_{ji} b_{ik} = 0$ for $j \neq k$. This then gives

$$\sum_i a_{ji} b_{ik} = \delta_{jk} \tag{3-51}$$

a statement that, if expressed not in the language of expansion coefficients but in the language of matrices, becomes

$$AB = E \tag{3-52}$$

or

$$A = B^{-1} \tag{3-53}$$

This should not be surprising. The transformation from the basis
set $\{\phi^i\}$ to the basis set $\{\psi^i\}$ must be representable by a square matrix with nonzero determinant; hence, its inverse must exist. It is
only reasonable that the inverse transformation be directly related
to the reverse expansion of vectors.

We have not yet drawn upon the property that the orthonormality
of the vectors be preserved under this transformation. Equation
3-53 is a result of requiring that completeness be preserved. For
orthonormality of the ψ^i's, we have, in a Euclidean vector space,

$$\langle \psi^i \mid \psi^j \rangle = \delta_{ij} = \sum_k \sum_l \langle \phi^k b_{ik} \mid \phi^l b_{jl} \rangle$$

$$= \sum_{kl} \langle \phi^k \mid \phi^l \rangle b_{ik} b_{jl} = \sum_{kl} \delta_{kl} b_{ik} b_{jl}$$

$$= \sum_k b_{ik} b_{jk} \tag{3-54}$$

Equation 3-54 is almost a matrix product, but not quite. If we
again invoke the definition of a transpose, we derive

$$\delta_{ij} = \sum_k b_{ik} b'_{kj} \tag{3-55}$$

which implies that

$$BB' = E \tag{3-56}$$

or

$$B^{-1} = B' \tag{3-57}$$

We have thereby proven the following results.

> **Theorem** (a) The inverse of an orthogonal matrix is the transpose of that orthogonal matrix.
> (b) The inverse of a unitary matrix is the transpose complex conjugate of that matrix.
> (c) The rows of orthogonal or unitary matrices are orthonormal vectors.
> (d) The columns of orthogonal or unitary matrices are orthonormal vectors.

Part (b) can be proved by deriving Eqs. 3–54 through 3–57 again for Hermitian vectors by supplying complex conjugation at the appropriate places. Part (c) should be clear from Eq. 3–54, and (d) is analogous. The last aspect of the structure of orthogonal and unitary transformations is a statement about the determinants of their representative matrices. We know, for orthogonal transformations, that $BB' = E$; hence,

$$|B|\,|B'| = |E| = 1 \tag{3-58}$$

Since $|B'| = |B|$,

$$|B| = \pm 1 \tag{3-59}$$

Together with the analogous result for unitary transformations, we have proven the following theorem:

> **Theorem** The determinant of an orthogonal matrix is either $+1$ or -1; the determinant of a unitary matrix has modulus 1.

A particular, and useful, geometrical application of orthogonal transformations is rotation in two and three dimensions. We begin by considering a rotation in two dimensions. If a rotation through the angle α is carried out, the point p will be transformed into the point p'. The coordinates of p' are

$$\begin{aligned}
x' &= x \cos \alpha - y \sin \alpha \\
y' &= x \sin \alpha + y \cos \alpha
\end{aligned} \tag{3-60}$$

which is a set of linear equations. In matrix language, the rotational transformation may be represented by

$$R_{\text{point}} = \begin{pmatrix} \cos \alpha & -\sin \alpha \\ \sin \alpha & \cos \alpha \end{pmatrix} \tag{3-61}$$

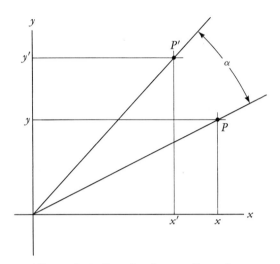

Figure 3–1   Rotation in two dimensions.

The student should notice that in this process the coordinate axes of Fig. 3–1 stay fixed but the point moves. The problem can also be described by a rotation of the coordinate axes in the opposite sense, that is, through an angle of $-\alpha$:

$$R_{\text{axis}} = \begin{pmatrix} \cos\alpha & \sin\alpha \\ -\sin\alpha & \cos\alpha \end{pmatrix} \tag{3-62}$$

Both these points of view occur, and the important point to remember is that a rotational transformation of a point has the opposite sense of a rotation of the coordinate system.

With the matrix representative of a two-dimensional rotational transformation in mind, we may now examine rotations in three dimensions. There are many possible ways to consider a three-dimensional rotation, but all these ways have two principles in common. First, three angles are, in general, necessary to describe the rotation of a three-dimensional object. Playing with an object, preferably unsymmetrical, will convince the reader of this. Second, the customary way of describing the rotation is by the following sequence.

(a) Rotation about one of the coordinate axes by an angle ϕ.

(b) Rotation about the new position of another one of the co-ordinate axes by an angle θ.

(c) Rotation about the new position of the original axis by an angle ψ.

This sequence of rotations is called a rotation through *Eulerian angles* (after the mathematician Euler). Modern writers have made different choices for the sequence, and the student should carefully note a particular writer's convention. In agreement with a number of well-known textbooks, we shall make the following choice, illustrated in Fig. 3–2.

(a) Rotation through an angle ϕ about the z axis to yield a new $x'y'z$ axis system (matrix representative A).

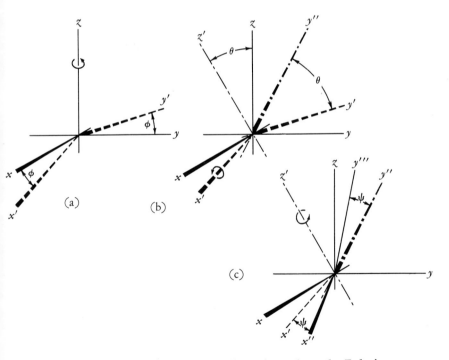

Figure 3–2 Rotation in three dimensions through Eulerian angles: (A) rotation about z by ϕ; (B) rotation about new x by θ; (C) rotation about new z by ψ.

(b) Rotation through an angle θ about the x' axis to yield a new $x'y''z'$ axis system (matrix representative B).

(c) Rotation through an angle ψ about the z' axis to yield a new, and final, $x''y'''z'$ axis system (matrix representative C).

This sequence of operations represents a rotation of the coordinate system. The matrix representatives of each separate transformation can be found by analogy with Eq. 3–62, and are

$$A = \begin{pmatrix} \cos\phi & \sin\phi & 0 \\ -\sin\phi & \cos\phi & 0 \\ 0 & 0 & 1 \end{pmatrix} \qquad (3\text{–}63a)$$

$$B = \begin{pmatrix} 1 & 0 & 0 \\ 0 & \cos\theta & \sin\theta \\ 0 & -\sin\theta & \cos\theta \end{pmatrix} \qquad (3\text{–}63b)$$

$$C = \begin{pmatrix} \cos\psi & \sin\psi & 0 \\ -\sin\psi & \cos\psi & 0 \\ 0 & 0 & 1 \end{pmatrix} \qquad (3\text{–}63c)$$

The over-all effect of these three separate rotations gives the general three-dimensional rotation matrix, R,

$R = CBA =$

$$\begin{pmatrix} \cos\psi \cos\phi - \cos\theta \sin\phi \sin\psi & \cos\psi \sin\phi + \cos\theta \cos\phi \sin\psi & \sin\psi \sin\theta \\ -\sin\psi \cos\phi - \cos\theta \sin\phi \cos\psi & -\sin\psi \sin\phi + \cos\theta \cos\phi \cos\psi & \cos\psi \sin\theta \\ \sin\theta \sin\phi & -\sin\theta \cos\phi & \cos\theta \end{pmatrix}$$

$$(3\text{–}64)$$

which, although complicated, plays an important role in the consideration of molecular rotation.

In conclusion of this section, and by way of offering a partial summary of the past two sections, the following lists show the interrelation between statements about transformations, matrices, determinants, and linear independence. The student should endeavor to realize the underlying unity of the subject, and to use it.

3–4   LINEAR OPERATORS

In this section we shall take a major step forward in realizing the application of the algebra of vector spaces to quantum mechanics.

Equivalence of statements: $n \times n$ matrices

Case 1. *Determinant is not zero.*

1. Linear independence of a set of vectors.
2. Row equivalence to unit matrix.
3. Matrix has an inverse.
4. Matrix has rank r equal to dimension n.
5. Linear transformation is a one-to-one mapping of n space onto n space.
6. Determinant of matrix is not zero.
7. Set of n simultaneous linear equations in n unknowns has a solution.

Case 2. *Determinant is zero.*

1. Linear dependence of a set of vectors.
2. Row equivalence to triangular matrix with at least one all-zero row.
3. Matrix has no inverse.
4. Matrix has rank r less than dimension n.
5. Linear transformation is a many-to-one mapping of n space onto r-dimensional subregion of n space.
6. Determinant of matrix is zero.
7. Set of n homogeneous simultaneous linear equations in n unknowns has a solution.

Equivalence of statements: $m \times n$ matrices with rank r

---

1. Linear independence of any r of the m vectors; dependence of $m - r$ of the vectors on the r independent vectors.
2. Row equivalence to triangular matrix with $m - r$ all-zero rows.
3. Linear transformation is mapping of n space onto r-dimensional subregion of m space.
4. Set of simultaneous linear equations has solution if rank of augmented matrix is also r.

Early in Chapter 1 we had mentioned the role of eigenvalue equations in quantum mechanics and seen the form which such equations take, such as Eq. 1–2. Although the description of specific operators will be left to a work on quantum mechanics per se, the general results can be set forth here. As has been our custom, we begin with a number of definitions.

> **Definition** An *operator* is a set of instructions, defined for some vector space, for changing one vector belonging to the space into another vector belonging to the space. Thus we shall write $\mathcal{A}\xi = \eta$ to mean that the result of applying a particular set of instructions, embodied in the definition of the operator $\mathcal{A}$, to the vector ξ is to form a new vector η. Operators will be notated in script letters.

We might well inquire into the difference between this definition of an operator and the definition of a transformation in the previous section. In the final analysis, there is none. The word *operator* is more often used in the context of quantum mechanics to represent particular physical quantities, whereas the word *transformation* is used to represent changes in a coordinate system. However, their definitions are identical in form, and furthermore, the definition of a linear operator is analogous to that of a linear transformation.

> **Definition** A *linear operator* $\mathcal{A}$ obeys these equations:
> (a) $\mathcal{A}(c\xi) = c\mathcal{A}\xi$, where c is a constant (perhaps complex).
> (b) $\mathcal{A}(\xi + \eta) = \mathcal{A}\xi + \mathcal{A}\eta$, where ξ and η are both vectors.

The definition of *operator* as a "set of instructions" leaves us with no way of representing operators. How may we represent linear operators? The result of operating an operator $\mathcal{A}$ on any vector can be found from the result of operating the operator $\mathcal{A}$ on the basis vectors. Suppose, for example, we know that

$$\mathcal{A}\phi^i = \sum_j A_{ij}\phi^j \tag{3-65}$$

where the set $\{\phi^j\}$ is a complete, orthonormal basis set for the vector space in question. Any vectors may be expanded in terms of the ϕ^j vectors:

$$\xi = \sum_i c_i\phi^i \qquad \eta = \sum_j d_j\phi^j \tag{3-66}$$

We may then use the operator definition, $\mathcal{A}\xi = \eta$, to relate the numbers $\{c_i\}$ and $\{d_i\}$:

$$\mathcal{A}\xi = \mathcal{A}\sum_i c_i\phi^i = \sum_{ij} c_i A_{ij}\phi^j = \eta = \sum_j d_j\phi^j \tag{3-67}$$

so that

$$d_j = \sum_i A_{ij}c_i \tag{3-68}$$

We have now only to discover what the numbers $\{A_{ij}\}$ are. This is easy if the basis set $\{\phi^i\}$ is orthonormal, for then

$$\langle \phi^j \mid \alpha\phi^i \rangle = \sum_k \langle \phi^j \mid A_{ik}\phi^k \rangle = \sum_k A_{ik}\langle \phi^j \mid \phi^k \rangle = A_{ij} \tag{3-69}$$

We often see the left side of Eq. 3-69 written with an extra vertical bar, $\langle \phi^j \mid \alpha \mid \phi^i \rangle$. This extra vertical bar adds nothing new, but only serves to call attention to the operator α in the center. An inner product like $\langle \phi^j \mid \alpha \mid \phi^i \rangle$ is often called a *matrix element*. It will be far more convenient to use these elements as we go further. For example, Eq. 3-68 can now be written

$$d_j = \sum_i \langle \phi^j \mid \alpha \mid \phi^i \rangle c_i \tag{3-70}$$

which has the form of a matrix product,

$$\begin{pmatrix} d_1 \\ d_2 \\ \vdots \\ d_n \end{pmatrix} = \begin{pmatrix} \langle \phi^1 \mid \alpha \mid \phi^1 \rangle \cdots \langle \phi^1 \mid \alpha \mid \phi^n \rangle \\ \langle \phi^2 \mid \alpha \mid \phi^1 \rangle \cdots \langle \phi^2 \mid \alpha \mid \phi^n \rangle \\ \vdots \qquad \qquad \vdots \\ \langle \phi^n \mid \alpha \mid \phi^1 \rangle \cdots \langle \phi^n \mid \alpha \mid \phi^n \rangle \end{pmatrix} \begin{pmatrix} c_1 \\ c_2 \\ \vdots \\ c_n \end{pmatrix} \tag{3-71}$$

This being the case, we shall do away with the expansion coefficients A_{ij} (small capital letter), and replace them with the usual matrix elements $a_{ji} = \langle \phi^j \mid \alpha \mid \phi^i \rangle$:

$$d_j = \sum_i A_{ij}c_i = \sum_i a_{ji}c_i \tag{3-72}$$

Here we have made use of a column matrix (an $n \times 1$ matrix) to represent a vector. An inner product may be formed from two vectors in matrix notation if the left vector is written as a $1 \times n$ row matrix and the right vector as a $n \times 1$ column matrix. Their product is, of course, a 1×1 matrix, or a scalar:

$$\langle \xi \mid \eta \rangle = [c_1 \; c_2^* \cdots c_n^*] \begin{pmatrix} d_1 \\ d_2 \\ \vdots \\ d_n \end{pmatrix} = [\;\;] \tag{3-73}$$

In our case, $\eta = \alpha\xi$.   Hence,

$$\langle \xi \mid \eta \rangle = \langle \xi \mid \alpha \mid \xi \rangle = [c_1^* \cdots c_n^*] \begin{pmatrix} a_{11} & \cdots & a_{1n} \\ \vdots & & \vdots \\ a_{n1} & \cdots & a_{nn} \end{pmatrix} \begin{pmatrix} c_1 \\ \vdots \\ c_n \end{pmatrix} \qquad (3\text{–}74)$$

Two features of importance have appeared so far.   The use of a *square matrix to represent a linear operator* and the use of a *column matrix to represent a vector*.   The particular matrices used were predicated on the choice of the basis set $\{\phi^i\}$, since the matrix elements were defined by $a_{ji} = \langle \phi^j \mid \alpha \mid \phi^i \rangle$.   Of course, *any* basis set would work. There are, therefore, any number of matrices which represent α, each matrix representative arising from a different basis.   Because of this, it would, in a strict sense, be incorrect to say that the matrix A whose elements are a_{ij} is the *same* as the operator α; accordingly, we say that the matrix *represents* α, or *is a representative of* the operator α in the basis $\{\phi^i\}$.   Similarly, we would not be strictly correct to say that the column vector

$$\begin{pmatrix} d_1 \\ d_2 \\ \vdots \\ d_n \end{pmatrix}$$

is the *same* as η, but that this column vector *is a representative of* or *represents* η.

We should then investigate the relations between two matrix representatives of a given operator.   Let A^ϕ be the representative of α in the $\{\phi^i\}$ basis, and A^ψ be the representative of α in the $\{\psi^i\}$ basis. The matrix elements are $a_{ij}^\phi = \langle \phi^i \mid \alpha \mid \phi^j \rangle$ and $a_{ij}^\psi = \langle \psi^i \mid \alpha \mid \psi^j \rangle$. Finally, let the two bases (which are orthonormal) be related by a unitary transformation,

$$\psi^i = \sum_k u_{ik}\phi^k,$$

and, in reverse,

$$\phi^i = \sum_j u_{ji}^*\psi^j = \sum_j u_{ij}'^*\psi^j.$$

The relation between the matrix elements a_{ij}^ϕ and a_{ij}^ψ is then

$$a_{ij}^\psi = \langle \psi^i | \mathcal{Q} | \psi^j \rangle = \sum_k u_{ik}^* \langle \phi^k | \mathcal{Q} | \psi^j \rangle$$

$$= \sum_{kl} u_{ik}^* u_{jl} \langle \phi^k | \mathcal{Q} | \phi^l \rangle = \sum_{kl} u_{ik}^* u_{jl} a_{kl}^\phi$$

$$= \sum_{kl} u'^{-1}_{ik} a_{kl}^\phi u'_{lj} = [U'^{-1} A^\phi U']_{ij} \qquad (3\text{-}75)$$

The structure $A^\psi = U'^{-1} A^\phi U'$ occurs often in algebraic equations. We say that A is obtained from B by means of a *similarity transformation* if $A = S^{-1}BS$. If S is unitary, as in the present case $(S = U')$, the transformation is called a *unitary transformation;* if S is orthogonal, an *orthogonal transformation.* From this we get the following result.

Theorem The matrix representative of $\mathcal{Q}$ in the ψ basis may be found by a similarity transformation of the representative of $\mathcal{Q}$ in the ϕ basis; this similarity transformation is the transpose of the transformation connecting the bases.

We have established the relations between linear operators and their matrix representatives; now it is only natural to extend to operators the features of matrix algebra, the matrix product, the inverse, and the transpose. A few further features are of importance, and are contained in the following definitions.

Definitions The *commutator* of two operators $\mathcal{Q}$ and $\mathcal{B}$ is the operator $\mathcal{Q}\mathcal{B} - \mathcal{B}\mathcal{Q}$, and is designated $[\mathcal{Q}, \mathcal{B}]$.

The *adjoint* of an operator $\mathcal{Q}$, denoted $\mathcal{Q}^\dagger$, is that operator whose matrix elements are related to those of $\mathcal{Q}$ by

$$\langle \phi^i | \mathcal{Q}^\dagger | \phi^j \rangle = \langle \mathcal{Q}\phi^i | \phi^j \rangle.$$

The operator adjoint to $\mathcal{Q}$ is represented by a matrix which is related by a transposition and a complex conjugation to the representative of $\mathcal{Q}$ itself, since

$$\langle \phi^i | \mathcal{Q}^\dagger | \phi^j \rangle = \langle \mathcal{Q}\phi^i | \phi^j \rangle = \langle \phi^j | \mathcal{Q} | \phi^i \rangle^* \qquad (3\text{-}76)$$

The dagger symbol is used to signify an adjoint.

Definition   The *trace* of an operator is the sum of the diagonal matrix elements of any representative of that operator: tr $\alpha = \sum_i a_{ii}$. (In German references, *trace* is called *Spur* and is abbreviated Sp.)

As an example of some of the principles that we have been discussing, let us consider a typical operator and its representatives in some bases.

Definition   A *projection operator* $\mathcal{P}_\epsilon$, which gives the projection of some vector in the direction of a unit vector ϵ, is defined by $\mathcal{P}_\epsilon \xi = \langle \epsilon \mid \xi \rangle \epsilon$.

The projection operator gives the component of a vector in a particular direction. We may very simply solve for the eigenvalue of $\mathcal{P}_\epsilon$ using only operator methods:

$$\mathcal{P}_\epsilon^2 \xi = \mathcal{P}_\epsilon(\mathcal{P}_\epsilon \xi) = \mathcal{P}_\epsilon(\langle \epsilon \mid \xi \rangle \epsilon) = \langle \epsilon \mid \xi \rangle \mathcal{P}_\epsilon \epsilon = \langle \epsilon \mid \xi \rangle \epsilon \quad (3\text{--}77)$$

Hence, $\mathcal{P}_\epsilon^2 = \mathcal{P}_\epsilon$. This is expressed by saying that the operator $\mathcal{P}_\epsilon$ is *idempotent*. Then, $(\mathcal{P}_\epsilon^2 - \mathcal{P}_\epsilon) = 0 = \mathcal{P}_\epsilon(\mathcal{P}_\epsilon - 1) = 0$, and either $\mathcal{P}_\epsilon = 0$ or $\mathcal{P}_\epsilon = 1$. We already know the possible eigenvalues for $\mathcal{P}_\epsilon$ —one or zero—without even setting down the matrix representative of $\mathcal{P}_\epsilon$. Now let us see what a matrix representative of $\mathcal{P}_\epsilon$ looks like.

EXAMPLE

The projection operator in a two-dimensional Euclidean vector space, with the projection direction vector $\epsilon = (1/\sqrt{2}, 1/\sqrt{2})$. Choose as the basis the conventional Cartesian basis $\phi^1 = (1, 0)$, $\phi^2 = (0, 1)$. Then, by direct evaluation,

$$p_{11}^{\phi} = \langle \phi^1 \mid \mathcal{P} \mid \phi^1 \rangle = \left\langle (1, 0) \,\middle|\, \left(\frac{1}{\sqrt{2}}, \frac{1}{\sqrt{2}} \right) \cdot \left(\frac{1}{\sqrt{2}} \right) \right\rangle = \frac{1}{\sqrt{2}} \cdot \frac{1}{\sqrt{2}} = \frac{1}{2}$$

$$p_{12}^{\phi} = \tfrac{1}{2}$$
$$p_{21}^{\phi} = \tfrac{1}{2}$$
$$p_{22}^{\phi} = \tfrac{1}{2}$$

The matrix P^ϕ is

$$\begin{pmatrix} \frac{1}{2} & \frac{1}{2} \\ \frac{1}{2} & \frac{1}{2} \end{pmatrix}$$

Consider now the basis $\psi^1 = (1/2, \sqrt{3}/2)$, $\psi^2 = (\sqrt{3}/2, -1/2)$. A calculation similar to the above gives the elements p^ψ_{ij}, and the matrix

$$P^\psi = \begin{pmatrix} \frac{1}{2} + \frac{\sqrt{3}}{4} & \frac{1}{4} \\ \frac{1}{4} & \frac{1}{2} - \frac{\sqrt{3}}{4} \end{pmatrix}$$

We must now confirm the transformation theorem, $P^\psi = U'^{-1}P^\phi U'$. Since

$$\psi^1 = \frac{1}{2}(1, 0) + \frac{\sqrt{3}}{2}(0, 1) = \frac{1}{2}\phi^1 + \frac{\sqrt{3}}{2}\phi^2$$

$$\psi^2 = \frac{\sqrt{3}}{2}(1, 0) - \frac{1}{2}(0, 1) = \frac{\sqrt{3}}{2}\phi^1 - \frac{1}{2}\phi^2$$

we have

$$U = \begin{pmatrix} \frac{1}{2} & \frac{\sqrt{3}}{2} \\ \frac{\sqrt{3}}{2} & \frac{-1}{2} \end{pmatrix} \qquad U' = \begin{pmatrix} \frac{1}{2} & \frac{\sqrt{3}}{2} \\ \frac{\sqrt{3}}{2} & \frac{-1}{2} \end{pmatrix} \qquad U'^{-1} = \begin{pmatrix} \frac{1}{2} & \frac{\sqrt{3}}{2} \\ \frac{\sqrt{3}}{2} & \frac{-1}{2} \end{pmatrix}$$

Then, by direct multiplication

$$\begin{pmatrix} \frac{1}{2} & \frac{\sqrt{3}}{2} \\ \frac{\sqrt{3}}{2} & \frac{-1}{2} \end{pmatrix}\begin{pmatrix} \frac{1}{2} & \frac{1}{2} \\ \frac{1}{2} & \frac{1}{2} \end{pmatrix}\begin{pmatrix} \frac{1}{2} & \frac{\sqrt{3}}{2} \\ \frac{\sqrt{3}}{2} & \frac{-1}{2} \end{pmatrix} = \begin{pmatrix} \frac{1}{2} + \frac{\sqrt{3}}{4} & \frac{1}{4} \\ \frac{1}{4} & \frac{1}{2} - \frac{\sqrt{3}}{4} \end{pmatrix} = P^\psi$$

We will soon find that in the basis $x^1 = (1/\sqrt{2}, 1/\sqrt{2})$, $x^2 = (1/\sqrt{2}, -1/\sqrt{2})$ $\mathcal{P}$ takes the form

$$\begin{pmatrix} 1 & 0 \\ 0 & 0 \end{pmatrix}$$

With these three examples we may (somewhat facetiously) illustrate the concept of matrix representation with Fig. 3-3.

We turn finally to the problem of finding the eigenvalues and eigenvectors of linear operators. Not all linear operators obey an eigenvalue equation, but, from the point of view of quantum mechanics, two classes of operators which do obey an eigenvalue equation are of great importance. These are *Hermitian operators* and *unitary operators*. We shall summarize the results first, and then offer the proofs.

> **Definition** An eigenvalue is said to be *degenerate* if the eigenvalue satisfies an eigenvalue-eigenvector equation for more than one eigenvector; the number of eigenvectors with the same eigenvalue is called the *degree of degeneracy* of the eigenvalue.
>
> **Definition** A *Hermitian operator* is a linear operator which is self-adjoint; that is, $\mathcal{3C} = \mathcal{3C}^\dagger$, or $h_{ij} = h_{ji}^*$. The diagonal elements of a Hermitian matrix are real.
>
> **Theorem** A Hermitian operator in an n-dimensional vector space has n *distinct eigenvectors* and n *real eigenvalues*. If the eigenvalues are nondegenerate, the eigenvectors are mutually orthogonal, and, with suitable normalization, form an orthonormal set. Even if some of the eigenvalues are degenerate, an orthonormal set can be constructed from the distinct eigenvectors.
>
> **Definition** A *unitary operator* is a linear operator whose adjoint is its inverse: $\mathcal{U}^{-1} = \mathcal{U}^\dagger$.
>
> **Theorem** A unitary operator in an n-dimensional vector space has n distinct eigenvectors (which may, as above, be made to constitute an orthonormal set), and n eigenvalues, all of which have unit modulus.

We begin by proving the Hermitian operator theorem. If $\mathcal{3C}\phi^i = h_i\phi^i$, then $\langle\phi^i|\mathcal{3C}|\phi^i\rangle = h_i\langle\phi^i|\phi^i\rangle$. Since $\mathcal{3C}$ is Hermitian, $\langle\phi^i|\mathcal{3C}|\phi^i\rangle = \langle\phi^i|\mathcal{3C}|\phi^i\rangle^*$; and $h_i = h_i^*$, so h_i is real. For two different eigenvectors,

$$\mathcal{3C}\phi^i = h_i\phi^i \tag{3-78a}$$

$$\mathcal{3C}\phi^j = h_j\phi^j \tag{3-78b}$$

From Eq. 3-78a we get $\langle\phi^j|\mathcal{3C}|\phi^i\rangle = h_i\langle\phi^j|\phi^i\rangle$; from Eq. 3-78b, $\langle\mathcal{3C}\phi^j|\phi^i\rangle = h_j^*\langle\phi^j|\phi^i\rangle$. However, $\langle\mathcal{3C}\phi^j|\phi^i\rangle = \langle\phi^i|\mathcal{3C}|\phi^j\rangle^* = \langle\phi^j|\mathcal{3C}|\phi^i\rangle = h_i\langle\phi^j|\phi^i\rangle$. Then, $(h_i - h_j^*)\langle\phi^j|\phi^i\rangle = 0$. Since h_j is real, if $h_i \neq h_j$, $\langle\phi^j|\phi^i\rangle = 0$ and the eigenvectors are orthogonal.

The proof of the theorem for unitary operators is very similar. If $\mathcal{U}\psi^i = u_i\psi^i$, then $\mathcal{U}^\dagger\mathcal{U}\psi^i = \psi^i = \mathcal{U}^\dagger u_i\psi^i = u_i\mathcal{U}^\dagger\psi^i$. Then $\mathcal{U}^\dagger\psi^i = (1/u_i)\psi^i$, or $\mathcal{U}^\dagger$ has the same eigenvectors as $\mathcal{U}$, but with reciprocal eigenvalues. Then $\langle\psi^i|\mathcal{U}^\dagger|\psi^i\rangle = u_i\langle\psi^i|\psi^i\rangle$ and $\langle\mathcal{U}^\dagger\psi^i|\psi^i\rangle =$

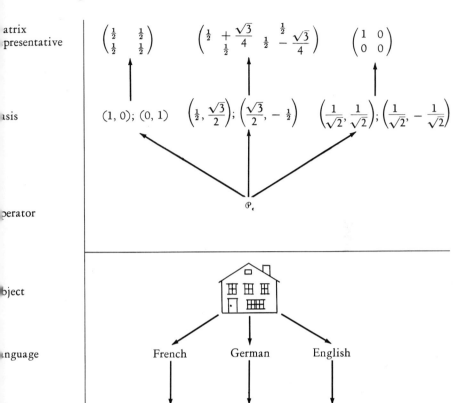

Figure 3–3 The operator $\mathcal{P}_\epsilon$, where $\epsilon = (1/\sqrt{2}, 1/\sqrt{2})$ and its matrix representatives in three bases; by analogy, the object *house*, and its word representatives in three languages.

$(1/u_i^*)\langle\psi^i \mid \psi^i\rangle$. However, $\langle \mathfrak{U}^\dagger\psi^i \mid \psi^i\rangle$ also equals $\langle\psi^i \mid \mathfrak{U} \mid \psi^i\rangle$. Hence, $1/u_i^* = u_i$, and $u_i u_i^* = 1$, or the eigenvalues u_i have modulus one. The orthogonality of the eigenvectors may be proved in a way analogous to the proof for Hermitian operators. The particular problems which arise for degenerate eigenvalues are discussed at the end of this section.

Neither of these proofs shows why Hermitian or unitary operators must obey an eigenvalue equation, and this is offered without proof at the present. However, each of these theorems has a corollary for Euclidean vector spaces.

> **Corollary** Corresponding to the theorem for Hermitian operators in a Hermitian vector space there is the analogous theorem for *symmetric operators* ($S_{ij} = S_{ji}$) in a Euclidean vector space; corresponding to the theorem for unitary operators in a Hermitian vector space there is the analogous theorem for *orthogonal operators* ($\mathcal{R}' = \mathcal{R}^{-1}$) in a Euclidean vector space.

All these theorems and corollaries have dealt with the *existence* of eigenvalues and eigenvectors, but nothing so far has shown us how to *find* these eigenvalues. We can undertake a study of the solution of eigenvalue equations in general terms from two points of view, the *secular equation* and the *similarity transformation*.

Consider the eigenvalue equation, Eq. 1–2, in matrix form:

$$Q\phi = q\phi \qquad (3\text{–}79)$$

This equation is a one-line statement of a number of linear equations in the components of the vector ϕ:

$$\begin{aligned} Q_{11}\phi_1 + Q_{12}\phi_2 + \cdots + Q_{1n}\phi_n &= q\phi_1 \\ \vdots \qquad\qquad \vdots \\ Q_{n1}\phi_1 + Q_{n2}\phi_2 + \cdots + Q_{nn}\phi_n &= q\phi_n \end{aligned} \qquad (3\text{–}80)$$

These, in turn, may be rearranged to give a set of simultaneous linear homogeneous equations in the n unknowns ϕ_i (the components of ϕ).

$$\begin{aligned} (Q_{11} - q)\phi_1 + \quad Q_{12}\phi_2 \quad + \cdots + \quad Q_{1n}\phi_n &= 0 \\ Q_{21}\phi_1 \quad + (Q_{22} - q)\phi_2 + \cdots + \quad Q_{2n}\phi_n &= 0 \\ \vdots \qquad\qquad \vdots \qquad\qquad \vdots \\ Q_{n1}\phi_1 \quad + \quad Q_{n2}\phi_2 \quad + \cdots + (Q_{nn} - q)\phi_n &= 0 \end{aligned} \qquad (3\text{–}81)$$

We have already learned that such a set of equations has a nontrivial solution only if the determinant of the coefficients vanishes. Hence, we obtain the nth degree equation for q, called the *secular equation:*

$$\begin{vmatrix} (Q_{11} - q) & Q_{12} & \cdots & Q_{1n} \\ Q_{21} & (Q_{22} - q) & \cdots & Q_{2n} \\ \vdots & \vdots & & \vdots \\ Q_{n1} & Q_{n2} & \cdots & (Q_{nn} - q) \end{vmatrix} = 0 \qquad (3\text{–}82)$$

Secular equations are commonplace in quantum mechanics. Think a minute about what Eq. 3–82 says. If we expanded Eq. 3–82 we would get a polynomial of degree n in the unknown q. Setting aside (for the moment) the practical question of solving that equation, notice that one significant feature appears: there are n roots to the equation. The theorems we proved above stated that there would be n eigenvectors and n eigenvalues, and now we see why. It is because the eigenvalues are the solutions of an nth degree equation. Of course, as we saw, some of these roots (the eigenvalues) may be equal, but we shall defer this problem.

Very well, we now have n eigenvalues. However, the set of equations 3–81 can then be solved for the components ϕ_i for the eigenvector, *for each of the n eigenvalues.* Hence, Eq. 3–81 gives, ultimately, n eigenvectors, one eigenvector for each eigenvalue. To conclude the calculation, we shall require that the eigenvectors be normalized.

By way of recapitulation, we solve a matrix eigenvalue equation by the following steps.

1. Set up and solve the secular equation; obtain eigenvalues.

2. Use eigenvalues (now known) in eigenvalue equation to get eigenvectors.

3. Normalize eigenvectors.

We may look at the eigenvalue problem from a second point of view as well. Imagine that we know the eigenvalues and eigenvectors of a matrix:

$$\begin{aligned}
Q\phi^1 &= q_1\phi^1 \\
Q\phi^2 &= q_2\phi^2 \\
&\vdots \qquad \vdots \\
Q\phi^n &= q_n\phi^n
\end{aligned} \tag{3-83}$$

We could line up all the column vectors side by side and make an $n \times n$ matrix of them, such as

$$\Phi = \begin{pmatrix} \phi_1{}^1 & \phi_1{}^2 & \cdots & \phi_1{}^n \\ \phi_2{}^1 & \phi_2{}^2 & \cdots & \phi_2{}^n \\ \vdots & \vdots & & \vdots \\ \phi_n{}^1 & \phi_n{}^2 & \cdots & \phi_n{}^n \end{pmatrix} \tag{3-84}$$

The eigenvectors ϕ^i form the columns of the matrix Φ. The effect of operating Q on Φ is simply to generate a matrix whose columns are $q_i\phi^i$:

$$Q\Phi = \begin{pmatrix} q_1\phi_1{}^1 & \cdots & q_n\phi_1{}^n \\ q_1\phi_2{}^1 & \cdots & q_n\phi_2{}^n \\ \vdots & & \vdots \\ q_1\phi_n{}^1 & \cdots & q_n\phi_n{}^n \end{pmatrix} = \begin{pmatrix} \phi_1{}^1 & \cdots & \phi_1{}^n \\ \phi_2{}^1 & \cdots & \phi_2{}^n \\ \vdots & & \vdots \\ \phi_n{}^1 & & \phi_n{}^n \end{pmatrix} \begin{pmatrix} q_1 & & \bigcirc \\ & q_2 & \\ & & \ddots \\ \bigcirc & & q_n \end{pmatrix} \tag{3-85}$$

$$= \Phi\hat{q}$$

where we have used the symbol $\hat{q}$ to represent the matrix which is composed of the n eigenvalues q_i on the diagonal, and zeros everywhere else. Multiplying each side of Eq. 3–85 by Φ^{-1} gives

$$\Phi^{-1}Q\Phi = \hat{q} \qquad\qquad (3\text{–}86)$$

This is a statement that *the similarity transformation of Q by the matrix composed of its eigenvectors taken columnwise gives a diagonal matrix whose entries are the eigenvalues of Q.*

Hence, if we can find a way of transforming Q to a diagonal matrix, called *diagonalizing the matrix Q*, the columns of that similarity transformation are the eigenvectors and the entries in the diagonal matrix are the eigenvalues. This procedure is readily transcribed for digital computation, and often forms the basis for computer solution of eigenvalue problems. Since, as we have proven, the vectors ϕ^i are orthonormal, the transformation $\Phi^{-1}Q\Phi$ is a unitary transformation. As an example of these ideas, we find the eigenvalues of the P_ϵ matrix discussed previously.

EXAMPLE

Consider the operator $\mathcal{P}_\epsilon$, where $\epsilon = (1/\sqrt{2}, 1/\sqrt{2})$ in the usual Cartesian basis. The matrix representative of this projection operator in this basis is

$$\begin{pmatrix} \tfrac{1}{2} & \tfrac{1}{2} \\ \tfrac{1}{2} & \tfrac{1}{2} \end{pmatrix}$$

as found before. To find the eigenvalues of this operator, we solve the secular equation.

$$\begin{vmatrix} \tfrac{1}{2} - p & \tfrac{1}{2} \\ \tfrac{1}{2} & \tfrac{1}{2} - p \end{vmatrix} = 0$$

which gives the quadratic

$$\tfrac{1}{4} - p + p^2 - \tfrac{1}{4} = 0$$

which has the roots

$$p^2 - p = 0$$
$$p_1 = 1 \qquad p_2 = 0$$

These roots, which are the eigenvalues of $\mathcal{P}_\epsilon$, are just what we had predicted before from operator properties alone. We now find the eigenvector ϕ^1 corresponding to the eigenvalue $p_1 = 1$:

$$\begin{pmatrix} \tfrac{1}{2} & \tfrac{1}{2} \\ \tfrac{1}{2} & \tfrac{1}{2} \end{pmatrix}\begin{pmatrix} \phi_1{}^1 \\ \phi_2{}^1 \end{pmatrix} = \begin{pmatrix} \phi_1{}^1 \\ \phi_2{}^1 \end{pmatrix}$$

which becomes

$$\tfrac{1}{2}\phi_1{}^1 + \tfrac{1}{2}\phi_2{}^1 = \phi_1{}^1$$
$$\tfrac{1}{2}\phi_1{}^1 + \tfrac{1}{2}\phi_2{}^1 = \phi_2{}^1$$

or

$$\phi_2{}^1 = \phi_1{}^1$$
$$\phi_1{}^1 = \phi_2{}^1$$

Note that the eigenvector-component equations are identical. To fully determine the components, we require normalization, which gives $\phi_1{}^1 = \phi_2{}^1 = 1/\sqrt{2}$, or $\phi^1 = (1/\sqrt{2},\ 1/\sqrt{2})$. The eigenvector ϕ^2 corresponding to the eigenvalue $p_2 = 0$ is found by an identical process to be $\phi^2 = (1/\sqrt{2}, -1/\sqrt{2})$.

Stop and think about these eigenvectors: the eigenvector with eigenvalue one is *exactly the same* as the projection direction ϵ; that is, a vector in the projection direction projects to a vector of the same length. On the other hand, the eigenvector ϕ^2 with eigenvalue zero is perpendicular to the projection direction ϵ; a vector perpendicular to the projection direction projects to a point (zero length).

We may also confirm the similarity transformation $\Phi^{-1}P_\epsilon\Phi$ which diagonalizes P_ϵ by direct substitution:

$$\begin{pmatrix} \dfrac{1}{\sqrt{2}} & \dfrac{1}{\sqrt{2}} \\ \dfrac{1}{\sqrt{2}} & -\dfrac{1}{\sqrt{2}} \end{pmatrix}\begin{pmatrix} \dfrac{1}{2} & \dfrac{1}{2} \\ \dfrac{1}{2} & \dfrac{1}{2} \end{pmatrix}\begin{pmatrix} \dfrac{1}{\sqrt{2}} & \dfrac{1}{\sqrt{2}} \\ \dfrac{1}{\sqrt{2}} & -\dfrac{1}{\sqrt{2}} \end{pmatrix} = \begin{pmatrix} 1 & 0 \\ 0 & 0 \end{pmatrix}$$

There is another technique for finding the eigenvectors which is somewhat simpler. The components of an eigenvector obey Eq. 3–81. Each line of Eq. 3–81 looks like the expansion of a determinant by cofactors. For, if $\phi_1 = [Q - \hat{q}]_{11}$, $\phi_2 = [Q - \hat{q}]_{12}$, and so on, then the first line of Eq. 3–81 gives

$$(Q_{11} - q)\phi_1 + Q_{12}\phi_2 + \cdots + Q_{1n}\phi_n$$
$$= (Q_{11} - q)[Q - \hat{q}]_{11} + Q_{12}[Q - \hat{q}]_{12} + \cdots + Q_{1n}[Q - \hat{q}]_{1n}$$
$$= |Q - \hat{q}| = 0 \tag{3-87}$$

where the numbers Q_{ij} are the matrix elements of Q, and the numbers

q are the eigenvalues of Q. Hence the cofactor of the secular determinant for *any* row, ith column, gives a number proportional to ϕ_i.

EXAMPLE

In the case of the operator $\mathcal{P}_\epsilon$ given above, the secular determinant for the eigenvalue $p_1 = 1$ is

$$\begin{vmatrix} -\frac{1}{2} & \frac{1}{2} \\ \frac{1}{2} & -\frac{1}{2} \end{vmatrix} = 0$$

and the eigenvector ϕ^1 has components proportional to $(-\frac{1}{2}, -\frac{1}{2})$, if we choose the cofactors of the first row; ϕ^1 has components proportional to $(-\frac{1}{2}, -\frac{1}{2})$ from cofactors of the second row; each of these gives $\phi^1 = (1/\sqrt{2}, 1/\sqrt{2})$ with suitable normalization.

The student might well inquire what conditions must prevail in order that two operators have the *same* set of eigenvectors. This question is of great importance in quantum mechanics, because it tells us when two operators can both assume definite eigenvalues in the same single, stationary quantum state. Our question could equally well be phrased by asking when two matrices can be diagonalized by the same similarity transformation. The result is beautifully simple.

Theorem Two Hermitian operators can have the same set of eigenvectors (eigenfunctions) if, and only if, they commute.

Let us prove first that if $\mathcal{A}$ and $\mathcal{B}$ commute, then they have the same eigenvectors. Suppose $\mathcal{A}$ has eigenvectors ψ^i; then $\mathcal{A}\psi^i = a_i\psi^i$. However, because $\mathcal{A}$ and $\mathcal{B}$ commute, $\mathcal{A}\mathcal{B}\psi^i = \mathcal{B}\mathcal{A}\psi^i$. Then,

$$\mathcal{B}\mathcal{A}\psi^i = \mathcal{A}\mathcal{B}\psi^i = \mathcal{B}a_i\psi^i = a_i\mathcal{B}\psi^i \qquad (3\text{–}88)$$

Equation 3–88 shows that the vector $(\mathcal{B}\psi^i)$ is also an eigenvector of $\mathcal{A}$ with the eigenvalue a_i. This can only be true if $(\mathcal{B}\psi^i)$ is a multiple of ψ^i; hence,

$$\mathcal{B}\psi^i = b_i\psi^i \qquad (3\text{–}89)$$

and ψ^i is also an eigenvector of $\mathcal{B}$. The student may detect that this argument fails if the eigenvalue a_i is degenerate; such cases are considered at the end of this section.

To prove the converse—that if $\mathcal{A}$ and $\mathcal{B}$ have the same set of eigenvectors, then they commute—we begin by showing how an operator's effect may be restated in terms of projection operators. A vector ξ may be expanded in a complete orthonormal set ϕ^i:

$$\xi = \sum_i \langle \phi^i \mid \xi \rangle \phi^i = \sum_i \mathcal{P}_\phi \xi \qquad (3\text{-}90)$$

That is, the effect of *expanding* a vector in a basis is equivalent to adding up the *projections* of that vector along the basis vectors. Suppose the eigenvectors of $\mathcal{A}$ are the set $\{\phi^i\}$. Then, because of the foregoing relation, we may write

$$\mathcal{A}\xi = \mathcal{A} \sum_i \langle \phi^i \mid \xi \rangle \phi^i = \sum_i \langle \phi^i \mid \xi \rangle a_i \phi^i = \sum_i a_i \mathcal{P}_{\phi i} \qquad (3\text{-}91)$$

which is an equation stating that the effect of operating $\mathcal{A}$ on a given vector is to generate the vector sum of the given vector projected along an eigenvector times the eigenvalue. If we represent $\mathcal{A}$ as

$$\mathcal{A} = \sum_i a_i \mathcal{P}_{\phi i} \qquad (3\text{-}92)$$

and $\mathcal{B}$, having the same set of eigenvectors $\{\phi^i\}$, as

$$\mathcal{B} = \sum_j b_j \mathcal{P}_{\phi j} \qquad (3\text{-}93)$$

then it is not difficult to show that $\mathcal{A}$ and $\mathcal{B}$ must commute, since

$$\left[\sum_i a_i \mathcal{P}_{\phi i}, \sum_j b_j \mathcal{P}_{\phi j} \right] = 0.$$

(The student should work out this commutator to his satisfaction.)

The final topic of this section is the discussion of how the properties of the eigenvalues and eigenvectors of linear operators must be modified in the case of degenerate eigenvalues. We consider first how to form an orthonormal set of eigenvectors from the eigenvectors of Hermitian (or unitary, or symmetric, or orthogonal) operators with a degenerate eigenvalue.

Suppose it happens that two eigenvectors, ξ_1 and ξ_2 have the same eigenvalue q. These vectors need not be orthogonal. Our theorems provide only that the eigenvectors corresponding to different eigenvalues are orthogonal. If $\mathcal{Q}\xi_1 = q\xi_1$ and $\mathcal{Q}\xi_2 = q\xi_2$, then any linear combination of ξ_1 and ξ_2 also obeys the eigenvalue equation $\mathcal{Q}(\xi_1 + c\xi_2) = q(\xi_1 + c\xi_2)$, where c is a constant. We want the vector $\xi_1 + c\xi_2$ (*which is an eigenvector*) to be normalized and orthogonal to ξ_1. Then we will have two vectors, ξ_1 and $\xi_1 + c\xi_2$, that are orthonormal. This is precisely the problem which confronted us in the Schmidt orthogonalization procedure. Suppose ξ_1 is already normalized. Then, requiring

$$\langle \xi_1 \mid \xi_1 + c\xi_2 \rangle = 0 \qquad (3\text{–}94)$$

gives

$$c = \frac{-\langle \xi_1 \mid \xi_2 \rangle}{\langle \xi_1 \mid \xi_1 \rangle} = -\langle \xi_1 \mid \xi_2 \rangle \qquad (3\text{–}95)$$

This equation is analogous to Eq. 3–9; the procedure can be repeated indefinitely as indicated by the degree of degeneracy of the eigenvalue q.

Degeneracy also affects our discussion of the simultaneous eigenvectors of commuting operators. We had pointed out that if $\mathcal{Q}$ and $\mathcal{B}$ are Hermitian and commute, and that if $\mathcal{Q}$ has the eigenvectors $\{\psi^i\}$ and eigenvalues $\{a_i\}$, then

$$\mathcal{Q}(\mathcal{B}\psi^i) = a_i(\mathcal{B}\psi^i). \qquad (3\text{–}88)$$

If a_i is a nondegenerate eigenvalue, then it must be the case that $\mathcal{B}\psi^i$ is a multiple of ψ^i, as we had noted. If a_i is degenerate, however, $\mathcal{B}\psi^i$ is, in general, a linear combination of all the eigenvectors belonging to the eigenvalue a_i. Suppose these are labeled by a second index, k, running from 1 to n (we say a_i is n-fold degenerate). Then

$$\mathcal{B}\psi^i = \sum_k b_{ik}\psi^{ik} \qquad (3\text{–}96)$$

The coefficients b_{ik} form an n-dimensional submatrix of the matrix representative of $\mathcal{B}$ that is not diagonal. To put it another way, if the matrix A is a diagonal, the matrix B is diagonal wherever A is nondegenerate. Where A is degenerate and B is not diagonal, we may find the eigenvalues of $\mathcal{B}$ by diagonalizing the smaller submatrix.

This section has introduced a number of ideas which are central to

a concise formulation of quantum mechanics. By way of conclusion, a summary of these concepts is presented.

1. Linear operators may be represented by matrices, once a basis set is specified. The matrix representative of the operator α is that matrix whose elements are $a_{ij} = \langle \phi^i \mid \alpha \phi^j \rangle$, where the basis $\{\phi^i\}$ is specified.

2. The effect of operating α on a vector ξ may be simulated by multiplying the matrix representative of α by a column matrix representative of ξ (both in the same basis).

3. Change of basis is effected by a similarity transformation.

4. Hermitian operators have real eigenvalues and orthonormal eigenvectors.

5. Unitary operators have eigenvalues of modulus one and orthonormal eigenvectors.

6. Eigenvalue equations may be solved by (a) setting up and solving the secular equation, substituting back into the eigenvalue equation, and normalizing; (b) solving the secular equation, using cofactors of the secular determinant to find the eigenvectors, and normalizing; or (c) finding the similarity transformation which diagonalizes the matrix.

7. Two Hermitian operators have the same set of eigenvectors if and only if they commute.

Problems

1. If the following vectors are linearly independent, form an orthonorma set from them; if they are linearly dependent, exhibit this linear dependence.
   (a) $(1, 1, 2)$, $(0, -1, 0)$, $(-1, 0, 1)$.
   (b) $(1, 2, -1, 0)$, $(0, 3, 4, 1)$, $(1, 1, 1, 1)$, $(2, 0, -4, 0)$.
   (c) $(i, 1, 2)$, $(2i + 1, -1, 3i)$, $(4, 5i, 6 + i)$.
   (d) $(0, 0, 2, 0, 0)$, $(1, 1, 1, 1, 1)$, $(1, 3, 1, 2, 2)$, $(0, 0, 1, 2, 2)$, $(1, 0, 1, 0, 1)$.

2. Are a set of mutually orthogonal vectors linearly independent? Why or why not?

3. Show that, in a vector space, $c\alpha = 0$ implies either $c = 0$ or $\alpha = 0$.

4. Form a multiplication table and compute the inner products of all vectors in Problem 1, parts (a), (b), and (c).

5. Show that matrix multiplication is associative.

6. Let
$$A = \begin{pmatrix} 1 & 2 & -1 \\ 3 & 0 & 2 \\ 4 & 5 & 0 \end{pmatrix} \qquad B = \begin{pmatrix} 1 & 0 & 0 \\ 2 & 1 & 0 \\ 0 & 1 & 3 \end{pmatrix}$$

Find AB and BA. Do A and B commute? Find A^{-1} and B^{-1}. Verify that $(AB)' = B'A'$, $(AB)^{-1} = B^{-1}A^{-1}$.

7. Evaluate the determinant

$$\begin{vmatrix} 1 & -1 & 1 & -1 \\ 0 & 1 & -1 & 1 \\ 0 & 0 & 1 & -1 \\ 1 & 0 & 0 & 1 \end{vmatrix}$$

by expansion in cofactors; by direct evaluation.

8. A determinant has zeros below the main diagonal and nonzero elements on and above the main diagonal. Show that the value of this determinant is simply the product of the diagonal elements.

9. Solve the following sets of simultaneous linear equations where possible. If a solution is impossible, comment.

(a)
$$2x - 3y + 5z = 0$$
$$x - y - 2z = 2$$
$$5x \quad\quad - z = -1$$

(b)
$$2x - y + 3z - w = 0$$
$$4x - 2y - z + 3w = 0$$
$$2x - y - 4z + 4w = 0$$
$$10x - 5y - 6z + 10w = 0$$

(c)
$$2x - y + 3z = 1$$
$$4x - 2y - z = -3$$
$$2x - y - 4z = -4$$
$$10x - 5y - 6z = 10$$

(d)
$$4x + 2y + z = 11$$
$$x - y - z = -4$$
$$x + y + z = 6$$

10. What orthogonal transformation carries the Cartesian basis $(\hat{x}, \hat{y}, \hat{z})$ into the spherical basis $(\hat{r}, \hat{\theta}, \hat{\phi})$?

11. A linear transformation maps the xy plane onto the uv plane according to

$$L = \begin{pmatrix} 2 & -1 \\ -3 & 0 \end{pmatrix}$$

Find the image of the points $(1, 2)$, $(-2, 1)$, $(1, 0)$, $(0, 1)$ under L.

12. Compute the rank of each of these transformations and comment.

(a)
$$\begin{aligned} u &= x + 2y - 3z \\ v &= 2x - y + 4z \\ w &= 3x + y + z \end{aligned}$$

(b)
$$\begin{aligned} u &= y - z \\ v &= 3x - y + 3z \\ w &= x + z \end{aligned}$$

13. In a two-dimensional Hermitian space, two bases are related by

$$\psi^1 = \frac{1}{\sqrt{2}}(\phi^1 + i\phi^2) \qquad \psi^2 = \frac{1}{\sqrt{2}}(\phi^1 - i\phi^2)$$

(a) Determine the unitary matrix U which transforms the ϕ vectors into the ψ vectors.

(b) If in the ϕ representation operator $\mathcal{A}$ has the matrix representative

$$A^\phi = \begin{pmatrix} \cos\alpha & -\sin\alpha \\ \sin\alpha & \cos\alpha \end{pmatrix}$$

what will be its representative A^ψ in the ψ representation?

(c) Show that a unitary or orthogonal transformation always has an inverse.

14. Show that the matrix

$$A = \begin{pmatrix} a & b \\ b & b \end{pmatrix}$$

a symmetric, real matrix is transformed into the diagonal matrix

$$B = \begin{pmatrix} c & 0 \\ 0 & d \end{pmatrix}$$

by the similarity transformation $B = T^{-1}AT$, where

$$T = \begin{pmatrix} \cos\theta & -\sin\theta \\ \sin\theta & \cos\theta \end{pmatrix}$$

Derive the value of θ for which this diagonalization transformation works, and evaluate c and d.

15. Prove the following properties of Hermitian operators.

(a) Any matrix representative of a Hermitian operator has a real determinant.

(b) The inverse of a Hermitian operator is Hermitian.

(c) The product of two Hermitian operators is Hermitian if and only if they commute.

16. Prove the following properties of the *trace*.

(a) $\operatorname{tr} A^\dagger = (\operatorname{tr} A)^*$

(b) $\operatorname{tr}(aA) = a \operatorname{tr} A$

(c) $\operatorname{tr}(A + B) = \operatorname{tr} A + \operatorname{tr} B$

(d) $\operatorname{tr}(AB) = \operatorname{tr}(BA)$

(e) $\operatorname{tr}(A)$ is independent of the basis in which α is represented by A.

17. Show that a unitary operator may always be written in the following forms.

(a) The form $\mathcal{U} = \alpha + i\mathcal{B}$, where α and $\mathcal{B}$ are Hermitian, and $[\alpha, \mathcal{B}] = 0$.

(b) The form $\mathcal{U} = e^{i\alpha}$, where α is Hermitian.

18. Prove the following properties of orthogonal and unitary operators.

(a) The product of two orthogonal operators is orthogonal.

(b) If α is symmetric, and $\mathcal{U}$ orthogonal, then $\mathcal{U}^{-1}\alpha\mathcal{U}$ is symmetric.

(c) The product of two unitary operators is unitary.

(d) If α is Hermitian and $\mathcal{U}$ unitary, then $\mathcal{U}^{-1}\alpha\mathcal{U}$ is Hermitian.

19. Verify the matrix representing a rotation in 3D space through Eulerian angles given in Eq. 3–64.

20. What happens in the determination of eigenvectors if the eigenvalues are degenerate?

21. Find the eigenvalues and eigenvectors of the operator $\mathcal{K}$, whose matrix representative in 3D space is

$$K = \begin{pmatrix} 7 & -3 & -\sqrt{2} \\ -3 & 7 & \sqrt{2} \\ \sqrt{2} & \sqrt{2} & 10 \end{pmatrix}$$

Check your result by applying an appropriate similarity transformation to K to diagonalize K.

22. Show that the eigenvectors of a unitary operator are orthogonal.

23. Find the eigenvalues and eigenvectors of

$$\begin{pmatrix} 1 & i & 0 \\ -i & 1 & 0 \\ 0 & 0 & 0 \end{pmatrix}$$

4

Classical Mechanics

O ur purpose in this chapter is twofold. We shall first formulate classical mechanics in such a way that the connection between classical and quantum mechanics is clear.

Our second purpose is to learn to handle two mechanical problems of importance in quantum chemistry, vibrational and rotational motion of molecules. These two kinds of molecular motion lie at the center of infrared and microwave spectroscopy.

We begin with a section of review and basic definitions, proceed from there to Lagrange's and Hamilton's equations to point up the connection with quantum mechanics, and conclude with applications to molecular motion.

4–1 INTRODUCTION AND THE CONSERVATION LAWS

In considering classical mechanics, we shall freely use vector quantities. The world in which we, and our experiments, live is a three-dimensional Euclidean vector space, so that we may quickly summarize the properties of vectors in this space as follows:

(a) A vector $\mathbf{V}$ will be specified by three components, all real, usually in the Cartesian basis,

$$\mathbf{V} = (V_x, V_y, V_z) = V_x\hat{x} + V_y\hat{y} + V_z\hat{z} \qquad (4\text{-}1)$$

Vectors in this chapter are given their usual symbols, and rendered in **bold face**. Unit vectors are notated with the circumflex, or caret, or "hat" mark.

(b) The *dot product* or *scalar product* of two vectors is

$$\mathbf{V}_1 \cdot \mathbf{V}_2 = V_{1x}V_{2x} + V_{1y}V_{2y} + V_{1z}V_{2z} \qquad (4\text{-}2)$$

and is precisely the same as what we had called the *inner product* in Chapter 3. By analogy, then, the length of a vector $\mathbf{V}$ is $(\mathbf{V} \cdot \mathbf{V})^{1/2}$; two vectors are perpendicular if their dot product is zero.

In mechanics there is also defined another type of vector product.

> **Definition** The *cross product* of two vectors is defined by
>
> $$\begin{aligned} \mathbf{V}_1 \times \mathbf{V}_2 = &(V_{1y}V_{2z} - V_{1z}V_{2y})\hat{x} \\ &+ (V_{1z}V_{2x} - V_{1x}V_{2z})\hat{y} \\ &+ (V_{1x}V_{2y} - V_{2x}V_{1y})\hat{z} \end{aligned} \qquad (4\text{-}3)$$

Notice that a *cross product* of two vectors gives a *vector*, while the *dot product* of two vectors gives a *scalar*. The cross product of a vector with itself, that is, $\mathbf{V} \times \mathbf{V}$ is $\mathbf{0}$, if all the components of the vector commute with each other. If the components are numbers, they obviously commute, and $\mathbf{V} \times \mathbf{V} = \mathbf{0}$; however, if the components are operators, it will be necessary to apply the commutation rules of the operators in order to evaluate $\mathbf{V} \times \mathbf{V}$.

All our considerations in this chapter will proceed from a number of definitions, and Newton's laws. We shall, however, remain unconcerned with relativistic effects. We begin with just one particle and offer two definitions.

> **Definition** The *linear momentum* of a particle (or simply the *momentum*) is
>
> $$\mathbf{p} = m\mathbf{v} \qquad (4\text{-}4)$$
>
> where m is the mass of the particle, $\mathbf{v}$ the velocity, and $\mathbf{p}$ the momentum.
>
> **Definition** The *angular momentum* of a particle about a point is
>
> $$\mathbf{l} = \mathbf{r} \times \mathbf{p} \qquad (4\text{-}5)$$
>
> where $\mathbf{r}$ is the distance vector from the point to the particle, $\mathbf{p}$ is the (linear) momentum of the particle, and $\mathbf{l}$ the angular momentum.

For the sake of compacting notation, we shall use the conventional dot to represent time derivatives. Thus, $\dot{\mathbf{r}} = d\mathbf{r}/dt = \mathbf{v}$; $\dot{\mathbf{v}} = d\mathbf{v}/dt = \mathbf{a}$, the acceleration, and so forth. Newton's second law is expressed as

$$\mathbf{F} = \dot{\mathbf{p}} \qquad (4\text{-}6)$$

This equation, very compact, is equivalent to the familiar $\mathbf{F} = m\mathbf{a}$, if the mass is constant, since then $\dot{\mathbf{p}} = d(m\mathbf{v})/dt = m(d\mathbf{v}/dt) = m\mathbf{a}$. The simplicity of Eq. 4–6 actually includes a conservation theorem that is tantamount to Newton's first law.

Theorem If the total force on a particle is zero, then the (linear) momentum of the particle does not change in time, or the momentum is *conserved*.

We may well ask whether or not a similar conservation theorem holds for angular momentum. We may show that there is such a theorem by taking the cross product of $\mathbf{r}$, the distance vector to a point of interest, with both sides of Eq. 4–6.

$$\mathbf{r} \times \mathbf{F} = \mathbf{r} \times \dot{\mathbf{p}} = \mathbf{r} \times \frac{d}{dt}(m\mathbf{v}) \qquad (4\text{-}7)$$

However,

$$\frac{d}{dt}\mathbf{r} \times m\mathbf{v} = \mathbf{v} \times m\mathbf{v} + \mathbf{r} \times \frac{d}{dt}(m\mathbf{v})$$
$$= \mathbf{v} \times m\mathbf{v} + \mathbf{r} \times \dot{\mathbf{p}}$$
$$= \mathbf{r} \times \dot{\mathbf{p}} \qquad (4\text{-}8)$$

since $\mathbf{v} \times \mathbf{v} = 0$ identically. Then,

$$\mathbf{r} \times \mathbf{F} = \frac{d}{dt}(\mathbf{r} \times \mathbf{p}) = \dot{\mathbf{l}} \qquad (4\text{-}9)$$

The essence of Eq. 4–9 may be summarized with a definition and a theorem.

Definition The *torque* about a point exerted on a particle is
$$\mathbf{N} = \mathbf{r} \times \mathbf{F} \qquad (4\text{-}10)$$
where $\mathbf{r}$ is the distance vector from point to particle, $\mathbf{F}$ the total force, and $\mathbf{N}$ the torque.

Theorem If the total torque about a point, $\mathbf{N}$, exerted on a particle is zero, then the angular momentum about that point is conserved (is unchanged in time).

The last important conservation theorem we shall discuss for a one-particle system deals with energy, and will be expressed in terms of two definitions.

Definition   The *work* done in moving a particle through the distance $d\mathbf{s}$ is

$$dW = \mathbf{F} \cdot d\mathbf{s} \qquad (4\text{–}11)$$

Definition   A *conservative force* is one that may be related to a scalar *potential* by a negative derivative[1]:

$$\mathbf{F} = -\frac{\partial V}{\partial x}\hat{x} - \frac{\partial V}{\partial y}\hat{y} - \frac{\partial V}{\partial z}\hat{z} = -\boldsymbol{\nabla} V = -\mathbf{grad}\, V \qquad (4\text{–}12)$$

With these definitions we can calculate the work required to move a particle from point 1 to point 2.

$$
\begin{aligned}
W_{12} &= \int_{(1)}^{(2)} \mathbf{F} \cdot d\mathbf{s} = \int F_x \, dx + \int F_y \, dy + \int F_z \, dz \\
&= -\int \frac{\partial V}{\partial x} dx - \int \frac{\partial V}{\partial y} dy - \int \frac{\partial V}{\partial z} dz \\
&= -V_2 - (-V_1) = V_1 - V_2 \qquad (4\text{–}13)
\end{aligned}
$$

On the other hand, since $\mathbf{F} = \dot{\mathbf{p}} = m\dot{\mathbf{v}}$, and $d\mathbf{s} = \mathbf{v}\,dt$, we also obtain

$$
\begin{aligned}
W_{12} &= \int_{(1)}^{(2)} m\dot{\mathbf{v}} \cdot \mathbf{v} \, dt = \frac{m}{2} \int \frac{d}{dt}\,(\mathbf{v} \cdot \mathbf{v})\, td \\
&= \frac{m}{2} \int \frac{d(v^2)}{dt} dt = \frac{mv^2}{2}\Big|_{(1)}^{(2)} \\
&= \frac{m}{2}\,(v_2{}^2 - v_1{}^2) \qquad (4\text{–}14)
\end{aligned}
$$

The quantity $mv^2/2$ is the kinetic energy, which we shall symbolize by $T;$ hence,

---

[1] The symbol $\boldsymbol{\nabla}$, called *del* or *nabla*, is a vector differential operator: $\boldsymbol{\nabla} = +(\partial/\partial x)\hat{x} + (\partial/\partial y)\hat{y} + (\partial/\partial z)\hat{z}$. The operation of $\boldsymbol{\nabla}$ on a scalar gives a vector result, the *gradient*, abbreviated **grad**. The operation of $\boldsymbol{\nabla}$ on a vector takes two forms: $\boldsymbol{\nabla} \cdot \mathbf{a} = \text{div } \mathbf{a}$, the *divergence* of $\mathbf{a}$, a scalar; $\boldsymbol{\nabla} \times \mathbf{a} = \mathbf{curl\ a}$, a vector. The operator $\boldsymbol{\nabla} \cdot \boldsymbol{\nabla}$, or ∇^2, is called the *Laplacian*. These terms are used in a thorough examination of mechanics, electricity, and magnetism, but will be of only casual interest in this chapter.

$$W_{12} = T_2 - T_1 = V_1 - V_2 \tag{4-15}$$

whence

$$T_2 + V_2 = T_1 + V_1 \tag{4-16}$$

We have proved the following theorem.

Theorem Energy $(T + V)$ is conserved in motion that is the response to a conservative force.

We have discussed only one particle so far. Extending the analysis to many-particle systems is straightforward, if we agree on some additional definitions.

Definitions (a) The total force on a particle i which is one of a system of particles is made up of two parts, the *external force* $\mathbf{F}_i^{\text{ext}}$ and the sum of *interparticle forces*

$$\sum_{j \neq i} \mathbf{F}_{ij}^{\text{inter}}.$$

Newton's third law gives $\mathbf{F}_{ij} = -\mathbf{F}_{ji}$.

(b) The *center of mass* is located by a vector

$$\mathbf{R} = \frac{\sum_i m_i \mathbf{r}_i}{\sum_i m_i} \tag{4-17}$$

where m_i is the mass of the ith particle and $\mathbf{r}_i$ the position vector of the ith particle.

(c) The *total mass* of the system is $M = \sum_i m_i$.

(d) The momentum of the center of mass is $\mathbf{P} = M\dot{\mathbf{R}}$.

(e) The angular momentum of the center of mass is $\mathbf{L} = \dot{\mathbf{R}} \times \mathbf{P}$.

These five definitions allow three theorems that are the many-particle analogs of the three previous theorems, as well as three *separation theorems*. These theorems, although important, are stated without proof.

> **Theorems** (a) If the *total external force* applied to a system of par-
> ticles is zero, the total linear momentum is conserved.
>   (b) If the *total external torque* about a point applied to a system of par-
> ticles is zero, the total angular momentum is conserved.
>   (c) If both *external* and *interparticle* forces are conservative, then
> the energy $(T + V)$ is conserved.

The following separation theorems show how the motion of the
entire system of particles may be separated into two parts.

> **Theorems** (a) The total linear momentum of a system of particles
> equals the linear momentum of one particle of mass M located at the
> center of mass.
>   (b) The total angular momentum of a system of particles about a
> point equals the angular momentum of a single particle of mass M about
> the point plus the angular momentum of the particles about the center
> of mass.
>   (c) The kinetic energy of a system of particles equals the kinetic
> energy of a particle of mass M moving at the velocity of the center of
> mass $(\dot{\mathbf{R}})$, plus the kinetic energy of the particles with respect to the
> center of mass.

The author acknowledges the assistance of complete textbooks on
classical mechanics, particularly that of Goldstein,[2] in this and
following sections. Proofs of the foregoing theorems may be found
there for those interested. The six proofs are not particularly difficult, however, and appear in the problems at the end of this chapter.

In this section we have begun a study of classical mechanics by
reforming Newton's laws to give conservation theorems for the
momentum $\mathbf{p}$, the angular momentum $\mathbf{l}$, and the total energy,
$T + V$.

4–2   GENERALIZED COORDINATES AND LAGRANGE'S EQUATIONS;
HAMILTON'S EQUATIONS

In this section we shall derive forms of Newton's laws that have
two particularly useful properties: these equations will be scalar

---

[2] Goldstein, H., *Classical Mechanics*, Chapter 1. Addison-Wesley, Reading, Massachusetts, 1959.

equations, not vector equations, and these equations will be suitable for use in any coordinate system. Heretofore we had discussed both the equation of motion $\mathbf{F} = m\mathbf{a}$ and the conservation theorems—all of which are vectorial except for conservation of energy—with particular reference to a Cartesian coordinate system.

One of the tricks in solving physical or chemical problems in either classical or quantum mechanics is to choose a coordinate system judiciously, with full respect for the symmetry of the problem. For example, the motion of the earth about the sun, Kepler's problem, is difficult to describe in Cartesian coordinates, but natural in spherical coordinates. The motion of an electron about a nucleus, the quantum-mechanical hydrogen atom problem, is intractable in Cartesian coordinates, but straightforward in spherical coordinates. The advantage gained by casting the equations of motion for a system into a judiciously chosen coordinate system is great; the student will probably also appreciate the ease of handling scalar, rather than vector quantities. Of course, we wish to be absolutely *general* in examining mechanical problems. Being able to set up the equations of motion in spherical coordinates alone is not enough: we want equations of motion in a coordinate system that is *generalized*, so that any concrete coordinate system we choose is a special case of our fully generalized coordinate system.

Definition The $3n$ Cartesian coordinates required to describe the mechanics of n particles may each be given by $3n$ functions of $3n$ *generalized coordinates* q_i and time:

$$x_1 = x_1(q_1, q_2, \ldots, q_{3n}, t)$$
$$y_1 = y_1(q_1, q_2, \ldots, q_{3n}, t) \qquad (4\text{-}18)$$
$$\vdots$$
$$z_n = z_n(q_1, q_2, \ldots, q_{3n}, t)$$

A general position vector will be notated $\mathbf{r}_i$, meaning the vector $\mathbf{r}_i = (x_i, y_i, z_i)$. Time is allowed for explicitly in Eq. 4–18 because of the possibility of moving coordinate systems, but it will not occur in the remainder of our discussion.

We begin our derivation of equations of motion of a system of particles with Newton's second law, Eq. 4–6. This is true for each particle, so that

$$\mathbf{F}_i = \dot{\mathbf{p}}_i \qquad (4\text{-}6)$$

Our derivation commences with a statement of work. This at once gives us a scalar quantity. The work done in moving particle i by an infinitesimal distance $\delta\mathbf{r}_i$ is[3]

$$\mathbf{F}_i \cdot \delta\mathbf{r}_i = \dot{\mathbf{p}}_i \cdot \delta\mathbf{r}_i \qquad (4\text{-}19)$$

We now apply the transformation equations 4–18, leaving out explicit time dependence for simplicity.

$$\mathbf{r}_i = \mathbf{r}_i(q_1, \ldots, q_{3n}) \qquad (4\text{-}20a)$$

$$\mathbf{v}_i = \dot{\mathbf{r}}_i = \sum_{k=1}^{3n} \frac{\partial \mathbf{r}_i}{\partial q_k} \frac{dq_k}{dt} = \sum_k \frac{\partial \mathbf{r}_i}{\partial q_k} \dot{q}_k \qquad (4\text{-}20b)$$

$$\delta\mathbf{r}_i = \sum_{k=1}^{3n} \frac{\partial \mathbf{r}_i}{\partial q_k} \delta q_k \qquad (4\text{-}20c)$$

The left side of Eq. 4–19 in generalized coordinates is, summed for all particles,

$$\sum_{i=1}^{n} \mathbf{F}_i \cdot \delta\mathbf{r}_i = \sum_{i=1}^{n}\sum_{j=1}^{3n} \mathbf{F}_i \cdot \frac{\partial \mathbf{r}_i}{\partial q_j} \delta q_j = \sum_{j=1}^{3n} Q_j \delta q_j \qquad (4\text{-}21)$$

A word of warning: the sums in Eq. 4–21 have different ranges, since there are n particles, but $3n$ generalized coordinates. What about the quantity Q_j that appears in Eq. 4–21? The right and left sides of Eq. 4–21 are somewhat parallel, and this prompts a definition.

Definition The *generalized force* Q_j is a scalar corresponding to the generalized coordinate q_j, and defined by

$$Q_j = \sum_{i=1}^{n} \mathbf{F}_i \cdot \frac{\partial \mathbf{r}_i}{\partial q_j} \qquad (4\text{-}22)$$

Then both sides of Eq. 4–21 have the form of (some kind of force) $\times$ (some coordinate). We have left to consider the right side of Eq. 4–19, which is more difficult. We begin with two brief statements, which are not proven here but are given as problems.

---

[3] We might be concerned about work done by forces of constraint. It is very often the case that the forces of constraint act in a direction normal to the direction of motion; hence, the work they do is nil. We shall be restricted to such cases.

$$\frac{d}{dt}\left(\frac{\partial \mathbf{r}_i}{\partial q_j}\right) = \frac{\partial \mathbf{v}_i}{\partial q_j} \qquad (4\text{-}23a)$$

$$\frac{\partial \mathbf{r}_i}{\partial q_j} = \frac{\partial \mathbf{v}_i}{\partial \dot{q}_j} \qquad (4\text{-}23b)$$

Then,

$$\sum_i \dot{\mathbf{p}}_i \cdot \delta \mathbf{r}_i = \sum_i m_i \ddot{\mathbf{r}}_i \cdot \delta \mathbf{r}_i = \sum_i m_i \ddot{\mathbf{r}}_i \cdot \sum_j \frac{\partial \mathbf{r}_i}{\partial q_j} \delta q_j$$

$$= \sum_{ij} \left\{ \frac{d}{dt}\left(m_i \mathbf{r}_i \cdot \frac{\partial \mathbf{r}_i}{\partial q_j}\right) - m_i \dot{\mathbf{r}}_i \cdot \frac{d}{dt}\frac{\partial \mathbf{r}_i}{\partial q_j}\right\} \delta q_j$$

$$(4\text{-}24)$$

Substituting from Eq. 4–23, we obtain

$$\sum_i \dot{\mathbf{p}}_i \cdot \delta \mathbf{r}_i = \sum_{ij} \left\{ \frac{d}{dt}\left(m_i \mathbf{v}_i \cdot \frac{\partial \mathbf{v}_i}{\partial \dot{q}_j}\right) - m_i \mathbf{v}_i \cdot \frac{\partial \mathbf{v}_i}{\partial q_j}\right\} \delta q_j$$

$$= \sum_j \left\{ \frac{d}{dt}\left(\frac{\partial}{\partial \dot{q}_j} \sum_i \frac{m_i v_i^2}{2}\right) - \frac{\partial}{\partial q_j} \sum_i \frac{m_i v_i^2}{2}\right\} \delta q_j$$

$$= \sum_j \left\{ \frac{d}{dt}\frac{\partial T}{\partial \dot{q}_j} - \frac{\partial T}{\partial q_j}\right\} \delta q_j$$

$$(4\text{-}25)$$

since $T = \sum_i m_i v_i^2/2$. Thus we have reduced the right side of Eq.

4–19 to an expression involving scalars and generalized coordinates. Equations 4–21 and 4–25 both involve sums over displacements δq_j. Since the generalized coordinates are independent, the comparison of Eqs. 4–21 and 4–25 may be made termwise. Thus, combining the results of Eqs. 4–25 and 4–21, we establish the following theorem.

Theorem First form of *Lagrange's equations.* The equations of motion of a system of n particles in $3n$ generalized coordinates are $3n$ equations of the form

$$\frac{d}{dt}\frac{\partial T}{\partial \dot{q}_j} - \frac{\partial T}{\partial q_j} = Q_j \qquad (4\text{-}26)$$

$j = 1, \cdots, 3n$, where Q_j is the generalized force of Eq. 4–22, and T is the kinetic energy.

To complete our discussion of classical mechanics in generalized coordinates, we return to the generalized force. Just as we were able to express the term $\dot{\mathbf{p}}_i \cdot \delta \mathbf{r}_i$ in terms of the kinetic energy T, we shall be able to express Q_j in terms of the potential energy V, and thereby achieve a measure of esthetic symmetry in the equations. The definition of Q_j is given in Eq. 4–22. If the forces $\mathbf{F}_i$ that appear there are conservative, they may be written as derivatives of a potential, as in Eq. 4–12. Combining Eqs. 4–12 and 4–22, we obtain

$$Q_j = \sum_i \mathbf{F}_i \cdot \frac{\partial \mathbf{r}_i}{\partial q_j} = \sum_i \left\{ F_{ix} \frac{\partial x_i}{\partial q_j} + F_{iy} \frac{\partial y_i}{\partial q_j} + F_{iz} \frac{\partial z_i}{\partial q_j} \right\}$$

$$= -\sum_i \left\{ \frac{\partial V}{\partial x_i} \frac{\partial x_i}{\partial q_j} + \frac{\partial V}{\partial y_i} \frac{\partial y_i}{\partial q_j} + \frac{\partial V}{\partial z_i} \frac{\partial z_i}{\partial q_j} \right\}$$

$$= -\frac{\partial V}{\partial q_j} \tag{4–27}$$

The first formulation of Lagrange's equations, Eq. 4–26, then becomes

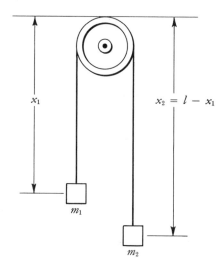

Figure 4–1   Atwood's machine, consisting of an ideal pulley and two masses.

$$\frac{d}{dt}\frac{\partial T}{\partial \dot{q}_j} - \frac{\partial T}{\partial q_j} = -\frac{\partial V}{\partial q_j} \tag{4-28}$$

To complete the symmetrical structure of these equations we shall impose the restriction that the potential energy be independent of velocity.[4] Then, $\partial V/\partial \dot{q}_j = 0$, and Eq. 4-28 may be rewritten

$$\frac{d}{dt}\frac{\partial (T-V)}{\partial \dot{q}_j} - \frac{\partial (T-V)}{\partial q_j} = 0 \tag{4-29}$$

which leads directly to a definition and the second formulation of Lagrange's equations.

Definition The *Lagrangian* is a scalar dynamical quantity defined by

$$L = T - V \tag{4-30}$$

Theorem Second form of *Lagrange's equations*. The equations of motion of a system of n particles in $3n$ generalized coordinates are $3n$ equations of the form

$$\frac{d}{dt}\frac{\partial L}{\partial \dot{q}_j} - \frac{\partial L}{\partial q_j} = 0 \tag{4-31}$$

where L is the Lagrangian, defined in Eq. 4-30.

The Lagrangian formalism helps the recognition of constants of motion, that is, the statement of conservation theorems. In particular, we find the following theorem.

Theorem A generalized conservation theorem. If $\partial L/\partial q_j = 0$, then the dynamical quantity $\partial L/\partial \dot{q}_j$, which is a generalized momentum, is conserved.

As a brief example of the Lagrangian framework, we shall analyze the motion of the pulley-and-weight system shown in Fig. 4-1.

EXAMPLE

The system of two particles of masses m_1 and m_2, and a frictionless, weightless pulley and strings shown in Fig. 4-1 could simply be analyzed using

---

[4] This restriction is not always necessary, but it simplifies the discussion appreciably. Goldstein shows how this restriction can be circumvented.[2]

$\mathbf{F} = m\mathbf{a}$. By way of illustration, however, we work this problem in the Lagrangian framework. First, we find the potential energy (due to gravity)

$$V = -m_1 g x_1 - m_2 g(l - x_1)$$

where l is as shown in Fig. 4–1. Then, the kinetic energy is

$$T = \frac{m_1 \dot{x}_1^2}{2} + \frac{m_2 \dot{x}_2^2}{2} = m_1 \dot{x}_1^2$$

since $\dot{x}_1 = -\dot{x}_2$. The generalized coordinate system is the single coordinate x_1. The Lagrangian is

$$L = T - V = \frac{\dot{x}_1^2}{2}(m_1 + m_2) + g(m_1 - m_2)x_1 + m_2 g l$$

For Lagrange's equations we need to evaluate

$$\frac{\partial L}{\partial x_1} = (m_1 - m_2)g$$

$$\frac{\partial L}{\partial \dot{x}_1} = (m_2 + m_1)\dot{x}_1$$

There being but one coordinate, there is but one of Lagrange's equations 4–31, which is

$$\frac{d}{dt}(m_2 + m_1)\dot{x}_1 - (m_2 - m_1)g = 0$$

or

$$(m_2 + m_1)\ddot{x}_1 = (m_2 - m_1)g$$

which is precisely equivalent to the Newtonian $\mathbf{F} = m\mathbf{a}$.

The problems at the end of the chapter illustrate Lagrange's equations in situations where Newton's equation would be more clumsy.

As a consequence of expressing Newton's laws in the form of Lagrange's equations, we were able to derive a general conservation theorem: $\partial L / \partial \dot{q}_j$ is conserved if $\partial L / \partial q_j = 0$. If L is expressed in Cartesian coordinates,

$$L = T - V = \frac{m}{2}(\dot{x}^2 + \dot{y}^2 + \dot{z}^2) - V(x, y, z) \qquad (4\text{-}32)$$

then $\partial L / \partial x = F_x$, the force in the x direction, and $\partial L / \partial \dot{x} = m\dot{x} = p_x$, the momentum in the x direction. Thus, the conservation theorem in Lagrangian form reproduces the original conservation of momentum theorem. We might, then, to give parallel structure and equal weight to coordinate (or position) and momentum, define a generalized momentum.

Definition The *generalized momentum* p_i, which is said to be *conjugate* to the generalized coordinate q_i, is defined by

$$p_i = \frac{\partial L}{\partial \dot{q}_i} \qquad (4\text{-}33)$$

With this definition, Lagrange's equations can be rewritten

$$\dot{p}_i = \frac{\partial L}{\partial q_i} \qquad (4\text{-}34)$$

The advantage of reexpressing mechanics in terms of position and momentum, rather than in terms of position alone, is twofold. First, a striking parallel structure between position and momentum emerges which underlies much of the significance in mechanics, both classical and quantum. Second, we may rewrite the equations of motion in terms of $6n$ first-order differential equations in the $3n$ q_i's and $3n$ p_i's rather than $3n$ second-order differential equations in the q_i's alone. That is, by considering both position and momentum to be independent variables, we buy mathematical simplicity at the price of twice as many equations. To do this, that is, to write equations of motion in terms of q_i's and p_i's, we begin by defining a new dynamical quantity of mammoth significance.

Definition The *Hamiltonian* for a system of n particles is defined by

$$H = \sum_i p_i \dot{q}_i - L \qquad (4\text{-}35)$$

Considering, as we had before, generalized coordinates with no explicit time dependence, and a potential energy independent of velocity, we may write

$$dH = \sum_i \left\{ \frac{\partial H}{\partial q_i} dq_i + \frac{\partial H}{\partial p_i} dp_i \right\} \qquad (4\text{-}36)$$

where, from Eq. 4-35,

$$\frac{\partial H}{\partial q_i} = \sum p_i \frac{\partial \dot{q}_i}{\partial q_i} - \frac{\partial L}{\partial \dot{q}_i} \frac{\partial \dot{q}_i}{\partial q_i} - \frac{\partial L}{\partial q_i} \qquad (4\text{-}37a)$$

$$\frac{\partial H}{\partial p_i} = \dot{q}_i \qquad (4\text{-}37b)$$

Since $\partial L/\partial \dot{q}_i = p_i$, and $\partial L/\partial q_i = \dot{p}_i$, substituting into Eq. 4-36, we obtain

$$dH = \sum_i \{-\dot{p}_i dq_i + \dot{q}_i dp_i\} \qquad (4\text{-}38)$$

or

$$\dot{q}_i = \frac{\partial H}{\partial p_i} \qquad \dot{p}_i = -\frac{\partial H}{\partial q_i} \qquad (4\text{-}39)$$

Equations 4-39 are often referred to as *Hamilton's equations*. However, what are the properties of the Hamiltonian? So far, we have little more than an abstract definition, Eq. 4-35. One of the particularly important properties of H is that it is conserved, or a constant of the motion.

$$\frac{dH}{dt} = \sum_i \left(\frac{\partial H}{\partial q_i}\dot{q}_i + \frac{\partial H}{\partial p_i}\dot{p}_i\right) + \frac{\partial H}{\partial t}$$

$$= \sum_i (-\dot{p}_i\dot{q}_i + \dot{q}_i\dot{p}_i) + \frac{\partial H}{\partial t} = \frac{\partial H}{\partial t} \qquad (4\text{-}40)$$

Thus, unless H is *explicitly* time dependent, it is time independent, or a constant of the motion.

Lastly, to correlate H with more commonplace terms, we examine the kinetic energy more closely:

$$T = \frac{1}{2}\sum_i m_i v_i^2 = \frac{1}{2}\sum_i m_i \left(\sum_j \frac{\partial r_i}{\partial q_j}\dot{q}_j\right)^2 \qquad (4\text{-}41)$$

if $\mathbf{r}$ is not explicitly dependent on time. Then,

$$T = \frac{1}{2}\sum_i m_i \sum_{jk} \frac{\partial \mathbf{r}_i}{\partial q_j} \cdot \frac{\partial \mathbf{r}_i}{\partial q_k} \dot{q}_j\dot{q}_k$$

$$= \frac{1}{2}\sum_{jk} t_{jk}\dot{q}_j\dot{q}_k \qquad (4\text{-}42)$$

where

$$t_{jk} = \sum_i m_i \frac{\partial \mathbf{r}_i}{\partial q_j} \cdot \frac{\partial \mathbf{r}_i}{\partial q_k} \tag{4-43}$$

Then,

$$\frac{\partial T}{\partial \dot{q}_i} = \sum_k t_{ik} \dot{q}_k \tag{4-44}$$

and

$$\sum_i \dot{q}_i \frac{\partial T}{\partial \dot{q}_i} = 2T \tag{4-45}$$

The definition in Eq. 4-34 of the generalized momentum may now be invoked. For, if, as before, the potential energy V is independent of velocity,

$$p_i = \frac{\partial L}{\partial \dot{q}_i} = \frac{\partial T}{\partial \dot{q}_i} \tag{4-46}$$

Finally,

$$H = \sum_i p_i \dot{q}_i - L$$

$$= \sum_i \frac{\partial T}{\partial \dot{q}_i} \dot{q}_i - T + V$$

$$= 2T - T + V = T + V \tag{4-47}$$

or, for conservative systems whose potential is independent of velocity, the *Hamiltonian is the total energy*. All these results may be expressed in a single theorem.

Theorem The Hamiltonian H, for a conservative system with a velocity-independent potential energy, is a constant of the motion if it is not explicitly time dependent; it is the total energy of the system, so that, for these conditions, (total) energy is conserved. Finally, if H is independent of a (generalized) coordinate, the momentum conjugate to that coordinate is conserved; if H is independent of a momentum, the coordinate conjugate to that momentum is constant.

As a final topic in classical mechanical theory, which, together with the Hamiltonian formulation constitutes a way of bridging the gap between quantum and classical mechanics, we introduce one final definition.

Definition The *Poisson bracket* of two dynamical quantities, F and G, is defined by

$$\{F, G\} = \sum_i \left\{ \frac{\partial F}{\partial q_i} \frac{\partial G}{\partial p_i} - \frac{\partial F}{\partial p_i} \frac{\partial G}{\partial q_i} \right\} \qquad (4\text{-}48)$$

One important application of Poisson brackets is in showing conservation properties, for

$$\frac{dF}{dt} = \frac{\partial F}{\partial t} + \sum_i \left\{ \frac{\partial F}{\partial q_i} \dot{q}_i + \frac{\partial F}{\partial p_i} \dot{p}_i \right\}$$

$$= \frac{\partial F}{\partial t} + \sum_i \left\{ \frac{\partial F}{\partial q_i} \frac{\partial H}{\partial p_i} - \frac{\partial F}{\partial p_i} \frac{\partial H}{\partial q_i} \right\}$$

$$= \frac{\partial F}{\partial t} + \{F, H\} \qquad (4\text{-}49)$$

Thus, if F is not explicitly time dependent, F is a constant of the motion (is conserved) if the Poisson bracket of F with the Hamiltonian is zero.

In this section we have developed two powerful formalisms of classical mechanics.

1. *Lagrange's equations.* $3n$ second-order differential equations in the $3n$ generalized coordinates:

$$\frac{d}{dt} \frac{\partial L}{\partial \dot{q}_i} - \frac{\partial L}{\partial q_i} = 0$$

2. *Hamilton's equations.* $6n$ first-order differential equations in $3n$ generalized coordinates and $3n$ generalized momenta:

$$\frac{\partial H}{\partial p_i} = \dot{q}_i \qquad -\frac{\partial H}{\partial q_i} = \dot{p}_i$$

These formalisms have helped us spot conservation theorems. One is particularly important: an explicitly time-independent Hamiltonian is a constant of the motion. The Hamiltonian, under certain common circumstances may be equated with the total energy of the system. Chapter 5 will show how Hamiltonian classical mechanics can be related to quantum mechanics.

4-3 VIBRATIONS OF A MECHANICAL SYSTEM

In this section we shall study the vibrational motion of a system of particles using the Lagrangian mechanics developed in the previous section.

There are $3n$ degrees of freedom for a system of n particles; of these, three may be accounted for in translation, and three more in rotation. Therefore, there are $3n - 6$ degrees of vibrational freedom. This brief calculation must be amended for linear molecules in which there are but two degrees of rotational freedom, and therefore $3n - 5$ degrees of vibrational freedom.

The Lagrangian is $L = T - V$. We need, therefore, to write T and V in generalized coordinates. We have, from Eqs. 4–42 and 4–43,

$$T = \tfrac{1}{2} \sum_{jk} t_{jk} \dot{q}_j \dot{q}_k \tag{4-42}$$

$$t_{jk} = \sum_{i} m_i \frac{\partial \mathbf{r}_i}{\partial q_j} \cdot \frac{\partial \mathbf{r}_i}{\partial q_k} \tag{4-43}$$

or, that T is a *quadratic function of the generalized velocities.* Furthermore, T may be represented by a matrix whose elements are the numbers t_{jk}.

The potential energy of a real vibrating molecule is a complicated and not completely understood function. However, the *harmonic* potential function that may be used for a simple calculation of the vibrational motion of a mechanical system is often a good approximation to the true molecular potential energy, when small displacements from equilibrium positions are considered. The mechanical system with this potential energy is called a *harmonic oscillator;* this potential energy function is identical with that which describes a system of particles obeying *Hooke's law:*

$$V = \tfrac{1}{2} \sum_{jk} v_{jk} q_j q_k \qquad (4\text{-}50)$$

or, the potential V is a *quadratic function of the generalized coordinates.* Also, V may be represented by a matrix whose elements are the numbers v_{jk}.

We may now write the Lagrangian as

$$L = T - V = \tfrac{1}{2} \sum_{jk} \{ t_{jk} \dot{q}_j \dot{q}_k - v_{jk} q_j q_k \} \qquad (4\text{-}51)$$

and, from Lagrange's equations in Eq. 4-31,

$$\frac{d}{dt} \frac{\partial L}{\partial \dot{q}_i} - \frac{\partial L}{\partial q_i} = 0 \qquad (4\text{-}31)$$

obtain

$$\frac{d}{dt} \left\{ \frac{1}{2} \sum_k t_{jk} \dot{q}_k \right\} + \frac{1}{2} \sum_k v_{jk} q_k = 0$$

$$\sum_k \{ t_{jk} \ddot{q}_k + v_{jk} q_k \} = 0 \qquad (4\text{-}52)$$

This equation bears a formal similarity, not unexpected, to that for simple harmonic motion; hence, we may try a solution of the form $q_k = \phi_k \sin \omega t$ where ϕ_k is the amplitude of the motion and ω is the vibrational frequency. This gives

$$\sum_k [v_{jk} \phi_k - \omega^2 t_{jk} \phi_k] = 0 \qquad (4\text{-}53)$$

This is just a set of simultaneous linear homogeneous equations in the variables ϕ_k. They have a solution only if the determinant of the coefficients is zero:

$$\begin{vmatrix} v_{11} - \omega^2 t_{11} & v_{12} - \omega^2 t_{12} & \cdots & v_{1N} - \omega^2 t_{1N} \\ v_{21} - \omega^2 t_{21} & v_{22} - \omega^2 t_{22} & \cdots & v_{2N} - \omega^2 t_{2N} \\ \vdots & \vdots & & \vdots \\ v_{N1} - \omega^2 t_{N1} & v_{N2} - \omega^2 t_{N2} & \cdots & v_{NN} - \omega^2 t_{NN} \end{vmatrix} = 0 \qquad (4\text{-}54)$$

This equation strongly resembles the secular equation for the eigenvalues of an operator shown in Eq. 3-82. Our present Eq. 4-54 may also be called a secular equation, in spite of the appearance of the eigenvalues ω^2 on and off the main diagonal and always multiplied by a matrix element of the kinetic energy matrix T. There will be $3N - 6$ (or $3N - 5$) roots ω^2, and as many values of the ϕ_k's. Similarly, the set of equations in 4–53 could be written as an eigenvector equation:

$$V\phi^i = \omega_i{}^2 T\phi^i \qquad (4\text{-}55)$$

That is, the effect of operating V on ϕ^i is to give a multiple, $(\omega_i{}^2)$, of the effect of operating T on ϕ^i.

Theorem The eigenvalues, $\{\omega_i{}^2\}$, must be nonnegative and real.

This theorem may be proven along the same lines as given in the previous chapter.[5] It is satisfying that ω^2 is nonnegative, for then the frequency ω will be real. We may answer the eigenvalue problem for molecular vibrations in the form of another theorem.

Theorem The eigenvectors, $\{\phi^i\}$, are such that a matrix Φ, whose columns are the vectors ϕ^i, simultaneously diagonalizes V and T by transformations

$$\Phi'V\Phi = \Omega \qquad (4\text{-}56a)$$

$$\Phi'T\Phi = E \qquad (4\text{-}56b)$$

where Ω is a matrix whose diagonal elements are the possible values for ω^2, and E is the unit matrix.

The transformations here are not similarity transformations, which would have the form $\Phi^{-1}V\Phi$ and $\Phi^{-1}T\Phi$. The transformations that appear in Eqs. 4–56 are called *congruent transformations*. The eigenvalue equation 4–55 may be rewritten using the matrices Ω and Φ as

$$V\Phi = T\Phi\Omega \qquad (4\text{-}57)$$

Multiplying from the left by Φ', we have

$$\Phi'V\Phi = \Phi'T\Phi\Omega \qquad (4\text{-}58)$$

Compare this with the corresponding result for the conventional eigenvalue problem, as in Eq. 3–86, which could be rewritten

$$\Phi'Q\Phi = \Phi'\Phi\hat{q} \qquad (3\text{-}86)$$

---

[5] Goldstein, *op. cit.*, p. 323.

since Φ' is orthogonal. In Eq. 4–58, we have replaced $\Phi'\Phi$ in Eq. 3–86 with $\Phi'T\Phi$; this may be compared to the difference between Eq. 4–54 and Eq. 3–82. In fact, just as in Eq. 3–86, $\Phi'\Phi = E$, the unit matrix, we may show that $\Phi'T\Phi$ in Eq. 4–58 is also the unit matrix. For, taking the inner product of Eq. 4–55 with ϕ^j on the left,

$$\langle\phi^j\,|V|\,\phi^i\rangle = \omega_i^2\langle\phi^j\,|T|\,\phi^i\rangle \tag{4–59}$$

and, on the right,

$$\langle V\phi^i\,|\,\phi^j\rangle = \omega_j^2\langle T\phi^i\,|\,\phi^j\rangle$$
$$\langle\phi^j\,|V|\,\phi^i\rangle = \omega_j^2\langle\phi^j\,|T|\,\phi^i\rangle \tag{4–60}$$

Comparing Eqs. 4–59 and 4–60, we see that

$$(\omega_j^2 - \omega_i^2)\langle\phi^j\,|T|\,\phi^i\rangle = 0 \tag{4–61}$$

or, for different eigenvalues $\omega_j^2 \neq \omega_i^2$, $\langle\phi^j\,|T|\,\phi^i\rangle = 0$. Finally, by scaling the vectors $\{\phi^i\}$ appropriately, we may require $\langle\phi^j\,|T|\,\phi^j\rangle = 1$ for all ϕ^j. These statements are analogous to the orthonormality of eigenvectors in the usual eigenvalue problem.

It therefore follows that $\Phi'T\Phi = E$, as in Eq. 4–56b, and Eq. 4–58 becomes $\Phi'V\Phi = \Omega$ as in Eq. 4–56a.

This section concludes with a brief example of how this formalism may be applied to molecular vibrations. It should be pointed out at the outset that far more sophisticated methods than are considered here are available, and have been applied to the vibrations of complex molecules. However, the general features of the problem and its solution are the same.

EXAMPLE

Consider a molecule which is constrained (this is an unreal simplification) to vibrate only along a straight line. The molecule is symmetrical, as shown in Fig. 4–2.

We need first to evaluate, in the coordinate system shown (as an example—others could be chosen) the potential and kinetic energies, and then to express the potential and kinetic energies as matrices. Let us begin with the potential energy. The potential energy, in the harmonic oscillator approximation, is given by a number of terms, each of which is the square of the distention of a bond times a Hooke's law force constant:

$$V = \frac{k}{2}(x_2 - x_1 - b)^2 + \frac{k}{2}(x_3 - x_2 - b)^2$$

We are required to write the potential energy in displacement coordinates. Define the equilibrium position of the leftmost particle by x_{01}, of the center particle by x_{02}, and of the rightmost particle by x_{03}. Then define the displacement coordinates as follows:

$$q_1 = x_1 - x_{01}$$
$$q_2 = x_2 - x_{02}$$
$$q_3 = x_3 - x_{03}$$

Since

$$b = x_{02} - x_{01} = x_{03} - x_{02}$$

the potential energy is now

$$V = \frac{k}{2}(q_2 - q_1)^2 + \frac{k}{2}(q_3 - q_2)^2$$
$$= \frac{k}{2}(q_1^2 + 2q_2^2 + q_3^2 - 2q_1q_2 - 2q_2q_3)$$

We may now write down the matrix for the potential energy. The matrix elements v_{ij} are the coefficients of the term q_iq_j in the potential energy expression. This means that the potential energy matrix is

$$V = \begin{pmatrix} k & -k & 0 \\ -k & 2k & -k \\ 0 & -k & k \end{pmatrix}$$

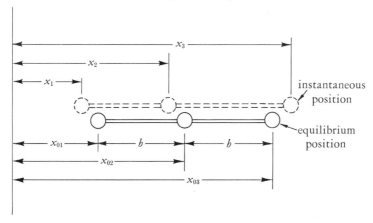

Figure 4–2 **Coordinate system used to describe a linear triatomic molecule.**

The kinetic energy is somewhat simpler. In the coordinate system shown in Fig. 4–2, the kinetic energy is

$$T = \frac{m}{2}(\dot{x}_1{}^2 + \dot{x}_3{}^2) + \frac{M}{2}(\dot{x}_2{}^2)$$

If we substitute into this equation the displacement coordinates and their time derivatives (notice that $\dot{x}_{01} = 0$, and so on), we obtain for T

$$T = \frac{m}{2}(\dot{q}_1{}^2 + \dot{q}_3{}^2) + \frac{M}{2}(\dot{q}_2{}^2)$$

Again taking the various terms in T (only three in this case) and placing them in a matrix where t_{ij} is the coefficient of $\dot{q}_i\dot{q}_j$ in T, we get the kinetic energy matrix

$$T = \begin{pmatrix} m & 0 & 0 \\ 0 & M & 0 \\ 0 & 0 & m \end{pmatrix}$$

The eigenvalue equation is

$$V\Phi = \omega^2 T\Phi$$

and the secular equation which must be solved is

$$|V - \omega^2 T| = 0 = \begin{vmatrix} k - \omega^2 m & -k & 0 \\ -k & 2k - \omega^2 M & -k \\ 0 & -k & k - \omega^2 m \end{vmatrix}$$

It is easy to expand the secular determinant by cofactors of its first row:

$$0 = (k - \omega^2 m)\begin{vmatrix} 2k - \omega^2 M & -k \\ -k & k - \omega^2 m \end{vmatrix} + k\begin{vmatrix} -k & -k \\ 0 & k - \omega^2 m \end{vmatrix}$$

$$= (k - \omega^2 m)\,[(2k - \omega^2 M)\,(k - \omega^2 m) - k^2] + [-k(k - \omega^2 m)]$$

$$= (k - \omega^2 m)\,[(2k - \omega^2 M)\,(k - \omega^2 m) - k^2 - k^2]$$

$$= (k - \omega^2 m)\,[-\omega^2 k(M + 2m) + \omega^4 Mm]$$

$$= (k - \omega^2 m)\,(\omega^2)\,[\omega^2 Mm - k(M + 2m)]$$

This has the solutions

1. $\quad k - \omega^2 m = 0 \quad \omega^2 = \dfrac{k}{m} \quad \omega = \left(\dfrac{k}{m}\right)^{1/2}$

2. $\quad \omega^2 = 0 \qquad\qquad\qquad\qquad \omega = 0$

3. $\quad \omega^2 Mm - k(M + 2m) = 0 \quad \omega = \left[\left(\dfrac{k}{m}\right)\left(1 + \dfrac{2m}{M}\right)\right]^{1/2}$

The presence of a zero solution to the eigenvalue problem is not forbidden by the theory which has been developed. We found only that the eigenvalues, ω^2, could not be negative. If the reader went back and examined the development of the theory at that point, he would conclude that the eigenvalue $\omega = 0$ corresponds to some sort of motion where the potential energy *for that degree of freedom* is zero. Zero potential energy is not a harmonic oscillator at all; it is some sort of motion with no restoring or opposing force. In other words, it represents a free translation or free rotation.

This is what we should expect at this point, too. We have set up the problem in three generalized coordinates, but there should be only two. We have failed to eliminate the generalized coordinate which corresponds to a translation parallel to the x axis. This illustrates an important point. *Motions of the molecule that are not vibrations will, if allowed to remain in the generalized coordinate system chosen, give a zero eigenvalue for ω^2.*

We could now reformulate the problem, using a set of coordinates containing only the two which are connected with the vibration. In order to do this, we would have to formulate an equation representing our wish to forbid translation, and use it to eliminate one of the three coordinates q_1, q_2, q_3 that we had before. This equation could be chosen by requiring that the center of mass of the system remain at the origin:

$$m(x_1 + x_3) + Mx_2 = 0$$

The succeeding development would yield the same nonzero eigenvalues, but on zero eigenvalue ω^2.

We are now faced with the problem of finding the eigenvectors in our problem that are the normal modes of vibration. In order to do this, we must substitute back our (now known) eigenvalues ω^2 into the eigenvalue-eigenvector equation, and use the equation to solve for the components of the eigenvector. There will be an eigenvector for each eigenvalue, so we must carry out this process as many times as there are eigenvalues. In the case of vibrational problems, unlike the normal sort of eigenvector problem, we shall not require that the eigenvectors be normalized to one, but that $\langle \phi^i | T | \phi^i \rangle = 1$.

The eigenvalue equation reads $V\Phi = \omega^2 T\Phi$. Choosing for our first calculation the eigenvalue $\omega^2 = k/m$, we obtain

$$\begin{pmatrix} k & -k & 0 \\ -k & 2k & -k \\ 0 & -k & k \end{pmatrix} \begin{pmatrix} \phi_1{}^1 \\ \phi_2{}^1 \\ \phi_3{}^1 \end{pmatrix} = \frac{k}{m} \begin{pmatrix} m & 0 & 0 \\ 0 & M & 0 \\ 0 & 0 & m \end{pmatrix} \begin{pmatrix} \phi_1{}^1 \\ \phi_2{}^1 \\ \phi_3{}^1 \end{pmatrix}$$

Writing the matrix equation as simultaneous linear equations (homogeneous), we obtain

$$k\phi_1^1 - k\phi_2^1 \qquad\qquad = k\phi_1^1$$
$$-k\phi_1^1 + 2k\phi_2^1 - k\phi_3^1 = \frac{km}{M}\phi_2^1$$
$$- k\phi_2^1 + k\phi_3^1 = k\phi_3^1$$

From either the first or last of these equations, we see that

$$\phi_2^1 = 0$$

whereas, by substituting this result into the second of these equations, we get

$$\phi_1^1 = -\phi_3^1$$

An acceptable eigenvector (before normalization) would be the vector $(a, 0, -a)$. We require the analog of normalization, namely, $\langle \phi^i | T | \phi^i \rangle = 1$. In matrix form, this is

$$(a \quad 0 \quad -a)\begin{pmatrix} m & 0 & 0 \\ 0 & M & 0 \\ 0 & 0 & m \end{pmatrix}\begin{pmatrix} a \\ 0 \\ -a \end{pmatrix} = (a \quad 0 \quad -a)\begin{pmatrix} am \\ 0 \\ -am \end{pmatrix}$$
$$= 2a^2 m = 1$$

So $a = (2m)^{-1/2}$. The normalized eigenvector is therefore $((2m)^{-1/2}, 0, -(2m)^{-1/2})$.

The same process for the eigenvalue $\omega^2 = (k/m)(1 + 2m/M)$ gives, for the unnormalized eigenvector, $(a, -2ma/M, a)$. With normalization, the eigenvector is quite complicated, $((M/\{2mM + 4m^2\})^{1/2}, -(4m/\{2M^2 + 4Mm\})^{1/2}, (M/\{2mM + 4m^2\})^{1/2})$.

The eigenvector can also be computed for the eigenvalue $\omega^2 = 0$. Unnormalized, it comes out to be (a, a, a); normalized, each component a is equal to $(2m + M)^{-1/2}$.

As a final check of this solution to the vibrational problem, we perform the transformation on the nondiagonal V matrix and on the T matrix. The result should give, for the V matrix, a diagonal matrix with the eigenvalues ω^2 on the diagonal, and, for the T matrix, the unit matrix.

For the sake of simplicity, consider a homonuclear triatomic linear molecule, such as N_3^- or I_3^-, so that $m = M$. The eigenvectors are then $((2m)^{-1/2}, 0, -(2m)^{-1/2})$, $((6m)^{-1/2}, -2(6m)^{-1/2}, (6m)^{-1/2})$, and $((3m)^{-1/2}, (3m)^{1/2}, (3m)^{1/2})$. We may interpret these eigenvectors graphically. The eigenvector $((2m)^{-1/2}, 0, -(2m)^{-1/2})$ indicates that whenever the leftmost atom moves left, the rightmost atom moves right, and vice versa. This is called the symmetric stretch mode of vibration, and may be diagrammed as shown in Fig. 4–3a. On the other hand, the eigenvector $((6m)^{-1/2}, -2(6m)^{-1/2},$

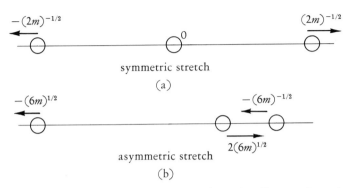

$-(2m)^{-1/2}$ $(2m)^{-1/2}$

0

symmetric stretch

(a)

$-(6m)^{1/2}$ $-(6m)^{-1/2}$

$2(6m)^{1/2}$

asymmetric stretch

(b)

Figure 4–3   Normal modes of vibration of a linear triatomic molecule.

$(6m)^{-1/2})$ involves a motion of the end atoms (1 and 3) in the same direction, and the center atom (2) in the opposite direction. The center atom moves twice as far so as to keep the center of mass fixed. This is called the *asymmetric stretch* mode, and may be diagrammed as shown in Fig. 4–3b.

The last eigenvector, $((3m)^{-1/2}, (3m)^{-1/2}, (3m)^{-1/2})$ does not (as do the first two) keep the center of mass fixed. In fact, this eigenvector corresponds to a uniform translation of the molecule. This was the eigenvector that corresponded to the eigenfrequency of zero.

4–4   ROTATIONS OF A RIGID MECHANICAL SYSTEM

In the previous section we developed the equations of motion for a vibrating mechanical system, and showed how that analysis could be applied to molecular vibrations. In this section we develop the equations of motion for a rotating mechanical system, and show how these may be applied to molecular rotations. As was pointed out at the end of the previous section, far more elegant methods than those presented here are available; the ensuing discussion is intended only to outline the general problem.

For mechanical systems, we seek solutions to Lagrange's equations, Eq. 4–31, with the Lagrangian function defined in Eq. 4–30.

This function is particularly simple for rotations of a rigid system,[6] where $V = 0$, so $L = T$.

The kinetic energy, however, takes on a particularly simple form for rigid rotations. Since, by definition,

$$T = \tfrac{1}{2} \sum_i m_i v_i^2 \qquad (4\text{-}62)$$

we must interpret $\mathbf{v}_i$ in terms of rotations. A simple diagram will convince the student that, for circular motion,

$$\mathbf{v}_i = \boldsymbol{\omega} \times \mathbf{r}_i \qquad (4\text{-}63)$$

where $\boldsymbol{\omega}$ is the *angular velocity*. It happens that Eq. 4–63 is true in general. Using Eq. 4–63, Eq. 4–62 becomes

$$T = \tfrac{1}{2} \sum_i m_i \mathbf{v}_i \cdot (\boldsymbol{\omega} \times \mathbf{r}_i) \qquad (4\text{-}64)$$

One can show further that the order of vectors in the product of Eq. 4–64 may be permuted, giving

$$T = \frac{\boldsymbol{\omega}}{2} \cdot \sum_i m_i (\mathbf{r}_i \times \mathbf{v}_i)$$

$$= \frac{\boldsymbol{\omega}}{2} \cdot \sum_i \mathbf{l}_i = \frac{1}{2} \boldsymbol{\omega} \cdot \mathbf{L} \qquad (4\text{-}65)$$

where $\mathbf{l}_i$ is the angular momentum of the ith particle, and $\mathbf{L}$ is the angular momentum of the whole system.

In turn,

$$\mathbf{L} = \sum_i m_i (\mathbf{r}_i \times \mathbf{v}_i)$$

$$= \sum_i m_i (\mathbf{r}_i \times (\boldsymbol{\omega} \times \mathbf{r}_i))$$

$$= \sum_i m_i (\boldsymbol{\omega} r_i^2 - \mathbf{r}_i (\mathbf{r}_i \cdot \boldsymbol{\omega})) \qquad (4\text{-}66)$$

---

[6] The assumption of rigidity of the molecular framework is, of course, incorrect, since the molecule does vibrate. However, this assumption simplifies the discussion and yet allows some features of interest to be manifested. Similarly, the statement $V = 0$ is not correct for the (very interesting) case of hindered rotation.

Equation 4–65 may be compactly rewritten using the definition of the moment of inertia tensor.

Definition The *moment of inertia tensor* for a body, about some point, is a symmetric matrix, defined in a Cartesian coordinate system as follows. Let $q_1{}^p$, $q_2{}^p$, $q_3{}^p$ be the x, y, z coordinates of particle p. Then the i, j element of the moment of inertia is defined by

$$I_{ij} = \sum_p m_p(r_p{}^2 \delta_{ij} - q_i{}^p q_j{}^p) \qquad (4\text{-}67)$$

where r_p is the distance of the particle p to the particular point.

With this definition for I, we may write

$$\mathbf{L} = I\boldsymbol{\omega} \qquad (4\text{-}68)$$

and therefore

$$T = \tfrac{1}{2}\boldsymbol{\omega} \cdot I\boldsymbol{\omega} = \tfrac{1}{2}\langle \boldsymbol{\omega} \, |I| \, \boldsymbol{\omega}\rangle \qquad (4\text{-}69)$$

The question before us now is precisely how we can simply interpret the role of the moment of inertia tensor in the formula for rotational kinetic energy.

We learned in Section 4–1 that the angular momentum of a system of particles about a point may be broken up into the angular momentum of the particles about the center of mass plus the angular momentum of the center of mass. Therefore, if we focus our attention on just the rotations of a molecule, that is, if we view the molecule in a coordinate system where the center of mass is fixed, we greatly simplify the problem, for, in such a coordinate system, the angular momentum is just the angular momentum about the center of mass. Then, in Eq. 4–67, r_p may be taken to be the distance from the center of mass to the particle p.

If it is possible for us to choose a coordinate system in which I is diagonal, say the ξ, η, ζ coordinate system, then the kinetic energy would take on the particularly simple form

$$T = \frac{\boldsymbol{\omega} \cdot I\boldsymbol{\omega}}{2} = \frac{1}{2}\left[I_{\xi\xi}\omega_\xi{}^2 + I_{\eta\eta}\omega_\eta{}^2 + I_{\zeta\zeta}\omega_\zeta{}^2\right] \qquad (4\text{-}70)$$

where $I_{\xi\xi}$, $I_{\eta\eta}$, $I_{\zeta\zeta}$ are the three diagonal elements of I, and ω_ξ, ω_η, ω_ζ are the components of the angular velocity vector.

Can I be diagonalized? Yes, since I is symmetric and real. For $i \neq j$,

$$I_{ij} = \sum_p (-m_p q_i{}^p q_j{}^p) = \sum_p (-m_p q_j{}^p q_i{}^p) = I_{ji} \qquad (4\text{-}71)$$

We may therefore appeal to the theorem of Section 3–4 dealing with the eigenvalues of Hermitian operators, for I is a Hermitian matrix. Hence the eigenvalues of I, called the *principal moments of inertia*, are real, and its eigenvectors, called the *principal axes*, are orthonormal. The similarity transformation which relates an arbitrary Cartesian axis system to the principal axis system is called the *principal axis transformation*. By diagonalizing the matrix for I, we may use at once the more simple expression for T, Eq. 4–70, in considering the energy of a rigid rotor.

It is customary to name rigid rotors according to the number of equivalent principal moments of inertia, as follows:

Moments of inertia	Name for rotor
$I_{\xi\xi} = I_{\eta\eta} = I_{\zeta\zeta}$	Spherical top
$I_{\xi\xi} = I_{\eta\eta} \neq I_{\zeta\zeta}$	Symmetric top
$I_{\xi\xi} \neq I_{\eta\eta} \neq I_{\zeta\zeta}$	Asymmetric top

EXAMPLE

Calculate the principal moments of inertia of water. If the water molecule is oriented in the coordinate system shown in Fig. 4–4, we may easily compute the elements of the moment of inertia tensor in this coordinate system. Notice that the molecule is oriented symmetrically with the center of mass at the origin of the coordinate system. We must first calculate the positions of the nuclei, given the molecular geometry. This can be done with simple trigonometry and the center-of-mass equation,

$$\sum_i m_i \mathbf{r}_i = \mathbf{0},$$

since the center of mass is at the origin. The positions of the nuclei are $\mathbf{r}(O) = (0.00, 0.07)$, $\mathbf{r}(H_a) = (-0.76, -0.55)$, and $\mathbf{r}(H_b) = (0.76, -. 55)$; $|\mathbf{r}(O)| = 0.07$, and $|\mathbf{r}(H_a)| = |\mathbf{r}(H_b)| = 0.94$. Using Eq. 4–67, we may

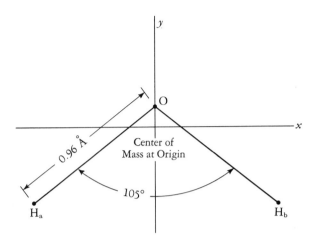

Figure 4-4   Principal axes of water molecule.

now compute the moment of inertia tensor for water about its center of mass. For example,

$$I_{xx} = \sum_p m_p(r_p^2 - x_p^2)$$

$$= [16(0.0049 - 0.0000) + 1(0.881 - 0.578)$$
$$+ 1(0.881 - 0.578)](M)(10^{-16}) = 1.21 \times 10^{-40} \text{ g cm}^2$$

where M is the mass of the proton, 1.67×10^{-24} g, and 1 Å^2 = 10^{-16} cm^2. Likewise,

$$I_{xy} = - \sum_p m_p x_p y_p$$

$$= -[(16)(0)(0.07) - (1)(-0.76)(-0.55)$$
$$-(1)(0.76)(-0.55)](M)(10^{-16}) = 0$$

In a similar fashion, we calculate the tensor I to be

$$I = \begin{pmatrix} 1.21 \times 10^{-40} & 0 & 0 \\ 0 & 1.93 \times 10^{-40} & 0 \\ 0 & 0 & 3.08 \times 10^{-40} \end{pmatrix} \text{ g cm}^2$$

We find the principal moments of inertia at once, since the tensor is diagonal. Furthermore, we find that the x, y, and z axes of Fig. 4-4 are the principal axes.

This classification of molecules, and the methods of matrix algebra devoted to finding the principal moments of inertia have motivated the preceding section.

Problems

1. Prove the properties of the cross product mentioned beneath Eq. 4–3.
2. Prove the three conservation theorems for systems of particles suggested in Section 4–1.
3. Prove the three separation theorems for systems of particles suggested in Section 4–1.
4. Two particles of mass m are joined by a rigid, weightless rod of length l; the center of the rod is constrained to move frictionlessly on a circular wire loop of radius a. Choose a suitably simple set of generalized coordinates and express T in this set.
5. Obtain the Lagrange equations for a pendulum which may move in three dimensions: a particle of mass m suspended under the influence of gravity by a rigid, weightless rod.
6. Two particles of unequal mass are connected by a (weightless, inelastic) string. One particle slips over the side of a table while the other rests on the (frictionless) table top. Describe the motion using Lagrangian mechanics.
7. A ball of mass m is attached to the center of a smooth flat table by means of a spring. The force constant of the spring is k, and its equilibrium length is r_0. Find the equations of motion for the system, and comment.
8. (a) Derive Eq. 4–23a; (b) derive Eq. 4–23b.
9. A particle is held inside a flat rectangular box by four springs, two each of two different force constants. The particle is given a small displacement from equilibrium. Describe its motion.
10. Derive Eq. 4–53.
11. Reformulate and work out the normal modes of the linear triatomic molecule in the center-of-mass coordinate system as hinted at in the example of Section 4–3.
12. Find the normal modes and frequencies of vibration of water.
13. Find the normal modes and frequencies of vibration of carbon dioxide.
14. Derive Eqs. 4–63, 4–65, and 4–66.
15. Prove Euler's theorem: The most general displacement of a rigid body with one point fixed is a rotation about some axis.
16. Work through the example given in Section 4–4 to calculate the moment of inertia tensor for water in a coordinate system where the oxygen atom is at the origin and one O—H bond lies in the x axis, rather than in

the coordinate system of Fig. 4–4. Compare the results from your calculation to those of the example.

17. The molecules CCl_4, NCl_3, OCl_2, and FCl are all chlorides of first-row elements. Compute the principal moments of inertia of each, and classify each as a particular kind of "top." Sketch each, and show the principal axes. You will have to look up the structure of these molecules.

18. Show that tetrahedral and cubic molecules are spherical tops.

5

Conclusion

The four preceding chapters of this book have been designed to prepare the stage for quantum mechanics, and especially for molecular spectroscopy. To finish this stage setting—in fact, to raise the curtain a bit—we touch briefly on two points. The first is the connection between classical and quantum mechanics; the second is the synthesis of the wave-mechanical and matrix-mechanical points of view.

5–1 THE BRIDGE BETWEEN CLASSICAL AND QUANTUM MECHANICS

To introduce quantum mechanics properly, one should become aware of the thrilling experiments performed around the end of the nineteenth and beginning of the twentieth century which begged a theoretical explanation not afforded by Newtonian mechanics and Maxwellian electromagnetism. To review this background would carry us away from the purpose of this book. This section is accordingly confined to a comparison of classical and quantum mechanics at the level of elementary theory, and the experimental basis for quantum mechanics is left for the enjoyment of the reader elsewhere.

Traditionally, quantum mechanics courses begin with a review of the evidence for the failure of classical mechanics. They approach quantum mechanics most often through the (quite natural) point of view of wave-particle duality, exemplified by the work of de Broglie. It should be understood at the outset that the conventional admixture of classical wave equations with the de Broglie momentum-wavelength relation does not constitute a derivation of the Schrödinger equation, the basic equation from which wave mechanics proceeds. The Schrödinger equation may be taken only as a postulate from which an outlook on the physical world can be built, for better or for worse. As such, this outlook has been enormously successful in describing submicroscopic matter, requiring assistance only in the directions of relativity and field theory. Wave mechanics, however, is not *derived;* it is *postulated.* An alternative approach to quantum mechanics—one which is at the same time more abstract and more fundamental—is to establish a connection between operators and corresponding dynamical quantities. In this direction, one can propose a simple and self-consistent set of postulates for quantum mechanics which are at once elegant, abstract, and basic.[1] Again, it should be understood at the outset that the approach to be presented here is not *derived,* but *postulated.* As such, it has neither more nor less physical content than Schrödinger's mechanics. The author hopes only that an alternative formulation of quantum mechanics, using the terminology of Chapters 3 and 4, rather than the (perhaps less familiar) terminology of wave motion will at least cast new light on the comparison of quantum to classical mechanics, and perhaps even make bridging the gap between the two physics less a leap of faith and more one of reason.

It was Bohr[2] who realized that, because classical mechanics was "right" for macroscopic systems, the introduction of quantum mechanics could not totally eradicate the classical theory which had

---

[1] See, for example, the excellent treatment in Dicke, R. H., and Wittke, J. P., *Introduction to Quantum Mechanics*, Chapter 6. Addison-Wesley, Reading, Massachusetts, 1960.

[2] Bohr, N., "The Quantum Postulate and the Recent Development of Atomic Theory," *Nature* **121,** 580 (1928).

gone before. Somehow, quantum mechanics must contain classical mechanics as a limiting case.[3] This statement itself may be thought of as the *correspondence principle*. How may we formulate the nature of the limit in which quantum mechanics yields classical mechanics? This question can be answered at many levels of sophistication. We offer here only one way of pointing out the classical limit of quantum mechanics and also the correspondence between them; there are other methods—some very elegant—for demonstrating this correspondence.

Following Dicke and Wittke,[4] for example, we might begin a postulatory formulation of quantum mechanics by saying that to every physical observable there corresponds an operator; for physically measurable quantities the operator must be Hermitian; the result of measuring the physical quantity is one of the eigenvalues of the operator which corresponds to that quantity.

In the limit of classical mechanics, the operator nature of physical quantities is lost; or, to be more precise, the operator for a physical quantity Q, denoted $\mathbb{Q}$, must be defined by the instructions "multiply the operand function by Q," that is, $\mathbb{Q}f \rightarrow Qf$. If this is so, then, in the classical limit, all operators corresponding to physical quantities commute. In the situations wherein quantum mechanics alone "rightly" describes the problem, all operators do not commute. Hence the nature of the classical limit of quantum mechanics must be

$$[\mathbb{Q}, \ \mathbb{B}] = (\text{small number})(\text{operator corresponding to}$$
$$\text{some function of } A, B) \qquad (5\text{-}1)$$

In the development of quantum theory, one "small number" appears time and time again. This number is Planck's constant. In fact, $i\hbar$ is just the right number for Eq. 5–1, as was verified by eventually comparing theory to experiment. We have now

$$[\mathbb{Q}, \ \mathbb{B}] = i\hbar(\text{operator corresponding to some function of } A, B)$$
$$(5\text{-}2)$$

Our search for a correspondence between classical and quantum me-

---

[3] Landau, L. D., and Lifschitz, E. M., *Quantum Mechanics: Non-relativistic Theory*, p. 19. Translated from Russian by J. B. Sykes and J. S. Bell (Volume 3 in *Course in Theoretical Physics*). Addison-Wesley, Reading, Massachusetts, 1958.

[4] Dicke and Wittke, *op. cit.*, pp. 91 ff.

chanics (which is here obviously not derived) is almost over. For reasons of dimensions, the "function of A, B" which we have yet to supply, must have the dimensions of $(AB/\text{erg-sec})$, since $i\hbar$ has units of erg-sec. Such a function is the Poisson bracket of A and B, whence

$$[\mathfrak{A}, \mathfrak{B}] = i\hbar(\text{operator corresponding to } \{A, B\}) \qquad (5\text{-}3)$$

which is precisely the seventh postulate of Dicke and Wittke.[5] Equation 5-3 is a "prescription" or a "helpful guide" rather than a derivation. Proceeding from this statement of correspondence and limit between classical and quantum mechanics, we may derive (and now *derive* is the right word) some consequences of importance.

First, compare the Poisson bracket of a quantity with the classical Hamiltonian to the commutator of the corresponding operator with the Hamiltonian operator.

$$df/dt = \{f, H\} + \partial f/\partial t \qquad (4\text{-}48)$$

Again appealing to the principle that in the classical limit, the operator $\mathfrak{F}$ must behave just like the function f,

$$\frac{d\mathfrak{F}}{dt} = -\frac{i}{\hbar}[\mathfrak{F}, \mathfrak{IC}] + \frac{\partial \mathfrak{F}}{\partial t} = \frac{i}{\hbar}[\mathfrak{IC}, \mathfrak{F}] + \frac{\partial \mathfrak{F}}{\partial t} \qquad (5\text{-}4)$$

which is *Heisenberg's equation of motion for the operator* $\mathfrak{F}$. Heisenberg's point of view, which placed emphasis on linear operators and their matrix representatives, put all the time dependence for a quantity into its corresponding operator through Eq. 5-4. This equation allows us to state the correspondence principle in terms of a conservation theorem: *Quantities which are constants of the motion in classical mechanics remain constants of the motion in quantum mechanics.* In particular, if the classical Hamiltonian is not explicitly time dependent, then energy is conserved:

$$\frac{dH}{dt} = \{H, H\} + \frac{\partial H}{\partial t} = \{H, H\} = 0 \qquad (5\text{-}5a)$$

This has the quantum-mechanical analog

$$\frac{d\mathfrak{IC}}{dt} = \frac{i}{\hbar}[\mathfrak{IC}, \mathfrak{IC}] + \frac{\partial \mathfrak{IC}}{\partial t} = \frac{i}{\hbar}[\mathfrak{IC}, \mathfrak{IC}] = 0 \qquad (5\text{-}5b)$$

---

[5] Dicke and Wittke, *op. cit.*, p. 102.

An alternative point of view,[6] that taken by Schrödinger, is to leave operators implicitly independent of time, and to make their eigenfunctions time dependent. To do this, begin with the equation of motion of an eigenvalue f of the operator   whose eigenfunction is ϕ. Then

$$\frac{d\mathfrak{F}}{dt} = \frac{d}{dt}\langle\phi\,|\mathfrak{F}|\phi\rangle = \left\langle\frac{d\phi}{dt}\,|\mathfrak{F}|\,\phi\right\rangle + \left\langle\phi\,\Big|\mathfrak{F}\Big|\frac{d\phi}{dt}\right\rangle \tag{5-6}$$

From Eq. 5–4,

$$\frac{d\mathfrak{F}}{dt} = \left\langle\phi\,\Big|\,\frac{i}{\hbar}[\mathfrak{IC},\mathfrak{F}]\,\Big|\,\phi\right\rangle = \left\langle\phi\,\Big|\frac{i}{\hbar}\mathfrak{IC}\mathfrak{F} - \frac{i}{\hbar}\mathfrak{F}\mathfrak{IC}\Big|\,\phi\right\rangle$$

$$= \left\langle-\frac{i}{\hbar}\mathfrak{IC}\phi\,|\mathfrak{F}|\,\phi\right\rangle + \left\langle\phi\,|\mathfrak{F}|\,-\frac{i}{\hbar}\mathfrak{IC}\phi\right\rangle \tag{5-7}$$

whence, in order to have agreement between Eqs. 5–6 and 5–7, we require

$$\mathfrak{IC}\phi = i\hbar\frac{d\phi}{dt} \tag{5-8}$$

which is Schrödinger's equation.

Thus we have seen that a neat correspondence can be established between classical and quantum mechanics which introduces both Heisenberg's and Schrödinger's equations of motion, and concomitant conservation laws.

5–2   THE SYNTHESIS OF MATRIX AND WAVE MECHANICS

We have mentioned the two points of view of eigenvalue-eigenvector problems. In the first, the operator is a differential operator and the eigenvalue equation is a differential equation. In the second, the operator is represented by a matrix and the eigenvalue equation by a set of simultaneous linear homogeneous equations. The syn-

---

[6] The words *point of view* have been used here in describing the way in which equations of motion are cast in quantum mechanics. Others use the word *representation* for this concept; thus, *Heisenberg representation* or *Schrödinger representation*. We, however, have used *representation* to mean something quite different, and therefore avoid using it here.

thesis of these two points of view is found in the concept of Hilbert space.[7]

We need to show how the algebraic methods of Chapter 3 remain applicable for problems with a continuous variable (as many quantum-mechanical problems have). If we define a *Hilbert space* as a vector space spanned by normalizable functions with a defined inner product (Eq. 3-1), then we may establish a synthesis of matrix and wave mechanics. The concept of Hilbert space allows a vector space with infinite dimension. This infinite number may be discrete and denumerable, as in the index n in the basis set $\{H_n(x)\}$, $n = 0, 1, \ldots$. Or, this infinite number may be continuous and non-denumerable, as the number of points on the line.

Further discussion of Hilbert space would carry us too far afield; the author hopes only to indicate the nature of the similarity between an eigenfunction and an eigenvector. In Hilbert space, the matrix representative of an operator might be of infinite dimension; an eigenfunction would be representable by an infinitely long column vector. For example, consider the operator for position, $\mathfrak{X}$, which has a continuous range, or *spectrum* of eigenvalues, say $\{x'\}: \mathfrak{X} \mid x'\rangle = x' \mid x'\rangle$. Any eigenvector $\mid \xi\rangle$ in the Hilbert space may be expanded in terms of the eigenvectors of $\mathfrak{X}$ (since they comprise a complete, orthonormal set).

$$\mid \xi\rangle = \sum \mid x'\rangle\langle x' \mid \xi\rangle = \int \mid x'\rangle\langle x' \mid \xi\rangle \, dx' \qquad (5\text{-}9)$$

Since the Hilbert space is of infinite dimension, we replace the sum by an integral over the continuous variable x'. The coefficients $\langle x' \mid \xi\rangle$ are (complex) functions which make up the representative of the vector $\mid \xi\rangle$ in the basis $\mid x'\rangle$. We may call this collection of complex functions the *wave function:* $\Psi_\xi(x') = \langle x' \mid \xi\rangle$. The inner product of two Hilbert space vectors, $\langle \xi \mid \eta\rangle$, provides the final link to the theory of Chapter 2:

$$
\begin{aligned}
\langle \xi \mid \eta\rangle &= \int dx' \int dx'' \, \langle \xi \mid x'\rangle\langle x' \mid x''\rangle\langle x'' \mid \eta\rangle \\
&= \int dx' \, \langle \xi \mid x'\rangle\langle x' \mid \eta\rangle \\
&= \int dx' \, \Psi_\xi^*(x')\Psi_\eta^*(x')
\end{aligned}
\qquad (5\text{-}10)
$$

which is the same as Eq. 2-1.

---

[7] For a somewhat more detailed discussion, see Jackson, J. D., *Mathematics for Quantum Mechanics*, Sections 5-10 and 5-11. W. A. Benjamin, New York, 1962.

Thus we conclude our foray into the mathematics and physics which are relevant to quantum chemistry. The author's hope is that the student's mastery of the principles and applications of quantum mechanics will not be needlessly fettered by a simultaneous strain to grasp the mathematical language in which the subject is couched.

Problems

1. Show that Eq. 5–3 is dimensionally correct.

2. Using the correspondence principle as expressed in Eq. 5–3, find the commutation relations between Cartesian coordinates and Cartesian linear momenta.

Appendix

Mathematical Background
and Bibliography

The purpose of these brief appendices is to summarize some formulas of importance that may be unfamiliar to students with two years of college mathematics, and yet are important to the development of the text.

A–1 COMPLEX NUMBERS

(A) ARITHMETIC OF COMPLEX NUMBERS
1. Definition: $i = \sqrt{-1}$.
2. Addition: If $z = x + iy$, $z' = x' + iy'$, then $(z + z') = (x + x') + i(y + y')$.
3. Modulus: $|z| = (x^2 + y^2)^{1/2}$.
4. Multiplication: $zz' = (xx' - yy') + i(xy' + yx')$.
5. Division: $z/z' = \{(xx' + yy') + i(xy' - x'y)\}/\{x'^2 + y'^2\}$.
6. Conjugation: $z^* = x - iy$.

(B) ALGEBRAIC THEOREMS
1. Modulus of sum of two numbers is less than or equal to sum of moduli: $|z_1 + z_2| \leq |z_1| + |z_2|$.
2. Decomposition into modulus and argument: $z = x + iy = r(\cos\theta + i\sin\theta)$, where $r = |z|$, $\theta = \tan^{-1}(y/x)$.

3. De Moivre's theorem: If $z = r(\cos \theta + i \sin \theta)$, then $z^n = r^n(\cos n\theta + i \sin n\theta)$.

(C) SPECIAL FUNCTIONS

1. Exponential. Defined by the power series, $\exp[z] = 1 + z + z^2/2! + z^3/3! + \cdots$, the exponential function has all the same properties as the exponential of a real variable. In particular,

$$e^z e^{z'} = e^{z+z'} \qquad e^{iy} = \sum_n (iy)^n/n! = \cos y + i \sin y.$$

Hence, $e^z = e^x(\cos y + i \sin y)$.

2. Trigonometric. Defined by power series, these functions are apparently identical in all respects to their real counterparts. Notice, from paragraph 1 above, that

$$\cos z = \frac{e^{iz} + e^{-iz}}{2} \qquad \sin z = \frac{e^{iz} - e^{-iz}}{2i}.$$

A–2   CALCULUS: PARTIAL DERIVATIVES

(A) DEFINITIONS

1. Total derivative:

$$\left.\frac{dy}{dx}\right|_{x_0} = \lim_{\Delta x \to 0} \frac{\Delta y}{\Delta x} = \lim_{\Delta x \to 0} \frac{y(x_0 + \Delta x) - y(x_0)}{\Delta x}$$

2. Partial derivative:

$$\left.\frac{\partial z}{\partial x}\right|_{x_0, y_0} = \lim_{\Delta x \to 0} \frac{z(x_0 + \Delta x, y_0) - z(x_0, y_0)}{\Delta x}$$

(B) THEOREMS

1. Inversion.

$$\left.\frac{\partial z}{\partial y}\right|_x = \left(\left.\frac{\partial y}{\partial z}\right|_x\right)^{-1}$$

2. Chain rule. Example: suppose $w = w(u, v)$, $u = u(x, y)$, $v = v(x)$. Ultimately, w is dependent on x and y. Evaluate this dependence by tracing through the intermediate functions u, v:

$$\frac{\partial w}{\partial x} = \frac{\partial w}{\partial u}\frac{\partial u}{\partial x} + \frac{\partial w}{\partial v}\frac{\partial v}{\partial x}$$

$$\frac{\partial w}{\partial y} = \frac{\partial w}{\partial u}\frac{\partial u}{\partial y}$$

3. Implicit differentiation. Example: If u, v, x, y are interrelated by

$$F(u, v; x, y) = 0 \qquad G(u, v; x, y) = 0$$

then solve the two simultaneous linear equations

$$0 = \frac{\partial F}{\partial x} + \frac{\partial F}{\partial u}\frac{\partial u}{\partial x} + \frac{\partial F}{\partial v}\frac{\partial v}{\partial x}$$

$$0 = \frac{\partial G}{\partial x} + \frac{\partial G}{\partial u}\frac{\partial u}{\partial x} + \frac{\partial G}{\partial v}\frac{\partial v}{\partial x}$$

for $\partial u/\partial x$ and $\partial v/\partial x$; similarly for $\partial u/\partial y$ and $\partial v/\partial y$. Application of the theory of Chapter 3 will simplify such a calculation by defining the *Jacobian*,

$$J(F, G; x, y) = \begin{vmatrix} \dfrac{\partial F}{\partial x} & \dfrac{\partial F}{\partial y} \\ \dfrac{\partial G}{\partial x} & \dfrac{\partial G}{\partial y} \end{vmatrix}$$

Then, $\partial u/\partial x = -J(F, G; x, v)/J(F, G; u, v)$, and so forth.

4. Triple product.

$$\left(\frac{\partial x}{\partial z}\bigg|_{y}\right)\left(\frac{\partial z}{\partial y}\bigg|_{x}\right)\left(\frac{\partial y}{\partial x}\bigg|_{z}\right) = -1.$$

A–3 BIBLIOGRAPHY

The following bibliography is not intended to be complete, but rather a survey of works that the author has found useful.

(A) MATHEMATICS FOR PHYSICS AND CHEMISTRY
Chisholm, J. S. R., and Morris, R. M., *Mathematical Methods in Physics.* W. B. Saunders, Philadelphia, 1965.
Courant, R., and Hilbert, D., *Methods of Mathematical Physics*, Vol. I., 1st English ed. Interscience, New York, 1953.
Irving, J., and Mullineux, N., *Mathematics in Physics and Engineering.* Academic Press, New York, 1959.
Jackson, J. D., *Mathematics for Quantum Mechanics.* W. A. Benjamin, New York, 1962.
Margenau, H., and Murphy, G. M., *The Mathematics of Physics and Chemistry.* Van Nostrand, Princeton, 1956.

Matthews, J., and Walker, R. L., *Mathematical Methods of Physics*. W. A. Benjamin, New York, 1964.

Sokolnikoff, I. S., and Redheffer, R. M., *Mathematics of Physics and Modern Engineering*. McGraw-Hill, New York, 1958.

Sokolnikoff, I. S., and Sokolnikoff, E., *Higher Mathematics for Engineers and Physicists*. McGraw-Hill, New York, 1934.

(B) CALCULUS AND ALGEBRA: TEXTBOOKS IN PURE MATHEMATICS

Birkhoff, G., and MacLane, S., *A Survey of Modern Algebra*, 3rd ed., revised. Macmillan, New York, 1965.

Buck, R. C., *Advanced Calculus*. McGraw-Hill, New York, 1956.

Courant, R., *Differential and Integral Calculus*, Vols. I and II, 2nd English ed. Interscience, New York, 1937.

Thomas, G. B., *Calculus and Analytic Geometry*, 2nd ed. Addison-Wesley, Reading, Massachusetts, 1953.

Weiss, M. J., *Higher Algebra*. Wiley, New York, 1949.

(C) CLASSICAL MECHANICS

Goldstein, H. J., *Classical Mechanics*. Addison-Wesley, Reading, Massachusetts, 1959.

Landau, L. D., and Lifschitz, E. M., *Mechanics*. Translated from Russian by J. B. Sykes and J. S. Bell (Volume 1 in *Course of Theoretical Physics*). Addison-Wesley, Reading, Massachusetts, 1958.

Synge, J. L., and Griffith, B. A., *Principles of Mechanics*, 3rd ed. McGraw-Hill, New York, 1959.

(D) QUANTUM MECHANICS: TEXTS WITH CHAPTERS ON CLASSICAL MECHANICS AND MATHEMATICAL BACKGROUND

Dicke, R. H., and Wittke, J. P., *Introduction to Quantum Mechanics*. Addison Wesley, Reading, Massachusetts, 1960.

Dirac, P. A. M., *The Principles of Quantum Mechanics*. Oxford Univ. Press, New York, 1947.

Eyring, H., Walter, J., and Kimball, G. E., *Quantum Chemistry*. Wiley, New York, 1944.

Kauzmann, W., *Quantum Chemistry*. Academic Press, New York, 1957.

Landau, L. D., and Lifschitz, E. M., *Quantum Mechanics: Nonrelativistic Theory*. Translated from Russian by J. B. Sykes and J. S. Bell (Volume 3 in *Course of Theoretical Physics*). Addison-Wesley, Reading, Massachusetts, 1958.

Pauling, L. C., and Wilson, E. B., *Introduction to Quantum Mechanics*. McGraw-Hill, New York, 1935.

Schiff, L. I., *Quantum Mechanics*. McGraw-Hill, New York, 1955.

Answers to Problems

Chapter 1

1. Solve $df/dx = kf$; solutions are all functions $\{e^{kf}\}$.

Chapter 2

1. Evaluate all integrals of Eq. 2–16.

2. (a) even; (b) odd; (c) even; (d) odd; (e) even; (f) odd; (g) e^x = $\sinh x + \cosh x$, $\sinh x$ is odd, $\cosh x$ is even; (h) $e^{ix} = i \sin x + \cos x$, $\sin x$ is odd, $\cos x$ is even.

3. The norms are $\pi/2$, except $N(\sin 0x) = 0$, $N(\cos 0x) = \pi$. The expansion coefficients are $b_n = (2/\pi)\langle \sin nx \mid f \rangle$, $a_n = (2/\pi)\langle \cos nx \mid f \rangle$ in the series $f = \Sigma\, b_n \sin nx = a_0/2 + \Sigma\, a_n \cos nx$.

4.
$$x - x^2 = -\sum_{n \text{ even}} \frac{4}{\pi n^3} \sin nx$$

$$= -\sum_{n \text{ even}} \frac{4}{n^2} \cos nx + \sum_{n \text{ odd}} \frac{4\pi - 4}{\pi n^2} \cos nx$$

$$+ \left(\pi - \frac{2\pi^2}{3} \right)$$

Sine series converges faster.

5.
$$\sin x = -\sum_{m \text{ odd}} [4/\pi m(m - 4)] \sin mx = \tfrac{1}{2} - \tfrac{1}{2} \cos 2x.$$

Cosine "series" is the usual trigonometric identity.

6. $\frac{1}{4} - \pi/6 + \frac{1}{2}\pi$.

8. Square wave is odd, so must involve only sine terms:

$$f(x) = \sum_{m \text{ odd}} (4a/m\pi) \sin mx.$$

9. Triangular wave is even, so must involve only cosine terms:

$$f(x) = \pi/2 + \sum_{n \text{ odd}} (4/\pi n^2) \cos nx.$$

11. Taylor series is not an expansion in orthonormal functions. The Schmidt process using different intervals and different orders of the powers of x will give different orthonormal functions.

12. Take the functions in this order: $f_0 = \sin^0 x$, $f_1 = \cos^0 x$, $f_2 = \sin^1 x$, $f_3 = \cos^1 x$, and so forth, and use the Schmidt process.

13. Multiply Eq. 2–114 for P_l^m by $P_{l'}^m$; multiply the equation for $P_{l'}^m$ by P_l^m, and subtract. Integrate by parts.

Chapter 3

1. (a), (c), (d) are independent; (b) is dependent.

2. Yes.

6.
$$A^{-1} = \begin{pmatrix} \frac{10}{9} & \frac{5}{9} & -\frac{4}{9} \\ -\frac{8}{9} & -\frac{4}{9} & \frac{5}{9} \\ -\frac{15}{9} & -\frac{3}{9} & \frac{6}{9} \end{pmatrix} \qquad B^{-1} = \begin{pmatrix} 1 & 0 & 0 \\ -2 & 1 & 0 \\ \frac{2}{3} & -\frac{1}{3} & \frac{1}{3} \end{pmatrix}$$

A and B do not commute.

7. Determinant $= 1$.

8. Use successive applications of expansion in cofactors.

9. (a) $x = -17/54$, $y = -63/54$, $z = -31/54$.
   (b) For example, $w = 7z/5$, $2x = y - 8z/5$.
   (c) $z = 5/7$, $y = 2x + 8/7$.
   (d) $x = 1$, $y = 2$, $z = 3$.

10.
$$\begin{pmatrix} \sin\theta\cos\phi & \sin\theta\sin\phi & \cos\theta \\ \cos\theta\cos\phi & \cos\theta\sin\phi & -\sin\theta \\ -\sin\phi & \cos\phi & 0 \end{pmatrix}$$

11. $(0, -3)$, $(-5, 6)$, $(2, -3)$, $(-1, 0)$.

12. (a) Rank 2; (b) rank 3.

13.
$$\text{(a) } U = \begin{pmatrix} \dfrac{1}{\sqrt{2}} & \dfrac{i}{\sqrt{2}} \\ \dfrac{1}{\sqrt{2}} & -\dfrac{i}{\sqrt{2}} \end{pmatrix}$$

$$\text{(b) } U'^{-1}A^\phi U' = A^\psi = \begin{pmatrix} e^{-ia} & 0 \\ 0 & e^{ia} \end{pmatrix}$$

14. $\tan 2\theta = 2h/(a - b)$.
16. (e) Show $\text{tr}(S^{-1}AS) = \text{tr } A$, where S is unitary.
21. Eigenvalues: 4, 8, 12.
23. Eigenvalues: 0, 0, 2.

Chapter 4

3. Let (a, θ, ϕ) be the coordinates of the center of mass of the rod on the circle, and let $(l/2, \theta', \phi')$ be the coordinates of the masses about the center of the rod. Then, $T = ma^2(\dot\theta^2 + \dot\phi^2 \sin^2 \phi) + (ml^2/4)(\dot\theta'^2 + \dot\phi'^2 \sin^2 \theta')$.
4. In spherical coordinates,

$$-mr(\dot\theta^2 + \dot\phi^2 \sin^2 \phi) + mg \sin \theta = 0$$
$$mr^2\ddot\theta - mr^2\dot\phi^2 \sin \theta \cos \theta + mgr \cos \theta = 0$$
$$mr^2\ddot\phi \sin^2 \theta + 2mr^2\dot\phi \sin \theta \cos \theta = 0$$

5. Use spherical coordinates about the point where the string passes over the table.
6. Using polar coordinates,

$$m\ddot r - mr\dot\theta^2 + k(r - r_0) = 0$$
$$2m\dot r\dot\theta + mr^2\ddot\theta = 0$$

Angular momentum is conserved.
8. $\omega_1 = (2k_1/m)^{1/2}$, $\omega_2 = (2k_2/m)^{1/2}$. Motion in different directions is not coupled.
14. Hint: Think of orthogonal transformations.

Chapter 5

2. $[x, p_x] = i\hbar$.

Index

THE REMOVES

This Large Print Book carries the
Seal of Approval of N.A.V.H.

THE REMOVES

TATJANA SOLI

WHEELER PUBLISHING
A part of Gale, a Cengage Company

Farmington Hills, Mich • San Francisco • New York • Waterville, Maine
Meriden, Conn • Mason, Ohio • Chicago

Copyright © 2018 by Tatjana Soli.
Owing to limitations of space, illustration credits appear on pages 607-609.
Wheeler Publishing, a part of Gale, a Cengage Company.

LIBRARY OF CONGRESS CIP DATA ON FILE.
CATALOGUING IN PUBLICATION FOR THIS BOOK
IS AVAILABLE FROM THE LIBRARY OF CONGRESS.

ISBN-13: 978-1-4328-5464-5 (hardcover)

Published in 2018 by arrangement with Sarah Crichton Books, an imprint of Farrar, Straus and Giroux

Printed in Mexico
1 2 3 4 5 6 7 22 21 20 19 18

For Mom, with love

A very great vision is needed and the man who has it must follow it as the eagle seeks the deepest blue of the sky.

— Crazy Horse

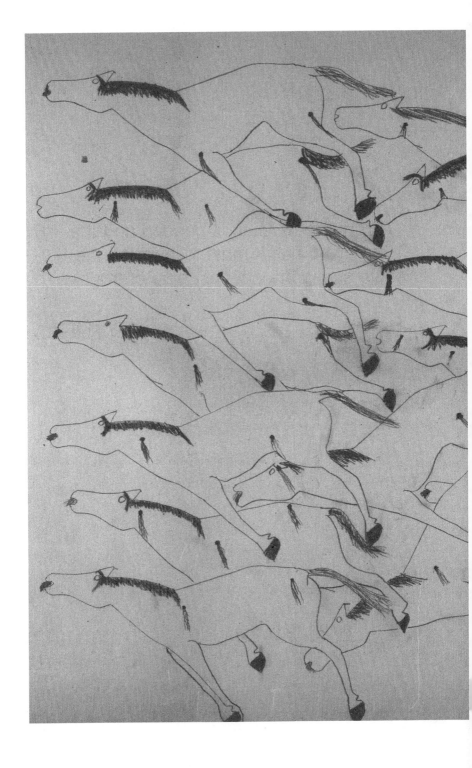

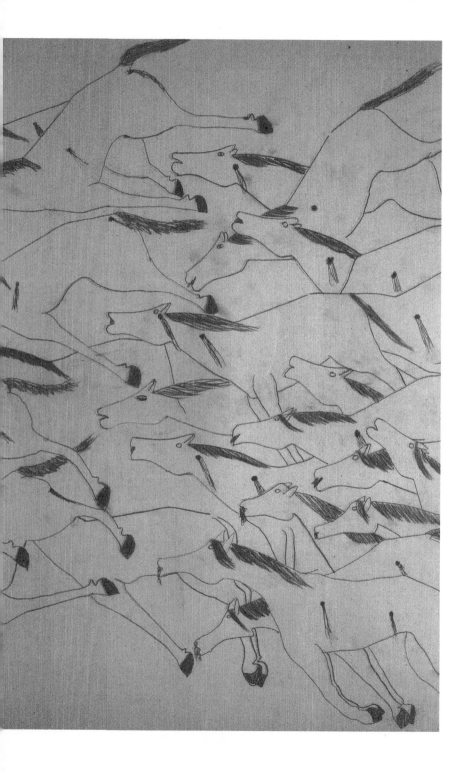

THE FIRST REMOVE

Indian attack — Fighting alongside
the men —
The massacre — Family — Taken captive
— The march

The thunder of the rifle inside the house so blasted Anne's ears that she forgot for a moment the reason for her father's firing it, so caught up was she in the physical pain of the noise. She cupped her palms over her ears to shelter them but too late. When she took her hands away, her hearing had fled, vanished so that events unfolded before her in eerie silence. From her mother's pious beliefs, she wondered briefly if this was a gift of God, this shielding deafness, but decided against such interpretation because if God had willingly allowed the sights before her eyes it would be blasphemy to his goodness. The silence proved both blessing and curse. Not the war cries of the

11

Indians, nor the screams of her relatives in their death throes as they departed from this earth, had the power to frighten her, but the lack of sound endowed her sight with a magnified strength. The acts committed before her turned into visions burned on her mind's eye that she would revisit, voluntarily or not, for the rest of her days.

In the morning the men had left to work the fields, leaving the small group of homesteads unguarded except for old men, the blacksmith, and some stragglers, including her beau, Michael, who loitered in the communal barn with the hope of a stolen meeting with her.

A party of Cheyenne rode in, one warrior in the lead, waving a dirty white piece of cloth on a stick. Immediately her mother's face went slack with fear. The tribes had become habituated to handouts, and they demanded charity whether given freely or not. She hissed to Anne's six-year-old brother, Nevin, to run out the back.

"Be careful, don't be seen. Bring the men back! Quick!"

Anne's grandfather went out to offer the band provision and delay any possible aggression till the men were returned to defend the homestead. Anne watched from the window as he walked up to the leader

and within seconds was surrounded by mounted warriors. Only the back of his graying head was visible above the ponies. It would be the last moment the world would appear safe to her. As quickly as she drew her next breath, an Indian behind him raised a hatchet even as he parleyed with the leader in front. Anne screamed as the blow came down, a bloom of horror. He staggered a moment from the impact, the circle of warriors still and calm, only mildly curious as he crumpled to the ground between their horses' feet.

Her father and some of the neighbors had run in through the back door, loaded down with rifles and bags of ammunition. In the part of Kansas they farmed, it was necessary to work the fields *with hoe in one hand and rifle in the other,* so the men had been ready to protect their families. The Indians already surrounded the other houses so that the men had no choice but stay and defend Anne's homestead before reaching their own. With one look outside, her father roughly pulled Anne from the window and directed her mother to gather the children against the back wall, low against the ground to avoid the ricochet of bullets. Her father's first firing, the one that deafened her, hit the warrior who killed her grand-

father, the shot taking off the side of his head, and he slumped over and rolled off his horse. Within moments, as if his blood nourished the earth he fell on, fifty more equally fierce fighters sprang into view.

Anne pressed against her mother and sisters, her arms around Nevin to keep him from squirming away to join the men. Having sounded the alarm of the attack, he was filled with fearlessness and childish belief in his own invincibility. Anne closed her eyes. Again she saw the Indian's concave head, his face fierce as a hawk's, and then the dip of his body to earth. The darkness under her eyelids combined with the lack of sound to calm her. Did her grandfather share this same darkness with her? She pretended that this was a nightmare from which she could soon wake. Her mother poked her up.

Her father, manning the window, motioned for Anne to rise and travel between the shooters along the front of the house, resupplying them with ammunition. The neighbor whose task it had been now lay facedown in the doorway, blood pooling under him, and Anne had no choice but to step over his legs each time she must hand out bullets. She would never be able to explain it, but with the duty to attend her fear went away. Her greatest preoccupation

14

was to lift her skirts clear so that they should not sop the blood. If she accomplished that, it seemed everything else would be okay. She stayed dry-eyed and calm as yet another man slumped over the window frame, and she must pull him back inside and lay up his rifle against the wall. One man who raised dairy cows cried as he shot blindly, and another who tenant-farmed wheat soiled himself, yet Anne glided between them as if serving cakes at one of her mother's teas. There were five dead inside the house when she finally glanced at the clock and realized two hours had passed. Outside the number of Indians had grown so that they appeared a hive of angry bees.

"Take up the rifle!" her father yelled, and realizing his daughter's impairment he pointed his chin at a gun.

It had come down to her father, an elderly neighbor with poor eyesight, and herself as defense for her mother and siblings. Without hesitation she crawled to the window and pointed the weapon's barrel out.

Several homesteads were burning, and the sunny morning had grayed in the thickening smoke. She fired as best she could, the recoil paining her shoulder, but as far as she could tell the bullets did not come close to a single target. As she watched, the

blacksmith's family attempted escape across the fields. First the father was shot and fell down. The mother and children continued running, but they seemed to have lost compass and moved in an arc that they retraced like chickens in the farmyard running from the approach of the axe. Warriors on foot trotted after them, easily nabbing all three. When the mother begged to have her children back and offered money, the warriors knocked her on the head, then proceeded to strip off her clothes and scalp her. Her long reddish gold hair had been the envy of all the women. Anne would not talk of the other things they did to the body. She whispered a prayer, entrusting the woman's immortal soul to the Lord. After the mutilation was over, Anne turned away and daintily vomited onto the dining room floor.

Her head throbbed, a mix of fear, noise, and smoke making her dry-heave the contents of her empty stomach. Dully she wondered where Michael was, and why had he not come to save her? She had allowed him to kiss her and touch underneath her blouse. Had he run away and left her behind? If he was such a coward she would not marry him after all. Her heart quaked at the thought she might not survive long

enough to reject a suitor.

Now the warriors on horseback turned their attention on Anne's house, which was the last left standing. They rode full speed circling it, throwing up a cloud of dust that mingled with the heavy burning smoke from the other buildings and the crop fields farther on that had been set aflame. She could not hear the terrifying shrill of their cries, nor the beating of the horses' hooves, although she imagined she felt their percussion through the floor, the rumble and awful pound of danger, unless it was simply the thud of her own despairing heart.

Anne fired in a haphazard way, slowed down both by fatigue and inaccuracy. She had only practiced still targets while shooting with her father, never at anything moving, definitely never anything threatening to shoot back at her. Even that limited practice had been grudged by her father, who thought it unbecoming for a fifteen-year-old girl to learn such. Strange that now she was the one tasked with defending them.

Two young men, friends of her Michael, fearful of Indians surrounding their barn in the northwest corner of the settlement, tried to flee along the south field and were shot down as easily as quail. So taken up was she by the plight of their neighbors, Anne at

first did not notice Indians had climbed on her own roof. Soon flames could be seen licking the corner of the ceiling, smoke thickening the air so that her father had to set down his gun and beat out the nascent fire with a blanket. It was at that moment that a bullet fired through the doorway caught him in the throat. Surprised, angered, he could offer her no last words, but she read in his eyes how sorry he was to leave them in such danger. A moment later, he was no more.

His old carbine was unwieldy in her hands, too heavy to hold, but she carried it over to her mother and siblings and crowded over them. The weapon's metal was warm. She imagined it still held the life from her father's hands. She was determined she would blast the first Indian who made it through the door, even if she could do nothing about the second, third, and fourth.

What happened instead was the entire roof caught ablaze at once and formed a fiery crown above them. With no one to extinguish it the heat grew unbearable inside the room, like sitting in the oven where the bread baked. Hot ash fell like snowflakes and ate small burning holes in their clothing. As soon as the beams were softened enough, the entire structure would

collapse and incinerate the family whole. The unbidden thought came into Anne's head that perhaps this was her father's parting protection as he waited in heaven above for them to join him.

"We must leave, Mama," Anne yelled, but her mother shook her head, already entered on the path of her Christian martyr's death.

It was a commonplace that any death was preferable to the fate to be found through the door, leaving oneself at the mercy of the Indians. Anne sat, the heavy, oily smoke scratching her lungs, tearing her eyes. An active girl, she preferred movement, wanted to bolt out the door for a last gulp of sweet air and risk being shot rather than sit and roast to death. Already her skin prickled red and tender.

"We should run to the river," she said aloud to no one.

Her mother had gone blank with fear. Blind and helpless and ultimately doomed as the kittens her father regularly gunnysacked and dropped into the river. She would be of no help. Her baby sister, Dottie, and her middle sister, Emma, were already weak from coughing. After witnessing his father die, Nevin had reverted to his usual timidity and was now crying at full volume. He had wet his pants.

19

"Mama, please?" Anne pleaded.

They all felt a shifting of the house as if it were seeking a more comfortable seating, and as the roof crashed down inside the room, Anne in one motion grabbed Nevin and ran out the door. Why him? Nevin because he was the youngest and the only boy in the family?

Outside was unutterable relief. She gulped the cool air and held her brother closer as she ran along the front of the house, a hail of bullets so strong the wall looked as if it were being chewed apart. She would not think about the arrows also raining, would instead pretend she was making her way through a storm, but then Nevin spasmed in her arms, forcing her to stop. A bullet had shattered his leg; it dangled down bloody and useless at her hip. He howled so loudly that even she could hear the small, astonished roar.

A warrior took advantage of her distraction to grab her from behind while another tore Nevin from her arms. She fought with all her remaining strength, regretting, too late, that she had not remained by her mother's side. She lunged for her brother and was butted in the stomach with a rifle stock. The wind sucked out of her, pain made her forget where she was while in its

grip. After a moment, despite the jab of something sharp at her back, she crawled on hands and knees to Nevin's crumpled form, wanting to cover him and go back inside. She ignored the feet at each side of her, too frightened to look up.

A warrior lifted Nevin above her and stood blocking her path. When he set the boy down on the ground like a toy, holding each arm for balance, her brother was queerly calm as he stepped down on the shattered leg. It buckled unnaturally under him, the white of thin bone protruding through skin while he screamed himself to delirium. The warrior chuckled as the child fell to earth, and then clucked his tongue, grabbed the boy by the feet like a rabbit, and dashed him against the building.

Anne prayed for the Lord to claim her. She was guilty of having taken the boy from their mother and then failing him. His last moments on earth filled with cruelty and terror, and it was her fault. Stupid, stupid girl, she deserved whatever now happened.

When the warrior came at her and preemptively grabbed her hair, he found all resistance gone. Frontier children were always taunting one another in games with scalping, and she had the idle thought that now she would know what it was like. She

21

endured his punches and kicks as penance, sure they were only preliminary to her being killed. Her only prayer was that she would die with her honor left intact to please God and her mother.

It surprised her when instead she was led to a small, bedraggled group of neighbor women gathered in a field. A group of ten children, including Emma, was corralled under a tree. How had she gotten out? What had become of Dottie and Mama? None of the rest of her family had come out of the burning house. This indeed was not a nightmare — reality was far worse than anything imagination could conjure.

The Indians motioned for the women to start walking, and one of them, a young mother whose babe was nowhere in sight, began crying aloud that they would be killed.

"If they so wanted, we would no longer be breathing," Anne said.

Unhearing, the woman collapsed on the ground and commenced a primitive baying. One of the warriors came and prodded her, conveying by sign language that the captives would soon be fed, but she was beyond caring of their intentions. Years younger than her, nevertheless Anne was impatient with the woman's obtuseness.

"We live only at their mercy, which you now test. Come, please. Get up now," Anne urged, but there was no help for her. The woman was lost inside her own horror as surely as if it were yet another conflagration. The warrior in charge of them looked in exasperation at Anne as if the two of them had somehow become conspirators, then quickly brought out a knife and in a single motion slit the woman's throat.

Anne turned away and began walking. She did not blame the woman for her weakness. She herself had promised that she would rather die than suffer capture, but when the moment came she found an unwillingness to give up her life so easily, despite the immediate dangers and afflictions. She prayed for rescue.

VIRGINIA, 1863

That morning Custer used the lull after battle to cross enemy lines, handed off from a Union picket to a Confederate second lieutenant, who promised to get him safely to his destination. It was risky, madness really. If not taken prisoner, he would be skinned alive by McClellan if found out, but a gentleman's word was his honor. He treasured his. Besides, it was a thrill to change out of his Union blue for the Rebel gray, even donning the wide-brimmed hat. If things had been slightly different, the Confederacy might have been the side he fought for.

They skirted camps, Custer listening, looking for a glimpse of his old roommates, especially Rosser.

Only a scant two years ago at West Point, Rosser had slapped down his plate at dining hall. It being Washington's birthday, they had been rewarded with an extra dessert

and entertainment by the marching band. The cadets shouted over one another, the Southerners vowed to resign to join the forming Confederate forces. There was talk of secession, but no one believed it would lead to war.

Rosser looked fondly over at Custer and grabbed his hand.

— We're going to have a war. There's no use talking. I see it coming.

— Then I'll fight alongside you.

Rosser pursed his mouth as if he were testing something gone bad.

— No, my friend. You belong to the North, whether you like it or not.

It felt like a rebuke, and Custer swallowed hard to hide his disappointment.

— I suppose.

— One day soon, we will face each other in battle, Rosser said, his eyes filled with a perverse joy.

— That would be the darkest day for me. I would be so sorrowful to defeat you.

With that, Custer banged his hand on the table and ran out to the parade ground, Rosser in hot pursuit.

When the flag had been lowered, the band struck up "The Star-Spangled Banner," and Custer led a cheer that the cadets took up. Rosser jumped up on a bench and led

"Dixie" to a small but loud subset of men. The moment their cheers went up, Custer jumped on a low wall and led another round of "The Star-Spangled Banner." Back and forth it went, everyone in high spirits.

Leaving barracks at dawn, Custer failed to notice the effigy of Lincoln that hung outside until he almost ran into its dangling feet. He had a country boy's respect for those in power, especially a president, and he found such an act reprehensible. Of course his Southern brethren were the culprits. Nonetheless, to avoid their being punished, he cut it down before any staff noticed and demanded the perpetrators' dismissal.

It didn't matter. In the morning, Rosser and the rest of the Southerners, young men Custer had lived the last three years with, whom he considered brothers and friends worthy of sacrificing his life for, rode away to become his enemy.

Now in the middle of the War of the Rebellion, Custer and his guide were rounding a bend in the path when a Rebel soldier jumped from behind a tree and demanded a password. Custer's skin tingled at the danger he'd gotten himself into, the possibility the passed message had been a ruse. What a coup to single-handedly apprehend

him without a shot fired. They would of course invent circumstances of the capture, portraying it as fierce and demanding of bravery.

But the password was accepted.

His heartbeat slowed. They traveled unmolested and in a few minutes ducked inside a barn where the ceremony was to take place. His friend Forester was now entirely recovered from the wounds that the Southern belle at his side had tended. Months before, while searching a battlefield for survivors, Custer's attention had been drawn by a young Rebel's moan. He had personally delivered Forester to the makeshift dispensary, had even given him a pair of warm socks and money.

In the barn a parson somehow had been persuaded to squeeze a wedding among the continual last rites with which he was overwhelmed. The clergyman was exhausted and sick at heart from the waste of war he had the job to bless. The sight of a Union soldier disguised and behind enemy lines hardly fazed him.

— You simply had to be my best man, Forester said.

Custer dusted his uniform off, stood as witness for the couple, and kissed the lovely bride on the lips. He repeated for the

umpteenth time that the beauty of Southern women never ceased to ensnare him. When Forester turned his trouser pockets inside out to show how empty they were, he also paid the clergyman's fee, as well as bought the black-market ale for the small party to toast the nuptials. He was back in camp before McClellan had a chance to notice him missing.

LIBBIE

The first pull was the worst, the air squeezed out of the lungs, the ribs bent inward into the chest, the second yank buckling the stomach, and woe to the foolish girl who dared eat anything in advance. When Jane had finally finished tying closed the corset, Libbie stood for a few moments trying to regain her breath, which wouldn't fully come again until the stays had been loosened hours later after the tea. She would remain light-headed the entire afternoon, but when she glanced into the looking glass her form inspired her — she resembled exactly a fluted vase of flowers, the nipped twenty-and-a-half-inch waist, the flare of bosom above and hips below.

Jane helped her step into the collapsed hoops — steel blades held together with tapes that when extended fully resembled nothing so much as metal birdcages — then lifted the contraption up to her waist and

belted it. Libbie wore her fancy extra-wide one for the holiday, the one that she had just ordered from New York. Her father and stepmother indulged her to an alarming degree. Once the hoops were attached she positively pushed her way through the room like a sailboat. Next came the petticoat, then finally the yellow silk dress, one consisting of nothing but ruffles and flounces, the fabric imported from France. She wore her late mother's amber bobs and necklace, and her brown hair was coiled up with small yellow silk roses tucked in. She resembled the most delicious confection, waiting in the baker's window for a passerby to purchase her.

Jane would help her get through her father's front doorway, down the steps, and into the carriage — the logistics of the larger crinoline were more difficult than Libbie was used to. Of course she could have changed at her friend's house but the intention was to make a grand appearance. That was the goal — all the artifice must look effortless and unstudied. What would these young men do when the women they were so enamored by were sprung free from their restraints?

When at last she arrived in her friend's parlor for the Thanksgiving Day party,

Libbie looked around the room at the other women similarly tethered and immobilized. They appeared like a garden of full-blown roses, the men bees circulating among them, bringing them sustenance in the form of dainty china cups of tea and small plates of cake. Had the crinoline been invented as an aid to virtue, it being near impossible for a man to get close enough for a kiss?

On arrival already she was bored.

It would be hours until she got back home, was undressed and untied, and Jane served her bread and jam as reward for her suffering. She'd gratefully lie abed and read her books the rest of the evening.

But the afternoon loomed long ahead. Libbie stood in the middle of the too-warm parlor, breathless, hungry, her legs already tired from standing, her feet pinched into low-heeled slippers that she must be careful not to catch in her bottom hoop else the whole meringue-like edifice topple. She dared not risk even sitting down. Although she had heard of fine ladies in New York performing the balletic maneuver of flipping the back of the hoop up onto a chair with a flick of their foot and then reversing onto the seat, Libbie was too unskilled with hoops to attempt it. There were too many

cruel stories of girls tipping their skirts up and showing off their pantaloons to mixed company.

Even navigating around the food table was fraught. They had all heard of ladies squeezing past a tight corner and their dresses catching fire from burning candles or oil lamps. One girl in a town fifty miles away had actually burned to death in her parlor when unbeknown to her an ember caught in her dress flounce, and in panic she was unable to untie the hoops in time to run out the door.

Libbie laughed and flirted with the men as was expected of her but found it hard to concentrate. Her mind instead was fixated on her discomfort, her enraged, crushed interior. The dresses, however beautiful, were a torture. At that moment nothing would have pleased her so much as a stout pair of trousers.

Not only could the women in their splendid exile not approach men due to their steel boundaries, they could not even get close enough to each other to pass whispered information — which men were up for promotion, which had a stern mother, which had short-lived fidelity — so both their bodies and minds remained drifting and isolate. It was their destiny and their

job to be husbanded, so the girls had no alternative but to compete for manly attentions.

Libbie Bacon, Libbie Bacon, Libbie Bacon — she loved the sound of her own name, perfectly compact, self-contained. The thought of adding a third, a cumbersome, awkward appendage to Libbie Bacon [_____] didn't seem necessary or desirable. She'd devoured the books of Fanny Fern and Grace Greenwood as a young girl, even toyed with the idea of becoming a lady author herself, and had decided that spinsterhood had many things to recommend it. She wished she could confide in someone that she just didn't see the point in being married.

People felt pity for the maiden aunts and spinsters in town, Miss Townsend, for example, who taught piano, or Miss Girard, who assisted her brother in the dry goods store, but Libbie detected a fire in the eyes of these women, a straightness to their backs that the married women, burdened with the cares of husband, children, and household, distinctly lacked. Libbie had extravagant fantasies of waking up and spending her mornings drinking coffee and reading books in bed. People gossiped that her indepen-

dent streak came from the early loss of her mother.

Brown-eyed and dimpled, by age eighteen she was not embarrassed to say she had more than her fair share of beaux. While not a great beauty, she was not unpleasant to look at either. Her strength was in putting people at ease. She always tried to be straightforward and pleasant, never to put on airs like some of the other girls. The best way to describe her life up to that point was that it was gloriously ordinary. She longed for that to change.

A recent graduate of the nearby ladies' seminary, her activities at that time consisted of an unending round of teas, dinners, and socials whose sole aim was matrimony. Libbie enjoyed her feminine powers over men, and pretended she did not understand the ultimate reason for these gatherings. She herself reveled in the chase. A young male teacher at her school was so tormented by her rejection of his suit that he quit his job and moved away. At hops, she danced till the last instrument was packed up to go home, never wanting the night to end. It was the magic of youth that despite evidence to the contrary she believed it could go on forever. Her admirers made the natural mistake of thinking her enthusi-

asm was stirred by them.

One by one the young women succumbed to one or another beau and announced engagements. Her father doted on Libbie far too much to openly state the fact that she was expected to come to a similar conclusion. Already she had turned down a fair number of proposals, claiming to her father that none of them were at all satisfactory.

Growing up in a small town, it did not escape her that matrimony was a kind of gilded cage, as restricting and unwieldy as her dress, that after a couple of years those same gay girls that had eagerly married became so weighed down with domestic work and childrearing that they turned into different people entirely.

Already one or two girls with whom she had been friendly in school pleaded that they no longer had time to do something as frivolous as read books. They looked at her knowingly as if she were a child who would soon be initiated into the adult female world. Well, if that was the way it would be, she would stay a child!

All the married ladies wanted to do was recall their days of courtship, culminating with their wedding day, as a kind of high point in their lives. *Remember the orange*

blossoms in my bouquet? Did you ever taste such a buttercream wedding cake? They urged Libbie to settle on a life of the same *before it was too late.* The Council of Matrons, she called them behind their backs.

Perhaps it was the lack of maternal influence that allowed Libbie such a cool, unsentimental eye. She would soon be nineteen but was in no hurry. She loved her life at home, coddled by her father and stepmother, so that she wouldn't have minded becoming the newest spinster in town, the kind of lady everyone pitied but who Libbie suspected didn't feel nearly as sorry for herself. Would the most eligible girl in town be allowed to refuse marriage?

She was too ignorant to know that what she longed for was freedom, a freedom not on offer to pampered girls like herself.

Poor Libbie Bacon, judge's daughter. Two baby sisters taken to heaven so quickly she hardly knew them. An only child with the loss of her brother, Edward, who had been the pride of his parents. Three years older than her, always getting into boyish trouble, yet he was as kind and gentle to his baby sister as could be. It scared her when he became bedridden. He had hurt his spine falling through a stair. Libbie nursed him in

36

her childish way, spending long days sitting on his bed, inventing games. Often while reading him endless stories from her books, she fell asleep and had to be carried to her own room.

Edward had only just recovered from his back injury when he came down with a fatal disease. Quickly her parents sent her away to stay with relatives, worried she would sicken also. Every afternoon at her relatives' house there were intense thunderstorms, and since there was no one to comfort her she hid under the bed. Each night she prayed for Edward's recovery, but the sum total of her efforts was that when she was allowed to return home at last, he was already in the ground. To her six-year-old mind it was a punishment. As far as she understood he'd moved to a different house, and whenever she went outside she still looked for him. His loss devastated their little family.

Her parents predictably became fearful and overly protective of their only daughter. When Libbie disobeyed and went to play with the neighborhood children that her mother considered too "rough," she was dragged home and locked in a closet as if she were a piece of fine porcelain in danger of breaking. Libbie remembered the close

darkness, the smell of leather shoes and talc, the stale perfume on her mother's clothes. Often she fell asleep listening to her mother on the other side of the door praying for her salvation. Even at that young age she sympathized with her traumatized parents while at the same time having no intention of obeying them.

The tragedy of her young life was still to come — her melancholic mother passed when Libbie was twelve. Her father and she remained alone until he remarried years later. Everyone said loss at a young age affected one, and she came to blame that for her moods. Regularly her father would find her shut inside her closet, sleeping. Sometimes she dreamed she still heard her mother's prayers through the door.

Her favorite way to escape the cloistering of her family was to walk the fields outside Monroe, although her father had strictly forbidden it. What if an Indian attacked her? There hadn't been an Indian around Monroe in quite a while, she answered.

One day she was sitting on a tree stump, crying, when a boy her own age rode up on a rough-looking nag.

"You okay?"

Libbie wiped her face, not pleased at having a witness to her anguish. In public she

always aimed at a determined cheerfulness to mask the sorrow everyone expected. She recognized the boy from his blond hair and thin, long face as one of the Custer clan.

"Leave me be. I'm fine."

"You don't seem it."

Libbie sighed. "That's not polite to say to a lady."

"You're a girl, even if you are a pretty one."

The Custers lived on the other side of town. Although she recognized this boy from school, which he attended sporadically, the two families did not move in the same social circles or go to the same church. The uncharitable judgment was that the family had too little money and too many children to support.

"Want to ride my horse?"

"No."

"You should. When I'm blue it makes me feel better. No place as good as on top of a horse."

She surprised herself when she said yes. Its main lure was that it was forbidden. She knew there would be the devil to pay if her father found out, but her mother had been gone only a year, and he was lenient about her transgressions so far.

"I'm George Armstrong, in case you

39

wanted to know, but my family call me Autie."

"What kind of name is that?"

He didn't answer right away, and when he did she could hear the hurt in his voice.

"Mine."

His face had turned pink, and she regretted being so unkind.

They were the same height, both slight of build, and could almost have passed for brother and sister. He had the feel of a runt. When he laced his hands together to form a stirrup for her to step up on, though, she was surprised by his strength, easily boosting her onto the horse. She was surprised, too, how her leather boot felt small and dainty in his hands.

Although she took riding lessons and was mastering sidesaddle, there was no way to attempt it while bareback so she lifted her skirts and sat the horse astride. Autie's eyes flicked over the glimpse of petticoat offered. Girls hinted that riding in this posture might ruin one's marriage prospects as well as being unladylike, but Libbie didn't give a fig. She enjoyed the feel of warm horseflesh against her legs.

When Autie lifted himself up in front of her on the horse, she began to protest but realized how ridiculous it would be to make

him walk all the way home. She'd make him dismount when they came close to her house. At first she tried to lean back so that there would be no direct contact between them, which was equally impossible. Soon she was resting herself along his back, her legs against his. The horse moved in a drowsy gait that almost lulled her to sleep, her head on Autie's shoulder, then he reined the horse hard to the right, unbalancing her and making her put both arms around his waist.

"I ride out here when I'm sad. It helps," he said.

"Are you sad now?"

"Not anymore. Not when I have company. I hate to be alone."

She smiled and was pleased he could not see her face, the unexpected flush of pleasure his words gave her. She rocked forward and let the manhorse heat touch every part of her body.

"My name is Libbie."

"I know that."

She blushed a deeper pink. He smelled of hay and sunshine and horse, a perfectly pleasing combination to her. It crossed her mind briefly that his riding by might not have been purely accident, that she was an

object of his admiration. Too bad he was a Custer.

"Fact is I've had my eye on you."

"Is that so?"

"Since first grade. You used to swing on your front gate when I walked back from school."

"Didn't see you."

"You always shouted, 'Hello, you Custer boy!' "

Libbie of course remembered but would not admit to what a brat she'd been.

"We should ride regularly. You seem to enjoy it."

Her face burned. She adjusted her weight away from him.

"No."

"Why?"

"Because you are the son of a farmer."

Six years later, on the cold, dark afternoon of a Thanksgiving party, Libbie was being bored to tears by the conversation of the man in front of her when Autie burst through the door. Of course she was aware of his enormous change in fortune. The whole town talked of nothing else than their newly minted war hero. She wanted to say that when their eyes met this time it was love at first sight, that in a lightning flash

she could see her life joined to his, but that would be untrue. She was a practical girl, not prone to exaggeration. No, it was more the novelty of him, the stir he caused due to his recent successes in the War.

How could she explain this? He had always been around town, but then suddenly there he was! A war hero! It was like knowing a gawky neighbor girl who after a period of absence returns transformed into a graceful young woman. A swan. Well, Autie was a swan if there ever was one, and for a small-town girl it didn't get more exciting than that.

He was the most intoxicating mixture of familiar and strange. Physically he was still the same young man of ordinary height, on the slight side, with pale skin easily prone to burn, and those famous golden locks that the newspapers crowed over so much: the Golden Boy General. Some people could not reconcile his newfound fame with the unremarkableness of his presentation, but Libbie saw his extraordinary confidence. He was electric, with a vitality that charged a gathering. Everyone wanted to bask in that glow as if he were the sun that they orbited. But when he looked at you with those cool, appraising eyes you felt his danger. It was perfectly believable that he'd killed men.

He expected the world to live up to his expectations, and it had obliged so far. Libbie understood why men followed him into battle, to death if need be. Rumors were that women followed him into bed.

What she cared for less was that every other girl in the room, unmarried *and* married, young and old, was also trying to catch his eye, and he played this up for all its worth. The center of attention, he basked in it. At this provincial fete, he had the air of a cosmopolitan, the fairy dust of the larger world clinging to his shoulders. Ladies jostled all around him, bumping his legs with their skirts. The men were not jealous but just as eager to approach him. What really irked, though, was how totally he ignored Libbie, as if he had forgotten her altogether.

Not for her his type, that was certain. Full of himself.

She was at the buffet table later, serving a gentleman and herself slices of cake, when she felt a burning on her neck and turned to find Autie standing behind her, staring.

"Libbie Bacon."

Standing beside him, she noticed he was now considerably taller than her. His shoulders were broad, his body muscled, and his golden hair was handsome beyond words.

"Autie."

"You have certainly filled out in the most pleasing of ways."

She flushed.

"So have you."

"We've both grown up."

He laughed out loud and clapped his hands as if this were some bit of genius on their part. His gesture was so ridiculous she laughed too. She knew then without a doubt that he had staged his behavior that whole evening for her benefit, to build to that moment.

"Can I bring you a glass of punch?" he asked.

"She already has punch," the gentleman at her side said, but neither of them paid him the slightest attention.

"I'd love some," she said.

Her companion angrily crammed great forkfuls of cake into his mouth as they stood awaiting Autie's return.

With great ceremony he carried a dainty glass of punch across the room, catching his finger in the delicate ring handle and spilling some on the floor in front of her. A man who had killed Rebels at the point end of a bayonet now blushed at his clumsiness. Drops of red punch had splashed up on her pale dress, and he kneeled, mortified, hold-

ing the hem in his hands, looking distressed out of all proportion to the offense. She kneeled down, too, collapsing her skirt, drowning in a pool of wilted silk. She forgave Autie, as she would forgive him over and over again through the years, for ever greater offenses.

That evening they danced and laughed, and there was no hope left for her.

Shenandoah Valley, 1864

Custer was returning late at night from reviewing the picket. The rain had fallen hard all day, pummeled the dirt roads until they were ground thick as tar, bogging down both camps in stasis, and he could think only of falling asleep in his tent, its rare patch of dryness. He'd wake Eliza and have her prepare a hot cup of coffee to warm his insides.

This made the presence of the Rebel soldier all the more galling. He stood under a clump of trees waiting out the rain, calm as if returning from a Sunday dance, holding the reins of a magnificent horse. Although it was pitch outside, Custer could make out a grizzled face, a body heavy and probably slow. He guessed he was an old man of at least forty years if not more. Had the Rebel drawn a weapon, he would have already been shot dead. Instead the man stood unmoved, barely acknowledging the

intrusion. Custer gave the order of surrender and received no reaction. He wondered at the possibility of the man being deaf or mute. Next he threatened use of his gun. The Rebel turned away, dismissive, and made to mount his horse and continue his homeward journey.

The bullet penetrated the abdomen through the Rebel's greatcoat although he seemed bent on ignoring its effect. A few blood pumps later, the man dropped the horse's reins and walked from under the sheltering branches out into the storm as if the rain might provide some healing balm. Custer, acting the prig, demanded the prisoner not attempt escape and swiped his saber across the man's coat front, slicing fabric and flesh. Even as he did it, he felt his action excessive, the man's insolence angering him out of all proportion. If there was an emotion in the Rebel's eyes, it was mere pique. Custer had yet found a man convinced of the surety of his own death.

— Ordered you to fucking surrender, he complained.

War wasn't a game. Proximity to death was enough to knock out any such foolish notion, and yet there was protocol. Warfare should be conducted with honor and bravery by the best soldiers. The notion that one

George Armstrong Custer

was set on killing men that one might just as easily be fighting alongside made gentlemen's rules essential.

The man's lips puckered as if to make a sharp reply. He sucked in breath and made a stuttering step forward as if he found being in Custer's company a moment longer unseemly. Gently his hands cradled his stomach as it flooded out something unwinding, gelatinous, and black-red.

Already in his short career in the army Custer had killed men or had seen them be killed — bullet wounds, saber cuts, punctured chests, hands and legs disabled or lopped off entirely, heads split open — so that the idea of the sacrosanct body had been destroyed. Some men did not recover from the discovery. In each case the victim appeared shocked as if the reality of a body, his body, being so violated were a betrayal. Such thinking explained why so many men were willing to go to war: the belief that through intelligence or ability they were somehow exempt. Veteran soldiers realized the fallacy of such thinking, but even so the most hard-hearted, practical men regularly became mystical when the subject was their own corporeal survival. Custer had come through unscathed too many times. His men wanted to believe in a divine luck that

maybe would shield them, too.

Carefully he rode around the man and fetched the horse, noting the fineness of the saddle and reins, the heft of the expensive sword that remained sheathed even as its owner writhed in his death throes. It exasperated him, the man's contrariness in not allowing himself to be taken prisoner, or at least fighting back like a gentleman. Turning his back on the dying fool, Custer made ready to move out along the suck of road, mud fetlock-high on the horses, saying a quick prayer that the poor man's eternal soul not be judged by distinctions such as the gray or blue of his uniform, but rather the quality of his cowardly soul.

A shattering rent the black night.

When Custer recovered he realized the Rebel had raised up and parted a last shot at his back. Quickly he spurred his horse to return and pumped a pincushion of holes into the Rebel's body, experiencing not a moment's more remorse. Providence shone on some and not on others, and whoever denied it was either a fool or liar.

When Custer returned to camp, blood somehow covered his hands though he had not been in near proximity to the man. He washed it away but could not rid himself of

its stick that night. The horse, a magnificent thoroughbred much loved by Custer, accompanied him for years even as memory of its owner faded until he accidentally shot the animal in Kansas.

The sun burned against the tea-colored tent canvas. It was unheard of to be still lying asleep with the sun already up, and his body tensed into panic before he remembered the battle was over, victory assured, commendations and promotions accomplished.

There had been grumbling at his fast promotion, but during the last battle he'd stopped the Rebels in their tracks, turned them around, and made them run. The charge had been magnificent, fifty mounted cavalry racing down the gentle hill, sabers drawn. Soldiers petitioned to be under his command.

Custer sat up too quickly, black washing over his eyes. When he reached to rub sleep off his features he felt a tremoring in his hands that was new and yet not unfamiliar. It came as an expected penance, a rite of passage in its way no different than the coming of maturity in the sprouting of beard, the heat inspired by a pleasing female form. Sure that it would go away, he resolved to ignore it, and took soap, tooth-

brush, and powder to the river to bathe. Walking through the camp in his undershirt with his toiletries tucked under an arm, he nodded at men who stopped and saluted as he passed.

The trembling grew more pronounced as he scrubbed his hands with the soap, unable to erase the shadow of rustblood stain on them. In exasperation he picked up the razor before the impossibility of using it without a major bloodletting became obvious. He surrendered the blade, laying it back down. The betrayal by his body troubled him. He refused to allow for any weakness.

The cavalry was the eyes and ears of the army yet his eyes and ears were poisoned. In his mind he tried to connect the carnage he'd witnessed — scores of bodies torn apart until the individual pieces lost meaning — with the fact that he was being praised and honored as a hero, for delivering thirteen captured Confederate flags, each signifying untold death on both sides. He'd buried soldiers younger than his brother Tom, each boy wrapped in his own blanket as if being put down for eternal slumber. Not even a coffin for these heroes, who were simply commended to the embrace of bare earth.

It was a devil's bargain that, being a soldier, he could rise to prominence only by dealing out death, killing as many of the enemy while preserving his own forces as possible, but above all *winning*! Napoleon bragged that he could inspire men to fight for bits of colored ribbon. General Sheridan would have said the same if he'd thought of it first. The man reveled in brutality, yet it did not escape Custer's notice that it won him power.

Custer had worshipped General McClellan, as had all the men under his command, but that great warrior had been mocked for walking the battlefield, crying over his dead soldiers. A perception grew that he had grown wary of attack, choosing the safety of his men instead of victory. Soon after, he was relieved of his duty. Custer would not make that same mistake.

Was victory delivered to Custer simply because he was left alive to claim it? Few understood that war became its own reward. The veterans called it "going to see the elephant," the excitement and then desolation of battle unlike anything else in ordinary life. One paid dearly for the knowledge, but some went back for more. War was a hunger satisfied only by glutting on itself.

When the culmination of his ambitions

arrived a scant two years from leaving West Point, promotion to brigadier, youngest in the army, he decided the poor farmer's son needed an overhaul in appearance. He had been struck by the Rebel general Jeb Stuart's attire — gilded braid, golden spurs, a black plume on his hat, anchored by a golden star. Sheridan disdained such theatrics, but they called to Custer. He scatted his boy to dig up a star while he bought himself a black velvet suit and enough gold lace to cover it. Eliza sewed the star on the sailor collar of his oversized dark shirt.

The first time he looked in the mirror, he was well pleased with the effect he made, complementing it with a red neckerchief and the Rebel hat he'd never discarded. Some soldiers, who didn't understand that one wore something of the enemy's to take his power, complained of the hat. He'd heard stories of Indians out on the frontier who painted color both on their bodies and their horses for protection, carried dead birds strapped to their heads for swiftness, wolf pelts on their shoulders for fierceness, buffalo skin shields for strength. The biggest effect was on the wearer's belief in its power, the disequilibrium it created in the enemy.

He walked through the camp conscious of

the glances and curling lips the impression created. So be it. After his victories they'd be scrambling for anything to match his successes. Ridicule of his appearance would, after victory, turn to emulation. What the eccentric uniform could assure was that he would be remembered. He would be seen both by those who could promote him and those that he would lead, forcing him to courage from both ends. One could not hide behind one's men dressed in such manner.

One in four in his unit had died, the highest rate in the cavalry, yet the Michigan Brigade received the greatest glory. His men donned red kerchiefs to announce being under his command, part of his tribe. When he was transferred from the 1st to the 3rd Cavalry, many of the men were distraught. Others threatened to resign if not transferred with him. His men were thrilled to be under his command because he would lead them to glory, and they wrote of the honor they felt sacrificing themselves. The battles continued — Antietam, 24,000 casualties.

Every man killed now remained as an otherworldly afterimage. He stared in the mirror and thought, *What a poor thing is man. What a poor thing am I.*

■ ■ ■ ■

He came across Tom in camp, bawling like a baby over the death of a friend in battle the day before. Custer stood in silence until he looked up.

— Have you lost your heart, brother? Tom asked.

— The men rely on me to win and keep them from dying.

— You've grown hard.

— You can mourn your soldiers, or you can lead them. You will go mad trying to do both.

When they advanced through the Shenandoah Valley, Sheridan's orders of scorched earth shook many of the volunteer soldiers, farm boys who understood the value of what they destroyed. The shame in setting a barn, a silo, on fire. Even professional soldiers rued the destruction of food when they lacked enough to eat, houses that could no longer be sheltered in. *Eat out Virginia clear and clean . . . so that crows flying over it for the balance of the season will have to carry their provender with them.*

It was not a new tactic. Kearny, the first general Custer had served under, taught

him that success in battle alone did not guarantee victory unless there was also thorough devastation of the enemy's support, no matter how distasteful the task. Mercy led to revenge. The enemy's will must need be broken, and the best way to accomplish that was to strike at his home and livelihood.

Custer had studied history enough to know that carnage on such a scale could be found since the days of Genghis Khan and the Bible. Privately he thought this conflict too close, violence of brother against brother destroying both.

He rode past fields set on fire. Burning a man's crops felt more disrespectful than taking him prisoner. Raised on a farm, he knew the hard labor it required. Humble shanties and great antebellum mansions alike were set ablaze, loss the great equalizer. The waste was an affront to a poor boy trained to frugality.

Down one country lane, Custer was overwhelmed by the rotting smell of dead cattle. Soldiers butchered the beef to feast on as much as they could, and laid out more for Union passersby, a regular carnivorous smorgasbord. Most of the meat went to spoil, which was preferred to feeding the enemy. The soldier in Custer was reconciled

to the cost of war, but the man in him still shrank back.

Thin, underfed women wept to watch their homes destroyed, their faces twisted by want and the beginning lines of hate. Long, unkempt hair trailed down their backs like weeds. He choked at the thought of his Libbie brought to such low circumstance. Libbie with her dimples, her innocence, her plummy taste of wine.

He passed mothers who walked ghostlike past their bawling children, shamed at not being able to provide succor. Their land now dried-out dugs, no longer able to nourish.

His soldiers, at first shy, were now made bold. They broke into houses, ransacked cellars for alcohol, stole at will. It felt very much like the end times. Officers tried to rein them in, but reports came of women disrespected, their menfolk shot for protecting them. What were they destroying, and what would replace it?

One of his West Point friends came and asked for protection for his family. Custer stationed guards outside the home. When he rode by a day later, the guards were gone, commissioned to more important duty. Any leader worth his salt admitted that controlling one's men was like riding a bull, one must know when to apply control and when

to let go. In battle he knew his men would be brave wherever he led. In murky times such as they were going through, baser nature took over.

In the beginning he was not convinced in the wisdom of Sherman's total war. It all changed when under the Gray Ghost, the infamous General Mosby, a band of Confederates acted as thugs. It was a new, unholy kind of bedouin warfare, comprised of small groups making strategic raids and then disappearing back into their surroundings. They dressed to blend in with the population, even wore Union uniforms to assassinate soldiers at close range when off their guard. They shot them in the back, while eating, while taking a shit. They acted without honor. Custer would not again meet such tactics until he was sent out to the Territories to conquer the Indians. When Sheridan's engineering officer was murdered in such fashion, the culprits melted away before they could be caught. Sheridan ordered Custer to burn all the houses in a five-mile radius to punish those harboring the fugitives.

— Are you willing?

— Look out for smoke, Custer answered.

He understood exactly Sheridan's directive to act as judge, jury, and executioner. It

was his appetite in carrying this out that earned him special notice. When he at last captured a group of Mosby's men, four were shot while he had the band play on and then the other two were hanged, a note pinned to the toe of one:

This will be the fate of Mosby and all his men.

Mosby retaliated by hanging seven of Custer's men taken as prisoner, although two managed to escape and tell of it. The War had grown personal and brutal, beyond the civilities he had studied at West Point.

Unable to gauge the change in himself, he saw it in his brother Tom. Poor Tom, good sport, had always followed in his big brother's footsteps. An unspoken agreement between them held that although Tom was as good or better a soldier, he shunned the spotlight and would allow Custer the lion's share. Tom in battle, though, was fearless. He captured two enemy flags and was still not ready to rest after he had been shot in the cheek. Custer had to order his arrest to get him to accept leaving the field to have the wound attended.

The War of the Rebellion was an education without parallel, and unlike at West Point, here Custer was an avid student. From Kearny he learned to be a strict

disciplinarian with his men. With McClellan he learned the importance of being loved by them. If so, they would follow you to the most dangerous battlefield because you inspired something in them of which they were unsuspecting. They did not grudge you their death if it came to that. Sheridan, his final mentor, taught him the most valuable lesson: be ruthless and without mercy when necessary.

Custer rode out of Virginia on the victory train to Washington, traveling at the dizzying speed of forty miles per hour. A cavalryman, the fastest he ever wanted to go was on top of a horse running dead out. There was nothing as soul-filling as man and beast crossing the earth together at such speed. The trains were progress, the progress the army was fighting to ensure, yet he did not know if progress set that well with him. Out West the Indians regularly tore up tracks and attacked trains, attributing to the iron beast a particular malevolence rather than it being a simple manifestation of the white man's greed.

The train was forced to stop often due to burned timbers across the tracks. He watched as hungry, owl-eyed soldiers-become-marauders leered in. Along some

sections it did not pay to open the windows or breathe in too deeply; burial was an indulgence when the living struggled to survive. He was glad that he did not have Lincoln's burden to stitch the nation back together once the War was done. How to unite the population when the South had turned feral, savage in its desperation? But Custer's mind wasn't a philosopher's. He did not have the clarity for politics that he had on the battlefield.

Being a soldier was in his blood. He must be humble about it or be labeled a war lover, suffering the same slander as Sherman and Sheridan. What they all shared was the military's universal admiration for the soldier who was without fear. To be such and lead men who fought bravely was the highest calling he could conceive.

He'd seen much these last months and longed for the balm of Libbie's company, to burrow into her velvet. Nothing counted except when she saw and approved her boy's victory, saw how his men loved him and thus made it real. She had written to him: *I'm so proud of my Bo.*

. . . Don't expose yourself so much in battle. Just do your duty, and don't rush out so daringly. Oh, Autie, we must die

63

together. Better the humblest life together than the loftiest, divided. My hopes and ambitions are more than a hundred times realized in you. I have dreams of us in old age, sitting side by side in rocking chairs, hair as white as snow, surrounded by a big, loving family such as yours was growing up. Oh, how happy I was when I woke up to dream of our future together . . .

In Washington, Pennsylvania Avenue was packed with cheering crowds, the captured Confederate flags hung out the window of the omnibus as they rode down the street. The new nation was newly proud of itself, like a babe taking his first wobbly steps. Troopers climbed down only to be lifted again off their feet. Earnest veterans with gray in their hair came up to Custer, kissed his hand. He burned, he delighted, although it was that same stained hand they touched. The dead marked him like the rings inside a tree, another rite of passage. He pulled back, wondering at the lie, the thinness of victory.

He prayed no one saw the quiver in his hands, the blood under his fingernails. He stood at rigid attention as the dead men in his regiments presented themselves one at a time — the long line of loyal Union men

who had followed him to their death thinking his enchantment extended to them. Only he could see them. Confederate soldiers were there, too, with their surprised eyes and bloody black wounds, waiting patiently to pass in review. Last was the Rebel from that lonely, rainy night. He walked past slowly, limping, which detail Custer did not recall. The majority of the men he did not recognize but understood that he was responsible for. He was to accept the blame for all.

He swallowed a scream, tried to bolt forward, but the crowd pinned him back, unwilling to give him up. The paucity of the actual experience seemed wrong against this praise yet he hungered for its balm. Huzzahs and slaps on the back. Maybe the toll paid was not too high, a divine equation, adulation matching the destruction, a nation tearing apart at the seams of union, a hero elevated beyond his due to heal it back up. He did not create the War, but he determined to thrive within it. He was twenty-three years old.

ROCKY MOUNTAIN NEWS (1864)
The Battle of Sand Creek

Among the brilliant feats of arms in Indian warfare, the recent campaign of our Colorado volunteers will stand in history with few rivals, and none to exceed it in final results . . . Among the killed were all the Cheyenne chiefs, Black Kettle, White Antelope, Little Robe, Left Hand, Knock Knee, One Eye, and another, name unknown. Not a single prominent man of the tribe remains, and the tribe itself is almost annihilated. The Arapahoes probably suffered but little. It has been reported that the chief Left Hand, of that tribe, was killed, but Colonel Chivington is of the opinion that he was not . . . the utter surprise of a large Indian village is unprecedented. In no single battle in North America, we believe, have so many Indians been slain . . . A thousand incidents of individual daring and the passing events of the day might be told, but space forbids. We leave the task for eye-witnesses to chronicle. All acquitted themselves well, and Colorado soldiers have again covered themselves with glory.

The Fort Lyon Affair

Washington, December 20, 1864

The affair at Fort Lyon, Colorado, in which Colonel Chivington destroyed a large Indian village, and all its inhabitants, is to be made the subject of congressional investigation. Letters received from high officials in Colorado say that the Indians were killed after surrendering, and that a large proportion of them were women and children.

The Second Remove

Captivity and starvation — A falsehood —
The march —
Elizabeth — A smiting — Moccasins

The captive women walked behind the horses like chattel, guarded loosely but such was enough given their traumatized condition. Escape required resolve, and the women — many wounded, all grieving — had none. Many did not even have full clothing on, much less coats. Some had lost their shoes on the march and shuffled forth on bleeding feet. As she walked, Anne felt along her ribs and was convinced the bottom one was broken. She feared that if she bent over too quickly she might jab herself from within. The memory of Nevin's shinbone poking through skin haunted her.

On the first day they traveled many hours and stopped in darkness atop a hill. The prisoners fell to the ground in pain and

exhaustion and were left there for the night. Their captors gave no thought to providing food or drink or warmth. Instead they celebrated a victory feast unlike any the whites had ever imagined. All the night they were kept awake by the roaring and dancing of the warriors around a huge bonfire, their long, attenuated forms throwing dark shadows over the prone bodies of their captives.

At some point in their saturnalia, eight warriors came to the cowering women, and each picked one. The one who chose Anne was thick and squat, muscular, and when he pushed her down a short distance from the other women, her desperate slaps landed as futilely on his arms and chest as if she were striking at a boulder. He smelled of unwashed skin and mineral earth. Tired of her struggle, he hit her in the face, and the high, snapping sound of her nose and the feel of warm blood down her throat quieted her. If she did not concentrate to breathe, she was sure she would drown in her own blood. Nonetheless, at the thought of what was about to happen, she kicked at his groin as he ripped her skirt in half and used a knife to slice away her undergarments. He held a thin branch across her throat to pin her to the ground, and all she was left was to close her eyes and pray that she would be

dead before he defiled her.

When it was over, she stood up and walked back to the group of women who had been spared thus far. All averted their eyes, and not one word of solace was offered. After that, each time it happened it mattered less, until eventually it mattered not at all.

The smell of roasting meat knifed her stomach with hunger. The enemy had stolen horses, cattle, swine, and fowl, and now they butchered with the abandon of having received such bounty unearned. Much of the meat was boiled or roasted, but much else was wasted, either left burning to char or uncooked on the ground. Starvation drove one woman to crawl to the fire to grab at a piece of beef. A warrior observed the attempt and stepped on her arm, flinging the piece of meat into the bushes and promptly clubbing her hand so that it was broken and left her permanently crippled. Anne watched the scene in silence, without a thought of coming to her aid, an unthinkable act of cowardice and selfishness of which she would not have imagined herself capable only the day before.

Instead, like a bird of prey, she studied the trajectory of the beef, the slope of the bush it landed underneath. In the deepest

night when all was quiet, she slowly crawled to the bush and swallowed the meat without hardly chewing. She had not even considered sharing it. Only after it was safely in her belly did she beg forgiveness for her sins.

At dawn the captives were awakened by the prods of sticks. The Indians had torn down the camp and wanted to move out quickly, worried about retribution from the army for the previous day's killing spree. Those who refused to move were hit, and one grandmother who refused to rise due to her debilitated state was left behind. Anne pretended that the roll of dirty clothes and bonnet were merely a bundle and did not mask a poor, doomed soul within its folds. She also pretended not to recognize that the hanks of hair and scalp hanging from the saddles of the horses were the fresh scalps harvested from their homestead. One with long gray hair in particular must have belonged to her beloved grandfather.

Anne turned her back and concentrated merely on taking each step ahead, and that proved difficulty enough as the way became more steep and treacherous as her physical state weakened steadily.

It was unimaginable that they would travel such a way over many months through the vast and desolate wilderness, each night

stopping without comfort, each morning waking with more hunger than the day before. In retrospect she considered the hardship valuable only in that her extreme suffering denied any room for grief over the loss of her family.

During that period she traveled farther than she had in all the previous years of her young life combined. Her existence had been confined to a mile radius of the settlement, interspersed with infrequent, fearful wagon rides to the nearby small township. These trips were always hurried and defensive, with a wary eye turned to the possibility of encountering either inclement weather or Indians bent on destruction. The land itself was viewed as endless and treacherous, in need of taming, as were the natives who ruled over it.

The Cheyenne were not practiced in husbandry and seemed to give no thought that their valuable commodities, their captives, would likely perish before reaching their intended destination.

At some point the children were reunited with the women as the war party joined a larger group from the same tribe, presumably feeling safer now that they were no longer in danger of being pursued. Anne was frantic to find if Emma was among

them. She asked all the children, then the women, but none could give her an answer to the whereabouts of her young sister. It was as if the neighborly ties that bound the settlers had been erased, and each was estranged from the others. Had she only imagined seeing her sister that first, horrific morning?

Each woman who had strength enough took custody of a child. In lieu of her sister, Anne took care of Elizabeth, a golden-haired girl of five whose parents she had known. The mother had been a delicate transplant from Massachusetts and had raised the girl to be ignorant of country ways compared with the other children. Anne had babysat the girl and spent an afternoon acquainting her with the most common plants in her yard. Elizabeth had a damaged shoulder and whimpered at the jarring it received during movement. She was unable to grab undergrowth during rocky climbs, causing her to fall behind, to the displeasure of their guards. It proved a difficult parenting.

Undeterred, Anne continued to ask her captors where her sister Emma had been taken and if she had survived. Eventually one of them answered in broken English that she had been a bad girl and so was

wasted. The warrior made a circle the size of a plum in his palm.

"I eat this much of her. She taste good."

The hooligan burst out in laughter and started bragging in his language to his accomplices. They all howled in mirth and made supping noises.

Anne walked on. She would learn not to ask questions, because her captors used words simply as one possible tool in an arsenal of torture. Only later did she learn that the Cheyenne were as horrified by cannibalism as were the white settlers. The care of Elizabeth somewhat salved her worry over Emma, and she prayed another woman took equal care of her dear sister.

It began to snow. The first storm of the year came much earlier than usual. Anne could not help but think them cursed. Elizabeth had only slippers, and cried piteously at the pain in her feet. Anne took off her apron, ripped it in half, and wrapped the pieces around each of Elizabeth's tiny feet, appalled when the yellow cloth quickly turned brown with blood. She had never experienced such biting hunger in her own life, it was like a rooting beast let loose, hollowing one out from the inside. Now the child's pleading for nourishment undid her. In

desperation she invented a game — naming what they would eat when they returned home. Turkey, beef, fried chicken, cornbread, rhubarb pies, cookies and biscuits. Eventually, even porridge and brown beans sounded extravagant. A fellow prisoner frowned and asked them to stop, the memories of such meals driving her mad with hunger.

A few mornings later Anne rose with such lightness in her head she did not care if she lived to see that day's sunset. She strode to the man she presumed was chief, who did not deign to deal directly with the captives, and demanded food and shoes for the girl. Her eyes blazed. She swore her heels lifted a few inches off the ground. She could already feel at her elbows the lift of angels readying her for the final ascension. After a moment's silence she realized she was yet standing on earth, corporeal, and so she dared add that enough provision should be given to all the children and the women also, herself included.

Without a word, the chief clubbed the back of her head with his arm, smiting her, and she fell unconscious to the ground.

When she woke, she found the camp had been halted for the day. A broth of sorts, consisting of boiled grain and the leg bone

of a horse, had been distributed to the prisoners. As Anne sat up, Elizabeth carried her a cup of the brew, her feet adorned in her new leather moccasins.

LIBBIE

Almost as soon as the courtship began so did the problems.

Autie had known only a bounty of familial happiness in his youth, and it gave him an unshakable optimism that all remarked upon. Libbie, on the other hand, was always waiting for the next stroke of misfortune that was surely just around the corner.

Her father, although a fan of the local hero, still did not see Autie as suitable for his daughter. Rumors of various women and drunkenness abounded. Judge Bacon didn't want his brilliant girl to live the straitened life of an army wife so he forbade Autie to even visit the house. Their meeting elsewhere was strictly banned.

Libbie had her own doubts. Autie was a terrible flirt. During his leaves, her girlfriends reported sightings of him at parties all over town in the company of other women. There was one especially, Fanny,

Libbie Bacon Custer

whom Libbie considered vulgar and of loose character. In fact Fanny was quite pretty and outgoing; she came from an affluent family. Libbie was simply eaten up by jealousy. She sat alone in her house brooding on the nights she suspected them together. Her father was right — she would do best by forgetting him.

But then she would receive a barrage of notes begging for her to meet him at a mutual friend's house. She went, fully intending to give him her mind and break off their flirtation. People wondered at Autie's quick rise through the ranks during the Rebellion, but Libbie understood it. Unlike regular army, cavalry commanders were successful to the extent that they could react quickly, instinctively — a trait Autie had on the battlefield as well as in the parlor. His was a charm offensive.

So magnetic was he that everywhere he went in the world, he made fast friends. He was a singular burning flame, as if destiny had put her finger on him and nobody else would satisfy. It was the unfairness in his good fortune that would eventually earn him a number of detractors, but that was in the future. During those first months Autie laid siege to win her heart.

Angry at his latest indiscretions with

Fanny, Libbie would sit next to him at a party and look away. He brought her flowers. A chain of paper cutout hearts. When she allowed him to hold her hand, he quite forgot himself and kissed her fingertips. What to make of such a man?

Once when he was escorting her home, they came to a mud puddle. Instead of walking around it, which they could have done easily, he insisted on taking off his jacket. Waiting for a nearby group of revelers to notice, he laid it with a flourish in the mud so she could step across and not dirty her skirts.

"No, Autie!"

The revelers stopped what they were doing and came to watch. A few clapped.

"Allow me. It gives me pleasure," he said.

"It's not necessary!"

"The jacket will be precious to me forever."

After they were married, she saw his brother Tom wearing said jacket, and realized it had been borrowed and had been his all along. But it was more than these courtship antics that had won her over.

How could she explain? They extinguished each other's loneliness simply by being together. Except for her father, she lacked family, and he filled that need for her. What

did he see in her? He came from a large, boisterously loving tribe. The Custers' copious tears and kisses at every reunion, however brief the absence, never ceased to astonish and faintly repulse her. His mother would need be put to bed, so overwrought with grief was she at his departures to the War. For his part, he fled the house with his own face bathed in tears. He needed someone to understand him and cheer him on, and this Libbie was perfectly willing to do.

One afternoon on the street, Judge Bacon and Libbie passed an obviously inebriated Autie staggering along with friends, his arms over their shoulders, belting out a bar ditty. Her father gave a deep frown, and she was furious with the knowledge that now he would never allow Autie to step foot in the front door, much less permit courtship or marriage. Fanny would win him by default. Libbie gave Autie an ultimatum to give up alcohol as she could not abide such behavior, and he surprised her by vowing never again to touch a drop.

Although her father forbade their correspondence, Autie, undeterred, sent her heady letters through her best friend, Nettie, detailing battles and victories that would be in the newspapers. His ardor was the most exciting thing that had ever happened in

her life. Autie was in the grip of an important fate. They never talked of it, but she knew he felt it. It was what led to his moods later when that good fortune deserted him. The youngest brigadier general in the Union army, then after his part in the Battle of Gettysburg he became a national hero. And he loved *her.*

All was not perfect. Even though he was supposed to be head over heels about Libbie during their courtship, he still kept up a relationship with Fanny, sending them an equal number of letters while away. It goaded Libbie into despair. After all she had been through she needed someone for her very own. She forgave him when he promised to court only her while at the same time she stopped believing his excuses. She had to endure Fanny bragging all over town of his proclamations of love. That summer Fanny even hinted that there was an understanding they would be engaged in the fall.

If Libbie really was decided on him, this would be her first battle.

She had an expensive ambrotype taken of herself and sent it to him, only to find out later that he was so pleased with it he showed it off to Fanny. He also shared Libbie's letters, which infuriated her. Nothing was private between them. But the

indiscretion went both ways. He told her that Fanny had attended a drunken party and actually sat in his lap, kissing him.

"She is a girl who Does Everything," Autie said, smiling when Libbie confronted him.

Libbie blanched. "Really?"

"Everything. And that's exactly why I love only you."

"I'm sure I don't understand what you mean."

But of course she did. Libbie sat alone in her house playing out a strategy no different than that of a general on a battlefield, calculating her behavior to win the moniker of Mrs. General Custer.

When Autie left to return to the War, her merry handful of suitors took their old place, joined by yet new ones. Perhaps she would do better to forget Autie, but it was as if she had been gifted with the Sight. Instead of enjoying the suitors' glances, their compliments, instead of reveling in their attentions as she had formerly, she understood that these were simply the opening feints in a war. They aimed to win her, to carry her away in her white lace dress to a life of drudgery and homemaking.

She caught glimpses of possible futures. One night at supper she regaled the table

with a story about Nettie and herself on an adventure.

"Then we returned by a dirt path. It looked like the one we had come on, but then —"

"Pass the rolls, Libbie," one of her beaux said, clearly not having heard a word of her story.

"Excuse me?"

"The bread. And butter."

Her father coughed into his napkin.

For the first time Libbie noticed her admirer's small eyes, his wide, dull forehead, the ungenerous mouth that did not promise passionate kisses.

He looked up at her, puzzled that she had not done what he asked.

"The rolls, Libbie, please! For my gravy before it gets cold."

One could only imagine such a marriage, such a fate.

Only one man could give her the extraordinary life she craved. She read his letters as if they were nourishment.

. . . I am longing and anxiously hoping for the time to come when I can be with my darling little one again. I bury my nose in your scented handkerchief that you gave your Bo on leaving. Ah, how it brings back

sweet memories of snuggles. Prepare for being attacked with tickles once we are together again . . .

Autie, for all his philandering, his endless lies about no longer corresponding with Fanny, hung on Libbie's every word. He would retell something she had said months before, treasuring it as if it were the wisest, most learned thing he had ever heard on the matter. Words from her, Libbie Bacon, girl from Monroe.

Their courtship was conducted through absences and letters, much as their marriage would end up being lived. Although it was an agony to live through, she admitted it created an unusually bright flame of passion between them. She was always realistic about herself — she was nothing particularly special except for Autie's love for her. She was determined to win him.

THE THIRD REMOVE

The deserted township — Starvation —
An untruth — Arrival at the Indian village
—
Her mistress — A fellow captive

A northerly struck, driving the temperatures
down so low that water froze in a cup and
even those with the benefit of heavy buffalo
robes shivered. Custom was for each teepee's family to extend shelter to all members, but when Anne sought accommodation for the child and herself, she was
roughly thrown out. She begged shelter
from others, who sometimes offered it.
Hearing of her actions, her chief forbade
her to go asking for aid and thus shaming
him. As punishment he denied her food
although Anne guessed nothing other than
the usual broth had been intended them.

Elizabeth and she lay down on the open
ground, huddling by a small fire that she

had kindled from brush and a stolen coal. Anne's limbs grew heavy and somnolent, and many a night she fully believed she would not survive till morning. Her only regret was no longer being there to protect Elizabeth, who was too fragile to survive without a guardian. One evening in particular Anne tried to prepare her thoughts to depart the earth and make peace with her Lord as her mother would approve, but found herself distracted by the night sky, which had at last cleared, revealing thousands of sharp silver daggers of light above, as well as the fairy-tale blanket of white that lay on the trees, bushes, and land around them. Nature, when not observed at a remove but up close, enchanted beyond anything she had previously imagined.

In the middle of the night a family of deer appeared at the edge of the tree line. She held her breath as they stood still a moment basking in the starlight, eyes that reflected the liquid night, pelts silvered, hooves like polished riverstone. Their ears twitched back and forth listening. She swore that they looked straight at her and yet were unafraid. Finally they moved off through the trees. She worried for their safety even though she herself wasted from starvation.

She drifted off to what she assumed was a

final rest only to be prodded awake in the glare of daylight. She covered her eyes with hands reddened and split from the cold. The two of them were so pitiable now that the Indians had no choice but to mount them on a pony that they then led. Elizabeth began an incessant crying over the pain in her stomach, which Anne recognized was simply hunger. The sound irritated their captors, and they threatened to knock the girl on the head if she did not quiet. Anne was hard-pressed to calm her.

"I want my mama," Elizabeth whimpered.

"That's where we are going," Anne answered without hesitation. "But you must promise to be very, very quiet."

She, who had been such a careful tender of the truth, now spouted lies when convenient as easily as if she had been doing such her whole life. What would happen when they reached their destination and no mother appeared? Wasn't it a sin to engender hope that had no possibility of fruition? But Anne could not think beyond the successful navigation of the next few steps ahead of them. She needed the girl to survive. That would be her victory. Survival was the beginning, without which the child would soon enough be joining her mother in eternity.

Worn from another day's march, they entered a small township Anne recognized from past visits with her family. It had been a special treat to stop there on the way to or from their home while stocking provisions or visiting relatives. The main attraction had been a passable luncheon café and sundry dry goods store where the children were allowed to pick out bits of sweets such as maple sugar candy or Necco wafers.

The place was now deserted, the people having fled, most of the buildings burned down. Anne remembered her parents talking of whole towns disappearing due to Indian attacks. Nonetheless the sight of the few remaining wooden structures was a comfort, evidence of a civilization that was fast becoming strange to her. Granted, that relief was small given the town's abandonment. There would be no one to rescue them.

Down the main street, they passed the half-decayed, flyblown carcass of a horse still tethered to the welcome post of the local flophouse. In one house, Anne could see a smashed bedstead and the green, heavy silk of a dress that still clothed its owner. Idly Anne recalled her coveting a friend's pretty dress and wondered at her former callowness. How much she took for granted.

An amazing array of artifacts lay scattered along the ground — a cracked looking glass, boots, pots, pans, apothecary items — things totally superfluous to her current existence. A lady's whalebone corset. The funeral card of a young man in uniform. Anne picked up a sterling fork that an Indian quickly snatched away from her. She found a dog collar and a few books much abused by the weather. It was disturbing to contemplate the likely fates of the owners of these worldly belongings.

The Indians, tired of the wailing of the women, allowed the captives to take abode in a half-standing warehouse for the night. Although the floor was dirt and the sky visible, having walls seemed a rich luxury to them.

Anne could not sleep, and as she lay there she heard the scurrying of mice. Curious, she waited till all was quiet outside then she crawled on her hands and knees to find what she suspected — stray grains of wheat and corn that had been stored in the building. She gathered the pitiful kernels into her pockets, little guessing that these would provide the bulk of her sustenance in the days ahead.

They traveled over a week through rough terrain without anything more than a few

cups of weak broth and melted snow for nourishment. The cold was so bitter that even when they had a fire to sleep against, Anne felt that warmth was something foreign to her body. It could no longer penetrate to her frozen core. She did not credit her survival each day to anything less than a miracle.

When at last they reached what she guessed was the main encampment in Indian Territory, the arrival occasioned a frenzied atmosphere. They remained in the winter camp for more than a week, but even such rest did not recuperate Anne from her fallen condition.

Within hours they were traded to another chief for the price of a hunting blade. Captives were valuable as labor. Her new master's woman put her to work day and night. Her first duty was to stay out all night guarding his pony herd, a job usually reserved for men, as horses were a tribe's main wealth. It was grueling labor in the freezing cold. One night, bone tired, she lay down for a quick nap and did not rise till morning when a warrior had to lift her to standing and then slap her face for circulation. Such an easy solution, to simply freeze to death.

Grudgingly, a sour, greasy buffalo hide

was given her to wear over her cotton dress. With its warmth the task became the smallest bit more tolerable. A gift of clean undergarments would have brought her to tears.

Allowed only a few hours' sleep in the morning, her daytime duty then began, of stripping bark from the saplings to provide fodder for the animals. She was told that if she tried to escape not only would she be killed but also Elizabeth. If a single horse went missing, she would be killed. If the animals were not fed properly, she would be killed. Anne held firm to the belief that it was only a matter of time before they found an excuse to kill her regardless of her actions. Observing their hardship, Anne understood she was the unwelcome enemy.

Whenever she had a rare free moment, her main task became begging for food. Hunger was a constant that crowded out all other thoughts. She had observed that the members of the tribe were generous with one another but acted miserly toward captives. If her teepee was preparing a large pot of stew over the fire, the family only rarely allowed her to dip her cup in and take the smallest amount away.

Even when she was lucky, she knew better

than to look too closely at the contents of her bowl, or she would lose her appetite. Soldiers had conducted winter campaigns, and the camp had had to flee to save their lives, leaving behind their winter stores of food. Mice and squirrels went in whole. Parts of dogs, deer, and horses. Birds and snakes and grubs. With starvation pressing close, everything was fair game, everything palatable.

Although she endeavored to make their provisions last longer to stave off hunger, Elizabeth and she were forced to eat everything they received immediately or risk it being stolen. It led to a cycle of starvation, satiation, starvation that broke their strength. When Anne was successful enough to hide away a handful of nuts or pemmican, the chief's wife would often find her hoard, and then she would be beaten for begging rather than be given enough provender to survive.

In light of these restrictions and cruelties, Anne was surprised at the freedom of movement she was allowed. The Indians knew she was too frail to run far. She had lost all compass of where they were but assumed it was far from Kansas.

Wilderness lay impenetrable in every direction, civilization a forgotten dream.

Could the great cities of the world still exist simultaneously with this primitive world?

During her explorations of the larger camp, she discovered another white woman, who had been taken a month before from Texas and found herself traded to her current location. Anne hugged her, overwhelmed at the companionship, but the woman shrugged off her touch. She was big with child and could talk of nothing but escape.

"But in what direction would you go?" Anne asked, as she had already studied the matter and determined any attempt futile.

The woman bowed her head and began crying. "The Lord shall guide me. Come with me."

Anne pitied the woman for her expectant condition, her thinness, the weathered roughness of her face, which clearly once held beauty.

"You will never survive an escape," Anne whispered.

The woman reached out her hand and placed it atop Anne's. She said nothing, an expression of great disappointment in her eyes. She got up with difficulty and moved off. It felt like a judgment, but Anne dismissed it. She had grown shrewd in survival

and calculated the woman had no chance of success.

The escape attempt was the news of the camp. The woman had been caught within one short hour's time and killed. The method used was slow torture as a cautionary lesson to others against attempting the same.

There were no words to describe Anne's desolation. Her desire to escape redoubled.

LIBBIE

A scant year before, she had been preparing for spinsterhood, and now here she was — a bride. Not just any bride, but one marrying a national hero. She had escaped being poor, motherless Libbie Bacon forever.

Her original plans were for a modest family wedding during Autie's leave. She had always pictured an intimate ceremony, followed by a family party, but once word got out the occasion drew interest all out of proportion to what they expected. Important social figures in Monroe waylaid Judge Bacon and asked for invitations, and then townspeople wanted to know if there would be some type of public celebration of the nuptials in which they could take part. Libbie refused, but Autie was quite flattered at the attention and allowed the town to commandeer their wedding.

"I just hope," her stepmother said, "you

are strong enough to stand up to such a man."

That was Libbie's first inkling that her savior might also be her tormentor.

Libbie had picked out a pea-green silk for her wedding dress, adorned with yellow military braid. A green silk veil and a corsage of red roses would complete it. But when one of the matriarchs of an important family in town heard of her plans from the dressmaker, she hurried to the Bacon house and demanded to talk with Libbie and her stepmother, Rhoda.

"What can you be thinking? It won't do at all. This wedding reflects on all Monroe. A description of your dress will be in the national papers!"

Libbie grew quite alarmed at the realization of how Autie's fame was already changing them.

The wedding plans swelled to an evening affair with the whole town invited, hundreds of people packed in the church with as many again milling outside. Libbie ended up going down the aisle in a stiff white dress that Autie joked could walk into church by itself. Its extensive train dragged at her steps as if it were reluctant to allow her to give up her girlhood status. A lace veil attached to an orange-blossom crown floated behind,

and Autie got briefly tangled in it, much to the amusement of the front-pew guests.

Autie's brother Tom obtained furlough and surprised them. She had not spent time with him before, but now as Autie was whisked away by people craving his attention, Tom looked after her. Both were content to be wallflowers. Tom was handsome, an impressive soldier in his own right, but he was quiet and self-effacing compared with Autie. It occurred to her that he might have been the easier man to marry.

The reception was grand, too grand for her taste. Tables were piled high with oysters, turkeys, hams, plates laden with wedding cake, blancmange, and fresh pineapple in February (luxury unimaginable during the lean war years), all washed down with champagne. A room was filled floor to ceiling with gifts, which later had to be left behind in storage. A military family traveled light.

Libbie wanted Autie to come dance with her, but he was marooned in a crowd of men wanting his opinion about the outcome of the War of the Rebellion. As a military hero, he was the stuff their boyhood dreams had been made of and they wouldn't let him go. As she walked the rooms, Libbie heard talk of people heading out to the Territories

to make their fortunes. Farmland was being sold at bargain prices, along with equipment, animals, and seed to create enticement for new settlements.

She passed a beautifully gowned woman with her back to the room who caught her attention. Her perfection of form — chestnut hair, ivory shoulders, tiny beelike waist, blue silk dress — had Libbie's admiration. But as the woman turned around from speaking with her circle of friends, Libbie feared she may have let out a gasp on seeing an angel's face entirely covered over in scars, a map of torture and brutality impossible to imagine in that civilized and genteel setting. The scars did not end at her chin but continued down her neck, scrolled over her arms and chest before disappearing under the fabric of her luxurious dress.

The woman, from a prominent family, had traveled out to New Mexico Territory to visit her fiancé, when she was captured by the Apache. She was held in captivity four months before being ransomed.

Later that evening Libbie was searching for Autie for a nuptial toast when she found the two on a settee in the library in front of the fire, drinking small glasses of sherry. He had put his hand on top of the woman's briefly as they exchanged some confidence,

and she bowed her head to him.

When Libbie approached she saw his face was flushed, his eyes watery. He was deeply affected by the meeting, and it cast a momentary pall on the evening. Libbie felt she was indeed what he jokingly teased — a silly, frivolous schoolgirl. Her earlier peeve had been childish. Even on this happiest day of their lives, he could not help but involve himself in the plight of others. A chill came down her spine. What if she was not equal to his fame? He looked up and saw her, joyfully waving her over.

"I want you to meet the love of my life," he said to the woman.

It wasn't until that moment that she truly loved him, loved him as a mature woman loves a man, for his whole being, and not just as an infatuated girl worships a hero.

It was the happiest day of her life, not for the obvious reason of marrying the man she loved, nor even for the minor celebrity of becoming a war hero's bride, but because she was never again to know another day, before or after, so filled with hope. Most times hope was more satisfactory than its fulfillment, which often fell short. For the moment theirs was a true marriage. They filled each other's heart. Generals and officers who later complained about her pres-

ence on military campaigns simply did not understand that together they were strongest.

Their honeymoon barely begun, Autie was called back to Washington to rejoin his regiment.

When the order came to move out to Virginia, all her promises of being strong and brave as a soldier's wife flew out of her head. Having so recently found true love, the possibility of his dying quite unnerved her. She could not endure another loss. At the least, Libbie refused to be left behind. Being separated was infinitely harder to bear than the threat of danger.

"I just want to be a little mouse, curled up safe in your pocket," she said.

To her surprise, Autie allowed it. A choice that ended up being the most fateful decision of their marriage, setting the tone for their future life.

General Kilpatrick was her baptism into the ignoble reality of the military, something not covered in the glowing tales written in newspapers. She was introduced to the novel concept that not only did one fight the enemy, one fought one's own side, where dangers sprang from both above and below.

Kilpatrick, nicknamed Kill Cavalry, was a vain man, full of hubris. He ordered Autie on what amounted to a suicide mission simply to serve as decoy. He was to draw troops away from the Confederate capital to clear the path for the main maneuver of Kilpatrick "single-handedly" capturing Richmond. That her Autie succeeded while his commander aborted his mission spoke for itself.

In the privacy of their rooms, Autie confided that the men despised their general. Although he was brave, he was reckless, and profligate with his men's lives. He exhibited bad judgment at Gettysburg and again at Falling Waters, and men had died needlessly. Autie's men, on the other hand, spoke of their confidence at being under his lead. He squeezed Libbie's hand.

"It means everything to me. I must be worthy of their trust."

A large plantation house had been converted into Union headquarters, and there Autie readied to leave at dawn. She began to cry hysterically, the realization of the danger he was going to suddenly palpable.

"Be brave, Libbie," he said, disappointed by her lack of composure.

A guard unit would arrive to look after her.

All day she waited alone and still they did not come.

The house was large and rambling, unknown, the circumstances under which she was staying there unclear. Had the owners been forcibly evicted, or was the army renting it? Coerced or volunteered? Could an angry family member be lurking inside a cabinet, bent on revenge? The floorboards creaked in an unhappy way, without the pressure of feet. The woods around Stevensburg were dense and menacing. She did not even consider venturing outside, a target to any outraged Southerner.

She scurried upstairs and barred herself in the bedroom, sitting by the large window overlooking the front of the house to read and wait. The memory of her earlier behavior burned in her. Nothing in her life to that point had ever been asked of her, other than to be pretty and cultured, certainly not courage. Last night Autie had trusted her enough to confide in her about generals, and she had returned the favor by acting like a silly child, scared of her own shadow.

What if he refused to let her come in the future? She took out pen and paper, determined to set his mind at ease: *I will learn to*

be brave, but you know, dear, I can't learn all at once.

How slowly time crawled.

Hours later she heard the sound of men marching. Finally! All manner of metal things — sabers, guns, pots, pans — clattered like a tinker's wagon from the din of it. Joyfully she raised the window sash to call out a greeting to her "rescuers." Unused to being solitary, those few hours taught her the necessity of always surrounding herself in company. She would always try to envelop both Autie and herself in a large, loving circle of family and friends.

She hung out the window so far as to threaten pitching out entirely, straining to see the soldiers through the trees, when she stopped. Although she hardly could make out distinct words, she could tell from the cadence those voices did not come from the North. Sure enough, as they skirted the woods along the property, she saw gray rather than blue wool uniforms. Quickly she drew back, pressing against the inside wall. Stories of crimes committed against women filled her head. Depending on the rank of the commanding officer, it could range from gentlemanly house arrest to the unthinkable. She had never before known such fear.

No gun had been left her, although she hadn't an idea of how to use one if it had, but just the idea of holding a weapon sounded preferable to wielding a book, even one as ponderous and heavy as *The Woman in White.* If she survived the next hours, she promised she would remedy the situation by having Autie supply her with both gun and shooting lessons.

For the moment, no other options available, she hid. There being no closet, she chose beneath the bed as she had done since she was a little girl frightened of thunder. She slid against the tight wooden struts supporting the four-poster honeymoon bed. The afternoon sun burned against the cotton ruffle. Underneath was not as clean as she would have liked, not nearly as clean as her girlhood bedroom in Monroe. With every inch of her being she regretted not listening to her father and going home like the other wives. What a foolish woman she was. Dust tickled her nose, and she pinched her nostrils shut in order not to sneeze.

Hours passed. She was embarrassed to say that she fell asleep, waking at evening to the sound of boots and the clanking of a saber up the stairs. Her heart tried to escape her chest. She held her breath and mouthed her last prayers as the door banged open.

"Libbie!"

She crawled out, unsteady, dress twisted around her legs, face gritted with dust. She tried to pin her fallen hair but gave up as tears welled.

His eyes were lit with hilarity at the sight of her, but he knew better than to utter a sound. She glanced miserably at him, and he could bear it no longer. He burst with laughter.

"There were Rebels passing not twenty yards from me!"

"They wouldn't dare touch a hair on the pretty head of Custer's wife."

"How do you know that?"

"Well, dear, I hope they wouldn't," he said. "You do understand there's a war going on, don't you?"

She cried hot tears at being so poorly treated. Only after he begged her forgiveness, pleading exhaustion and relief at finding her, did she move on to white-hot anger.

"You give no thought to my safety. You are not worried in the least."

His face turned red. "Men died today in battle, Libbie. If I worried about everything I should, I would go mad."

He had brought his black cook Eliza, and she was already installed in the kitchen preparing dinner for no less an illustrious

guest than General Sheridan, commander of all the cavalry.

"He wants to meet the beauty who stole my heart."

At table, Sheridan beamed at her Autie for his accomplishment on the battlefield that day. The whole house was aware of the newlyweds' tiff. In his awkward attempt at mollifying the teary bride Sheridan bragged that Autie was "the only man who matrimony has not spoiled for a charge." The comment had the opposite effect of making Libbie feel even more dejected.

They sat down to an excellent meal of roast beef, baked potatoes, and peas — unheard-of luxury in a war zone short of food. The crown jewel of the meal was the lightest, fluffiest of biscuits. Eliza was a wizard both in procuring in the black-market economy of the camp and in her cooking skills. Libbie was filled with admiration.

A year before Eliza was contraband, an ex-slave following the army, when she got a job cooking for the regiment. Impressed by her cooking skills, Autie had asked her to manage his private household on the campaign.

"You are fighting the War for me, the least

I can do is cook for you," she answered.

They had been together through thick and thin since. Eliza went into battle with him, cooking over a stewpot as bullets flew by her head at the front lines. The Confederates had even captured her twice, along with his personal wagon, but she remained undaunted and found her way back to him. She welcomed Libbie and coddled her like a mother even though they were close to the same age.

Now Sheridan furnished a lovely bottle of claret to complete the dinner. Libbie noted that Autie poured them each a glass without comment. He gave her a pointed look, and she nodded, allowing him this one time to drink.

But it wasn't until dinner was over and they had spent the night in the four-poster bed that Libbie was finally able to laugh at her foolishness. However ungracefully, she had managed to survive her baptism into military life.

Autie took for granted she would be safe because she was his wife. She wondered if this was true. How did he know for certain? It bothered her that he didn't worry more over her, that he treated the whole episode as a grand joke, an anecdote to be told over

the campfire. No doubt she would soon be the butt of jokes between Autie and Tom. Every embarrassment was grist for the Custer humor mill.

After being entrusted with the lives of thousands of men, a callus of sorts had grown over Autie's heart. For the first time she noticed something about her new husband — his exuberant optimism had devastating effects on those around him. He did not live in the same world as those less brave than he, and he made them pay the price for their cowardice. Nonetheless, she had endured, even if in such a timid way. After that first experience she never willingly went home to wait out a campaign.

LIBBIE

Within hours the farmhouse was vacated and again they were on the move. She rode sidesaddle on Autie's favorite horse, Custis Lee. She traveled beside her husband, and when she tired she moved to an ambulance specially outfitted for her comfort, behind the command escort. That special privilege began a slow burn of resentment in the soldiers.

The road was bumpy, the journey a long one, the wagon's bouncing rattling her bones till she was sore when she climbed down to her tent at night. When a snake crawled into the tent with her one evening, she ran back to the wagon to sleep, but she dared not show displeasure, fearing any tantrums would be cause to send her home.

One morning they were to cross swampland up a narrow, tree-choked trail. Up at dawn, they rode till mid-morning, when they stopped for a meal and to rest the

horses, then carried on. Late morning sun poked through the tree limbs overhead, poured a yellow, pollened light over the land. The creak of saddles, the percussion of metal against metal, the thud of hooves and boots were a soothing cadence that gave a sense of progress despite their torpid speed.

She nodded off in the heat, the wagon's hot canvas smelling of starch, daydreaming of being again a young girl at her mother's side as she ironed, when an explosion shook the wagon and made the horses jump in their stays. The sound was so loud her ears rang afterward.

The column came to a ragged stop. Her driver climbed down to quiet the animals, their eyes white-rimmed in fear. Orders were shouted up and down the line to remain in place, but it wasn't until one of Autie's staff rode back that it was confirmed — a soldier had tripped a new weapon called a land torpedo. It was a barbaric way to wage war. Sherman called it a coward's way to murder. They could not move forward without knowing the extent of the mining done to the road ahead.

They remained at a standstill for hours in the sweltering heat, restricted from going off the road to relax in the woods. Even

pack animals and horses were not allowed to refresh at the nearby stream. She found the scene strangely bucolic, soldiers stripped down to shirts, the lace of trees against the noon sky, the greenish gloom of forbidden woods, the stamp of horses in their stays. Mosquitoes descended as numerous as raindrops to feast on any exposed skin.

It became stifling in the wagon. Perspiration rolled down her back, her chemise and petticoats thoroughly wet under the heavy blouse and skirts she wore. Trying to stay cheerful, she shared apples and water with the driver. She was fortunate to have a wagon full of food and water. Theoretically she could last days in such a privileged cage.

Hours passed.

She simply had to have fresh air, but her escort stopped her before she could place a footstep on the earth. Autie's orders. She whipped the curtains closed, and quickly shed her corset and petticoats. She would wear only her cotton dress, modesty be damned. So freed, she stood up out of the wagon, lapping up any freshness in the heavy air like a dog. She was aware of the looks of soldiers around her: even though married she still enjoyed an admiring male glance, so she lengthened the time of her pose.

It was then that she heard a man's screams, then the louder, ringing silence. Minutes later a stretcher went past, the wounded man blanketed with a sheet, his bloody leg still in its boot nestled next to his side like a newborn. Mercifully, he had passed out. Libbie bowed her head and said a prayer.

She offered to go and sit with the wounded soldier but was refused. The doctor must have thought her too will-o'-the-wisp to be of support. No one would say it to her face, but she guessed that hers was the only ambulance empty enough to accommodate the wounded man. She volunteered it, happy to ride her horse or join a supply wagon. The doctor accepted, but within a few minutes Autie countermanded her, to Libbie's horror.

Later the doctor told her that it wouldn't have mattered, the soldier never regained consciousness and died that night. She said another prayer for his mother, knowing the enormity that such loss would mean to the poor woman. Libbie could bring tears on just by picturing her own dear mother's face. She resolved to read aloud passages from the Bible to comfort all close enough to listen. The men told her it was the closest to home they had felt in months.

In the afternoon, activity could be heard from the rear. Mounted cavalry herded a large group of soldiers between them. Libbie was shocked as they came close enough for her to recognize gray uniforms. Prisoners. Autie must have "borrowed" them from the latest battle. They were shoved to the head of the column.

What happened next haunted her for many years. Threatened by the end of a rifle or saber, the prisoners were poked down to a crawling position, shoulder to shoulder across the road, three rows deep. They proceeded to crawl like small children, no, like beasts of burden, forced forward to trip any land torpedoes with the weight of their own bodies if they did not manage to disable them first. No one cared how unlikely it was that a common soldier would have such advanced technical ability.

Travel became agonizingly slow. In the period while the prisoners were prodded ahead several hundred yards, all eyes watched the road, everyone dreading the concussion of yet another explosion. In between it was so quiet one could hear the wind in the trees, the chafing drone of insects. Libbie imagined she heard the whoosh of her own blood in her ears.

The column would come into motion and

catch up in minutes only to endure yet another equally long wait.

The sight of men used in such fashion shamed her. She believed it lessened her husband's mission, and she would speak to him about it. It did not seem moral, but she reconciled herself that, being a woman, she didn't understand the ways of war. What strain Autie must have labored under and hid from her daily. She thought of his silences, which she formerly had attributed to displeasure with her, and now guessed their true cause.

Was it unforgivable weakness on her part that she wished to return to the ignorance of childhood? She had not imagined such cruelty of one man toward another. Worse, the man who ordered it was also the man she loved. She felt herself aged a decade in the first few weeks of her marriage.

What if Autie stepped on one of those traps and was wounded or even killed? Rather than sacrificing him she would gladly have a hundred Rebels, a thousand, crawl on their bloodied hands and knees. She knew this was an unforgivable Christian failing, this selfishness, this pride. She chose virtue and charity when it suited, ignoring its call when its practice became too difficult.

Bereft of other options, she prayed once more, as she did each morning, noon, and night for an end to this savage war.

Appomattox Station, April 1865

The military inculcated in its officers the need to quantify every battle in terms of loss and spoils, so after each victory Custer dispatched men to count. The tally of the Shenandoah campaign: 2,556 prisoners taken, 71 guns, 29 battle flags, 52 caissons, 105 army wagons, 2,557 horses, 1,000 horse equipments, 7,152 beef cattle. As important as what was gained to the victor was what was destroyed for the loser: 420,742 bushels of wheat, 780 barns, 700,000 rounds of ammunition.

The numbers in a ledger, of course, did not begin to quantify the impression on the senses: fields of grain burning in broad daylight with no one allowed to douse them. Black plumes of oily smoke that rose straight up then feathered across the blue sky. Slaves suddenly free but without provision of the next meal. Men under fifty conscripted to the Union war effort, or taken prisoner if

they refused, or shot if they were too much trouble. Houses plundered, left aflame.

Women for the most part were spared. They expressed little gratitude over the fact. Their eyes scorched Custer's back as he rode by. Once he stopped to offer a tin of biscuits, and the lady spat on him. He did not stop again. He understood the temptation to blame him due to the color of his uniform. Female arms and stomachs hollowed from the want his army inflicted. Skin stretched over the filigree of pedigreed bones. Being gentlemen, the officers spared the women every indignity but starvation. At night some in desperation came to offer themselves for a handful of flour or a cup of sugar. In the morning, like bruised fruit, the most fragile souls had swung themselves from tree limbs, starched petticoats floating in the breeze.

At the end of the War, 359,528 Union dead and 258,000 Confederate dead. Three thousand horses dead during the battle at Gettysburg alone. Unreal numbers. In the balance of things it seemed easier to die than live. During war the border between the two became porous. The people called the Shenandoah campaign "The Burning," as if it were a plague brought from above, but Custer understood it was only a small-

ish hell made by man.

Even then, the Confederates in their death throes did not give up. He was ordered to Appomattox, his soldiers exhausted, enduring terrible cannon fire, he leading a charge. Nothing was as beautiful in all of creation — men and horses steeled of intent, moving as one to engage death and hopefully wrest glory from it. The memory brought tears to his eyes still. Years later he retrieved a little of that feeling when buffalo hunting and attending horse races. When a horse went all out and began pulling ahead, years of breeding and training paying off, it came close to the meaning of life. At least to a cavalryman.

He captured 24 cannon, 5 battle flags, 200 wagons, and 1,000 prisoners. As the prisoners filed past on their way north, Custer had the band strike up "Dixie." The steps of the prisoners quickened and by the fifth repetition a discreet cheer rose up. Despite the tremors and ghosts, he did not believe in disrespecting the brave. Defeat yes, disrespect no.

Sheridan told Custer to prepare to attack again, when it finally came — a lone rider coming forward with a white towel on a stick. It was over. Even as they stood battle ready, waiting, a cheer rose up and spread

from both sides. Custer only knew he could at last rest. He sat on the ground still holding his horse's reins in his hand and fell asleep.

When Lee rode in to sign the surrender, Custer had tears in his eyes. The War had been the most formative experience of his young life. Two years before as a mere boy he had written to a friend that he would be perfectly content to be in battle every day. Now at the ripe age of twenty-five he realized the foolishness of his words. The world had come close to extinguishing itself, and the sooner the War ended, the better.

The next day Sheridan sent Libbie the signing table as a gift, including a note to her stating that her Armstrong was as responsible for the victory as anyone. Could one accept praise for victory without also accepting blame for carnage? He was in some ways still a child. Proud fool, he carried away the trophy table, flattered as a silly schoolboy by Sheridan's praise.

The lowly Custer clan had done its country proud in the War. Brother Tom was awarded two Medals of Honor, and Custer became the youngest brigadier general in the army. He determined to put out of his mind those burning houses, lace curtains of ash, fine clothes trampled, smoldering

furniture. The endless, endless dead. He felt the Southerners' hatred, palpable like a sharp rock in his boot. It was deserved. As simple as this — in war one side won, the other lost. He was a soldier who followed orders. During the War he had turned from boy to man. When lucky he saved the day. So far he had been lucky more often than he had not.

The Fourth Remove

Work camp — Neha — Rattlesnake bite
—
With child — In mourning

Two summers later Anne took Elizabeth with her while she worked as buffalo skinner. The work crew consisted of four men who were unfit for battle due either to age or infirmity; three older women unfit for anything else; Neha, the newest woman of her chief, Snake Man; and Anne, with her charge. As the youngest, Neha and Anne were given the most grueling work. Work camp was for those too unlucky to get out of the labor of butchering. They had the camaraderie of being the lowest level of the tribe.

They dried meat like laundry on long suspended poles. They scraped the skins clean and aired them on bushes. Anne's job was the laborious one of tanning the hides.

This involved stretching them along the ground and tacking them down with small wooden pins. Day after day, she would kneel over the skin and rub it very hard with a sharp stone, till it was pliable and white. Her hand cramped, her arms ached, her back was tender, and yet she had no reprieve the long day. Her belly hung heavy with her first child, which would be birthed in the fall.

It pleased her that it was only women and old men in camp, that the senior wives of her master disdained such labor. No one objected to stopping early and sitting by the fire to eat and tell stories as long as the work got done.

Away from the drama of the chief and the cruelties of his wives, Anne had the rare luxury to sleep deeply. The cool nights and nearby river lulled her to a peaceful state. For the moment, she was content. Human happiness was like a flower insistent on burrowing its way out despite the most inhospitable conditions.

During the last years, Elizabeth and Anne had been traded from chief to chief three more times, the first time for a gun, the second for a sack of grain, and the third to Snake Man for Anne's sewing ability, which

had gained her a small measure of status. Bearing witness to the killing of other captives due to ill health or escape attempts, Anne understood her only refuge was in appearing to submit to captivity and in being useful to the tribe's survival. The native way of life brooked no tolerance for delicate sensibilities or melancholia. A captive without use was one quickly dispatched.

During raids on settlers one of the great prizes was clothing, but these garments needed to be sliced and refitted. Always a proficient seamstress for her mother, Anne was now much in demand for her ability.

At first the bloody, arrow-pierced nature of the clothing repulsed her and led to sleepless nights, but with time she adopted a more sanguine attitude toward the clothes' resurrection. She viewed their new afterlife much as she did her own, of adapting to a second life that bore no resemblance to her former one.

Members of Snake Man's family came to her with sewing demands, including the embroidery of war garments, tobacco pouches, and gun cases, but other members of the tribe also sought her out and paid by barter, mostly food of which she felt the constant shortage, so that after a time Elizabeth and she ate well enough.

A new element in her life was the unexpected gift of companionship that Snake Man's acquisition of the half-breed Neha provided. The two women had formed an alliance against the cruelties of his older women. Anne had grown used to solitariness, learning not to get too close to anyone in the tribe — members came and went so frequently that attachment proved difficult. Yet she found she enjoyed the girl's company and grew to depend on it.

When Neha first arrived at the teepee, Anne was quite awed by her appearance. She somehow had stolen only the best from both races. She stood tall and lean, with dusky skin and gold-flecked eyes. All the chiefs had their eyes on her, and Snake Man impoverished himself of his horse herd to buy her out from under them.

Neha was the daughter of a powerful chieftain. Despite her mixed blood she had been the favorite of her father, who insisted on an exceptionally large payment of ten horses to give her in marriage. This did not endear her to Snake Man's wives, who considered her prideful. The outcast white woman became her only consolation.

Younger than Anne, Neha was unhappy at the age and sullenness of her new husband. The two women commiserated on the

randy, vain ways of Snake Man, who had more wives than means. The new woman's presence had the effect of curtailing his visits to Anne, for which she was grateful.

As a regular part of their year, the tribe went in search of buffalo to add to their stores for the winter. On one such journey they came upon railroad tracks that cut through their favored hunting valley, a pristine landscape that was one of the main routes of the herd.

The warriors stopped their horses and glared down at the metal-and-wood track as if it were an animate power, an adversary of supernatural strength. Anne felt her heart pound in excitement at this scarce, longed-for evidence of her civilization in such remote wilderness. Civilization came on rails, each track shortening the distance between herself and home. Did it not seem possible after all that she might be discovered? Discovered instead of rescued, because after so much time it was not credible that they searched for her still.

The Indians went to work destroying the track, a Sisyphean task even if they were successful in derailing a single cargo. Anne tried not to think of the danger to the passengers, but rather that the damage would

necessitate repairmen who might be able to deliver her from her captivity.

After crossing the mangled tracks, the tribe was not jubilant over such destruction but remained morose with foreboding. Noting Anne's quickened step, one of the women weighed her down with more to carry as punishment. Behind their ill temper, Anne sensed despair.

Anne meekly shouldered her added burden, sensing the volatility of the tribe's collective mood. She continued to hope, despite the bitter thought that she knew of no rescue attempts nor ransom offers having been made on her behalf. Most likely she was counted dead to the greater world.

She was sixteen years old the winter she was first with child but had mercifully miscarried due to malnourishment. The chief's women had been filled with spite toward her, hitting her about the head for the slightest mistake, denying her food, making her sleep outside the teepee's shelter, but after the loss of the child their rancor stopped.

Anne could not account the reason but was grateful. She supposed it was much like introducing a dog to an established household: a new pecking order must be ham-

mered out. She was a servant of the family, certainly not on the level of a wife. Perhaps their anger had diminished due to her clothes-making ability, which rendered the chief's women among the most fashionable in the camp.

The following spring she again became pregnant, and she beat her stomach with rocks and ate dirt, and again she lost the child. She made long and complicated prayers to God begging forgiveness for her damning actions.

The winter of her seventeenth year she was again pregnant, and this time she prayed that with the food she earned from her own labor she might be strong enough to deliver. She could explain her change of attitude in no other way than that she longed to have something of her own, something for which she would have reason to survive. She considered it God's gift and not to be questioned. It was a time of relative peace within the tribe, and she used it to rebuild her strength and plot an escape.

Once she had accepted the fact of the growing baby inside her, she assumed that it would diminish her hunger for freedom, but the pregnancy had the opposite effect. She could not imagine bearing a child within captivity, even if that captivity was

by its own people. Far from a child giving her a sense of belonging, its imminent arrival made her even more restive.

Anne wanted the boons of civilization for this next generation while also fearing for the child's safety within the camp. Would there be jealousy among the wives? Would its white blood make it an outcast? If the infant were hardy enough to survive till childhood, would its rude upbringing make it unable to later return to its white origins, just as an animal, once tasting the elixir of freedom, cannot again be domesticated?

The meat-drying process was under way when the women decided to take a break from the noontime sun. They went to lie in the shade to sleep, Neha joining them, but Anne told Elizabeth to follow her to the river, where she would bathe away the blood and animal fat that coated her arms.

Elizabeth had spent the morning picking wildflowers and braiding them into a crown to put atop her gold-white hair. That hair and her blue eyes made her an object of much adulation among the Indians, who allowed her to be lazy compared with Indian children her age, who were expected to work to the maximum of their abilities. Elizabeth sat on the boulders by the stream, the red,

gold, and blue blossoms in her headband giving her the appearance of a wood fairy.

The girl had changed much in her two years of captivity. Although she no longer cried, she also hardly talked. Her mother was a topic she refused to bring up. Anne did not know if the child had figured out her lie, or if she had blissfully forgotten. What she did do was make Anne her keeper, never letting her out of her sight. When the chief came to pay his attentions she turned the girl's sleeping face away and endured his rutting without protest to not waken the child. They ate and slept together, the girl curled in her arms so that Anne was made a mother before ever giving birth. The child's love gave her the courage to accept her approaching maternity.

When Anne explained that she soon would be joined by a baby, Elizabeth grew more cheerful, and often she would lay her small hand on the minor protrusion of Anne's belly and talk to the child as if it were her personal confidant.

"Baby will be my brother. He will grow up strong and protect me. He will take us away from the Injuns."

Anne did not know how to broach the fine point that the baby would indeed *be* one of the *Injuns* she wished him to take them away

from. She had avoided such thoughts herself as it was easier to continue on that way. One foot down and then another. However cowardly, such thinking had allowed them to survive thus far.

The sun was hot; light sparked on the moving water of the river like a flint against stone. How good it would be to join the women under the trees and nap. Anne rubbed her swelled belly and felt round and ripe as a fruit, her baby a sweet wild plum. At moments like these she felt not exactly happiness — she refused the description in such captivity — but animal well-being. She had survived. Just to be alive and filled with life felt akin to victory. These were her drowsy thoughts as she closed her eyes in the shade by the other women. She told Elizabeth not to wander too far off.

Sometime later she felt a rough jabbing at her side and instinctively rolled away to protect her stomach, the juicy burgeoning pit. Her first unhappy thought was that the wives had reverted to their rough ways before she realized that something else was wrong. The women's faces were grim as they shoved her back toward the river, where she found the prone form of her Elizabeth. Neha stood over her.

The child had continued picking flowers

and had crawled into some undergrowth after a particularly lovely bunch of red clover when she'd heard a strange rattling sound. An Indian child would have been taught that the sound warned of danger, the area likely infested with venomous rattlers, but Elizabeth simply sat back mesmerized by the toylike, seemingly harmless baby rattlesnake only as long as her hand. Did she reach for it, or it her? Impossible to tell except that there were fang marks right on her chest, far too close to the heart for an adult, much less a child. The women had pulled the girl away from the nest of serpents, knowing that the presence of one indicated others, but had otherwise given up on her.

"How did it bite you?" Anne asked.

"It was so tiny," Elizabeth replied, already dazed.

Now Anne held the small body, Elizabeth moaning as her chest swelled and turned an angry reddish purple that carried like blush to her neck and then face. Her frightened blue eyes were quickly buried within pillows of flesh. Each breath came more ragged than the one before, her lungs compressed within her bloated chest. In desperation Anne yelled to Neha to help her carry the girl down to the river. She sat Elizabeth

neck deep in the shallows, thinking perhaps the cold water would draw off the poison. Elizabeth started a forlorn wailing, which caused the women to frown and then turn their backs on the whole futile enterprise.

"I feel hurting," Elizabeth whispered. "Hold my hand."

"I am."

"I can't feel you."

Anne squeezed harder and held the other hand also.

"Listen to me. This is important. Remember your mother?"

Elizabeth looked across the water with great finality.

"She died," the child said.

Anne bit her lip.

"She is happy in heaven. She waits for you. You will go straight from my arms to hers. Do not be frightened."

"I'll try. I can't be sure."

An hour later, the child was gone.

In front of the girl Anne had forbidden herself tears, but afterward she remained dry-eyed as well. The ability to express sorrow seemed to have left her. She sat next to the small form and experienced a loneliness that she did not think a human could endure. Why were beings thus made to experience such ravaging emotion?

She scoured her memory for biblical verses that she might recite to honor the girl, but they all felt false and absurd under the hard circumstances of her short life. If any believer had been most certainly forsaken, it had been this poor child.

When the women tugged on Anne to move away, she growled sharply at them and spent the entire night in vigil beside the last human being that linked her to her old life. She felt as alone in the world as it was possible to be.

Up the hill, Neha sat watching over her. She swayed back and forth and sang the death song that expressed their pain.

At dawn Neha came to Anne and held out her hand. There was nothing else to do but take it.

Anne rose without protest, her bones stiff from sitting on the ground the night long, and went to the river to wash her face while Neha and the women dug a shallow grave. Together they inhumed the small body.

The buffalo meats and skins were bundled up and set on travois poles to be pulled by the ponies, and the small party moved out to rejoin the main camp.

KANSAS, 1867

Hancock didn't have the first clue about how to fight Indians and made the 7th suffer for his ignorance, driving them mercilessly across the plains to go against the southern tribes, with nary a contact to reward their labors.

How could Custer describe the grimness of the scout to Libbie? A description of the plains was beyond him for the simple reason that they were so singularly lacking in feature. Constant wind shredded the parched prairie grass. Waves and swells of grass as far as the eye could see, restful as the waves of an immense arid ocean. Riding the prairie was like being in a small boat on a vast inland sea.

Custer was dead tired of flat.

If he had been one of the creatures who burrowed underground, a worm or prairie dog, he could have described the vibration of the unseen buffalo herd passing miles

away, how it tumbled through the earth, how his dogs felt it thrum through their feet, a blood pulse that livened them although he could not guess the cause, attributing their excitement to the long column of horses, mules, and wagons that stretched out behind him like some slack, shedding animal across the plains.

He must not forget to mention the heat — how the sun scoured the hills, burned the low, nondescript bushes, pulled the last wet from the grass, faded the wildflowers in their bloom. It was so dry he couldn't find the saliva to spit, but he wouldn't write to Libbie about that.

The wind's direction shifted and carried a strong scent to the dogs' noses — not the everyday ones of flour, oil, dried meat, or even the stink of thousands of unwashed men, or the fresh stench of their shit along the sides of the trail, or the sweeter reek from cattle and horses — but an ancient, greasy, unctuous odor, unfamiliar and unsettling. In spite of the dogs' exhaustion, their wiry bodies set to prancing, with whinging barks as they circled around the horses' legs until Custer gave them the command of release. The hounds rocketed away across the prairie.

Far behind, a calf bawled its misery. Along

the line he heard dust-caked men mumble a dirge of complaint about the trail, the length of the march, the poor quality of their food and drink, the paltriness of the pay, and the stinginess of praise given by their martinet commander. Most of the postwar military were there simply to secure rudimentary employment, the low wages and hard conditions ensuring men of a desperate order.

Did they know or care how much he had been loved by his men during the War? Ask any of them, they would sing his praises. He had letters by the boxful. One soldier told the newspapers about Custer rescuing him on the battlefield after a bullet struck him in the leg. Not only did he carry the man from harm's way but also made sure he got treatment. *I would have given my right arm to save his life — aye, I would have died in his place!*

If these men wanted his praise, they must earn it. They couldn't hold a candle to his Michigan Brigade, no matter how hard he drilled them. His last hope was that he could forge the 7th Cavalry into a fighting unit in the heat of battle, but finding a battle also proved less satisfactory than it had before.

He likened the difference fighting Confed-

erates and fighting Indians to being attacked by a bear or a mosquito. The bear had overwhelming force, he stood big, square in front of you, and moved predictably. The Indians fought like the mosquito. They stayed invisible except for the high whine in the ear as one flailed against them and felt the sting of their bite, but only the luckiest swipe crushed them, usually after they were already gorged with blood. Endless, itching irritation.

The dull rock of horses, the rub of Custis Lee's saddle underneath, lulled him into dreaminess. The sun beat down against his felt hat, which shaded his eyes and nose, leaving chin and cheeks sunburned through his sparse mustache and beard. He pulled a kerchief from his pocket and wiped at the sand that crusted his eyes, blew his nose clean of mudsnot. He glanced at the men filing past — bowlegged, underfed, ill-bred. Soured faces and horned hands. Half were immigrants who had come after the War, unskilled laborers culled from the eastern cities who had no idea what they signed up for. They were squalid compared with his old Union volunteers. The only thing for sure was that such men were difficult to defeat because defeat already ran strong in their blood, and thus they had no fear of it.

A disturbance traveled through the column. The slightest threat from their surroundings registered physically through the men as if they formed a single entity. He shaded his eyes and saw far off on the blurred horizon dark human shapes. His heart added beats. The horses, sensing the new tension in the bodies of their riders, enlivened their gaits.

He halted the column, gathered his lead officers around him, good men who had weathered their postwar demotions as he had. Orders were given for arms to be made ready. Teamsters pulled rifles out from under wagon benches. He looked through his field glasses, but the waver of heat over salt pan made identification impossible. Was it a returning war party, or part of a larger camp on the move? He picked out an officer, and the two left the main body at a gallop to make contact. At hardly a quarter of the distance, the figures began to ride in a circle. His chest loosened at this signal of parley. He checked his relief with the thought that it might be an ambuscade, commonly employed by Indians.

When half the distance had been covered, he realized the horses were white men's animals, not Indian ponies. His breath evened. Again he was aware of the burning

sun on his back. Closing the final distance, he greeted herders who had lost their mules and then lost themselves on the deceptive plains. He pointed them in the right direction and then turned back.

Indians sparse as water, he thirsted for battle.

He twitched with anger at the sun, the dust, the runty men, the nag horses, the endless land that poured off in every direction like spilled tar. A passing soldier tilted a whiskey flask to his mouth in full view. All Custer could do not to order a lashing was set reins to horseflesh and follow the hounds away, over the nearby hillock where they had vanished.

His heart slowed, his throat loosened at the sound of pounding hooves. There was no glory like horses who ran not because they were spurred or whipped but from sheer animal joy, even if it was into battle.

Alone, the aspect of an inland grass sea was not as oppressive. He listened to the sound of dry thunder roll endlessly, unhalted by mountains.

If only he had Tom's company, their roughhousing would alleviate his utter boredom. Where had those cagey dogs gone off? Disappeared again over yet another

imperceptible swell of land like the barely visible but essential lift and fall of a breathing chest. And then he saw the cause of the dogs' agitation.

Black against the burning light. The beast stood at least six feet high; if it wasn't the biggest he'd ever seen he'd eat his hat. The head massive, winched down, so big and heavy it already seemed detached from its body. He could imagine it trophied above his mantel, the long horns unnicked and perfect wholes, sharp as cutlery. The body stood monstrous, broad chest tapering to the pure ironmuscle of hindquarter. The whole specimen deserved to be sent back east to be stuffed and set behind glass for posterity.

His attention, formerly scattered, now narrowed to a pinpoint. He was a wolf who had caught the whiff of prey. He hardly needed to goad Custis Lee to give chase; they were off. Air hot as if from an oven seared its way in and out of his lungs as he came alongside. Up close the animal grew even larger and more forbidding; he felt like he was trying to subdue a mountain. The coat was dusty as if the beast molted earth, creating the very ground beneath its feet as it ran. Maybe the Indian myth was true, of it being the source of all. Its acrid smell

repelled him. Breath pumped through the bellows-like lungs of the animal as Custer drew close, leaned down, and placed the rifle's muzzle to kiss the chest, but the moment was too perfect. He pulled off to prolong it, and the manbeast moved together in tandem a few more strides.

His horse was running full out, as fast and hard as during a charge. He wished they could go on tied like this across the vast, scrubbed emptiness forever. In pure joy he leaned down almost tenderly to deal the death shot. The molten power and rage of the animal made him want to crawl inside it, he felt such perfect awe. He was awake for the first time in days, nay months, years. It was almost as good as battle.

Just when he decided enough was enough, the bull, too, sensed a changed intention. It swung its giant head around toward the horse's belly, the horn so close it could easily plunge through to the intestines or else rip the man's leg off. The horse shied away, spooked either by the scrape of deadly horn or else the animal's feral stink. Custer's finger completed its downward pressure on the trigger as the sudden motion swung around the muzzle and instead exploded the equine head.

His Pegasus lost contact with the earth

and for a divine moment became airborne before he crashed down into the ground with an impact so hard it broke both his front legs. Barely did Custer have time to pull boots from stirrups before the impact of horse against earth pitched him over the body, pushed him facedown, his mouth bloodied, nostrils packed with dirt. Many horses had been shot out from under him during the Rebellion, scores more he had ridden to death, or they had perished from scant forage and water, but the loss of a mount never ceased to be unique and painful to a cavalryman. It was an amputation of a part as essential as an arm or leg, and infinitely worse this time, because he had caused it in sport.

During the War things had happened quickly, there had been no time to feel. Now he lay in his man-sized earth depression, and time dragged along behind him. Weariness weighed him down so that he was tempted to not move but rest until the pious thought occurred that soon enough he would be resting for all eternity, so he picked himself back up.

In his stupor he'd forgotten the cause of his present affliction. The bull had not. It stood waiting, its small, prehistoric eye studying him while its flanks heaved great

shovelfuls of air. Probably it was ailing, which was why it was alone, away from its herd. Solitude in the animal kingdom was an indicator of defeat and inevitable death.

Had he culled himself also? Where had his regiment disappeared?

Motionless, man and bull each eyeballed the other. At some invisible signal he knew the bull might turn its ragged anger toward him, and could easily outrun a man. It could impale him on one of those same spectacular horns that already he had mentally separated from its owner and mounted behind the fancy case of a museum. If Mr. Bull could read his thoughts, Custer was already as good as gone. A shame to die in such an ignoble fashion, but it could not be helped. A man was not always the master of choosing his final hour.

The wind notched stronger, the dusted sky yellowing to an unhealthy pallor. The bull lifted his head and scented the slightest degree right of the man. Was it hearing the lowing call of home? Longing for the comfort of being surrounded by a herd of his own kind, the distraction of mother bull, or was there a Mrs. Bull, or better yet a Miss Bull? The fall must have played tricks with Custer's head; he felt both fear and not fear. For some inexplicable reason, he knew the

animal would not charge. Never once was he tempted to reach for his shotgun. If one showed either Indians or buffalo one's back, one was as good as gone. Both were warriors, each carried the bloodlust, just as he, a soldier, had the bloodlust. The most beautiful thing in life was to have an opponent worthy of oneself.

The ancient inspiration deciphered, the great beast tossed its head as if to clear it of cobwebs. Its comical small tail whipped up and down like a lady's dainty riding quirt and off it trotted, stiff-necked, proud, without even a backward, menacing goodbye, stating clearly, *Fool!* Dismissive as if even he, Mr. Bull, understood that hidden in the surrounding bluffs and ravines lay fates far worse than he.

Custer's legs buckled. Danger born, matured, and died away. Now on his knees a tremor shook him like he was a rag doll. Fear, although he refused to name it such. The sky howled overhead, a hollow and jaundiced thing, the featureless plains around him ominous as a bare stage.

He crawled over to his beloved Custis Lee, stroked the lathered shoulder, cursed his recklessness, not able to bear the mash of blood and bone and brain. He had truly loved the horse. His living link to his War

was broken. Ashamed, he fiercely swiped at his eyes although there was no danger of witness. He had faced far worse than this on a daily basis during the Rebellion, both in numbers and kind, but here solitary mortality pierced him, made him feel exactly how small and inconsequential as a flea was the single passing of either man or beast.

He blubbered like a babe. He mourned Custis Lee in inverse proportion to how he had been unable to mourn his men during the rush of battle. He bawled and in the quiet afterward realized he was utterly forsaken. Out on that endless plain not a soul cared who he was, what he'd done, or what would become of him. It was his darkest nightmare: to die unknown.

The dogs were nowhere to be seen. Either they had returned to the regiment or had fallen back. Had he given chase to the bull farther than he remembered? He pulled himself to his feet and decided to walk to the highest nearby bluff in order to spot the column.

What should have taken him ten minutes took more than an hour. His feet ached, his mouth went dry so that his tongue matched the ground under his feet. He had not intended to be gone long enough to require more than the canteen of water that he had

long before emptied. The top of the swell revealed prairie pulling away in all directions, devoid of human form. He had been mistaken about the distance and height of the bluff. When he finally climbed it — his only compass point the carcass of the recently deceased Custis Lee — higher ones surrounded him.

Unless he spotted the column he was helpless to guess what direction to take. He smarted at his unkept promises to Libbie — stay with the column, no hunting side trips, only leave accompanied in case of running into trouble. It was then that it occurred to him he needed not only to locate his regiment but must avoid Indian contact. He was a prime, coup-earning trophy, dismounted, armed only with carbine and pistol. Even Mr. Bull had forsaken him, disappeared from sight as if deliquescing into the raw earth.

Over the next hours he summited two more swells only to find that the geography remained unchanged at the top of each. He was marooned in a still ocean of grass, no end in sight, no human in sight either. The exact sorriest spot on earth. He had lost the marker of his Custis's corpse, and until the sun began its decline he had no sense of direction. His eyes swam. Despite the heat,

sweat dried on him, his insides wicked of moisture. In the distance were lovely lakes of water that he knew to be traps. Skeletons all over the prairie attested to the power of the *ignis fatuus,* which always hovered just out of reach, capable of driving a man over the edge. He resolutely shut his eyes.

At the foot of yet another bluff, he was tempted to lie in the nonshade of afternoon although he wouldn't yet concede defeat. If you lay down, you didn't get back up. Knowing better, he stretched out anyway, the hard ground as beckoning to his hurting self as a feather bed. He repeated the transporting lullaby of names: Bull Run, Antietam, Gettysburg, Yellow Tavern, Trevilian Station, Richmond, Appomattox. Fairytale names from another time so far from this stunted present, his change in fortune pained him. A hallowed time that created hallowed men, himself privileged to be among them. If there was a God, it was a time never to be repeated. The end of one thing that augured the beginning of . . . nothing.

He closed his eyes and was just about to fall asleep when he heard the wondrous call of a bugle. He blinked. Never had the nearness of such wretched soldiers swelled a heart so. His officers would find him soon,

must be on his trail even now, but until then he would remain part of the earth. He crossed his ankles and tilted his hat over his reclining head to hide the panic still etched in his face.

— 'Bout time you showed up. Set up camp here for the night. And bring me some whiskey while you're at it.

Might as well make his broken promises to the old lady an even half dozen before he reformed on the morrow.

LIBBIE

After the war and a brief posting in Texas, Autie was commissioned lieutenant colonel of the newly created 7th Cavalry and sent to Fort Riley, Kansas. Autie and Libbie put a good face on it for each other, but both were devastated. They had been famous, feted like celebrities in New York City. Even when alone, Libbie had been singled out in Washington by no less than President Lincoln and asked if the Boy General really had such a lovely wife.

All that traded in for endless empty prairie, crude clapboard buildings, poor rations. Anonymity. It was a reckoning. As if their pride had grown out of proportion, and they were being slapped down into their places. Autie spent long evenings in his study in silence. His moods, he called them, though she heard other soldiers had the same. She knew better than try to speak to him at such times. They no sooner moved into one rude

hovel than a higher-ranking family arrived to lay claim to it, and in turn they took a lower officer's, a domino effect that left all feeling ill used.

Part of the voyage out to Kansas they rode in a train. Through one valley there were reports of Indians having waylaid a small group of wagons. The settlers had been rescued by the army, but the provisions had to be left behind. Before the story was out of the officer's mouth, they could see those same wrecked wagons out the window.

A dozen or more Indians were still picking through the spoils, ransacking supplies. A hatchet busted open a sack of flour that flumed up in a cloud. The warriors were in high spirits, and one tied a bolt of calico to the tail of a pony. As the train passed, the rider took off at a dead run to outrace the locomotive, the calico unfurling in long curls like a streamer behind him.

The hairs stood up on Libbie's forearms at the unexpected wonder of the sight. How to describe his appearance? The body undressed except for a breechclout, the limbs lean, muscled, and bronze. Both rider and horse painted with yellow stripes so that they appeared melded together. The rider raised his arm and shook it at the train then veered away. Libbie realized with astonish-

ment that he was playing with them. It was a magnificent sight. Despite herself she felt like clapping and noticed Autie was thrilled as she by the startling beauty and ebullience they witnessed. The weight of their exile lightened the smallest bit.

They were a modest, ill-fitting troop dropped in the great, desolate wasteland known as the Great Plains, which stretched through the territories in all directions, with hardly a soul per square mile in population. It was still commonly referred to as the Great American Desert — a desert of the senses most certainly if not of the land. The vastness all around dwarfed its inhabitants. The wind was a constant that varied from breeze to gale, wicking away every drop of moisture and replacing it with dust. From the ramshackle, mud-spattered little fort one looked out on . . . emptiness . . . a maddening, gloomy landscape in its lack of feature. In every direction were gently undulating mounds of grass that changed from green to gold to gray as the seasons passed. The only objects above a man's height were the thirsty cottonwoods that huddled the reed-choked, stingy rivers.

The sky made up for the land's neglect, blooming in crimsons and yellows in the

morning, turning all shades of blue during the day until the very deepest hue, settling down to greens and purples at dusk. The moon rode high in the dark lead of night and gave one the sensation of a boat at sea. Libbie herself felt cut adrift, removed from all she had known, waves of land locking her in place.

Almost as soon as they were installed at the forlorn Fort Riley outpost, Autie was called away to Washington, and he claimed he could not afford the additional expense of taking her with him. Then began a series of letters describing his being wined and dined, enjoying the company of famous and wealthy women. He postponed his return for the ostensible reason of seeking advancement within the military, or alternatively, securing a more lucrative position outside it. The Kansas assignment had been a great blow and accounted for his many silences. Still, his prolonged absence made Libbie a prey to doubt.

Did he regret marrying so quickly, just on the cusp of the possibilities his fame offered? His effect was no less in New York City and the capital than it had been in poor, provincial Monroe. Although the War was now two years past, his status as hero

still had the power to charm heiresses and actresses. He always dressed in his self-styled uniform that had irked so many and now was thought to be dashing. The cavalier. An affectation, but he continued to wear it through the streets and into the parlors of New York. He understood more than anyone the ebbing tide of fame, knew that the more time passed, the less bright his star shone. Libbie's loneliness spurred unkind thoughts of his character.

He reveled in his conquests, eagerly sharing them in his letters to her, just as he had shared his earlier liaisons with Fanny. Did he not understand a woman's heart? Especially hers, riddled with insecurity? Or did he purposely ignite her jealousy? At an exclusive party, he met a baroness wearing such a low-cut gown that he wrote he had not *seen such sights since I was weaned.* Another night he and a group of male friends flirted with *nymphes du pave.* In the same breath, he assured her it was all done in fun and never did he forget his husbandly duties of faithfulness. Libbie was forced into the part of fool.

Alone at night, she was serenaded by howling bands of coyotes. The wives were instructed to never leave the fort unescorted for fear of Indian attack, so what could have

been unimaginable physical freedom instead became confinement. The only liberty she took in her isolation was to loosen her hated corset so that it barely changed her natural waistline. Surely she didn't need to follow the rigorous standards of New York or even Monroe out in the middle of the plains, with no one to watch or care? She wouldn't bother tightening back up until Autie came home.

The hours crawled along in a series of halfhearted efforts at self-improvement — reading inspiring tracts, painting vignettes, including one of a dog smoking a pipe as a present for Autie's return, knitting a misshapen sweater that her peacock of a husband would refuse to wear and quickly give away. She consoled herself that within a few years she would have the care of a family to distract her.

His absence lengthened, and she spent the spring without him. Then he wrote that he would be yet another month, saying that time hung heavily while he waited on the decisions of Very Important Men. In the meantime he distracted himself with operas and plays, late-night dinners. A drawing in a fashionable New York magazine showed him at a costume ball, dressed as the devil with two of their mutual women friends as

his consorts. Libbie thought the costume fitting, then chastised herself for the uncharitable notion. She felt much the country mouse and was on her way to turning into a shrew. What really did being the belle of Monroe amount to? Jealousy was eating away at her.

The last straw was when he began to escort a famous singer about town. He spoke of going backstage during performances at her request. She would leave the door only a few inches open as she dressed, but still he caught *occasional glimpses of a beautifully turned leg encased in purple tights.*

Life on the Kansas prairie proved an enervating combination of boredom and terror. That year the papers were full of the lurid details of a massacre that had occurred at Fort Buford in Dakota Territory. Indians had overwhelmed the garrison and butchered every white person there, soldiers and civilians alike. The part that especially haunted the women was that the commander of the fort, a Colonel Rankin, had shot his wife to prevent her capture. Even as Libbie longed for Autie's protection, she wondered if she might need fear it instead. The implications of the story hung heavily on all of them until a month later the news-

papers announced the even more shocking news that it had been only a false rumor, and that the fort and its occupants, including the colonel's poor wife, were all safe. But the damage had been done to her peace of mind.

Libbie made the acquaintance of many gentlemen who arrived at the post as officers of the 7th, and either stayed on or moved to even more isolated forts. Entertainments became essential to everyone's sanity, and as distraction she set her energy on organizing them. Dinner parties were arranged. In the background there was always Eliza's disapproving presence — her loyalty was to Autie, and she had a puritanical idea of a wife's duties — but Libbie ignored her. She led a crowd who spent long nights singing and dancing in the parlor.

One particular officer became a great friend. Thomas towered above the other men, sporting a big square face and the most fantastic of mustaches. He would take the wives out riding when they could no longer stand their restriction.

Alcohol was the great scourge of frontier life, and a bottle regularly kept Thomas company. It was his only failing. She counseled him to give it up, undergo conversion as Autie had, yet he only smiled at her,

changing the subject to a new amusement, knowing how easily she could be distracted. He especially liked to tempt her with the excuse of dances.

Libbie now became quite the flirt. She was surprised how she enjoyed it, both the pleasure it gave to the days and how it took the sting from Autie's neglect. With the protection of a wedding ring, she could be more bold than she'd ever dared as an eligible young lady.

She conquered her loneliness in this way, even as Autie's letters grew more passionate with the many months of separation, his suspicions mounting as he read between the lines of her letters, which commensurately grew more spare. Sensing their coolness, he chided her and reminded her of their infamous coach ride in Texas, how the window somehow broke. She wrote back that she'd quite forgotten. He was clever to remind her of their secret life, rocking in the saddle each morning as sunlight streamed down on their bed, bare flesh against white sheets. He owned her soul yet he did not know what to do with it. Autie was all about the chase and so she would pretend to run.

Urging her to join him at last, he wrote in their special language that he wanted

something much, very much better and be sure you bring *it* along. I am entirely out at present and have been so long as to forget how it tastes.

Letters months old that freshened at the moment of rereading quickened her pulse.

Thomas's eyes studied her as she folded the incendiary letters away. She sent Eliza to her room for the night. The girl's eyes flickered over the two before she left.

"You're flushed," he said, accusing when they were alone.

She would never belong to another man. Why had Autie delayed so long inviting her?

"I'm going to my husband."

The prairie wind howled ceaselessly, bending the grasses, bending the will of them all. Yet she had grown a liking for it over the last months. She had been weaned, developed a hunger for the chalky bite of freedom — the most irresistible elixir once one developed a taste for it. She loved Autie, but also what was beyond him, the whole untamed world out there in its infinite liberty.

She walked between houses to go visiting the other women, and the wind raised her skirt to reveal petticoats. She grabbed them down, but not before Thomas's eyes were

on her, thirsty, as if she were the whiskey in his bottle. She waited an extra moment, too long for propriety, blood on fire, and then let the cloth slip through her fingertips to fly free again. Only after Autie returned did she sew lead weights in the hems like the other good wives.

THE FIFTH REMOVE

Buffalo hunt — Attack —
The horse god is watching over us

It was the time of the buffalo hunt. Anne went out with other women to do the butchering and skinning. They sat and watched the warriors make preparation to attack the herd. One warrior was singled out and given the honor to ride first and take the first shot. Anne sat with the women as they cheered. The shot landed but did not disable. The enraged buffalo went running after the source of the attack, and with a hook of horns knocked the man off his mount. The horse ran a short distance and then stopped, waiting for his rider to mount again, when the buffalo turned and began to make another run for the man. The women screamed. The other warriors were too far away to be of help, when suddenly the horse was in motion, running between

the warrior and the buffalo. When the horse reached the beast, he used his teeth and bit its ear off. The buffalo shrieked as the horse reared up and hit him with his front hooves. Anne disbelieved her eyes as the two animals circled each other and fought. Finally the buffalo went under the rearing horse and dug a horn into his abdomen, ending his life. In the meantime the man had time to make his escape.

The main body of warriors surrounded the wounded bull and quickly dispatched him. Afterward, they cut off the head of the horse and took it also, hanging it in a place of honor in the camp as reminder of the animal's unusual loyalty. This proved to the people that they were looked after by the Great Spirit. The times were so difficult, they were in need of such assurance.

THE SIXTH REMOVE

Famine — Attack by the cavalry —
Fleeing —
The oasis — The birth of a daughter

Tribal life was defined by constant movement. In the early fall of Anne's second year in captivity there was much suffering from lack of food. The chiefs held council and discussed the incursions of settlers into their territory for illegal hunting, as well as the disruption caused by the hated trains that frightened the herds and sent them off course. What it meant in practice was that the tribe must travel farther and farther for less and less food.

With the new scarcity, the women complained about the hard pace and lack of provisions, especially hard on the children. Feeling despondent over her future, Anne dragged her steps, and this led to cuffs on the head or a switch taken to the back of

her legs. En route, horses and dogs died of starvation, their bodies immediately butchered and eaten, but it was never enough to satisfy too many empty bellies. In such a state of scarcity, feeding a captive was resented, and Anne worried that she would be killed.

A few times in the last weeks she had delivered requested items of clothing and been refused the agreed-upon item for barter, mostly food. When she protested, she was threatened with bodily harm. Captives had no redress to a higher power within the tribe. Anne had grown more bold and willing to defend herself within the camp, but with her unborn baby's safety to worry about she backed down from insisting on payment. She could be cheated with impunity while a theft by her would be punishable. In desperation she resorted to stealing bits of food although the penalty could well be death.

One old grandmother, Unci, observed her dilemma and invited Anne to her teepee for a mouthful of whatever she cooked that day. She was a medicine woman, much respected in the tribe.

Anne's prized possession was a blanket given from the chief in condolence for the passing of Elizabeth, and this she gifted the

old woman. Eerily the woman was aware of the source of the blanket.

"The child thanks you for being her mother in her need."

Anne grew pale.

"She is gone."

Unci spread her arms to encompass the entire camp.

"She is here. Your life is not yours alone any longer," she said, pointing to Anne's large belly. "You are now a part of the Cheyenne. You must keep your eyes open to find your place."

Unci described how, while she nursed her first child, a young orphaned bear cub came into camp. The men drove him away, but he returned each day, weaker. She could not stand his suffering and decided to give the cub her own milk. The moment the milk touched his lips the animal revived, and she realized it had been a test. She suddenly had the gift of strong medicine and visions.

Anne did not know what to make of such statements, whether the woman dreamed, or she herself had simply not understood the nuance of their language.

"I was at Sand Creek," Unci continued. "The soldiers sliced open my belly, but I lived."

Unci lifted her deerskin shirt and showed

a mass of ugly red scar tissue covering her stomach.

"I understood it was the price for my medicine. You are paying a high price, also. Someday you will go back to your people, and you will tell them to leave the Cheyenne in peace."

"No one would care what a girl says."

Unci nodded. "I was afraid this was true."

In Anne's early days of captivity she had refused the raw meat doled out during the butchering process of any animal, but now in her expectant state she waited hungrily and even begged for such morsels. When she got lucky to win some, she forced herself to eat the bloody meat and organs raw in the native fashion, not willing to risk the delay of cooking, which might attract attention and thievery. Often as not she would gag and throw up the meat, it not being suited to her digestion.

During this time of debilitation in the tribe, Anne was awakened one morning to find the camp in great panic. Wolves reported seeing a large contingent of the U.S. Army pursuing their trail. It was the 7th Cavalry, led by Yellow Hair, as he was known to the Indians. The mention of his name lent urgency to their escape, because

he was known to be relentless in his pursuit, and difficult to lose because he employed native scouts.

Anne felt sure that they referred to General Custer, a hero often mentioned by her father. He had seen the general while serving in the Union army, although he never fought under the great man. The Boy General was reputed to be so handsome with his long curling golden locks that women swooned in front of him. Her mother used to tease her father that if she had met the general first she might have married him.

The Indian camp hurriedly broke up into smaller units, scattering in each direction of the compass to throw the army off. Anne's heart drummed hard in her chest at the possibility that she might be delivered from her ordeal. If she was forgotten in the chaos she might be able to slip away. To her disappointment a warrior was assigned to watch her, as the tribe knew it would rest harder on them if the army discovered they harbored captives. If her group was captured, she would be killed by the warrior, and her body either thrown in the river or buried deep in the earth.

Their teepee joined four others and made its way across a barren plain devoid of vegetation. They carried dried meat but had

had no time to fill skins with water. The heat was excruciating. Many days Anne tasted hardly a mouthful of food, and she fretted about the health of her baby. Neha split her meager rations, urging her to take it for the unborn's sake.

Thirst almost drove Anne to madness. She observed the Indians' method of taking a big drink of water in the morning before moving out, then placing a small stick in their mouth to chew on during the ride. Miraculously it slackened thirst. It angered her that they saw her struggle and yet made no attempt at instructing her in survival.

She lashed out at Neha.

"How could you not know something so obvious?" Neha answered. "I cannot guess what you do not know."

One evening as they rested against a series of large boulders, each as big as a house, the wolves came running in, announcing an attack was imminent. The warriors mounted and rode off, directing the women and children to hide in the rocks.

Anne could hear the gunshots and considered running out to her deliverers, although in the murk of battle she was as frightened of the soldiers' bullets as of the warriors'. What if the army mistook her for an Indian in her native clothing and her sun-darkened

skin? Even within the tribe she traveled in, there were many with lighter skin that betokened white blood in their veins. Would her being with child make the soldiers recoil? By the same token, the Indians might well shoot her fleeing form for treachery, especially since she carried Snake Man's child away with her. So she made the only choice it seemed possible to make — she hid with her oppressors.

The warriors had ridden off in the opposite direction to lead the army away and buy the women and children time to make their escape. When they returned hours later they forecast that the soldiers would figure out their error and be back by morning. The camp dared not rest even a few hours but only stopped to chew on some dried corn and then took flight again. The ponies were exhausted and walked gingerly along the dimly lit caliche plain. The tribe's best chance was to go into the heart of the most inhospitable country and outlast the army.

The moon was new, the starlight faint, and the horses stumbled on stones and in holes dug by desert creatures. In her condition, Anne was allowed to ride a pony while the others walked to alleviate the strain on the animals, but eventually her horse seemed to be doing a kind of drunken sideways stag-

ger. Worried that he might fall and roll over on her, she chose to dismount and walk. She put her hands underneath her stomach and tried to hold her belly still to avoid the pain of motion. Although as a girl she had witnessed women's lying-in, she did not know the particulars of what to expect and longed for the help of her mother.

Such a crippled caravan could have been overcome easily, but wolves reported that the cavalry instead made a lengthy stop at their abandoned camp and commenced to burn it down to the last bit. In that delay the Indians and Anne made their escape.

Days later, when the various branches of the tribe reunited, it was discovered that one group had not been as lucky as the others. Yellow Hair had gone in one direction; another commander went in the opposite. This captain had come upon fleeing Cheyenne consisting mostly of old people, women, and children. Only a small number of warriors were there to guard their flight. The soldiers opened fire and killed the warriors immediately. When the helpless hid in the rocks, refusing to surrender, they were all gunned down with no attempt to take them prisoner. Not only that, the bodies were scalped and some of the women defiled. Anne pondered over the veracity of

these stories. How could her own people act in such a barbarous fashion?

After a few particularly grueling hours of flight, Ann lay down on the hard ground and refused to get up, even at the threat of bodily harm. Finally one of the warriors handed off his weapons and allowed her to lean on his shoulder, and in such manner they made slow progress.

A more solid darkness replaced the black of night. Almost sleeping on her feet, Anne just missed walking into a wall of solid stone. Only the jerk on her arm by the warrior saved her serious collision. The path ahead narrowed and sloped downward, the hard earth gradually replaced by soft sand. Anne felt anxious, but the warriors appeared sure of the way.

The coolness of the air near the rock revived her. She held out a hand to trace her way along the wall, able to let go of her guardian's supporting shoulder. Although she could barely discern the human and animal shapes moving ahead of her, there was a feeling of constriction after the days and nights spent out in the wide open. She had no way to gauge the elevation, but bent her head back and looked up the height of four men to discern the midnight sky against

the surrounding rock walls. She felt entombed. They were descending into a kind of vaporous Hades, the cool air now growing moist, and over the thud of feet and hooves, she could make out the sweet sound of trickling water.

After a time, the men at the head of the line lit brush torches, and the walls turned a burnished copper as the passage widened again and disgorged the group into a small amphitheater, surrounded on all sides by high limestone parapets. The bottom was sandy, and a gentle stream ran through it. Tender grasses grew along its edges, and the ponies hungrily set to graze even before their bridles and saddles could be removed. Women and children collapsed where they stood, asleep almost before their heads touched the earth. The men sat and smoked a pipe before posting sentries and themselves resting. Not until morning did the women pitch teepees and start small, smokeless cooking fires.

As Anne sat drowsy in the morning light, a deer came out of the mist to drink along the stream and eat the succulent grasses. Before she could understand what had happened, the animal stumbled and fell on its side, an arrow poking out of its ribs. None had eaten in three days, and the deer was

cut up quickly. Inside the abdominal cavity they found the fetus of a fawn. All of it was put on the fire to cook. The women gave Anne a boiled piece of the fawn as big as her hand, a delicacy so tender they instructed that she should eat the bones as well as the meat and skin. In the past year she had eaten bear, frog, squirrel, and skunk in her captivity, besides boiled bones, roots, and tree bark, learning to be content with whatever was on offer. Her famished state made fastidiousness shy, although she still refused the great nourishment of drinking deer's blood, of which the others partook.

In their much depleted state it was decided they should remain in their rock fortress while the cavalry, having lost their track, moved farther and farther away. Anne found the cloistered location strangely comforting, the cool shade of the walls blocking off any view except the heavens directly overhead, which calmed her and directed her thoughts upward. Neha and she were allowed to wander the mazelike walls and found remnants of previous occupations, from the petrified remains of campfires to animal skeletons, either brought for slaughter or strayed in to die in solitude. The place had much the aspect of a natural cathedral, a refuge for man and beast away from the

relentless, devouring wilderness outside.

The weathered scrawlings of figures on walls resembled ones she had seen inside the teepees of her chiefs, which recorded the important victories of the tribe. In addition to warriors, horses, and buffalo, here were pictures of the vanished tribe's enemy, the white man, in both known and unknown uniforms. Curious, Anne looked for the evidence of captives, especially women, although she was unsure that she wanted to find it. There was none. Such persons were not deemed worthy of including in history.

Against the outermost walls were crude structures of mud and clay over wattle, with low barrier walls of stone. Ducking her head inside one such shelter she found a room feral and untamed, a veritable bear's den. In the tarry, dusty corner used as fire pit, she found a hammered silver frame holding a small cameo painting of the Virgin. Neha watched the tears come to Anne's eyes.

"Is this your God?"

"Not mine. But the Holy Mother."

Next to it was the tooled metal of a foreign helmet, much rusted.

She picked up both, amazed by the fine workmanship, which far surpassed any items that had been in her own family's possession. She knew from schoolbooks of the

Spanish conquistadors, who ultimately had been defeated by both the Indians and the land. She believed the two relics were signs: the first showing that Providence promised her eventual freedom, and the second pointing to the folly of the white man thinking he would conquer a land so cruelly indifferent to all human effort. The Indian, as far as she could tell, was the only race that could endure for any period the inhospitable clime, yet even for them the price paid was to remain in a perpetual state of vulnerability and want, abject and slave to capricious nature.

Ann slipped the palm-sized icon into her inner pocket, feeling its papist protection was as close as she could come to a Bible, heresy as such a thought would be to her family. Trying to win favor, she presented the antique helmet to Snake Man, who looked at it skeptically but slipped it on his head.

He had hardly spoken a sentence to her other than to give orders, but now he spoke over her head to a crevice in the rock wall behind her.

"Years ago with the Comanche we were attacked by the Texan soldiers. The chief was a very brave man. He rode in front of his warriors and stopped in clear view of

the enemy. No one understood why he was so fearless. He was killed immediately. When they pulled off his heavy robe, they discovered he wore the breastplate of a Spanish suit. One made like this hat. He thought by wearing it he would be as invincible as the white man. Ever since, I have known the white medicine does not work for us."

He threw off the helmet and spit in the dirt.

That night while Anne sat by the fire she felt a deep drag in her belly. The women indicated it was not yet time for the baby so she tried to ignore the insistent tugging, concentrating instead on the crescent of moon which rose silver in the narrow gap of sky, mixing with the rock walls lit copper from the fires. She fingered the icon in her pocket, longing to take it out and take comfort in it, yet knowing that it would excite the covetousness of the wives. Whatever came into her possession, they wished to take away, either stealing it for themselves or destroying it to demoralize her.

Had the owner of the icon forgotten it on his journey? Or, more ominously, had this unknowingly become his final resting place where he succumbed, sequestered in this foreign rock sarcophagus? The Spaniards

had been washed away from this country with only a few buildings and names to recall their ever having conquered it. She did not understand the confidence of her own people in thinking they would last better. She thought of her family's fate, thriving one moment, annihilated the next, and now her own desperate and tenuous condition.

Just then she felt an especially painful tug as if a small animal was trapped inside her and trying to claw its way out. A gush of warmth spread between her legs. When she let out a gasp, Neha looked at her alarmed.

In the midst of hiding and flight, a woman going through parturition was not a welcome burden. The men moved off impatiently and explained that on no account was she allowed to make any noise. Anne let Neha and the women lead her back to the wattle hut in which she had found the icon.

They set about making the sparse accommodation suit as well as was possible. One bundled sticks to sweep out the most offending debris, including animal bones. Neha started a flame in the ancient fire pit to ward off the damp, and laid down a buffalo robe for her comfort. Another went scavenging, returning with cut poles, which

she hammered into the floor next to Anne. She was made to understand that she should grip these during her pains. A knotted cotton cloth was given her to bite down on. Outside, two pits were dug. A woman heated water in one, ladled from the stream with the helmet that the chief had tossed away. The other pit was readied to bury the afterbirth. Once all was ready, the women settled down to smoke a pipe and spend long hours in storytelling. Neha, noticing Anne's cracked lips, rubbed hot fat on them. The act brought tears, Anne being so unused to tenderness of any sort.

The birth was a difficult one that lasted through the long night and the whole of the next day before a daughter was born. She gave her the name Solace to commemorate the loss of her dear Elizabeth.

Anne had not considered what a child might mean to her status within the community, but when she looked down into the eyes of her firstborn, she realized that everything must change. In earnest she began her plans for escape, no longer content to remain mired in apathy and despair, much less passive hope for release by death. The small face suckling at her breast had become her reason to live.

During the birthing process, the women

took off her deerskin dress. Anne tossed and turned in her only remaining garment from civilization, her cotton shift with the pocket that held the Virgin. In a spasm of pain, she had rolled over, and the icon had fallen out onto the buffalo robe. While Neha watched, one of the wives snatched it up, looked at it briefly, and tossed it into the fire.

Toward the aborigines of the country no one can indulge a more friendly feeling than myself, or would go further to reclaim them from their wandering habits and make them a happy, prosperous people . . . Humanity has often wept over the fate of the aborigines of this country . . . To follow to the tomb the last of his race and to tread on the graves of extinct nations excite melancholy reflections. But true philanthropy reconciles the mind to these vicissitudes as it does to the extinction of one generation of people to make room for another. In the monuments and fortresses of an unknown people, spread over the extensive regions of the West, we behold the memorials of a once powerful race, which was exterminated or has disappeared to make room for the existing savage tribes . . . What good man would prefer a country covered with forests and ranged by a few thousand savages to our extensive Republic, studded with cities, towns, and prosperous farms . . . and filled with all the blessings of liberty, civilization, and religion? . . . Doubtless it will be painful to leave the graves of their fathers; but what do they more than our ancestors did or than our children are now doing? To better their condition in an unknown land

our forefathers left all that was dear in earthly objects . . . Can it be cruel in this Government when, by events which it can not control, the Indian is made discontented in his ancient home, to purchase his lands, to give him a new and extensive territory, to pay the expense of his removal, and support him a year in his new abode? How many thousands of our own people would gladly embrace the opportunity of removing to the West on such conditions!

— PRESIDENT ANDREW JACKSON, "CASE FOR THE INDIAN REMOVAL ACT," DECEMBER 1830

The evil, Sir, is enormous; the inevitable suffering incalculable. Do not stain the fair fame of the country . . . Nations of dependent Indians, against their will, under color of law, are driven from their homes into the wilderness. You cannot explain it; you cannot reason it away . . . Our friends will view this measure with sorrow, and our enemies alone with joy. And we ourselves, Sir, when the interests and passions of the day are past, shall look back upon it, I fear, with self-reproach, and a regret as bitter as unavailing.

— EDWARD EVERETT,
SPEECHES ON THE PASSAGE OF THE BILL
FOR THE REMOVAL OF THE INDIANS
DELIVERED IN THE
CONGRESS OF THE UNITED STATES, 1830

SMOKEY HILL RIVER, 1867

Custer had strode through the war doing what he wanted, which neatly coincided with the wishes of his superiors, foremost of those being Sheridan. Now he felt the brunt of the workaday military that consisted of taking orders. Orders that more often than not were ill-considered.

As soon as he arrived in Kansas, he sensed that General Hancock did not have a grasp of the Indian situation. The tribes were suing for peace, yet Hancock niggled them with petty demands, threatened use of the army against them. How could anyone be won over in such manner? When depredations against settlers occurred, he did not see the obvious, that it was the work of a limited number of young warriors. Instead, he blamed the chiefs for not controlling their men.

Hancock had demanded a parley in a village, but when the army got there the

Indians had fled, obviously scared to have soldiers near their women and children after Chivington's massacre at Sand Creek in Colorado Territory. His response was to burn down the village and send Custer to hunt them down.

Custer chased up one hill and down another, the Indians always managing to stay out of sight. When moving targets were sighted on the horizon, the distance made it difficult to guess the threat. A native scout taught Custer the method of setting up two sticks and sighting over both to see if there was movement. Most often it was simply creosote bushes or boulders that in the mirage appeared to gain motion. Less frequently it would be a pack of lost mules or donkeys. The skeletons of these littered the prairie. Least often of all would appear Indians. Even when his cavalry did trap Indians, they protested they were on their way to a reservation.

— Are you peaceable?

— We are friends.

He guessed they would say the same even as they commenced to separate his scalp from his head.

Orders were to attack nonreservation Indians, but they were hard to find. After a

time, any Indians would do. Frontier people screamed for revenge, and Sherman wanted results.

Rumors spread about the Fetterman massacre the previous winter in Wyoming Territory, and it put fear in all. Eighty men dead. There were dark whispers that Fetterman, a war hero, and Captain Brown committed suicide by shooting each other at the moment of capture. It was the worst defeat in army history.

Custer drove his regiment hard, riding day and night, covering twenty-five miles of territory a day. The land was deceptive in its aspect: choked ravines, dead-end tabletop bluffs, landmarks that appeared to be only a mile away in reality taking ten miles to reach. The uniform terrain, on closer inspection, was gouged by deep ravines that could hide either a whole regiment or an entire Cheyenne war party.

Reduced to using the north star to lead them, his seasoned guides were like compasses with a broken north, regularly leading them astray.

It was a great relief when at last they reached the river and set up camp — the horses put out to graze on tender green grass, the men able to wash for the first time

in days. Teamsters rolled in with their wagons, and cooks started fires with the comforting smells of coffee and food. The night sky swung overhead like a great, dark, twisting carousel.

He knew no such contentment as camp after a long day's ride, the reward of tent and camaraderie. It put Custer in mind of his war days. He looked up and down the tented streets, the canvas glowing from the light within, reminding him of Chinamen's lanterns. If ever he mustered out of the army he would spend his summer nights sleeping in a tent under the stars, even if it must be in his own backyard.

He'd taught Libbie the joys of sleeping outdoors and believed she loved it almost as much as he. If only she was with him now, he'd feel more himself. In her letters it was clear her torment at their separations weighed on her.

The Cavalry's newest assignment was to police the stagecoach routes. In the middle of the night he'd sent a veteran officer of the territory with a troop from the west end of camp to determine their exact location on the river vis-à-vis the nearest station they were charged to guard.

Custer was dreaming he was still riding in

the saddle, the dream so sharp it was interchangeable with being awake, when a shot went off from the pickets.

— Indians!

Shapes could be seen in the murky distance of near dawn. Mounted warriors appeared spectral and nightmarish in war dress. The shriek of battle cries terrified his men unseasoned to the sound.

Dry throats. Soldiers raced to corral the remuda inside the wagon circle to prevent stampede. The Indians' first tactic was to steal the enemy's horses. Rifles loaded, the soldiers formed a skirmish line.

Ponies approached.

A lookout reported a group of eighty warriors. Custer's cavalry far outnumbered them so he held back for a closer target, knowing his soldiers' fingers itched.

The enemy lined up along a ridge, creating a magnificent, pagan phalanx. Custer had not felt such a thrill since he faced a line of Confederates. He recognized it was one of the finest and most imposing displays he'd witnessed: brilliant war bonnets, painted horses, lances, bows and arrows bedecked. Painted faces fierce as the devil. Riders so practiced they seemed a mythical manhorse beast. Worthy opponent indeed.

The sky lightened, though a heavy mist

still obscured the scene. His soldiers ached to fight.

The foremost line of ponies halted. Riders parleyed then withdrew to a bluff. Those behind turned and moved farther away.

The camp as a single entity let out a breath of relief, leavened with scorn. They grumbled about the "Injun reveille."

— Can't let us civilized sleep?

Custer cursed his own caution, and recognized he'd been bested. More important, he knew the reports he'd received were all wrong. The Indian was a canny fighter, and the army had some catching up to do if it hoped to win.

An hour later the heavy fog carried the sound of running horses on the east side of camp. A trick? Was the retreat a ruse to attack them unprepared?

Soldiers rushed to rearm only to discover they were being attacked by their own — the veteran's troop sent out the night before. They had drawn their guns as they galloped through the camp, thinking it an Indian one. They had mistaken their own corralled horses for ponies, Custer's conical Sibley tent for an Indian lodge, certain that they had headed in a straight line toward the overland trail several miles away, the land having tricked even a veteran tracker

of the area. The troop had inadvertently circumscribed a half circle and arrived at the other end of camp, the fog hiding the camp's true aspect until they landed inside it, the head of the column ready to eat its own tail.

After the initial confusion, great hilarity rose among the soldiers at the mistake. Diplomatically, Custer commended the attacking party's bravery at aggressing against an unknown and much larger camp in order to subdue it. Their mistake, he advised, was in not knowing the lay of the land and the size of the camp before charging. So unlike the chary Indians earlier who had reconnoitered and left. He omitted the likely fact that if the Indians had attacked they would now be dead, as would his misguided troop had the camp been foe instead of friend. Despite his ill-applied courageousness, this gray-haired veteran of many successful campaigns had to endure being remonikered He Who Rides in a Circle to Kiss His Own Arse, and his legend followed him for the next few years until he died at Summit Springs, Colorado, fighting against the Cheyenne.

Unsuccessful in their scout to look for camps, the column limped into Fort Hays.

There Custer discovered that Hancock, the harsh "father" to the Indians, had let himself be bamboozled by the oily-speaking Kiowa chief Satanta. He'd gone as far as to let the chief sup at his table. So infatuated was Hancock, he'd gifted the Kiowa with the uniform jacket of a major general, complete with sash and plumed hat, regalia soldiers had to work long and hard to earn the right to wear.

Mere weeks later, Satanta led a war party that attacked a nearby fort, stealing army horses while wearing his military booty. He had the courtesy to tip said plumed hat at his enemy and waggle his uniformed backside at them as he made off.

This was an enemy unlike that of the War. Custer felt sure that his superiors lacked sufficient knowledge of their adversary to successfully defeat them. He would remedy that to his own advantage.

He knew the Indians felt cheated because the government had not kept its treaty promises. Not enough annuities of food, clothing, ammunition, or guns had been issued over the winter when most needed. The presence of surveyors also had the tribes in an uproar. Surveyors meant railroads, meant fewer buffalo, meant starvation. The only item in surplus for the

Indians seemed to be whiskey, for which the young warriors had a great affinity, and peddlers managed to find their way through the most dangerous of territories to supply it. If only he could find soldiers as brave.

As his troops waited at Fort Hays for their own supplies, which were long in coming, they watched the cold rain beat down on the flat, iron-hard land without relenting. After days it had liquefied to a sticking muck that hindered the men and horses to the extent that they were discouraged from heading back out.

Custer was impatient at the inactivity, the lost momentum, and the strain of being separated from his Libbie. Everything had happened so fast during the Rebellion, constant battles and skirmishes, and during the rare lulls the distance between Virginia and Washington was short enough to be easily closed to see her.

At a stop on another thousand-mile surveil on the Platte River, he got a letter from Sheridan reprimanding him for his lack of engagement with the Indians. *Don't go soft like Sully and Hancock. I need my fighter. That's what I brought you here for.*

His orders were to continue policing stage stations, farms, and rivers, ridding them of hostiles.

What that meant in fact was long rides accomplished either in the rain or the heat or the wind or some unholy alliance of all three guaranteed to wear down both man and beast. Horses regularly dropped from exhaustion or starvation. No Indians took up residence at the locations reported, so by the time the troop arrived they found only fired houses and mutilated civilians. Not an Indian in sight.

Sometimes they arrived upon great gouged fields that indicated campgrounds recently abandoned, fields scratched by travois poles. Nearby fields shorn of grass by grazing herds. Sometimes they would find a lone teepee erected, a dead old woman inside, and they would wonder at the callousness of such a people. These sightings inspired fear, conjecture, mystery, as if they spoke of ancient beasts long disappeared from the face of the earth and not flesh-and-blood men such as themselves.

In his disgust at noncontact, Custer blamed the men, who in truth were for the most part happy to miss an encounter with the enemy. They marched with only the goal of their next meal. Their pay was paltry and used up on dearly priced alcohol as a palliative against the abuses of the march and their commander. The only thing that would

hold them together was battle, and for all Custer's efforts he could not scrounge them up one.

While camped along the Platte seven soldiers deserted on the strongest horses and another five walked out in plain sight of the command. They were headed for higher pay mining gold, unheard-of mutiny that if continued in such dangerous territory might end the whole troop. The army's only safety lay in its numbers. Official orders were to shoot deserters, and Custer made sure both officers and enlisted knew this. Now he gave the order to bring the deserters back dead or alive. The horsemen got away. The others were brought in, three wounded, one of whom died later that day. As far as Custer was concerned, the deserters had only themselves to blame.

Unlike the grief he'd experienced over each soldier's death during the War, writing a separate letter to each family, Custer didn't spill tears over this callow fellow. How was he supposed to fight with such apathetic talent? Among the Indians there was no such thing as desertion — those were the kind of men he should be leading — and these cowards could chew on that. There was a definite shift in his men's sympathies away from him, but he knew

that would be corrected later in battle.

Marching through the monotonous distances, what Custer would not have given to lie under the shade of even a single tree. Instead he laid his head under prairie milkweed, coneflower, and goldenrod. He could hardly remember the verdant forests of Virginia; they seemed to belong to someone else's life. In his current existence, all had turned stunted.

At times he wondered at this great hunger of conquest. The isolation of the plains was a terrible thing. It threw one back on oneself, and some men found themselves sorely failing the trial.

When the cavalry came upon a farmstead, the people were unused to society. They hunched against the wind and turned partly away. The leather-skinned men stood with legs squared apart, as if expecting the next blow of bad news. Their women, worn haggard by endless work, ran to fetch cups and spoons. The children, shy with the wobbly look of colts, stood silent and enthralled. Men in uniform were heroes. Custer recognized these people as his own, bludgeoned by the drear sameness of such a hard life. He felt sucked back into his past.

Custer's father had been town blacksmith

while he saved for years to buy a farm. Their big, always hungry, happy family could have been these settlers. He had been so determined to escape such a fate, but how far from it was he really? Tom, too, followed the call of adventure. The Custer boys were not meant to bend knee to the land. He knew the Plains tribes felt the same way and that the peace agreement, with its intention to turn them away from hunting and fighting to a life of agriculture, was a doomed one.

Permission was asked and granted to water at one particular homestead's well. The woman of the house offered the officers weak grain coffee, which they gladly accepted. Custer's hand shook as he reached for a cup, and he steadied it with the other. Out back could be found the small, mounded graves of departed children. It was not a life to which he wanted to subject his Libbie. Conversation centered on the ravages inflicted by the Indians in that part of the state, the cattle stampeded, the houses set afire, the neighbors killed. The army was there to deliver them from such scourges.

At another homestead, a man had his oldest daughter serve homemade bread with blackberry jam while he told of the mother's

abduction months back. She had traveled with neighbors to the nearest town for provisions. Their wagon was attacked. Some were killed, others taken captive. The daughter had tears in her eyes as the father voiced the commonplace that he sincerely hoped his beloved had gone to join the Lord.

All the land south of the Arkansas [River] belongs to the Kiowa and Comanche, and I don't want to give away any of it. I love the land and the buffalo and will not part with it. . . . I want the children raised as I was.

I have heard that you want to settle us on a reservation near the mountains. I don't want to settle. I love to roam over the prairies. There I feel free and happy, but when I settle down I grow pale and die.

A long time ago this land belonged to our fathers; but when I go upriver I see camps of soldiers on its banks. These soldiers cut down my timber; they kill my buffalo; and when I see that, it feels as if my heart would burst with sorrow.

— SATANTA, KIOWA CHIEF, SPEECH GIVEN IN 1867 DURING THE MEDICINE LODGE TREATY NEGOTIATIONS

LIBBIE

The separations were unbearable, but the reunions divine. When Autie at last returned, it was not to a tearful wife but to one with newfound vigor. She was thriving despite the harsh environment, like a flowering weed springing up in the most arid of soils. They settled into a period of marital bliss.

Nothing in her surroundings had changed. The accommodations were just as problematic. The wind blew as fiercely, lodging gritty dust in every corner of the house, in clothes, hair, eyes, and ears. Eliza complained that dirt even got into her cooking. Yet when Autie was there it was the difference between a gloomy, rainy day and a bright, sunny one.

Libbie felt guilty that her great happiness came at the expense of his. The obscurity of his present circumstances grated on him, led to his periods of silence, but now he

threw himself into consolations such as his hunting and taxidermy. He became a more attentive husband. They would lie abed late in the mornings to tickle, the dogs lying all around and on the bed, until Eliza brought a breakfast tray, *tsk, tsking* at the muddy paw prints on the sheets, and they were forced to behave. Those were honey-filled days.

When at last Tom's transfer to the 7th came through, Autie's happiness expanded because he was never so happy as when roughhousing and playing pranks with his brother, and then it was like having two unruly boys in the house. Their favorite game was "romps," chasing each other through the house playing tag. Tom created barricades between the rooms with furniture — he would stack the dining room chairs chest high in the doorway between the kitchen and dining room, then slide the table between the study and hallway. Eliza would be irate at the chaos and threaten to quit, and Libbie would retire to her bedroom and close the door, a signal that she was *off limits.*

Often, furious crashing sounds downstairs would be followed by thunder up the staircase, and the door would burst open to admit two grown men, cannonballing onto

the bed, dogs in hot pursuit. The three would lie there in silence, she in the middle determinedly reading her book, Tom and Autie on each side, breathing hard from their exertions, the dogs falling asleep, paws trembling in dreams of hunting. This was the happiness of family, one new to her. True, there was the usual shuffling of pride between siblings, but there was also deep love and respect between the brothers. They each knew the other's weaknesses, poked each other mercilessly for it, but were loath to admit any defect to the larger world.

Autie thrived on activity, not a natural condition on such a remote outpost, so Libbie made sure there were always people around. Regularly she invited single young ladies from Monroe to stay with them, in this way enticing Autie not to take flight back east again. The females were a natural lure to get the bachelor officers to come often for dinner, and it created the necessary frisson of social interaction. They all stayed up late at night playing the piano and singing. Dances were arranged. Many of the women returned from such a visit engaged. In the light of normal life, the girls were often mystified at their choice of romantic partner, claiming they had been enchanted by the extraordinary surroundings, and

called the nuptials off. Frequently, Tom stayed out courting, once prompting Autie to send a suitcase to the young lady's front door. Autie and Libbie hoped for a sister-in-law to materialize from these outings, but it never came to pass.

On the rare days when the wind died down and the temperature was tolerable, they took great pleasure in organizing riding parties for picnics. They traveled in a group of twenty or more, there being safety in numbers. Alongside these brave soldiers, Libbie felt brave, too.

Autie always rode far in front, restless and alert. He loved to race, and so challenged, she raced.

"First one to the bluff gets pie, the other gets nothing!"

They were off, their horses neck to neck. Autie never said it, but she knew he was impressed at her daring. The truth was Libbie was terrified and exhilarated in equal measure. After the novelty of racing wore off, his next favorite trick was to lean over and lift her out of the saddle as she rode. All she could do was hold on to her horse's reins and pray. One time he lifted her clear over to sit in his lap as the horses raced in tandem. There was no description of what it was like to be suspended above the

thundering hooves. One wrong move, she could have been trampled, but he held her as if she were his own life, so steady she gladly accepted whatever befell her. When they reined in and returned to the picnic, the company cheered and said they might get jobs in the California rodeo when their military days were done.

After one such picnic they returned late and collapsed into their bed. A young lady from Monroe was staying with them for the summer. Her room was the guest bedroom by the stairs. Autie mumbled something about getting a glass of warm milk and not to stay up. Libbie fell back asleep, waking hours later to a still empty bed.

She worried. A childhood habit that had strengthened in adulthood, she always imagined calamity in those days, and so put on her shawl and opened the bedroom door. There was Autie in his nightshirt coming out of the guest bedroom. Libbie thought she must be dreaming until after him the girl came to stand in the doorway. Naked. The golden glow of the candle cast light on her figure — long golden hair that fell to her waist, full milk-white breasts, and rounded thighs — so that she resembled the marble statues of Venus found in books.

When Autie reached out his hand and laid his fingers on her hip, the girl must have felt something, a quickening, because she lifted his hand to her lips.

Libbie stood transfixed, sickened. Her world slowly wobbled, teetered, threatening to break into a thousand pieces, her bold choice of husband a failure, raising the possibility that she might return to Monroe in humiliation. Refusing to go back to her old life, she slowly walked forward. When the girl saw her she gasped, covering between her legs with one hand, across her breasts with the other. Libbie went to Autie like a sleepwalker, raised her hand, and stroked his cheek. She came closer and kissed his lips. Then she moved to the stairs.

"I'm going to heat up the milk. Will you join me?"

The next day the whole fort readied for another picnic. They started out early with a site by the river as their destination, an area sheltered by cottonwoods and the rarity of lush green grass, from proximity to water. When they reached camp the mules were quickly unpacked and the cooks started fires. Libbie directed that blankets be laid out under the trees. Groups of men and women promenaded up and down the

banks of the river, and Libbie thought the scene compared to the idyllic resorts of the east coast.

Her Monroe friend avoided Autie and Libbie both, so nervous she circled around the large group without alighting on any individual. The poor thing probably waited for an avowal of intentions from Autie that would not be forthcoming. As was his habit, he slept in the grass under a tree, surrounded by his dogs, oblivious to the turmoil he had unleashed. The whole long day Libbie watched the two carefully. They refused to acknowledge each other, until she could almost convince herself that the night before had been only a fevered dream.

The day was a perfect one, a cool breeze tempering the hot sun, the grass fresh and moist in the shade so that they lingered well past lunch. Several of the men shared a flask of whiskey back and forth. Some had had the foresight to bring fishing poles and were making use of them. A group of women sat together and sang songs. It was a bucolic setting marred only by the presence of her erstwhile friend.

When Tom went to approach the lady, Libbie called him back. She hissed at him to stay away. His amusement turned to dismay. Since he was a Custer, he guessed

her reason. Showing his loyalty, he stayed by Libbie's side and rendered the lady in question invisible. Tom would prove himself loyal time and again in future years. Not for the first time did Libbie wonder if she had married the right brother.

Perhaps the girl sensed how quickly sentiment could turn in such a tight-knit community. A few of the other bachelor officers gallantly offered to walk with her, one in particular an aristocratic young man from New York with a narrow face and fine blond hair. Giddy over escaping her exile, she used the pretext of gathering wildflowers to distance herself from the group.

When the sun began to cast shadows, they gathered their things to begin the long ride home. Libbie was searching for Eliza to give her instructions when she heard a curious popping sound. Not until she saw the reaction of the men did she realize it was the sound of gunfire. In the large space it sounded toylike and harmless. Without more warning they saw through the trees a Cheyenne hunting party. The Indians raced at them full speed on their ponies, and the women ran, clustering in a group around some boulders while two soldiers watched over them. The rest of the men ran for their weapons and horses. Tom led the repulse.

Libbie was so frightened she buried her head in her hands and refused to look. The sound of gunfire quickly diminished. Once the soldiers were mounted, the two parties were evenly matched, and the Indians retreated. Autie explained that Indians pursued only when they had the clear advantage.

The men were ordered to stay in place and not pursue as there were too many women to leave alone. That's when Libbie heard the scream from her Monroe friend. She pointed as one of the remaining Indians, mounted on a particularly fine horse, came from behind the rocks. In their panic they had not noticed one of their number was missing — the aristocratic young officer from New York. They could see him lying in the grass with an arrow sticking out of his back. When the rider came up beside the fallen man, he leaned down as casually as picking a flower and with preternatural strength lifted the young man across his lap.

Libbie marveled at her thinking in that moment — she could only blame it on an imagination fed on too many serials — that the warrior would deliver the man to their care. This turned out to be far from his intention. What happened next took her years to reconcile. The officer wasn't dead.

Faint moans could be heard from him. The warrior rode back and forth in front of the party as he casually took out a knife and cut away the soldier's scalp. Even that was not the end. He then used a tomahawk and proceeded to smash the poor man's head.

Her Monroe friend got sick in the bushes. After three more passes, it was clear that the young man had mercifully passed, and then the Indian shifted him off his knee like a skinned animal and let the body fall to the ground. The hunting party left in a gale of war cries the memory of which made Libbie light-headed with terror.

They rode home in the silent dusk, stunned, subdued. Rifles ready, the soldiers rode on each side of the women, who were corralled in between, and even a rabbit would not have been safe crossing their path.

In her months spent on the plains so far she had yet to take their task on the frontier seriously. It had seemed a grand adventure, but there in front of her slung over a mule traveled the body for whom the posting had been a final one. Someone who that morning ate breakfast, planned on flirting with a pretty girl, and looked forward to a long life. It was a reminder of their tenuous position lest they forget. This early incident

formed the fabric of Libbie's life in the years that followed: constant, rational dread.

Early next morning at the fort, her Monroe friend was already packed and moved out. Although the plan had been for her to stay on through the summer months, she had a sudden change of intention no one cared to probe. At the sutler's where she waited for the mail train, she bade a frosty goodbye although Libbie remained cordial as could be. Something had changed in the girl's eye, something unhinged by the events she had witnessed. She disappeared from their life with the train. Autie made excuses of work as the reason he could not come see her off. At the very least Libbie hoped that he realized he had chosen rightly in a wife.

Upon suffering beyond suffering: the Red Nation shall rise again and it shall be a blessing for a sick world. A world filled with broken promises, selfishness, and separations. A world longing for light again. I see a time of Seven Generations when all the colors of mankind will gather under the Sacred Tree of Life and the whole Earth will become one circle again. In that day, there will be those among the Lakota who will carry knowledge and understanding of unity among all living things and the young white ones will come to those of my people and ask for this wisdom. I salute the light within your eyes where the whole Universe dwells. For when you are at that center within you and I am that place within me, we shall be one.

— CRAZY HORSE

THE SEVENTH REMOVE

Delay — Presentation of the child — Against the Crow

No opportunities for escape presented themselves after the birth of her daughter. Through the winter, she remained in a weakened state from her confinement and did not recover as quickly as she should have. A new mother was given no privilege of rest or increased food in the native culture. As a captive, Anne was treated exactly as she had been before, albeit now she had the added care of a baby.

After the child had survived to a month old, she was presented to Snake Man and his wives during a feast day. The chief chucked Solace under the chin but after that took little interest in the babe. He did insist that Anne again sleep inside the teepee, where he visited her nightly. Luckily, due to her poor health, she did not conceive the

whole following year.

Neha had gone for the winter to visit her father's tribe, and although Anne had begged to accompany her, such privileges were not given to a captive. The wives would not want to do without her labor. Anne was bereft without her company.

During the third year of her captivity the tribe covered twice the distance as the previous year in search of buffalo. The women lagged and complained that the pace was too arduous for the young and the old.

In the fourth year they traveled equally far but were not even rewarded with adequate hunting. They were reduced to scavenging nuts and berries, and the future held no promise of their lot improving.

On one particularly difficult journey, the grandmother of one of the chiefs, a woman so bowed and wrinkled as to appear beyond age, sat down roughly and dropped the sack she carried. The women around her stopped and urged her on, one even willing to shoulder her sack. The old woman would not yield.

Camp was made early, and a lodge erected specially for the old woman. The women cooked her dinner, and then sat with her all night telling stories of past exploits in which

she had figured. Anne was touched by their solicitousness, thinking it reflected well on them. In the morning they stored the food from the night before, along with dried meat, pemmican, nuts, and gourds of water, in the lodge, along with a supply of firewood. They exited, packed up, and readied to resume the trek.

Anne was stricken, realizing they meant to leave the old woman behind. The previous night's kindness had been a leave-taking. The cruelty stung her, more so because it had been done to one of their own. Anne crawled into the tent with the woman.

"Come, I will help you walk."

The woman would not meet Anne's eyes.

"Go, daughter."

"Then I will stay."

"I am going to the beyond country. It is not your time."

Anne stood outside, bawling, when a young warrior came up behind and gave her a hard kick. Her reactions shamed not only the family but the whole tribe. Her tears were judgment. This private necessity of survival was accepted by both the old woman and the family, by everyone except a stranger.

As was their custom, the chiefs met in

council and decided to solve the problem of scarcity by going to war against the adjoining Crow tribe and taking over the hunting lands they possessed. The territory had been ceded in a battle against the Sioux so long ago that only the eldest of the tribe could recall its legend from their childhoods. The area was so vast it could not be ridden across from sunrise to sunset, and the game on it was enough to again make the tribe fat.

The village operated at a feverish pace for days in celebratory preparation: warriors cleaned and sharpened their weapons; women prepared food to carry in case of a prolonged battle; horses and warriors were painted for strong medicine and bravery. The tribe was a warrior society, and this activity gave it life. In spite of herself, Anne was drawn into the excitement. The yearning for greatness among the young men matched that of young men back home. The warriors wheeled fearlessly around on their horses.

As was always the danger, the delay for preparation allowed the enemy to learn of the coming attack and take the offensive.

She woke to the high-pitched war cries of enemy Crow riding through their village and

shooting guns. Warriors quickly sprang to action and overcame the invading force. A half-dozen enemy fighters were killed; the survivors fled to regroup with a party waiting in the hills. While the women packed to retreat, the warriors prepared to counterattack.

Anne watched one old grandfather hurriedly paint his face. With difficulty he dressed himself in skins and needed help to climb onto his horse's back.

"He is too old," she said to Neha.

Neha shrugged. "In the old days, when the men became weak they would go to war. It is not so necessary now, but some still choose battle. They do not want to burden their families."

The grandfather did not return, and there was great mourning over his bravery after his passing.

The Cheyenne warriors followed the Crow back to the main enemy camp. Thinking themselves safe, the Crow had lodged along a river to repair from the rout they had suffered. When warriors appeared on the bluffs, crouching along the necks of their horses and draping themselves in buffalo robes, the disguise worked so well that a dozen Crow jumped on their horses for this easy target. The Crow were halfway to their

enemy when they realized their mistake, and by then it was too late. The fight would go down in legend, proving the cunning of the Cheyenne.

Back in the village, warriors went about torturing the enemy Crow prisoners left behind. The attack had breached the rules of warfare: why had they not simply counted coup instead of killing? Instead they had intended carnage, fighting as the white man, with as little mercy. The Crow had learned bad ways.

Anne was horrified by the hilarity and carnival atmosphere with which they went about the punishment. While one prisoner was still alive, they made a puncture in his abdomen and pulled out his intestines, unspooling them to wrap him around a small sapling tree. As he fainted they set brush and logs around his feet then roasted him alive. Unfortunately for him, he revived in time to understand his fate. His cries most certainly haunted his friends in the hills.

When the victorious warriors rejoined the tribe, they were proud and yelled in triumph at their victory over the Crow, yet it was clear that their numbers were diminished. As each family learned of its loss, anguished cries rose up. Anne was astonished at the severity of their mourning given how they

cherished warfare. Women cut off their hair in rough chunks. Both men and women made ritual gashes on their bodies to express their grief. Many painted their faces black, which combined with their bloodied bodies rendered the scene into a hellish vision.

Runs Swiftly, the brother of Snake Man, lost a grown son. He slashed his own arms and legs so severely he almost died from loss of blood. When warriors returned to him the bones of his son, he put up a special tent and set the bones inside it. Each day he had his wife bring a clay bowl filled with all the dishes prepared that day. He set the bowl outside the tent flap. Runs Swiftly spent each day sitting beside it, explaining to passersby that his son was sleeping inside, recovering from his wounds.

"When he wakes he must eat to gain his strength."

As Anne passed by, he stopped her.

"Child, my son needs fresh water."

Anne was confused, but the old man seemed so sorrowful she went along with his wishes. She brought a container of fresh water from the river and placed it by the food.

"Sit with me," Runs Swiftly said.

So she sat, enjoying the small respite from her duties. She flinched when one of her

chief's wives spotted her, afraid she would be beaten, but they dared not anger him.

At the end of the night when Runs Swiftly fell asleep by the campfire, exhausted by his vigil, Anne devoured the food and drank down the water.

The next morning, the grieving father seemed comforted by this evidence that his dreams were true. He demanded his wife bring another filled bowl. The woman suspected what was going on but did not dare upset her deranged husband.

No one begrudged Anne the food because it was clearly cursed, and she would suffer for it. At least she would suffer fat, she reasoned.

One night Runs Swiftly awoke as she was finishing the food. He stared into the fire without comment. Anne was unsure how much he understood of what had happened to his son and did not dare apologize.

"My son is a very brave warrior."

"I have heard."

"It was enough in the old days to be brave. I do not think it is enough any longer."

"No."

"He knows you are hungry and shares his food."

There was no reply that Anne could make to that.

She recalled the terrible days after the loss of her own family. Such self-torture as the Indians practiced might have been a relief, matching her turmoil inside. Or perhaps it would have been better to live in delusion as Runs Swiftly. Her only relief then had been to repeat her prayers, yet how bloodless and pallid a mourning that seemed by comparison.

Let them kill, skin, and sell until the buffalo is exterminated, as it is the only way to bring lasting peace and allow civilization to advance. —GENERAL PHILIP SHERIDAN

KANSAS, JULY 1867

The Cavalry were supposed to go out on campaign in the spring to protect the nascent railroads, but nature decided otherwise. In April the storm of the century descended so severely that the canvas of the tents hard-froze, water in buckets went solid, and Custer allowed his horse into his tent for fear of the poor beast expiring. Thankfully Libbie wasn't there to hear of it. She would think him going soft in the head.

Ferries full of supplies were encased on iced rivers. Their first major crossing over the Republican turned disaster. Then, with a warm spell, bridges were destroyed by the ramrod, swift-moving ice. Trains and wagons throughout the region became waterbound over a month.

Sent out to avenge attacks, Custer met with failure after failure. He gave chase yet never caught up. When he spotted a band, he pursued and learned his disadvantage.

The Indian ponies were faster and had greater stamina. They outdistanced the troops easily. Following a camp, the enemy quickly branched off into smaller and smaller groups, like a river dividing into tributaries, until the army ended up chasing a ghost. Not knowing which branch to follow, Custer pursued the largest until it petered to nothing. One time he lost the trail of more than a hundred warriors in such manner.

He had not experienced failure in the War of the Rebellion, and it did not sit well with him now. All he wanted was to go home and be with Libbie, his only remaining comfort. He had spent too much time away. He was losing the memory of her scent.

A reporter was assigned to accompany them and write articles about "the long-haired hero of Shenandoah" now on the plains, making the land safe for civilization. He readily sensed the reporter's disappointment with his changed demeanor. The soldiers' complaints of him had also colored the man's opinion. The men criticized he was too hard. Wrote one:

He keeps himself aloof and spends his time in excogitating, annoying, vexatious, and useless orders which visit us like the

swarm of evils from Pandora's box, small, numberless, and disagreeable.

When he at last read the treacherous newspaper months later the article claimed he was not the same leader he had been during the War. He flew into a black rage, deciding to ban future reporters unless they were proven loyal.

He was determined to work his way out of this purgatory. The rub of it for officers who had served during the War was that their rank dropped when entering the regular army from the volunteers. There were simply too many generals and not enough troops after the government mustered them out. The key to success would be to understand the Indians. The nomadic life they followed greatly resembled that of a cavalryman, a life Custer loved beyond all others.

The peace advocate Black Kettle admitted to not being able to control his young men. Warriors were still routinely murdering settlers and wreaking havoc. The only way for them to gain power was to make war, and so they clamored for it, just as Custer's only way to rise had been through his War. The native elders, secure in their status, tried to quiet the younger generation

and counseled an end to fighting. With age one could not help but fall into wisdom (he hoped the same for himself someday), and here wisdom was clear that the Indians were doomed for anything other than accommodation. If they managed to survive such a peace was another question.

Custer was of the hope that once introduced to the boons of civilization, they would embrace it and thus spare themselves extinction. The larger body of plainsmen — officials, ranchers, settlers — on the other hand, did not want to bother with the effort of salvation and instead would shuttle the natives immediately to history.

Diplomacy was needed for peace to be lasting. One of the main obstacles was the barrier of language. Most half-breed translators knew only their own tribe's language and the most basic English. Custer suspected much strife was due to poor translation or outright lies. Determined to learn as much as he could of the tribal languages himself, he would start with Cheyenne.

Custer and Libbie were having dinner when his favorite scout, Frank Gerard, asked to speak with him. A young Cheyenne man recently had gotten into a scuffle with the chief of his tribe and decided to leave. He was volunteering to scout. Should they

recruit him?

Golden Buffalo had gone into the mountains and fasted, looking for a sign for what he should do next. In a dream, he saw a military officer with long blond hair, and understood that he was to go live with him and learn the white ways in order to better advise his own people. He'd spent time with a trapper and learned a fair bit of English, had even written in a journal.

Custer looked bemused, not quite trusting the story, but ordered the young man to come in. The Indian was slight compared with the average warrior. He had dressed in a fighting breechclout and full war paint for the interview despite the implied hostility of such dress. Libbie blanched.

— What kind of fighter is he? Custer asked.

Gerard translated but Golden Buffalo answered directly.

— I am the best warrior in the tribe. The chief fears me because I earn more coup than any other.

Custer burst out laughing.

— Me too! Are you loyal? You are here consorting with the enemy.

— To those loyal to me, I am loyal. My leaders are blind. I see the future.

Custer stood up to look imposing, but

Libbie could tell he was holding in a laugh for all he was worth at the young man's preening.

— I know what I'll teach you. What will you do for me?

Golden Buffalo got effusive. He moved around the room with vigor, then came right up to Custer's face and yelled.

— I will teach you to find the Sioux. I will teach you to fight like the Indian. So you won't be slaughtered like dogs.

— Can you teach me to speak Cheyenne? Sioux?

— If your head is big enough to fit it.

Custer guffawed and clapped his hands, enjoying Golden Buffalo's braggadocio.

— Wash off that paint and put some military issue on. Welcome to the U.S. Cavalry.

Later, as insurance policy, Custer had one of his men steal the journal from Golden Buffalo's belongings and bring it to him. Only a few pages had been filled out. He read:

Stories tell a people's source. Their meaning is beyond the words used or the cleverness of the teller. They mean more than the truthfulness of the story. They are the people's beating heart.

I was born from the pairing of a buffalo and a tawny wolf. That is how the Cheyenne explained that I grew up Cheyenne but something different was inside me. The different thing was my father's Sioux blood.

We were asleep. Then the war came to us. I was a fifteen-year-old boy in my mother's tent the day Chivington came to our village on Sand Creek. Chief Black Kettle tied the American flag to his lodge pole, convinced by the promises of white men sympathetic to his cause that it would provide good medicine and prevent the soldiers from harming us . . .

Captain Soule refused to give the order to his men to fire. He saw my mother was wounded and took her to hide behind his men. Her leg was shattered, and he helped me to find a doctor to give her aid. My mother did not like their medicine and tore it off. The medicine man put earth on her wounds and she died of gangrene. Captain Soule testified against Chivington, and was shot shortly after in Denver. Some said it was in revenge.

At their first meeting Golden Buffalo came into Custer's study and promptly folded himself to sit on the floor. Favorably

impressed with the cleanness of his features, the straightness of his back, his confidence, Custer plopped on the floor opposite him.

— You like life here? he asked.

— It is fine. The barrack food is good.

— The food is abominable! I'll have Eliza let you sup in our kitchen.

— This is generous.

— This is bribery. So what are my first Cheyenne words?

Golden Buffalo thought. He put his hands on his chest.

— I am *Tsitsistas.* Cheyenne.

— *Tsitsistas.*

— Yes.

— What do you call me? The white man?

Golden Buffalo's face grew serious. He put his palm hard on Custer's chest.

— *Ve'ho'e.* White man. Trickster.

— Oh.

— *Motsé'eóeve.* Sweet Medicine. It is a sacred name.

Golden Buffalo nodded. He proceeded with an indecipherable spill of language. His eyes welled at one point, and Custer looked away as one did when another's pain is not understood. The Indians did not equate tears and crying with weakness.

— It is our tribe's prophecy. It is why I am here.

— Tell me.

— A person is going to come to the *Tsit-sistas*. He will be all sewed up [in clothing], nowhere will he not be sewed up, this person who is going to come to us. He is going to destroy for us everything that we used to depend on, he is going to destroy everything . . . And this one who is going to come to us will take over all the land throughout the world.

Silence lay between them long after Golden Buffalo finished his story.

Custer sighed and then asked — You believe this?

— It is ordained. I am here to find out if it is the white man. If it is you. Maybe I can learn your ways to save my people.

— But you said it was ordained.

— It is ordained that I try to stop it, even if I fail.

— You might . . . shoot me to do this.

Golden Buffalo looked aggrieved.

Custer assumed the young man intended to betray him at some point. Ever confident, he believed he would turn the young soul around before that time.

They rode in searing dryness, no water for the horses for days, before finally arriving at the Republican River when nature capri-

ciously decided to rain nonstop for a week. Custer sat out on the muddy plains immobilized. In their exhaustion, the men slept on saddle blankets and covered themselves with rubber ponchos against the rain, wrapped up like small leathery bats, some going so far as to cover their faces. In horror he blinked, seeing again the fields after battle during the War, bodies shrouded and collected in such manner for burial. This seemed a too-literal example of the parable that life was simply a preparation, a dress rehearsal, for death. He thought he would soon go mad.

He noticed Golden Buffalo on his periphery as the Indian mingled with the soldiers, earning their good will. He made sure the boy had a full uniform and a sound mount. Many nights they ate together in his tent, and as his store of language increased, he tried to explain things to the boy. When he described the War of the Rebellion, Golden Buffalo was shaken for days, not able to comprehend the size of such carnage. A friendship was developing.

Mail delivery became erratic, so his roaming thoughts over a week poured out to Libbie in thirty- to forty-page ramblings, convincing her that he must have turned

madman. When her letters arrived he snatched them hungrily and went off to savor the words like a dog with a prized morsel. The paper was scented with her Florida Water.

Her words were melancholy over their separation, although as time passed they grew more distanced. Some of the more recent ones described entertainments to while away the time. One particular officer's name kept recurring, her high opinion of whom he did not approve. He wrote back counseling caution, omitting mention of a letter he'd received hinting that she was creating a scandal with said officer. Instead he chided her for the perceived coolness of her letters. *Has my gurl already forgotten her beau?*

Even Tom complained over the paltriness of Libbie's communications. He said in a petulant tone that he was done with her if she didn't improve. Tom and he were like two starved tomcats waiting at the back door for a scrap of her affection.

Custer wrote a letter begging Libbie to join the wagon train of supplies for his camp, despite the path being considered rife with the possibility of Indian attack. He included a shopping list of personal supplies he lacked: one hundred pounds of but-

ter; cans of lard; any vegetables she might scrounge, including potatoes and onions. This delivery missed its recipient, and instead he received a letter that she waited for his signal to join him at another fort. More Indian raids stopped the mails altogether and then there were only silent imaginings.

Finally a rescue mission broke the malaise Custer struggled under. He felt his old energy marshal itself riding out in search of Lieutenant Kidder, sent from Fort Sedgwick with the 2nd Cavalry to deliver orders and reinforce them. The time to have met had long passed. Each day diminished the chances that the escort remained alive and unmolested. Custer pressed to cover as much area as possible. The horses were ridden till they were racks of bones. Rather than galvanized by the urgency of the search, his men were made sullen by the proximity to danger. They moved charily, doing no more than necessary to avoid reprimand. They looked without wanting to find.

His solution was to drive them harder.

Tom came to him in his tent.

— So, brother, there's grumbling in the ranks.

— Who?

Tom shook his head.

— You know I won't tell you. Maybe we should turn back for supplies. Hungry men don't fight well.

— Neither do cowards.

Tom looked away, took a deep breath.

— You'll lose their loyalty.

— That's enough, Captain.

Tom stood up to leave.

— Aren't you staying for dinner? Custer asked.

Tom shook his head again, put on his hat.

— Something in here made me lose my appetite.

The rain stopped, and the sun again scorched.

In the saddle for hours, over unyielding ground, the horses stumbling over their own tired feet, Custer spotted great black birds circling the yellow sky. Ill omen. He knew what it portended, and a great melancholy invaded his bones. In the way of such things, he felt relief that now the worst had come, he could face it and go on.

They were riding up a gravel gorge following the heavy trail leading to Fort Wallace when they saw an object far ahead. Slowing to a walk, they approached to

discover the shot carcass of a cavalry horse. Two miles farther, they came upon a second. The guide read the land and told its story: shod hoofprints from the missing party were joined by new pony tracks from the sides — the entire party had been forced off the path and down the slope of the valley.

The men's faces turned long and glum. He felt himself wobbling inside, his stomach knotted as if it could turn itself inside out. They climbed to a plateau, following the frenzied hoofprints, then made a gradual descent into a shallow valley where there was an unmistakable stench. The reek of battlefields. Deep, intimate, and mysterious death itself. He could not be sick or show fear in front of the men so he straightened his back, spurred his horse, and joined the advance guides.

Tom rode up beside him, ghostly despite his sunburn.

— You were right to push us on. Poor souls.

Custer nodded.

— You're a good officer. The men like you. Matter is, great men don't need to be liked.

It was petty to rub it in, but he did.

Officers and scouts spread out like spokes of a wheel through the rushes and willows

that led to a small stream. One of the guides gave a shout and all moved in his direction. Custer felt the same numbness descend on him as during the War when he walked the battlefields and witnessed the utter waste, the same whether in victory or defeat. The bodies lay in a small circle they had formed to protect themselves. Mounds of empty cartridge shells gave testimony to how desperate was the fight to avoid such an end.

All had been scalped, the skulls crushed. The one Indian guide, Red Bead, had been scalped, too, but the prize thrown down next to him. It was a mark of disgust at the treachery of turning on one's own. This pointed to the perpetrators being Sioux, led most likely by Pawnee Killer. Custer noticed that Golden Buffalo spent special long minutes examining the Indian and possibly contemplating his own future in the white man's employ.

The bodies lay in beds of ashes, tortured by fire, stripped of clothes that had been carried off. Noses and ears had been hacked off. Bristling with arrows, most were pierced twenty times or more. Sinews of arms and legs were cut away, a defacing by every imaginable method. Eyes torn out and laid on rocks. Teeth chopped out.

Custer's recourse was to fall back on

protocol. He ordered an official identification of each soldier. A mass grave was dug. He walked down to the stream, where he sat heavily, silent until his adjutant approached to ask final instructions. His hands trembled so badly he pressed them between his knees to still them. He stood up, stiff, determined to say the right words, to consign the bodies to the earth with dignity. First, though, he washed his hands in the stream and then, dissatisfied, went to his saddlebag for soap and brush. He scrubbed harder, until the skin was raw and abraded, but it made no difference. At last he quit. Inside him there was dread of the haunting to come.

Feeling a coolness at his neck, he turned to see Golden Buffalo watching him. Just at that moment he could not talk to the young man.

Even if it meant resigning his command, he would find a way to his Libbie, no matter the cost.

Golden Buffalo

Golden Buffalo dreamed things that were true but of which he had no understanding. This would be his way in life, holding visions in his mind until he found their meaning in the world, fitting them together like the broken shards of a pot.

The hunting had been bad for many years, the tribe growing poorer and weaker with each passing season. He decided to take himself off to the top of a ridge and seek guidance. The only way to enter the spirit world was to break the body, so he slashed his chest until it ran red. Although it was the height of summer, he brought no water, no food. He simply laid himself out on the rocky ground and stared at the sun until it blinded him. Inside and out.

After three days a vision came to him. He saw white people in numbers far greater than the largest Indian camp he'd ever known. So many people that he walked

through them for days and did not come to their end. He understood that his experience of the world was too small to understand what he saw. They crowded in narrow canyons created by more buildings than he'd ever imagined possible. He guessed that this was only one among hundreds of such villages of the white man, all of which could be emptied out to fight against the Indian.

He saw his people's futility in fighting such numbers, such rapaciousness. It was as useless as killing off coyotes. More would always come. They trailed out of their villages like ants looking for food, in their wagons and trains, because like the ant they were always busy with hunger. What did they want with the empty land? he wondered. Why did they enjoy shooting the buffalo when they had no use for its meat? Then he knew.

Long valleys covered with the lifeless bodies of buffalo, almost as many buffalo dead as there were white people, but these would not be replaced. The great bodies looked sorrowful — naked of skin or tongue or horn. The buffalo soul was shamed by this treatment and would disappear from the earth. The prophecy had started. The white man would destroy the Creator of All.

The long valley had snakes crossing it, snakes that turned out to be railroads and fences of wire, heralding the end of the great migration of both buffalo and Indians. It would be as if the sun in the sky was stuck in place and could not move the day forward. Fences of wire would impale the bodies of buffalo and men.

A mother buffalo and her calf ran through the great hilly fields, she smashing through the barbed-wire fence as if it were grass, trailing strands behind her even as the barbs embedded themselves in her flesh, partly tearing it away, red muscle showing, great ropes of blood flying off her as she ran. The calf by her side was drenched in his mother's blood, his eyes white-rimmed in fear. Then to Golden Buffalo's astonishment the mother ran over a cliff, her calf following behind.

The shock woke him from his dream, and he lay there bathed in sweat even though it was still early morning and the sun had not risen. His heart was fit to bursting. He sorrowed for the unborn future. It was a dream from which he would never entirely awake, that would haunt his daily life. The only thing he could do was to go to the heart of the enemy, learn his ways, and try to use that knowledge to save what was left.

LIBBIE

Autie came to her against all advice, against all reason, accused of abandoning his command, riding his horses to exhaustion, taking a night train, and thus almost ending his career in court-martial. He came like a little boy seeking comfort, a sinner seeking salvation. He came as an angry lover, infuriated over a slight. Perhaps in jealousy at false rumors over a certain officer. Maybe Libbie was a silly, vain woman for being gratified that he risked all for that *one long, perfect day* they spent together. He redeemed himself after his neglect of her. He was then quickly placed under arrest.

During the court-martial it became evident that he had created enemies among the officers who were outraged at his perceived ill-treatment of his soldiers. There was the perception that he no longer had the fire in his belly to pursue Indians. Why else abuse his men on such marches, only

to abandon them to run off to his wife?

Even to her, he seemed changed.

A vulnerability was in him, one she had first noted during the War. It had started in camp one night in Virginia. She found him in his tent, where he was bent over a washbasin, soaping his hands and furiously using a hard brush on his fingertips until they bled. When she came to him, he held up his hands as if under arrest, claiming grime under the nails. She assured him it was not so and put him to bed.

The search and then the grim discovery of the Kidder party had shaken him, a man who had seen thousands die during the Rebellion. They buried the mutilated remains and pushed on to Fort Wallace, exhausted, demoralized, only to find that base under siege from constant attacks, the supply line stopped, and food low. Provisions consisted of rotten bacon and hard bread. An outbreak of cholera struck down the weakened men.

Although the men were spent, something had to be done. He picked out seventy-five of the strongest horses and pushed on to Fort Harker for supplies. At the court-martial much was made of the brutal pace of the ride, but the select detachment rode through dangerous territory in a weakened

state. The shorter the period out, the better the outcome. They covered 150 miles in fifty-five hours of hard riding to Fort Hays. A smaller group covered another 60 miles without change of animals in twelve hours to Fort Harker.

She received long, frantic letters during this period, sometimes thirty pages or more, sections written only hours apart, complaining of his need and longing for her. *Last night the thought flashed through my brain that if ever I lost you, no other woman could or ever should reawaken it. You are irrevocably my first, my present, and my last love.* He said her letters back to him were more important than food or even air.

Autie's strength was being in motion, no hesitation, minimal reflection after making a decision. That was his greatness as a cavalry leader. His job done, he boarded a train in the middle of the night without leave to reach Libbie. That was when it happened, the perfect day that would make up for all the others, that assured her that she was the love of his life despite everything. She swore to him that she would never do anything to fan his jealousy again. The only sad thing was that the day had to end. *It was mine, and — blessed be our memory, which preserves to us the joys as well as the*

sadness of life! — it is still mine, for time and eternity.

Married life had turned her into a bit of a contrarian. More often than not she had found that the rosiest picture was run through with veins of gray. Undiluted satisfaction was almost an alien condition to the human mind, and conversely the bleakest hour could usually be mined for its thimble of gold. During and after the court-martial, they remained together, vowing to never again endure long absences, even if it meant Autie resigning his post. For a time she believed him.

Autie and Libbie both claimed that the trial was a diversion from Hancock's failures against the Indians. The charges during the court-martial were rancorous, fed by the brooding resentments that fester in the army. Sheridan supported them to the point of lending them his living quarters at Leavenworth. What especially rankled her were the accusations against Autie's character. In addition to the charges of abandoning his post, it was his response during the Indian attack at Downer's Station and subsequent treatment of the deserters that was brought into question.

Six soldiers had been sent back to find

Autie's straying horse Fanchon and found themselves attacked by a war party of fifty hostiles. Two soldiers were reported killed. During more clement times, the regiment should have gone back to bury the victims and possibly give chase, although experience forecast that the Indians would be long gone. Low on supplies and ammunition, it made no sense to risk further delay. Soldiers testified to Autie's lack of sympathy for the slain men, but emotion at this time would have wasted precious hours for a futile task, possibly endangering them all. Had Autie not just proven himself by his long, exhaustive search for the Kidder party?

Instead of being praised for his prudence, he was painted with a tar brush. At the trial, irritable, he made the further mistake of indelicately pointing out the flaw in the party's actions — to have fled instead of offering a tactical defense.

"You never run from Indians," he said, as if it should be self-evident. "They don't respect it, and they smell blood."

Such detached honesty was impolitic in the extreme of men asked to fight and die together. But Autie remembered General McClellan during the War, walking the battlefield and crying over the dead. This behavior had diminished him to his men,

and he was shortly after relieved of duty. Autie was determined to remain as tough as Sheridan, or even Sherman if need be.

He was found guilty as charged: absence without leave from his command; conduct to the prejudice of good order and military discipline; overmarching men and government horses; using public vehicles for private business; failing to care for two soldiers shot at Downer's Station; shooting deserters without trial; withholding care of wounded, resulting in one death.

The punishment was a year's suspension of rank, command, and pay. Sheridan told him it was considered a lenient sentence, account being taken of his past heroic conduct.

The months spent in Monroe were pleasant beyond words, an endless round of socializing, and the novelty of sleeping together in the same bed each night. Libbie did not like to admit that she wished the suspension would last even longer. What kind of harpy had she become, to revel in her husband's misery? She simply had found the silver lining.

Autie was pleased when, to show support, Tom came home to Monroe on leave of absence. While there, he went on his usual

rounds of the local ladies like a bee to a bed of clover. His leave finished, he returned to the army, but came back quickly at the behest of a certain lady. When he took Libbie aside, she was prepared to welcome a new sister, not for what he was about to tell her.

"With child?"

"She claims I'm the father."

"So it must be true." She struggled to not show her feeling of shock.

His face twisted for a moment. "Other women are not like you. Not as pure."

"Oh."

She had always felt an outsider to the Custer family secrets but now wished Tom had chosen Autie to share this confidence instead of her.

"I will die if I am forced to marry her."

"But —"

"Die! I say. She is nothing, *nothing* like you. Virtuous, loyal."

Libbie recognized the characteristic family theatrics in his words. She blushed.

"Then why did you court her?"

"Cruel words!"

"Perhaps Autie can talk to her —"

"You should hear the men in the regiment congratulating themselves for *not* being his brother! He jumps on me for every little

matter. They pity me."

Tom stopped in front of her chair and went down on one knee. He took her hand and placed it over his heart, which was hammering. The poor boy was in agony.

"Promise me on your life he will never learn of this."

"Oh, Tom."

"I couldn't bear his disappointment in me."

He wrapped his arms around her legs and buried his head in her lap. She felt his hot breath through the fabric. She stroked his head. The sweaty hair was fine and thin like his brother's.

"I'll talk to the lady in question. You and I will figure a course to take."

He held her face between his hands, beaming as he gave her a kiss on the lips, then jumped up, relieved, as if the difficulty were already behind him.

"Remember, I'd die of shame if it were ever found out."

On his deathbed, Libbie's father had warned her to never try to thwart Autie's ambition as a soldier, that he was born to the vocation and would be unhappy doing anything else. When the telegram came from Sheridan begging him to come back to head an

expedition against the Cheyenne, she pretended a happiness she did not remotely feel. The tearful leave-taking of kin was repeated, the packing away of most of their possessions was done once more. They would take only the most essential things because military life was not conducive to sentimentality, toward either things or people. Oblivious to it all, a euphoric Autie left in advance, taking three dogs with him, on the train back to Fort Hays.

My heart is filled with joy when I see you here today, as the brooks fill with water when the snows melt in the spring. I feel glad as the ponies do when the fresh grass starts in the beginning of the year.

My people have never first drawn a bow or fired a gun against the whites. There has been trouble between us. My young men have danced the war dance. But it was not begun by us. It was you who sent the first soldier.

Two years ago I came upon this road, following the buffalo, that my wives and children might have their cheeks plump and their bodies warm. But the soldiers fired on us. So it was upon the Canadian River. Nor have we been made to cry once only. The blue-dressed soldiers came out from the night, and for campfires they lit our lodges. Instead of hunting game they killed our braves, and the warriors of the tribe cut short their hair for the dead.

So it was in Texas. They made sorrow in our camps, and we went out like the buffalo bulls when the cows are attacked. When we found them we killed them, and their scalps hung in our lodges. The Comanches are not weak and blind, like the pups of a dog when seven days old. They are strong and far-sighted, like

grown horses. We took their road and we went on it. The white women cried and our women laughed.

But there are things that you have said to me which I do not like. They were not sweet like sugar, but bitter like gourds. You have said that you want to put us on a reservation, to build us houses and to make us medicine lodges. I do not want them. I was born under the prairie, where the wind blew free and there was nothing to break the light of the sun. I was born where there were no walls and everything drew free breath. I want to die there, not within walls. I know every stream and every wood between the Rio Grande and the Arkansas River. I have hunted and lived all over that country. I live like my fathers before me and like them I live happily.

When I was in Washington the Great Father told me that all the Comanche land was ours and that no one should hinder us from living on it. So why do you ask us to leave the rivers and the sun and the wind and live in houses? Do not tell us to give up the buffalo for the sheep. The young men hear talk of this, and it makes them sad and angry. Do not speak of it more. I love to carry out the talk I heard

from the Great Father. When I get goods and presents my people feel glad, since it shows that he holds us in his eye.

If the Texans had kept out of my country there might have been peace. But that which you say we must now live in is too small. The Texans have taken away the places where the grass grew thickest and the timber was best. Had we kept that, we might have done as you ask. But it is too late. The whites took the country which we loved, and we wish only to wander the prairie til we die.

— TEN BEARS, COMANCHE WARRIOR CHIEF, TO GENERAL WILLIAM TECUMSEH SHERMAN AT MEDICINE LODGE CREEK, KANSAS, OCTOBER 1867

Headquarters Department of the Missouri in the Field,
Fort Hays, Kansas
September 24, 1868

General G. A. Custer, Monroe, Michigan:
Generals Sherman, Sully, and myself, and nearly all the Officers of your regiment, have asked for you, and I hope the application will be successful. Can you come at once? Eleven companies of your regiment will move about the 1st of October against the hostile Indians, from Medicine Lodge creek towards the Wichita mountains.

(signed) P. H. Sheridan,
Major General Commanding

INDIAN TERRITORY, ANTELOPE HILLS, WASHITA RIVER, NOVEMBER 1868

Although those familiar with a plains winter claimed it a fool's mission, Sheridan gambled everything on the audaciousness of a winter campaign against the hostile tribes. He knew that one on one, the Indian warrior was the superior fighter, one that his conventional forces had not been able to defeat during the previous two summers. But catching them unsuspecting, burdened down by a village of women and children, ponies weakened by poor forage, he might bring a decisive victory that would have the Indians pleading to quit the warpath. What he needed to carry out the plan was a bold and fearless man, a man with something to prove, and that narrowed it down to exactly one.

Returning after nine months' enforced leave, Custer wrote to Libbie: *I experienced a home feeling here in garrison that I cannot*

find in civil life.

At Camp Supply, he drilled his new recruits for six weeks then begged Sheridan to let him go ahead of the delayed Kansas volunteer militia joining him. He feared they would hinder him in his movements. When permission was given, he readied eight hundred men to leave on the morning of a blizzard lest he waste any more time. Sheridan was gratified in his choice. *I rely everything upon you and shall send you on this expedition without giving you any orders leaving you entirely upon your judgment.*

At four in the morning, Custer paced, watching balefully as a group of officers, including Tom, lingered over their breakfast.

— Hurry, would you?

— Don't worry, brother. The snow and the Indians will still be there.

When he returned minutes later to a scene unchanged, he charged into the tent and kicked the mess table over.

— You're done now, he said, and stalked out.

The dozen Osage scouts assigned to the expedition pleased him much more. They were dressed for war, in brightly colored blankets and paint, their guns cleaned and at the ready, and they waited patiently by their groomed mounts. He could win the

plains with an army of men like these. The white scouts came over to discuss strategy for the days ahead with their counterparts. A bonus of one hundred dollars was offered for whoever led them to an Indian village first.

The troops traveled for days through one of the worst blizzards to hit the region, but it was no matter to Custer because he reasoned that, however they suffered, the hostiles would suffer the same. The key was to destroy their supplies, as they would not be able to replace them. If goaded into being peaceful, it was still the same result.

They barely made eight miles a day, the soldiers dismounting at intervals to walk in order to keep their feet from freezing. Snow balled under the horses' shod hooves, and if not regularly picked out, the animals slid, eventually going lame from the abuse. Men and animals were equally miserable.

Three days into the grueling trek they were in Indian Territory but did not find a single fresh trail. After conferring with the scouts again, Custer sent his second in command, Major Elliott, with three companies to reconnoiter the South Canadian River. Within hours a courier returned with the news that the trail of an Indian war party

had been found, estimated to consist of 150 warriors. Like a bloodhound, once Custer caught the scent of his quarry all else faded away. Cold, lack of sleep, hunger . . . all were immaterial except for how they affected his troops.

He called his officers together to give orders. The main wagon train would come at its own pace, guarded by eighty troopers with worn horses. The other eight companies would march immediately, each carrying one hundred pounds of ammunition. Seven wagons with the strongest teams would accompany them, carrying light supplies and extra ammunition. A risky exposure given the weather, but he would dare it. He noticed that Golden Buffalo had been assigned to stay with the train, and he called him up.

— You want to stay here or come with us?
— I will come.

He gave a curt nod, satisfied.

Riding all day, they didn't stop till nine at night, and then only to feed the horses and have a quick meal of coffee and hardtack. They joined back up with Elliott's troops at midnight and continued on.

Custer rode forward with the Osage scouts. Two on foot spearheaded the column. The body of the regiment was told to

stay back a half mile to avoid alerting lookouts. He worried that the sound of hundreds of feet on the crusty snow would be heard far ahead.

One of the forward scouts halted and signaled him to dismount and come look. The rest of the scouts stopped in place. A message was passed back for the main body to do likewise. The two crept to the edge of the ridge, and the Osage pointed in the darkness to a large herd of animals in the distance. He touched his nose.

— Fire.

Custer smelled nothing. He peered into the darkness, trying to ascertain if the herd was composed of buffalo or the hoped-for ponies. Elliott said the trail of the war party led straight ahead to the supposed camp.

A dog's bark echoed through the mineral air, and the Osage guide was pleased. According to him, war parties did not travel with dogs but instead left them in their village. Next, closer, they heard the tinkling of a bell, indicating a lead pony. Finally, proof incontrovertible came in the form of an infant's cry. A slumbering village lay ahead.

Custer brought his officers together and outlined the attack plan. Major Elliott and his three companies would pass behind hills, swing around, and charge upstream from

the northeast. The other eight companies would be divided up thus: Captain Thompson and two companies would cross the river, move behind bluffs, and come in from the south. Captain Myers and two companies would go into the woods, attacking from the west. He, with four companies, plus sharpshooters and scouts, would attack from the north. They must move in complete silence and in darkness. When in place they would wait, simultaneously attacking at dawn on his signal.

It was a classic battle plan learned at West Point, and he would rely on it again eight years later in the Little Bighorn valley in Montana.

—When I give the signal, I want a charge. Go *with a rush,* he said.

— General, suppose we find more Indians there than we can handle?

— *All I am afraid of is we won't find half enough. There are not Indians enough in the country to whip the Seventh Cav.*

They moved out, and then there was nothing for the companies under him to do but wait through the night as the others positioned themselves. He gave orders for absolute silence, down to removing sabers in case of clanking metal. Although they

were allowed to dismount, no walking, talking, smoking, or campfires were permitted. In the subzero temperatures, it was agony.

He saw that Golden Buffalo had now allied himself with the Osage scouts, and he went over to him. Custer knew the Osage were jumpy. They whispered among themselves of the probability that they might be traded as hostages if a pact were struck. He worried over their loyalty.

— Be careful they don't mistake you for the enemy down there. Once the fighting starts, stay back.

There was no way to overemphasize the importance of victory, but Custer knew it wasn't as clear-cut as during the War. The army was caught smack between two rocks and would likely be smashed to pieces no matter what they did. He wished for a decisive victory that would weaken Indian resolve. The goal was to have the Cheyenne and Arapaho safely on reservation land so the railroads and settlers could move unimpeded.

The problem was that the people living on the frontier were terrified by the latest depredations and demanded vengeance. The politicians and newspapers back east, safe from danger, nursed romantic notions of

259

the Indians roaming freely. There was no discussion of withdrawing from the plains, but they wanted a *humane* conquering, to turn the Indians into Christian farmers. Any student of history — Custer was making himself a fairly knowledgeable one — knew it was an impossible expectation.

Frontier perception was that the army had failed during the last years. A Kansas militia of volunteers was drummed up to ensure punishment for the latest crimes on the Saline and Solomon, as well as the captivity of two white women settlers. From Custer's point of view the problem was that the volunteers' training did not match their ambitions. He worried they would unleash another Sand Creek under his watch.

Luckily for him they had gotten lost and arrived too late to Camp Supply. Almost a thousand of their horses died from starvation on the way. Hopefully he would have the entire campaign over before they managed to catch up. Besides, if rumors were correct that this camp held the hostages Clara Blinn and her young son, their rescue would make him a national hero, and he did not need to share the spotlight.

It was common knowledge that the Medicine Lodge Treaty the previous year would be disastrous to the Plains tribes for the

simple reason that the U.S. government began breaking it almost before the ink was dry. Still, tribal leaders took the proceedings — set deep in their hunting grounds — seriously, stretching the signings over two weeks in their desire to gain some assurances for their people's future. The full import of being forced to give up their hunting grounds and traditional ways, being consigned to live at a remove on a bleak reservation, would soon be all too clear. Those who refused to sign were arrested and given nothing while their land was taken. The rub was that even those who co-operated were cheated of what they were promised. The government honored nothing, and the army had to deal with the resentment that caused. War was pre-ordained.

Dogs always followed the army, including Custer's own, but an Osage scout cautioned that a bark was the most common way Indians were alerted to army attack. Terrified that he would lose the painstaking advantage he'd worked so hard to achieve, he regretfully ordered the canines killed. For silence the animals were muzzled with rope, then stabbed or strangled. Two of his own hounds had followed, and he moved

away to not see the violence done to these loyal pets. Herculean were the sacrifices victory demanded.

After hours spent immobile in the freezing night, at last dawn lightened the horizon. The trees were like tombstones, gloomy with cold. The glow of a few teepees illuminated the darkness as fires were lit for morning. The light through buffalo hide was inviting, like sun against eyelids, illuminating dreams. Custer wished to be inside their close animal warmth, the fur smell of unshorn hide blanketing him.

Through the fog a more insistent light rose and pulsed, haloing icy motes in the air. Officers panicked, thinking this was caused by lighted arrows signaling the army's presence. Custer almost cried that the dogs had been killed for nothing, but then observed that the object was too long in its ascent for either arrow or firework. The light climbed higher and stayed aloft, freed of gravity, finally identifying itself as the morning star. It rose crystalline and remote from human concerns, golden at first and then all the colors of the rainbow. A sign, a portent of luck? He would not mention another name for the star: Lucifer, the fallen angel.

A shot rang across the village. From them

or the enemy? He wondered for the briefest minute if it could have been fired by Golden Buffalo to alert his people but dismissed the idea.

The moment of attack had shied out from under him, a skittish mount, but he regained mastery of it. He yelled the charge, told the band to strike up, but their first notes died a frozen spittle death within their instruments. Past caring, the men roared a big cheer as they charged. His overriding fear was that the village might still have somehow emptied like it had for Hancock. He nodded at his officers, spurring his horse.

— The ball has begun, gentlemen!

The hammering of iron hooves, running horses rousing the first inhabitants, who came out of teepees half undressed, rifles loaded. Within minutes the cold was forgotten. The smoke of fireearms and the screams of women and children replaced it. Orders were shouted demanding surrender, but surrender was unnatural when ordered at the end of a long gun.

Riding through the center of the village at Custer's side, Hamilton, the regimental favorite, was struck by a bullet. Grandson of one of the founding fathers of the country, Hamilton had begged and received permission to trade guard duties at the sup-

ply train in order to be part of the battle.

He was known for his fine caricatures. Good-natured, he always threw the drawings away after getting a laugh. The previous night Custer had stolen Hamilton's drawing of him and folded it away as a keepsake in his saddlebag.

Denying this claim on his mortality, Hamilton now rode carefully ahead as the blood rosetted at his back, an image not capable of being crumpled and thrown away. He slumped to the side and rolled off his horse.

A group of women and children fled the village, running down the valley as a company veered to chase them, opening fire when they refused surrender. One of the scouts and a wild-eyed Golden Buffalo hurried to Custer, asking if that was his order.

— No, not my intention. Stop them shooting!

They took off to halt the soldiers.

In ten minutes the cavalry controlled the village, gathering more than fifty women and children together as prisoners. They panicked over their fate, and he told Golden Buffalo to explain things to calm them. His troops were now being attacked by warriors from the perimeter. He ordered the troopers to hold fire as another group fled down the valley. On his own initiative, Major

Elliott pursued with a posse of nineteen soldiers.

Time moved queerly during battle.

A blur of motion, then moments of stillness and great clarity. On a small lookout point while directing the battle, Custer's attention was caught by a red-tailed hawk skying through the morning. Was it a trick of the light, its surreal beauty? The screams from the village were muffled, and fell flat like leaves to the ground, leaving no impression on the soaring bird. Custer fell deep in study of each detail of the whirling, feathered body as it rode the air currents. How small, how inconsequential from such a lofty perspective were the agonies caused by man.

An officer in great agitation reported to him that in pursuit of fleeing Indians, he'd ridden downstream.

— Far as I could see down the valley, teepees! Not only that, but warriors coming in our direction. My men barely made it back alive.

— Are you sure? You're not exaggerating?

— No, sir. And I heard shooting down in the valley. Maybe Elliott's men?

Custer shook his head.

— Myers's men went that way. Heard nothing.

■ ■ ■ ■

Custer walked the muddied village ground now mysteriously littered with the bodies of women and children — he'd given express orders to use extraordinary restraint to forbid it — in addition to warriors contorted in positions of violent death. How had it all happened with such speed? He gave orders to question the surrendered women and children to find out if the white hostages remained in camp. Indian custom was to kill captives when attacked, so the possibility was slight.

He ordered the firing of the village, razing everything that the Indians needed to survive the winter. During the War, Sherman had learned the trick of destroying an enemy's habitat and thus defeating him, and he relied on it still. Custer rationalized that depriving the enemy thus ended the violence more quickly.

Ruination of the village began at the upper end, troops tearing down lodges and using the poles as fuel, throwing goods on top. Custer was relieved when they found spoils from the murders along the Solomon and Saline, confirming that the killers had sheltered in this village. This would go far

in his report to defend the attack.

Despite his orders, the Osage had taken out their personal vengeance on their enemies. Custer saw one walk by with a scalp on his belt but knew better than to reprimand him. He would lose their loyalty thus. His favorite dog, Blucher, having somehow escaped the first slaughter, was found with an arrow stuck in his side. Weary, Custer rode out of the village to await the finish. The mopping-up part of battle never appealed to him.

The sun rested warm on his shoulders. Snow had melted along the shaded banks as if in grief. Hoarfrost sighed off tree limbs. Dismounted, he grazed his horse, laved his hands in the icy waters. Reddened by the extreme cold, still they remained unclean. The weight of the gray men on the other side of the river, their black caved-in eyes, stood in accusation, and already his Hamilton had joined them.

He turned sharply and spotted Golden Buffalo, his face so grave it could only be that he saw Custer's haunting. Or his own.

— You still with me? Custer yelled out.

Golden Buffalo nodded, but would not come closer.

The wind-scoured blue sky, the stain of dark

smoke from the burning village rifling its purity, was unconnected to him. Custer felt no absolving succor or reprieve. He knew this thing and its coming toll, how even now that same column of smoke would engender more violence from the Indians who witnessed its burning. The hecatomb of war would drive him to ground. Mortal men were not created to shoulder such burdens. Sand Creek begat the Saline and Solomon. The rape and massacre of settlers begat this holocaust morning. Did it matter if vengeance was wreaked on the right men, or were all men guilty, all men worthy of punishment, him most certainly?

When he returned to the village the adjutant informed him of a small group of warriors spotted along the bluffs. They sat mounted on ponies, joined by more even as they watched the destruction being wreaked by the army. If they had been inclined to peace before, now it could only be vengeance. Was that the meaning of the gray men?

He ordered that the prisoners be allowed to choose mounts from the herd and then the remaining stock killed. He had learned well from his mentors. A warrior on horseback was worth ten dismounted. To kill a horse was the most difficult thing for a

cavalryman, but his orders were clear: kill all warriors, capture surrendered women and children, destroy the village and ponies.

Soldiers were given the hellish task of cutting the throats of more than eight hundred horses. In terror at the look and smell of the white men, the ponies ran, making them difficult to capture. Custer went to the Osage scouts, but their disgust was so evident he did not ask for aid.

The soldiers closed in on the ponies in sad mimicry of the human slaughter hours before. Warriors watching from the clifftops yelled curses, pounded their own chests in agony. Horses were considered treasure, sacred.

There was the trouble of slow blood loss, the unbearable sound of equine screams. Horses returned to their fallen in camaraderie, then, smelling death, ran away in panic. When the soldiers' arms grew too weary as darkness approached, guns were brought out to finish the job, despite the dear cost in bullets. The whole snowy field turned rust-colored, cinerary. Wounded horses moaned like humans.

As evening fell the hills were thick with warriors many times more than the number at noon. Danger increased with the minutes. Camps downriver had been alerted by the

sounds of gunfire. Interviewing the female prisoners, the scouts learned that larger camps of Cheyenne, Arapaho, and Kiowa lay several miles farther along the river.

A temporary hospital set up in the middle of the village took care of the wounded. As Custer rode by, he saw the bugle boy sitting outside the medical tent on a pile of buffalo robes, his face covered in blood. The sight of children harmed undid him. He knew the boy, had let him come to his tent to eat sweets sent from Libbie and play with the dogs. Although he was too young to serve, he had replaced his fallen father to support their family. Once he was out in the field, Custer did not have the heart to return him. He stopped now.

— You okay, son?

— Got an arrow through me, General.

The boy pointed out the trajectory from above his eye and out the ear. A fraction of difference would have been enough to send him to the eternal rest. The barbed arrows were incapable of being backed out, so the surgeon had cut off the head and pulled the rest through.

— Fine job. You see the one did it to you?

The boy fished in a deep pocket and

270

brought out a bloodied hank of hair and scalp.

— Not only saw him, but shot him, then scalped him, too.

Custer burst out laughing, the child was so preternaturally beyond his years. War did that.

— The injury is slight?

— Reckon I'll survive.

— I'm most assured you will.

— Say I do survive, General, maybe you was to put me on your staff?

Little devil. Custer bit down on his lip so as not to mar the seriousness of the boy's request. The child had small, close-set eyes, high, slatted cheekbones, and a common mien when not covered in his own blood, but he had an uncommon confidence that Custer warmed to.

— You partial to dogs, young man?

— I could be, sir.

A genuine Machiavelli.

— Report to my adjutant when you're healed up.

When they returned to the fort, he would put the boy in charge of the dogs, out of harm's way, in Hamilton's memory. Maybe train him to become a groomsman.

The child was promptly forgotten as a detachment of warriors came off the bluff

and tried to break through army lines on the other side of the river. Custer ordered that the captives be brought as a buffer. As expected, the women's cries stopped the warriors from firing.

Village burned, ponies slain, military and civilian dead on both sides tallied, a quick search within the perimeter failed to account for Elliott and his party, and an assessment was made that they had been cut off by this new, encircling enemy. The wagon with the reserve ammunition had barely made it through the warriors, its wheels set on fire. If the main supply wagons were discovered and attacked, the regiment would be without food enough to return to Camp Supply.

As evening fell he organized the men in full formation, band playing, flags flying, and moved out in the direction from which the warriors had come. He knew, if the others didn't, that boldness was the true caution of the cavalry.

Convinced that their own villages would be next under attack, the warriors on the bluffs dispersed to defend them. Hours later, the feint successful, Custer gave the command to reverse and go back over the same territory covered, past the morning's death field, to rejoin the main supply train

the next day.

He had been in a slumber since the War, his best instincts unused, but now he was come to life again.

Killed: 103 warriors. Captured: 53 women and children. Killed: 875 ponies. Village property destroyed: 241 saddles, 573 buffalo robes, 290 buffalo skins for lodges, 160 untanned robes, 210 axes, 140 hatchets, 35 revolvers, 47 rifles, 535 pounds of powder, 1,050 pounds of lead, 4,000 arrows and arrowheads, 75 spears, 90 bullet molds, 35 bows and quivers, 12 shields, 300 pounds of bullets, 775 lariats, 940 buckskin saddlebags, 470 blankets, 93 coats, 700 pounds of tobacco, immense quantities of dried meat and other provisions.

Loss to the 7th Cavalry: 2 officers, 19 enlisted men, 3 officers wounded. He sent word of victory back to Sheridan:

We have cleaned Black Kettle and his band out so thoroughly that they can neither fight, dress, sleep, eat or ride without sponging upon their friends. It was a regular Indian "Sailor's Creek."

They rode for two days back to Camp Supply.

At one newly established ranch, Golden Buffalo stopped and stared at a barbed-wire fence, his eyes glassed as if he'd seen a ghost.

—What's wrong with you, boy? Too much whiskey?

Each night when they bivouacked, a scout made selections from among the captive women and delivered them like choice cuts of meat to officers' tents. Custer had watched the women carefully during the daylight as they rode the saved ponies from the herd. One in particular stood out both for her pleasing face and the deference paid her by the others. She rode a superior horse and mounted it well. He ordered another prisoner brought and had Golden Buffalo question her as to the girl's identity.

She was the daughter of a chief. Monahsetah had fetched a high price in ponies from the warrior who married her. But the duties of a wife did not suit her, nor did said warrior. She shot him in the knee and had just returned to her family village in time to witness this: her father slain, she herself taken prisoner.

In his tent he lay on his bed of buffalo skins before the blazing stove. When she was prodded in, he glimpsed Tom's face behind

her, outraged on Libbie's behalf and yet loyal despite that. His young brother was not yet married, could not understand that there was marital love and then there was also this.

He had caught enough of his words to gather that Golden Buffalo had urged the girl's accommodation. All men understood that women were the best insurance for loyalty. Golden Buffalo was bargaining to buy his. Custer would enjoy letting him try.

The tent flap closed behind the girl. Both were aware that a soldier with a loaded gun stood on the other side of the canvas. The night was a cold one, a howling wind blowing sporadically, causing the tent to shudder from each powerful gust. He propped himself up on an elbow and stared at her.

Stonily Monahsetah stared back. Wrapped in her blanket against the cold, she did not look away, showing neither anger nor fear, but frankly appraised him. Impressed, he thought her more cool-headed than many a general he had fought against. They both understood the proposed transaction; now it was more a settling on mutually satisfactory terms. He almost fell asleep waiting until some calculation had been reached, when at last she shifted her weight from one foot to the other and let the blanket drop.

Despite the dress and leggings, the fineness of her body had been obvious — the youth of unblemished skin, the inky hair that fell thick down her back as she unbound it, a veil covering her breast. She would not have been out of place, except for her exceptional beauty, if attending a social soiree in New York City, back in the States. There was none of the wilting delicacy of white women about her. Instead of seducing by helplessness she undid him by her strength.

After a prolonged silence, she coughed.

—You are handsome on a horse.

He flushed, knowing this was the highest criterion for leadership among the Indians. He, too, was being chosen.

—You mount a horse quite prettily yourself, he answered.

She tossed her head at the obviousness of his statement.

As she continued to undress, he realized he had indeed underestimated her charms. He tried to figure out this new enemy. He would need to be careful if it was true that she'd wounded and left her husband. The prisoner he'd questioned claimed she was a crack shot with a rifle, better than most warriors. What was she plotting now, when a day earlier she'd lost her father and a major portion of her tribe? Here she was dry-eyed,

scheming her best possible future. She canted her chin higher, not subservient in the least. A powerful protector among the enemy was essential. Raised in a warrior culture, used to the ways of the nomad, her life much resembled his as a soldier. For the moment he represented relative safety and shelter. They understood each other.

— *Hi'es'tzie,* Long Hair, she said, pointing at him.

He swept his hand over the nearby low table filled with officers' rations. She was a woman of appetite to match his, and he delighted as she fell on the food, ravenous, never taking an eye off him. Her inquisitive gaze probed to discover what kind of man he was while her sharp white teeth tore at the food.

GOLDEN BUFFALO

He spoke to the tribe at a feast in his honor. He had been sickened by the behavior of the soldiers at Washita the previous winter, how they fought without skill and then lied afterward about the number of women and children killed. He had returned to his people to regain his spirit strength.

"You do well to return," the chief said. "Tell us what kind of man this Long Hair is."

"He is a warrior. He has the heart of an Indian."

The chief bowed his head.

"He is smart and learns our ways," Golden Buffalo continued. "But he does so to defeat us and glorify himself among his people."

A large group of warriors left with Golden Buffalo for the hunt. They rode to a favorite buffalo watering hole in a secluded valley they had hunted in since Golden Buffalo

was a young boy. The warrior who called himself his new father had been proud of Golden Buffalo's abilities in riding and shooting and had him accompany the hunt before he allowed his own sons to do the same. He remembered the great excitement the men felt getting ready for the annual trek, and how he experienced a sense of belonging for the first time since he had lost his parents. He tried not to think that these men he rode among were the very tribe to kill his parents in warfare and then adopt him. The valley made him mindful of all these things.

They walked their horses leisurely in a scattered line, talking and joking, the chief turning around on his horse to tell Golden Buffalo the end of a story. No one could see the valley ahead, as a last hill still blocked it. The men at the head of the hunting party made a signal as they sniffed the air. Soon all of them noticed the awful stench of decomposition. Perhaps, they thought, a lone buffalo had died nearby. Cresting the hill in silence, the sight before Golden Buffalo's eyes made his heart sick — hundreds and hundreds of dead buffalo scattered across the valley floor, as numerous as the wildflowers, so many they darkened the ground they lay on. The animals

were bloated and rotting, the killing days old, some with their skin cut off, others whole except for a missing tongue.

The warriors shouted, outraged. They rode in angry circles and fired their guns into the sky. Golden Buffalo simply felt shame. Was he a fool to try to learn the ways of men who did such things? He turned his horse back and did not speak the rest of the day.

They had been expected to be gone a week, but came back in a few days. Urgent councils were announced among the Cheyenne, Sioux, and Kiowa, and ideas solicited to deal with the encroachment on their lands. Although it was illegal, the military would not enforce its own treaties. The majority favored going on the warpath against the settlers, who were easier targets than the soldiers.

They agreed on a plan to attack a fort in the migration path as a clear warning for the whites to leave. A medicine man claimed he could make the warriors immune to the whites' bullets. He told them he could cut a vein and bleed more warriors if needed. If he chopped off a finger, guns and ammunition would rain down from the sky. His breath would create a splendid shield pro-

tecting the warriors from the white man's bullets.

"Their guns will be no more powerful than sticks," he told them. "You will destroy them."

The warriors were empowered by his words, not allowing for the possibility of their being false. They rode in circles on their horses and gave the war cry, feeling invincible, stronger than they had in a long time. Golden Buffalo had been with the army long enough to be a skeptic. He viewed the warriors' belief as childish. With his white mind he did not believe the medicine man, but after Washita his Indian heart called on him. Faith rewarded made living worthwhile.

They charged the fort at dawn with great fanfare and little protection, propelled by their belief in the spell of the medicine man. The first warrior hit by a powerful rifle rolled off his horse, but they ignored it as an aberration. Another group charged but were repelled by a wind of bullets. Three fell to the ground, and the rest rode away to regroup. They had been presumptuous that the medicine would not still require of them their utmost skill and effort. They began their traditional circling attack, leaning

along the necks of their horses and shooting rifles through the fence and into exposed windows.

Horses were shot and rolled over, injuring the men who rode them. Some of the warriors argued that they must revert to their traditional way of fighting and stay out of range of the powerful weapons. Others argued that they must put their lives in the power of the medicine for it to work. A small subset of the most experienced warriors, including Golden Buffalo, would ride straight at the main building. The danger they put themselves in would impel the medicine to protect them. The man next to Golden Buffalo was killed. He himself was hit in the arm and fell off his horse, rolling to safety in a gully.

Golden Buffalo lay on his back and stared up into the blue sky. For a time, he could not vouch how long, he forgot about the battle raging around him, forgot about the soldiers who he served in order to defeat, forgot the tribe that he loved and had no faith in, but simply lost himself in the blueness of the sky overhead with its small white clouds speeding across. The wind had grown stronger without his noticing. A hawk was wheeling through the air currents, riding each swell with outstretched wings, glid-

ing effortlessly. Without a doubt Golden Buffalo would have traded his life for that of the hawk. He was weary of being human.

At last the war party made the decision to retreat.

The warriors rode away in pain and humiliation. They had lost ten men, an astonishingly high number given the small size of the action. Many more were wounded. Such a rout was possible only because they had so foolishly exposed themselves. When they were far enough away to be sure of their safety, they dismounted and accosted the medicine man.

"Why did you mislead us, *ma'háhke'so,* old man?"

One of the warriors whose brother had just been killed raised his quirt and lashed the man. Others joined in. Golden Buffalo felt the same rage, but he would not participate. What the man's failure told him was that his own vision was true — he must continue learning the way of the whites, hard as it was, because it was the only path to save his tribe. The prophecy of his dream was at last clear. His people would be lost otherwise.

The Eighth Remove

Indian council — On the warpath —
Waiting — Victory celebration

The spring and summer of her fifth year in captivity passed in unending movement that further deteriorated Anne's health. Nevertheless she did her utmost to survive and protect Solace and her unborn child. Although her belly was still flat she knew the signs — a tickling weight in her womb like that of a tendril pushing through soil deep, the tenderness and dark swell of breast, the muzziness of mind. Neha knew almost before she did, claiming that an expectant woman smelled differently.

The Indians were contentious after a series of routs by the army and stories of massacres of whole camps both on the reservation and off. It kept them distrustful. When Anne broached the subject of her being

traded for ransom to enrich the tribe, she was roughly told off. The Cheyenne had learned how duplicitous the whites acted.

Through the gossip of the women, Anne was learning of a world that was the inverse of the one she had previously understood.

The Sand Creek Massacre was long past but the memory of its treachery stayed fresh within the tribe. At the homestead, Anne had never heard mention of it before, but perhaps it had been kept from the children. Chief Black Kettle had been pledged safety for his people by Tall Chief Wynkoop. He had been told that if soldiers ever approached, mistaking them for hostiles, to hang the American flag and stand beside it, because it was strong medicine and would keep them safe.

But Wynkoop's defense of the Indians made him unpopular with the military, and he was replaced by a man they called the red-eyed soldier chief. The Indians did not trust him, with good reason. He was only pacifying Black Kettle while waiting for a large force of soldiers led by a devil named Chivington. Soon a force was gathered to go after the camp. Wynkoop's remaining allies protested that such action would dishonor the uniform of the army. They were threatened with court-martial.

When the soldiers approached the camp at dawn, there stood Chief Black Kettle in front of his teepee, his American flag blowing in the wintry wind.

Black Kettle was no fool. He understood the white man was seldom good on his word, but he reasoned appeasement was his tribe's only chance at survival.

The soldiers opened fire on six hundred Indians, mostly women and children, as the warriors were off hunting. Still Black Kettle yelled to his people to stand under the flag. Old men, women, and children huddled in a circle as White Antelope ran up a white surrender flag for good measure in case the army did not understand the American flag meant protection. Regardless, they were murdered.

A small number of Indians, including Black Kettle, managed to escape and tell of what happened. Later some of the soldiers there told the same story. The scene had been a chaotic one, a total lack of discipline combined with heavy drinking of whiskey. Forty or more women hid in a ravine to avoid gunfire. Offering no resistance, they sent out a small girl of six holding a white flag on a stick to show they were peaceful. The soldiers shot and killed the child after a few steps. One of the soldiers reported

seeing a woman with child cut open by other soldiers. After killing them, the soldiers systematically scalped or otherwise mutilated every body.

After the shooting ended, 105 Indian women and children lay dead; 28 Indian men were killed. Chivington had lost only nine soldiers, mostly due to reckless firing by his own men. Shaken, the Cheyenne and Arapaho tribes gave up their claims to the Colorado Territory. This had been the goal.

Recently, Long Hair/General Custer had gone after Black Kettle's camp again while it was in Indian Territory, on its own assigned reservation. Black Kettle, the strongest advocate of peace with the white man, had been betrayed and killed. The white man's word was deemed worthless.

Anne did not know what to make of such stories, but she saw the attitude toward her harden after the Washita Massacre. Members of the tribe who already resented her, if possible increased their hostility to her. Others understood that she was only a girl and could not be blamed for the sins of her people. It seemed to Anne that all the world had gone mad, she did not know who to trust, and it pained her to bring an innocent into such a world.

"Some want to do away with you to stamp

out your seed," Unci said. "I tell them no. Even if you are killed, the white seed will spread everywhere."

The buffalo herds had shrunk dramatically, and wherever one could be found the Indians invariably found the army and settlers also.

An Indian scout came into camp for the hunt. His name was Golden Buffalo, and he was rumored to be in the service of Long Hair. Anne tried to catch Golden Buffalo's eye with the idea that he might report her presence to Custer, but if he did notice her he gave no indication.

During the period of the councils, groups would arrive from the wilderness with their own captives in tow. At these meetings, chiefs from other camps noticed Anne and gave offers of goods in barter, but Snake Man was loath to part with her. Some warriors thought she, being white, should be put to death to avenge their losses, but cooler heads argued that she was innocent, besides valuable to the tribe for her dexterous fingers, which sewed such beautiful items.

In this way Anne met a tall woman who had been abducted the previous year in

Kansas. She was a doctor's daughter and a barrister's bride. She had known only the most protected life and had no idea of how to survive. Her dress was filthy. Anne helped rid her hair of the lice that were driving her mad. The women became friendly, Anne even offering to make her a dress, until the woman's chief noticed the two together and accused them of conspiring.

He dragged the woman by the arm back to his teepee and there tied her to a stake in the ground with a length of rawhide. She was denied food. Anne passed her regularly on errands and feared this new friend might perish from her unjust punishment. Unable to stand it any longer, when Anne next passed she surreptitiously threw a bit of seed cake into her lap while passing, which the woman stuffed in her mouth, not daring to chew but letting it dissolve down her throat. A few hours later Anne risked stealing pemmican out of her master's parfleche, although she knew the punishment would be severe.

The next day Anne again passed by but found the teepee empty, the stake bare. She feared the worst. While she sat on the riverbank doing her sewing, she was surprised when the woman approached her, this time in the company of a new master.

This man appeared kind and much pleased with his new trade. The woman had fetched a low price because she was accused of fomenting trouble. She handed Anne a kerchief of boiled venison and berries in thanks. She said she now had all the food she needed and was gaining strength hourly. She prayed her new chief would ransom her back to her husband.

Anne nodded with enthusiasm, knowing that hope, however unfounded, was the only grace available.

The day after, the chief left the council. Anne was never to see the tall woman again or know her fate. Her name was Dorotha.

They had reached the decision to make war on the whites. All rejected the idea of going to the reservation, to certain slow death. The women and children were sent to a place of safety to wait.

Anne was worked mercilessly, packing and carrying the teepee's belongings. When she was caught napping in exhaustion, the oldest wives kicked her, sometimes in the stomach, little valuing a captive's pregnancy although they would not dare such behavior in front of their Snake Man. This abuse worried Anne for her unborn's sake.

She had endured the same abuse while

carrying Solace, but she had been a different being back then, meek and afraid. Now she grabbed a branch from the cooking area whose endfire was coaled red. She poked the cruelest one's cheek with it, scarring her.

After that they left her in peace.

Neha was quiet when they were next alone.

"Do you fault me?" Anne finally asked.

"I fault myself for not coming to your aid."

"I had to win this battle myself. But your words please me."

Anne had learned that the Indians valued bravery and courage as Christians did meekness and charity, which they viewed as weakness. She resolved to change to the Indian way.

Once news of her defense spread within the tribe, her status rose greatly.

Still, she remained outcast but for a few exceptions. When Neha was busy, Anne would take the meager dinner either begged or earned from her sewing and go to sit with her babe, Solace, to watch the night sky alone. When the moon rose she reminded herself that it also shone down on her old home, on her friends and loved ones. She tried to convince herself that civilization did somehow still exist beyond the vastness of

the wilderness in which she languished, even though from all appearances the wilds seemed to have swallowed the rest of the world whole.

When the warriors came back in victory there was great rejoicing. The women said witnessing the celebrations would make the warrior inside Anne's belly grow brave. She could not guess how they knew she was with child, much less its gender. Forced to sit and witness these festivities, she had nightmares then and for years afterward.

Macabre dances were performed around the fire, especially the scalp dance, which featured a pole with all the grisly scalps flaunted, as well as the hands and feet of the victims. The warriors would make faces and utter war cries that caused Anne's blood to chill. They pantomimed their actions during the attack, most terrifyingly reenacting the death throes of their victims. At times their features seemed to mold to their victims' expressions so vividly, she imagined she recognized some of the people thus recently murdered.

LIBBIE

The battle at Washita was Autie's first great victory as an Indian fighter, and put to rest the sense that his best days were behind him. He again came to national attention, a hero and an expert on all things West. Libbie felt it gave him false confidence; he simply would not believe that his luck would ever end.

Two days after the battle, the troops arrived at the fringe of the valley created by the confluence of Beaver River and Wolf Creek. They had stopped to prepare for their victory march into Camp Supply. Some believed such pomp undignified, but Autie loved military ceremony, understanding its power over both the victors and the vanquished.

The crowd could not breathe for excitement as the soldiers rode down the slope of the valley with the band playing. General Sheridan and his staff had been alerted, and

waited mounted for the review. The 19th Kansas Volunteers, who had only just arrived at Camp Supply, missing the entire campaign, cheered on the men they were supposed to have fought alongside. It was magnificent. Pure spectacle. People talked about it for years afterward because it confirmed what they longed to believe, that they were the chosen and had divine blessing for their mission.

At the head of the column Osage guides rode in triumph, wearing full war regalia, chanting war songs. Periodically they would fire their guns into the air and spur their horses off on a dead run like errant rockets, returning with victory yells, gloriously fearsome. Faces made demonic in paint, they brandished spears on which were fastened the gruesome trophy scalps of their mutual Indian enemy. Guides worked for the army but settled scores first and foremost as Indians. Even their horses lost their natural animal innocence, implicated by the decoration on their bodies — painted stripes and dots — into beasts of a netherworld, with strips of red and blue enemy blankets woven into their manes and tails, scalps and ears tied to their bridles and saddles.

In front of Sheridan's staff and close enough for everyone to hear, the chief of

the scouts yelled out, "They call us Americans — we are Osage!"

No one in the audience responded, and soon the troopers' cheering covered the uncomfortable silence, answered by the volunteers cheering from the fort.

One young warrior carried a pole with the scalp of Chief Black Kettle, for which he was much honored. Even Libbie recognized the name as that of a great advocate of peace between the whites and the Indians. To celebrate his death seemed misguided. If their strongest chance of negotiated peace had just expired, surely that was no victory? They would later find out that the chief had indeed lost his life in the battle, but not his scalp.

Next came the scouts dressed in their pell-mell frontier outfits of buckskin and rags. Then the officers, with Tom among them, looking very much the knight-errant. A handsome figure he made, and Libbie felt the pride of a mother. He gave her a nod, then rode close to give her an Indian beaded pipe as battle prize. Autie rode alone, astride his favorite stallion, transformed once again into the conquering hero. He looked straight ahead, stopping in front of General Sheridan to sweep off his hat.

Behind him came the women and children

prisoners, wrapped in their bright red blankets, meekly astride their winter-gaunt ponies. Next came the band, playing the ubiquitous "Garry Owen" of which Autie was so fond. Next came the troops in formation, four across, in their patched blue uniforms, some with their feet wrapped in rags due to lost boots, giving the lie to the ease they pretended. Nothing quelled celebration like the admission of privation. As they passed General Sheridan they gave military salute with their raised sabers.

The irregular procession was thrilling and profane. Men returning from war in the same way they had from time immemorial, they could have been a victorious Napoleonic army. Autie had read excerpts of such historic parades out loud to her and had taken them as his template. It was heart-stopping in its pageantry and strangeness, its gruesome spoils of war down to the pipe that she held in her hand. There was an undeniable beauty in the sun glinting off sabers, the bright colors of guidons and blankets. The ear filled with music and war cries and cheers. The whole procession had the clear fingerprint of Autie, for better and worse. It was the turning point for them to finally leave behind the War of the Rebellion and feel their new destiny lying there on

that empty, wintery plain.

As the group of prisoners halted on their mounts, Libbie saw a young woman singled out, one to whom the others paid deference, and then she observed Autie's eyes on the girl, and she knew. Her heart froze. Gossip only confirmed it later. The girl was yet another spoil of war.

Washita River Indian Territory, December 1868

The ground was frozen hard. It clanged like metal under the horses' feet, the remaining snow stiff with its gloss of blood. Many of the Indian dead had been bundled in blankets and hidden under brush to keep the bodies from foraging animals. One figure, a woman, had been pulled out by wolves or coyotes and lay uncovered on the ground, her body bared. Her trunk had been cleaved as with a saber, breasts cut off.

Tom dismounted and threw a poncho over the woman.

Furious, Custer rode behind his young brother and took up the poncho at the end of his saber, appalled by such a display of sentimentality.

— That is the enemy.

— A woman. Tortured by us. Or the Osage under us.

The criticism by Tom was hard, and it galled him that it was just.

— Some of whom had guns and used them against us.

— Tell me, brother, surely you do not countenance such behavior.

Tom shook his head and moved off.

In the hyperborean air, decomposition was at a minimum, the bodies of the Indian ponies fresh as if only recently slain. Wolves had eaten out fleshy caves in their sides. His mouth went dry at evidence of ponies who had been merely wounded and slowly bled out, eating the grass in the vicinity of their heads before expiring.

Like most military battles, the nature of the engagement at Washita changed when it encountered public opinion. On first news of the victory broadcast by Sheridan to the press, Custer regained his status as national hero. Reporters wrote that he was continuing to show the brilliance he had during the War. Two weeks later the focus shifted to the fate of Elliott and his men thanks to an anonymous letter written to the papers by Captain Benteen.

Sheridan understood that one made decisions on the battleground with the limited information at hand. Custer's most pressing concerns had been victory over the village, and then with the appearance of the war-

riors, not getting overrun. His real mistake was attacking when he did not know the enemy's numbers nor the surrounding terrain.

Malcontents such as Benteen would go on about his abandoning the men, but Custer had sent Myers out on a quick reconnaissance. The officer had gone two miles downstream and found nothing. The recovery of the bodies might have endangered the entire regiment, including Benteen himself, but that didn't stop the crosspatch from complaining to the newspapers about the matter.

A commonplace in the military was that men under you thought themselves better qualified to lead. Benteen had been a good soldier in the War, but afterward his lack of success on the frontier, his being outranked by Custer, soured his temper. His constant long diatribes against his commander were well known and bored his listeners.

Newspapers praised the battle as the first victory on the frontier. That dimmed, though, when some of the eastern press began instead to call it a massacre, criticizing the bloodthirsty military, and hanging in effigy Sheridan and Custer. The country was bitterly divided on the Indian question. Expecting such treatment, Sheridan instead

concentrated on acting on their momentum by bringing in the remaining tribes. He would personally accompany the 7th Cavalry and the Kansas Volunteers back to the Washita Valley.

Custer broke out into a sweat, spurring his horse ahead to avoid the accumulation of sights that would otherwise lay him low. Absurd for a soldier to feel this way; more absurd to feel nothing. He resented what was now expected of him and took refuge in the fact that he had only followed orders, the utility and ultimate conclusion of which were someone else's responsibility, in this case precisely Sheridan's, who now rode ahead of him as if they were out on a hunting trip. Custer had killed for the man, wiped out a village, and then saved most of his men to boot. That should be enough for a day's work.

It had started during the War, Custer's separating the general from the man. Instead of grief, one mourned the loss of killing force. This was what one trained for, what one learned rising through the ranks, what he was now criticized for doing. He no more looked at his soldiers as individuals during the heat of battle than they looked beyond the general in him. Men craved leadership,

and this he performed ably. Each man wrestled with private torments in deepest night; that was the only place the human was allowed in war.

He'd been wrong to chastise Tom for covering the Indian woman. Tom was still a boy, still tenderhearted. That had all been squeezed out of Custer. Only Libbie fed the little bit of gentleness left him.

His thoughts turned to Monahsetah as they often did now, the pleasure of her, which he was not finished indulging in. Hard to think that these frozen forms along the ground were her people. What did it mean that he conquered her over and over again each night, and yet she remained with the upper hand? He did not for one moment believe she had surrendered; she was delaying revenge. Would a knife find his throat one night and would he mind the price paid? It was a mystery that from the same people came lover and enemy.

While Sheridan talked with the other officers, Custer told Tom to cover for him and rode away from the column, crossing to the south bank of the Washita. Brush and trees along the river were lustrous in casings of ice. He had entered upon an enchanted glass world.

During the battle he had shot at one warrior in the village before making his way to Headquarters Hill, unaware if the bullet had been fatal, yet when the dark shapes gathered around him at the river's edge, there was the Indian to confirm the bullet had done its work. He saw the young bugle boy with the bloodied face and was saddened that he had not survived. Added now were women, one in particular who resembled the one Tom had covered, although Custer had strictly forbidden any harmed. He wondered if his relationship with the girl was responsible for extending the guilt now to civilians. Then the children appeared, and he was undone.

Armies were impossible to keep on a tight rein at all times. Things happened in the mire of battle. Innocents suffered. The Osage guides had committed atrocities in their own name, yet he had been culpable by looking the other way. One allowed so much then pulled them back in line. Wasn't that the very thing for which the army had punished Black Kettle, his not being able to control his young men? Yet Black Kettle was at the bottom of a riverbed for it. The gray specters all stood there in bleak accusation, and there was no redress for him.

He was at pains to hide these visitations

from others, did not tell anyone of them, not even Libbie. Were they a version of soldier's heart, a condition he'd observed during the War, the sense knocked out of some soldiers after going through battle? He was loath to ever admit it and would not now.

A small detachment joined him, and they rode single file, ascending a divide, stopping at the top to let sunlight thaw them as they looked out over the desolate winter countryside.

They dismounted, made coffee to warm themselves, smoked cigarettes, and chewed hardtack to pass the time. Blasts of cold wind cuffed their backs, boxed their ears, stung the exposed skin of their faces. The flames of the fire bent flat against the ground. Conversation was subdued; they mostly said nothing, put in a mood by the death they had just surveyed, which presaged the death they would now surely find. Finally word came of Sheridan moving out.

A stain of ravens and crows flew up against the sky, their cries marking the scene. The soldiers came upon the uncanny sight of the naked body of a white man lying in the weeds, his corpse bristling with arrows. The frozen limbs glowed like white marble in

the sunlight. The search party stopped and looked down, sickened at the bashed-in head like a melon, its contents spilled onto the dirty snow. Custer felt a deep shame for the exposed body. Angered by his helplessness to change the outcome, he brusquely moved off.

— Cover the body, at least.

Tom raised his eyebrows. Sheridan continued downstream with the main body of soldiers. The horses faltered through a ravine, the deep shaded bottom preserving a high bank of clotted snow. Once across the river, more shapes stranded on a hill became visible. Frenzied spurs and whips were laid on, although time no longer mattered. They galloped to the scene as if after such a long delay a further one would not be accepted. The bodies lay in a circle in the high grass. Farther off were the carcasses of the slain horses. Wearily the rescue party dismounted, but they remained at the sides of their horses, reins in hand, made squeamish by the horror before them.

Sheridan dismounted and stood over the bodies, took off his hat, and crushed it in his hands.

The bodies, naked and frozen solid, had taken on the aspect of sculpture. Rendered anonymous by the fact of their lying face-

down, each was surrounded by a pile of spent shells. The mutilations were so macabre that the soldiers could only pray the men had already died and were not tortured alive. They bowed their heads in prayer. Custer closed his eyes, then blamed the wind for smarting tears. Later, Golden Buffalo explained that the Indian predilection for mutilation was to ruin the body so it could not haunt the afterlife or come back to avenge itself.

— I'll make the guilty suffer in this life, Custer said.

The soldiers marked the forlorn location for the wagons to recover the remains. It was a cruel irony that the dead should be interred on this hostile plain. Only Major Elliott's body would be taken for burial at Fort Arbuckle. Before it was consigned to a mass grave the camp doctor examined each body and made a report of wounds and mutilations at Custer's request. He would send that to the eastern papers to print if they dared.

Major Joel H. Elliott — two bullets in head; one in left cheek; right hand cut off; left foot almost cut off; penis cut off; deep gash in right groin; deep gashes in calves of both

legs; little finger of left hand cut off; throat cut.

Sergeant-Major Walter Kennedy — bullet hole in right temple; head partly cut off; seventeen bullet holes in back and two in legs.

Corporal Harry Mercer, Troop E — bullet hole in right axilla; one in region of heart; three in back; eight arrow wounds in back; right ear cut off; head scalped; skull fractured; deep gashes in both legs; throat cut.

Corporal Thomas Christie, Troop E — bullet hole in right parietal bone; both feet cut off; throat cut; left arm broken; penis cut off.

Private Eugene Clover, Troop H — head cut off; arrow wound in right side; both legs terribly mutilated.

Private William Milligan, Troop H — bullet hole in left side of head; deep gashes in right leg; penis cut off; left arm deeply gashed; head scalped; throat cut.

Corporal James F. Williams, Troop I — bullet hole in back; head and both arms cut off; many and deep gashes in back; penis cut off.

Private Thomas Downey, Troop I — arrow hole in region of stomach; thorax cut open; head cut off; right shoulder cut by a

tomahawk.

Farrier Thomas Fitzpatrick, Troop M — scalped; two arrows and several bullet holes in back; throat cut.

Private Ferdinand Lineback, Troop M — bullet hole in left parietal bone; head scalped and arm broken; penis cut off; throat cut.

Private John Meyers, Troop M — several bullet holes in head; skull extensively fractured; several arrow and bullet holes in back; deep gashes in face; throat cut.

Private Carsten D. J. Meyers, Troop M — several bullet holes in head; scalped; nineteen bullet holes in body; penis cut off; throat cut.

Private Cal. Sharpe, Troop M — two bullet holes in right side; throat cut; one bullet hole in left side of head; one arrow in left side; penis cut off; left arm broken.

Unknown — head cut off; body partially destroyed by wolves.

Unknown — head and right hand cut off; three bullet holes and nine arrow holes in back; penis cut off.

Unknown — scalped; skull fractured; six bullet and thirteen arrow holes in back; three bullet holes in chest.

Farther down the river, on the spot of the

campsites of the other tribes, they discovered the body of the white captive Clara Blinn. She had been shot in the head, and her emaciated frame and filthy clothes spoke of the harsh treatment she'd received since she'd been captured two months before. Beside her was the body of her two-year-old son Willie, plump compared with his mother, his skull crushed.

Mawisa, Black Kettle's sister, claimed the woman had been taken and held captive by Kiowa, under Satanta. Only later after she escaped did Custer find out that she'd lied to throw off suspicion from her own people and their allies the Arapaho.

During all of this Monahsetah said nothing. Foolishly he felt betrayed.

He lay in his tent, the canvas lit by the dim glow of the stove, and watched the smoke seep up out the opening at the top, obscuring the stars. Reveille would be in a few hours, yet sleep had fled. The mood was dark after the Elliott party discovery. Golden Buffalo had missed their language lesson. Custer wanted the solace of Monahsetah, but she was avoiding him, too. He gave her the freedom to come and go from his bed as she pleased because it gave him more pleasure when she came of her own volition. Many nights she told him stories of

her girlhood, and he fell asleep dreaming her life. He would be denied that distraction tonight.

The truth was Elliott had been a grand soldier and a bit of a fool, too. Searching for glory, he found the grave. *Here's for a brevet or a coffin,* he'd shouted, and found the latter. He had gone on his own resource, giving chase to a fleeing band of Indians, then found himself surrounded by warriors from the lower camps. Custer could not fault the officer's bravery, yet he was dead and in a most brutal fashion. It was not more complicated than rotten luck.

Custer was faulted for not having searched sooner, on the afternoon of the battle, as if it would have made a difference to the men's outcome. What if his little feint had failed, and their own larger regiment had found itself surrounded as well? He would be guilty of poor judgment like Elliott. No matter. They were dead, and he was their leader. In the way that mattered, it remained his fault, in the way that had nothing to do with the politics of the army, or the misguided altruism of the pacifists. He mourned his brave, foolish soldiers and knew already that they would join the others to haunt him. Soldier's heart indeed.

THE NINTH REMOVE

Thomas — Indian charity — Winter camp
—
Ransom — Deception at the fort

After Anne birthed her second child, Thomas, named after her father, the women did much reading of signs and prophesied he would grow up to be a great peacemaker in the tribe. That did nothing to sweeten her captivity.

Her camp joined a Sioux one, intending to winter together in an isolated valley. The location was chosen because they could be reasonably sure of being left alone by the army due to the difficulty of approach during inclement weather. Only Long Hair/Custer successfully managed winter raids, and rumor was that he had gone back east that year.

When she had first been captured, still a girl, she had daydreamed that Custer, wear-

ing his gold-braided uniform, his hair falling in long golden curls, would come to her rescue. He would be so taken with her that he would hand her up to sit behind him on his horse, and pressing against him, she would go home and live happily ever after.

Anne despaired at the prospect of another long, freezing winter. Although her children were cared for and fed by Snake Man's wives, she was still treated in a lowly manner, except the women never dared strike her again. During feasts of bear or venison, she was not allowed to join in, despite her growing reputation at sewing items of cotton, as well as buffalo and deerskin, which garnered her constant work. She more than earned enough to feed herself, but the majority of her money and barter items were taken by Snake Man. Regularly she resorted to begging for food and shelter from families that had taken a liking to her and did not turn her away.

Her favorite was Running Bear, whose family invited her in often. The family consisted of the old chief, his woman, their grown children, and many grandchildren. They considered her ill-treatment scandalous, that it gave a bad reputation to their tribe, especially considering her contribution of children and labor for Snake Man.

Living with this other family would make her life so much more tolerable. It was the first time that Anne looked at herself other than a prisoner and slave, but rather as an attenuated member of the tribe with her own desires.

During the worst blizzards she was given her own buffalo robe to use when curling up to Running Bear's fire. This was the first semblance of a home, a place where she was welcome, in many years. Often she would bring Thomas to suckle at night, and they would cuddle in the warmth. At peace, Anne would hold her infant and stay awake long into the night.

Having such time to reflect was a rare luxury. She marveled at how much she had endured. Removed from family and home, from love and friendship, from language, books, learning. Civilization, in short. She had been removed from the normal things one took for granted such as birthdays and holidays and faith. And yet. In her new existence there were things she could only describe as sublime. Her children couldn't be more loved by her. Neha was a true sister in all the ways that mattered. Her comfort in nature was a thing unfathomable in her previous existence.

■ ■ ■ ■

Anne was now barely guarded. She had been given more freedom after the birth of her second child for the simple reason that they were always on the move, traveling through treacherous areas where she would have clearly perished on her own. It was remarked upon even by Snake Man's women that she was a devoted mother. Too devoted to risk her children's lives in the wilderness; too devoted to abandon them. It would be impossible to attempt escape and survive the rigors of the landscape, and a sin to risk her children's lives in such effort.

All her hard-won equanimity vanished when she heard the tribe would register at a fort, vowing to reside on their assigned reservation, entitling them to "gifts" of provisions. The tribes had developed the ruse of receiving annuities and then disappearing with them, only to be wooed again the next year. They blamed their cheating on the agents who supplied worthless rotten blankets, moldy bread, barrels of sugar and flour that were half empty. Only a third of the quantity promised was in actuality delivered, and that was of shoddy quality,

making Indian compliance impossible.

Neha came and whispered in her ear. "In a few days' time we will be close to the fort. It is your chance."

"How will I manage with the children?"

Neha shrugged, unmoved. She was not yet a mother, could not understand. It would be Anne's last chance of rescue for the remainder of the year.

The next evening she spent with Running Bear and his wife. To her surprise they made her an extraordinary offer of adoption.

"If it pleased you, I would be happy to live here. You know my hardship at my chief's."

"Is it what you desire, child?"

Unable to stop, tears sprang to her eyes. Her misery surprised even her.

"More than anything."

"We will talk to Snake Man. He's a reasonable man."

"He is not. But I will work day and night to repay whatever it costs."

Running Bear laughed at her eagerness.

"I will arrange it."

Anne felt she had made great progress. When the right time came, she would convince the family to accept a ransom amount. If anything went wrong, she would escape alone, then beg the fort commander

to aid her in retrieving her children.

As they neared the fort, she was surprised to feel a vague guilt over the treachery of these machinations. After all, she had been taken against her will, her family slain, and been treated most harshly.

When at last she had saviors in the form of the kind Running Bear and his woman, their offer of two ponies, an unheard-of extravagance for a captive, enraged Snake Man, who refused to trade her. On top of that he forbade her visits to them. When he discovered she still went there, he came and dragged her home by the hair, beating her until she dislocated a shoulder.

Not only did he forbid visits to Running Bear but to other families as well. She was only to work for them. The rest of the time she was to stay near, defined not as eating and sleeping in their teepee, but being stranded and fending for herself until she was reduced to eating the dead grasses under the frost for nourishment. Her curse was in having ended up in Snake Man's household, which was harsh compared with many others.

Her only consolation was in watching the round, healthy bellies of her children, who were oblivious of her plight. She resolved that she would escape at all cost. She had

dreams for them, believing they were entitled to the gifts of civilization. She did not want to think too hard of the fact that Snake Man would feel differently on the matter. In truth, she hardly credited his fathering. She preferred to pretend her children's conception was immaculate.

Anne grew more and more determined as they neared the fort, but when it lay within a few miles' reach, a small party of warriors was instructed to shelter in the nearby woods and guard her so that she was not spotted. They could hardly sue as peaceful and deserving of provisions if they held a captive, much less if that captive informed that they had recently been on the warpath and did not intend to stay on the reservation.

Anne was in tears as she watched Snake Man and his women, along with her Solace and Thomas, join the rest of the tribe to visit the fort. They needed a show of numbers, especially children, to win the trust of the government agents. She prayed the obvious white blood in her children would give the lie to their charade but knew that the large number of half-breeds in the tribe would make this unlikely. Beside herself with distress at her plans unraveling, she ignored her guards, turned her back on

them and their fire, the smell of cooking, and instead sat dejected in the snow. Hours passed in this way, and she hoped that one of them might come and cajole her with a hot bowl of food, but they were perfectly happy to let her sulk as long as she made no attempt to escape.

The night was an especially sharp, cold one, the stars like knives overhead, and she began to feel pain in her extremities that turned to numbness. It tempted her, the idea of falling asleep and being rid of her troubles at last. She finally had surrendered to her fate, the likelihood that her hopes of rescue would come to naught, her life ending without ever returning home. Her heart froze, and she let it for fear of it otherwise breaking. Perhaps her end was the best remedy.

Against her own volition, she found herself struggling up, body stiff, legs unbending as poles. She shuffled to the low fire and sat down, her icy skin unfeeling even inches from the embers. Only as she warmed up and felt the pain of thaw did she fully perceive how far she had almost gone. The warrior on watch merely looked at her, then turned disdainfully away. It drove her to misery that he had witnessed her vice of despair, yet did nothing to help a fellow

creature. It was a hardness born of necessity, and yet that fact did not make it sit any easier. She longed for the balm of civilization.

After three days, the Indians returned from the fort, much relaxed as if they had enjoyed a prolonged time of leisure. They had been well fed and returned laden with flour, sugar, coffee, carrots of tobacco, as well as rifles and ammunition. Looking at such bounty — bribes — Anne grew angry. How had they made off with such supplies and not been required to stay? The chief bragged that they invented a story: they would go to the main body of the camp and hurry along the stragglers, which numbered in the hundreds. The commander had been only too glad to accept the bald lie, already writing a report of his victory. How had they not noticed the blood of her children, their light skin and fine features? The golden streaks in Solace's hair that matched her grandmother's locks? If at least the military had kept her children, Anne would have been at peace and sacrificed her own fate. Now she must fight on. There was no choice but to endure another long winter.

LIBBIE

Indians haunted Libbie, whether they were before her eyes or resided in her imagination. Long afternoons were the hardest. Between lunch and dinner duties, social calls put aside, it was the moment when she could brood.

There was the obvious fear of war parties, but there was also the more intimate fear of Monahsetah, a poisonous tale told by enemies. The truth — she was a princess, daughter of a chieftain, Little Rock, who was killed during the Battle of the Washita. By birth and by beauty she could not go unnoticed among the prisoners. Everyone knew Autie appreciated the female form and was himself admired by the opposite sex.

To outsiders Libbie went as far as praising Monahsetah as a forward-thinking advocate of peace. Many great chieftains spoke for peace and cooperation, and she prayed that those voices would prevail, saving both

Indians and themselves untold suffering. The main undoing of peace was the perfidy of the U.S. government. It did not help matters that Chief Black Kettle had been killed by the military.

The ranchers and settlers paid lip service to the idea of coexistence, but in practice they wanted the Indians off the land. The faraway peace advocates talked endlessly about the free-roaming Indians deserving the right to use the land they were born on, although this did not stop them selling that very land — at high profit — for ranching, farming, and mining.

In the spring of 1869, Custer asked Libbie to pay a visit to the Washita prisoners in the stockade at Fort Hays as a gesture of goodwill and cooperation. She resisted, fearful when having to come in contact with Indians, especially when they were unhappily being held captive. Above all she dreaded Monahsetah, who, having lost a father, might attempt revenge against the general by gleefully plunging a dagger into his wife. Yet he insisted it was her duty as the commanding officer's wife to extend her hospitality and show Christian charity. She did not know his aim other than to humiliate her, but phrased like this she had no choice.

Of course Libbie was also curious about this newest source of her distress.

She dressed as if paying a social visit, quite more than the company required, and immediately regretted it. The women and children were gathered in the common room, Autie chaperoning and mere steps away, and yet Libbie's heart pounded as if she were traveling a long, dangerous gauntlet quite alone. The women crowded around Libbie, as curious about her as she was of them.

Hands touched her jacket, gloves, boots. Her hat, on which perched a small stuffed bird, created a sensation. Excitedly one of the women related through the interpreter that her father, a great warrior, wore a bird, albeit a much larger one, strapped to his head for good medicine during battle. Libbie did not understand the meaning but smiled delightedly as if she had been told the most amusing anecdote at an afternoon tea. A bracelet was pulled from her wrist. An earbob was fondled. Libbie grew panicked, claustrophobic. So many bodies crowded around. The smells of grass, smoke, and leather dizzied her. She nodded as papooses were brought for her to admire, trying not to show her terror of babies, which she'd not had practice handling.

Monahsetah hung back from the crowd, watching. Libbie had been told the story of her outrageous behavior: shooting her husband in the leg, a potentially disabling injury to a warrior. How could such a headstrong girl stand her present circumstances? Wasn't she furious at her captors, who had killed her father? Wouldn't such a woman insist on exacting revenge? Libbie could almost see the blade come out of the folds of the girl's blanket and plunge into her chest, her heart's blood ebbing out. What a glorious coup that would be.

Finally the moment was right, and the girl chose to come forward. The other women meekly parted to make way for her. Up close she was not the perfection Libbie had conjured from a distance during the parade. Her hair was perhaps too thick and coarse? Her face too square? Her eyes too small? But when Monahsetah smiled Libbie sensed the joy and warmth of her, the vital, fertile youth, and her heart dulled. The girl held out her papoose, an adorable velvety-skinned baby with jet eyes, and Libbie nodded as Monahsetah pushed it into her lap. With an involuntary check, Libbie noted it appeared a full-blooded Indian child, born scant months after capture. Through the interpreter, it appeared she wished Libbie

to take possession of the child to care for during her imprisonment.

Libbie flushed a deep red as Autie came between them. Through a series of gestures and words he unequivocally conveyed how honored they both were, and yet firm in their refusal of her gift.

Somehow seeing Monahsetah in the flesh had done the trick. The venom of jealousy drained from Libbie, and she could wait dispassionately for what happened next. Would such an ambitious man end all prospects of advancement by pursuing such a union openly? She thought not.

They never spoke of that visit, nor did he ask her to repeat it. Shortly thereafter Autie was ordered out to bring in the remaining tribes or else declare war on them if they refused. He groused at the politicians back in the States who presumed to know better than the Indians themselves, or the soldiers familiar with them, what was best. If the government simply kept its promises of supplies, violence could be quelled immediately. The truth was that politicians cared for what filled their pockets, and that was railroads and settlements. Empty spaces did not.

After Washita there was a new moodiness in Autie, and when Libbie asked about the

campaign he refused to talk. She deemed it a kind of nostalgia caused by the War and not abated by Indian fighting. Tom simply shrugged his shoulders and said it was very different from the experiences of the War. Although Autie had been lauded in many papers, an equal number criticized him. He could not recapture the universal approval that he had during the War, and it ate at him.

To cheer things up Libbie decided to hold a masquerade ball. With such limited materials each person at the fort had to employ all his ingenuity to create witty costumes. Autie took no interest in the proceedings, but she suspected he worked in secret so as to make a grand entrance.

When the day came, the women decorated their makeshift ballroom with ribbons and candles. Members of the band picked up fiddles for the night. At the last minute she decided to dress up as an Indian princess. With much protest, Eliza was sent to the stockade with a request for a wardrobe and jewelry to be borrowed from the prisoners, counting on the universal that the women would have grabbed their best finery before leaving their homes. She would return the items the next day, along with quantities of sugar, coffee, and other luxuries as thanks.

By the time Libbie went downstairs, the party was in full swing. Their community was so habituated to one another's company, they did not rest on formalities such as waiting for the hostess's appearance before eating and drinking. She was surprised to see Autie in his old Union war uniform, his large hat shadowing his face, a smart black mask covering his eyes. Usually he excused himself from these soirees and went to his study to read until she begged him to come join in. Now he stood alone, pensively looking out the doorway, glum and unsocial.

Libbie danced with a few officers who grabbed her arm before she was through the doorway. She was much the sensation in her shocking native attire — a fringed deerhide dress sewn with patterns made of elk teeth and beads. It was heavy and clinging and felt like a sensuous second skin. She wore her hair down in two long braids with feathers woven at the side with suede straps. On her feet she wore a pair of beaded moccasins.

After drinking a small glass of punch to bolster herself she made her way to Autie. When she reached him, she gave him a big kiss, then immediately pulled back with a confused look.

"Libbie!" he said.

It was Tom, dressed in his brother's uniform.

"Why didn't you stop me? *You* knew who I was! Even if I didn't recognize you."

She blushed and walked away, never admitting that of course she would never mistake one brother for the other and had not this time.

Later, having drunk too much, Tom insisted on taking Libbie aside. Drink was the bane of the army and so it had become for him. She hated to see him in such a state and began to lecture him yet again on taking a vow of abstinence as Autie had.

"Yes, I'll abstain as he does," he said.

Libbie looked away.

"That was uncalled for. Forgive me. You suffer enough without my adding to it."

"Let's go dance."

"I've received a letter from a certain lady in Monroe."

"Oh."

Other than her husband, Tom was the closest person to Libbie's heart. They shared the status of being in thrall to Autie. Loyal to the death, still they kept their own council, feeling that he was too judgmental.

They moved away for privacy although Autie was in his study, giving the guided

tour to his taxidermied menagerie and quite oblivious to them. The room was so overwhelmed with his trophies it had the eerie feel of an Egyptian crypt, as if he intended to take his prizes with him to the afterworld.

"Did you hear?" Libbie asked.

"She gave birth to a son."

Libbie's eyes smarted. The announcement cut even though she knew it was coming.

"She married. A shopkeeper who agreed to the paternity."

"For the best." She patted his arm. "But just imagine — you are a father!"

Later, Libbie sat in the kitchen and poured herself a thimble of whiskey. Normally she never touched alcohol, but tonight the pain was too intense. Everyone was always curious about their childlessness. When they first married she took for granted that soon there would be pregnancies, her life filled with babies and children. Autie came from a large family and expected to have his own. After a year passed, she worried the failure was hers. To his credit Autie declared what a nuisance babies would have been in camp. She did not believe him for a moment, but she loved him all the more for the consoling fiction.

Months after the departure of her Monroe friend, Autie had gone to the infirmary and

received treatments of silver nitrate. He admitted receiving such treatments before while at West Point.

When he departed that spring to bring in the remaining Cheyenne tribes, three captives accompanied him: the senior squaw, Mawisa, sister of Chief Black Kettle, who was enticed with the promise that her co-operation would be rewarded with freedom; a friend of Mawisa; and, of course, Monah-setah. In the end they would be gone almost six months.

Libbie went home to Monroe and began her own treatments. The only mention of it between them was when she wrote in a letter, *A night with Venus, a lifetime with Mercury.*

Autie brought in the remaining tribes and solidified his new reputation. A photograph taken during this time captured his transformation. He had donned the dressed buckskin clothes of a scout. On his head was a fur cap, and he had grown out a beard — incarnated once more into the heroic. With the Washita victory, he had completed the changeover from Civil War cavalier to plains hero. Now, though, Libbie judged him with new, harsh eyes. He reminded her of an actor preening in a new costume, and she understood the scorn of his detractors.

Seemingly oblivious of their long separation, he bragged in his letters of how the nomadic life suited him. In retaliation she bought an expensive new dress that would cost him a month's pay and stayed out later than her habit at a great many parties. As further punishment she added another month to her stay, but he was gone by so much longer her chastisement went unnoticed.

Do you want to know what I think of him?
Tom should have been the General and I
the Lieutenant.

— GEORGE ARMSTRONG CUSTER

April 17, 1871

Dear Jimmi,

It has come to our attention, seeing as you are soon to be joined in holy matrimony to our beloved sister Maggie that you will need to be initiated into Custer family lore. Since Maggie has little to zero interest in this subject, Armstrong and I have taken it upon ourselves to explain certain stories to you. Of course Armstrong, as usual, has taken the General's prerogative, that is he decided on an action then promptly turned it over to a plebe to carry out. In this case you are lucky, though, because I, too, can spin a yarn, and probably a more interesting one than You-Know-Who. Let's see if I can't pen something for posterity. As there's a card game starting now, this will be continued.

— Tom

TOM CUSTER

BRAVERY

In our childhood I won't deny that the Custer boys were called many things but coward wasn't one of them. Then or later. We loved pranks and never tired of playing them on each other, on our dad, who gave as good as he got, and sometimes on outright strangers. After Armstrong left for West Point, I hit a low point, thinking I would spend the rest of my life up to my elbows in dirt, staring at the same dull horizon till the end of my days. As time passed the idea became more and more intolerable, and I twice tried to enlist, underage, before my father finally gave his consent. He understood we had adventure running in our blood.

After the War of the Rebellion, I was stationed away from Armstrong and Libbie at a fort being built deep in Indian Terri-

tory. As we drilled the soldiers, others were busy felling trees and erecting our shelter, always under guard due to the proximity of the warring tribes. We had just put up the guard tower when we were alerted to an ambush not two hundred yards from our location across the river. From our elevated vantage we could observe the action but were out of range, a fact that the war party had clearly predicted. We watched helplessly as the guard, frightened at the sight of real live warriors, not only failed to get off a single shot, but abandoned the wagon and mules — the object of the raid — and fled to a nearby hillock. A single courageous soldier could have held the dozen warriors off indefinitely but that is not what happened.

At the fort, the lieutenant made ready a troop to ford the stream even as the Indians were sawing through the traces and harnesses to carry the animals off. Our single cannon was fired, which soared harmlessly over the natives' heads and into the woods behind. This gave the Indians pause, but unmolested, they continued on. We watched as the party rode off with their booty and only then did our guard rise to give false chase, firing off a few rounds at their fast-disappearing backsides before returning to

camp. There were certain truths that were self-evident in the family, and one of the most important was that *Custers always pursue.*

The Indian cannot be himself and be civilized; he fades away and dies. Cultivation such as the white man would give him deprives him of his identity . . . If I were an Indian, I often think, I would greatly prefer to cast my lot among those of my people adhered to the free open plains rather than submit to the confined limits of a reservation, there to be the recipient of the blessed benefits of civilization, with its vices thrown in . . .

— GEORGE ARMSTRONG CUSTER

INDIAN TERRITORY, SPRING
1869

After Washita, Custer was happy to be removed from civilization for a time, even if it meant a prolonged absence from Libbie. Sheridan left him with orders to bring in the remaining tribes either by diplomacy or force. After his last drubbing in the papers, Custer vowed it would be the former.

They rode for weeks before coming on Indian camps that quickly sued for peace and then scattered like the virga, the rain that evaporated on its way from cloud to earth. Villages that had been full of people until minutes before were abandoned as if by magic, only lodges, blankets, pots, and weapons left behind when the soldiers arrived. By routine the men counted the spoils, put them in a pile, and set them ablaze.

He ordered half of the men back to Fort Sill in order to be more mobile and conserve food. The remainder, including more than

fifty Indian scouts, formed a strange hybrid thing crossing the plains. Golden Buffalo again came to him for his nightly lessons and sometimes stayed to eat supper with the two Indian women. Custer practiced his rudimentary conversation on them, and they would indulge him for a while before tiring of his slowness and talking among themselves for hours while he looked on.

The March was a demanding one. Low promontories that seemed only hours away with their promise of revealing camps required a full day of hard riding, and they would end up arriving in the dark to set up unsatisfactory bivouac. Field glasses revealed hints of habitation in the distance that turned out to be mirages, drying away upon approach. Tricks played on the eye and on the brain.

Traversing the salt plains took a week or more.

The land that appeared so flat and mute and hostile opened up to Monahsetah and Mawisa as they read signs invisible to the soldiers.

The terrain revealed itself to be as sweetly knowable as a woman's body, and Custer liked riding it all day, sleeping in his tent under the stars at night, nose filled with the

338

girl's scent of leather and grass and smoke. He was in no particular hurry to find the fleeing Cheyenne, who were rumored to be joining the Arapaho, heading to the Llano Estacado, where they figured to permanently elude the army.

The particular band they tracked was rumored to be holding two white women settlers captive, but after the Blinn defeat he was not ready for the violence that would surely come from another rescue effort. War, battle, and other violence were much like appetite, one had to build the hunger for them, and at the moment he was sated. For the first time since he'd come to the forbidding plains, he felt he understood the landscape. Subdued and conquered like the girl beneath him, he in turn had been conquered. Every morning was permeated by the taste of grass and smoke. Each night became a silken black river of hair over honey-dark skin. He did not write letters home to Libbie.

The nomadic lifestyle suited him, and he thought he understood what no politician in Washington could ever figure — even mansions of gold had no leverage to a people who craved space and movement, who considered all land in common and found a barrier of any sort to be a kind of

death. What they wanted was a floating world.

Monahsetah's spirits lifted, being on the open land, even though her prison traveled with her. Being tethered to one spot on the earth was the ultimate agony.

She taught Custer to use bow and arrow like an Indian. Done right, it was almost as effective as a gun. His competitive nature made him want to be as good with it as the warriors he fought against.

Years before, the Kiowa had tried to play Sheridan false. The chiefs had ridden along with the command, thick with promises that the village was on its way to Fort Cobb, but every few hours another chief begged off to go hurry the village along. Trackers discovered that the village was fast disappearing the other way. Lone Wolf and Satanta had promptly been made prisoner, but even then the village dragged its feet returning.

During long days of negotiation, Custer had occasion to get to know his forced guests through the interpreter, Satanta's son, a warrior of twenty. He served as liaison between the village and fort, carrying messages back and forth. In the course of things it came out that the young warrior was

renowned for his shooting skills, instantly igniting Custer's competitive streak.

During the interminable, dull hours of diplomacy, he soon had the boy engaged in contests of target practice. The smart thing would have been to let him win, but Custer could not. It was not in him. To soothe the chief's ego, the distance to the targets was varied and finally they even switched rifles, with no change in outcome. To Satanta these results were aberrations. He gazed into the campfire, his eyes glowing golden, as he explained that the result was as impossible as the buffalo disappearing, as impossible as the Kiowa not ultimately emerging triumphant.

Indian fighting, too, was fast disappearing, a way of life soon to be gone. The cavalryman was as dependent on the Indian as the Indian was dependent on the buffalo. Progress was as inexorable for him as it was for the tribe. He pitied them all.

Monahsetah's moods swung from carefree to dark, and one day during practice Custer turned to find her aiming the arrow straight at his heart.

— Do it, he said.

She said nothing, her face a mask of cold deliberation.

— I wondered when you would try. But if you kill me, imagine who will come after, he said, and spread his legs apart, squaring his hips, providing as big a target as possible.

Based on tracks left by Indian hunting parties, they pressed on westward. One morning the command was excited by the presence of smoke ahead and its promise of a main camp. The scout calculated that it could be reached by the afternoon of that day. After six hours of hard riding the smoke appeared just as distant as it had earlier, the only change being that the surrounding land had grown more rocky and forbidding.

He sent back to Fort Sill for provisions even as they continued on farther and farther into the barren landscape. The graying buffalo grass gave out so that they had to strip mesquite to feed the horses. The men were reduced to one meal a day and soon meat ran out entirely.

What infuriated him enormously was the short-changing they received from the Commissary Dept., and as soon as this campaign was over he was determined to roll heads, all the way up to President Grant if needed. They'd received no bread, only flour, the men reduced to baking something well-nigh inedible over a campfire. They'd

even run out of candles, and he was forced to hoard his stubs in order to write each evening. This was no way to take care of soldiers. He suspected much of the previous summer's mischief by the Indians had to do with the poor provisioning at the reservations, making the army's job even harder.

The smoke changed direction the second morning and fanned out before nightfall. When they at last reached its source, after almost ten hours of nonstop riding, it was discovered to be a prairie fire burning out of control, caused either by an old campfire or lightning. In the dark the orange embers snaked along the ground. When they reached a bush or tree, the possessed flames jumped and devoured the vegetation in a burst of fire before moving on. The soldiers' feet stirred up ash as they walked so that they had to cover their faces with kerchiefs to breathe. In this way thousands of acres were consumed, unseen except by them as sole witnesses.

Stopping for the night, one of the horses collapsed from starvation. No sooner had the body touched the ground than it was quickly dispatched into a meal. Soon campfires were lit from the existing conflagration, and ravenous men cooked roasts,

steaks, and broils on spits of coaled wood. Next morning it may have been his imagination, but he thought the horses moved more briskly, trying to minimize the degree to which their ribs poked against the skin, worried that they might be turned into the main course that night. His horse, Dandy, seemed happy to feast on sand and air.

He buried his hunger in Monahsetah's flesh while the rest of the soldiers shared out their whole month's ration of whiskey in mere days to dull their hunger pangs, all thus enjoying many an intoxicated night. None was more boisterous than Tom. As a matter of course, he had confiscated his brother's allotment of spirits because in the particular of his sobriety vow he was utterly faithful. Tom's behavior grew loud and disruptive, though, and Custer was forced to reprimand him. When that was not enough, he cuffed the cup out of his hand.

— Set an example, for God's sake.

— You should talk! Monster!

In his drunkenness Tom rose in anger, fists coming out before he realized his error, not only in defying an elder brother but his commander, too.

The unacknowledged truth between the brothers was they were matched in abilities, yet he had the role of leadership. Tom must

acquiesce.

He ordered Tom under arrest for insubordination and drunkenness. The next day he had him paraded before the troops with a placard bearing the word "drunkard" on his back. Tom sulked, refusing to go to his tent for meals as was their custom.

— Spend time with your damned Indians.

A few days later, Tom returned to his old self, except now he kept a special distance from the bottle when it was offered. Whether alcohol unleashed truth or its opposite, neither brother was eager to explore.

They rode another day, entering a wide valley with the promise of trees in the distance indicating water. As they approached, the trees wavered off. When at last they came upon streams, they found them alkaline and undrinkable, salt-crusted white along their banks. Both men and horses were near breaking point. Custer felt the men's hatred for him, both for his treatment of Tom, the camp favorite, and for pushing them to this doomed end.

Riding during the glare of noon, he squinted against the caliche burn from the ground when far in the distance he saw horses were being run, a large troop of soldiers following. Even before he saw them as more than blurs on the horizon, he

understood the horses would be the slashed ones from Washita, that some of the soldiers would be dressed in Union uniforms, some Confederate. There would be many cavalry and some Indians, women and children, and following would be buffalo, and even dogs beyond count. When they came close enough to be visible in his field glasses, they of course disappeared. He was pursued both within and without.

Tom Custer

MY BROTHER'S OBSESSION

He took us out weeks too long, to the most barren desert prairie, drove us to the point that the skeletal horses fell over from exhaustion and lack of food. Far from considering this a loss we counted it a bonus as at least we'd have nourishment that night. After eating we were still every bit as hungry as before. The men were on the verge of mutiny until the Indian trail was found, and then as if by magic Armstrong was again hailed a hero. Not to my thinking, but I had learned the hard way to keep my mouth shut. The possibility of glory, like gold-fever, blinded men.

To his credit, Armstrong managed to negotiate the captives' release without bloodshed. Once we had the women, we immediately headed to the closest fort. I'll never forget the look of the soldiers on duty

when we passed through the perimeter fence. A few men in undershirts on their way to the barber stopped to stare at us while still holding their bowls of lather.

We were a rough-looking bunch: half of us mounted, the other half walking as their horses had died underneath them; burned dark as Indians; our clothes in tatters; our boots fallen apart. We inspired apprehension.

What amazed me, though, was the appearance of the stationed soldiers. They had cheeks as full as pillows. I could not understand why they appeared puffy and bloated, why they moved so fast and spoke so loudly. It was as if the fort were under some spell. It gave me the most unnatural feeling. Only later did I realize that these men were not deformed at all, but it was we who had become the circus act. Cadaverous, filthy, weak, starved, the soldiers could not tell us apart one from another any more than one could tell apart skeletons on the prairie, which we had just missed becoming.

As I was about to comment on the strangeness in appearance of our hosts, I saw the mess tent where they were unpacking supplies. A great quantity of hard bread and sides of raw bacon were being laid out. We stood as one, enchanted, and then as

one dove down on the supplies like a flock of ravenous buzzards. The men from the fort watched speechless as officers, soldiers, and even scouts stuffed their mouths alternately with bread and raw pork. We ate it all down to the last scrap. For the rest of the month the fort had to make do without either on its menu.

Llano Estacado, the Palisaded Plain

They left Indian territory and kept heading west till they entered Texas then crossed into the Llano Estacado. They tracked the small hunting party for days, hanging back so as to not spook them. Custer's theory was they were on their way to reunite with the larger mother village of Cheyenne, who were thumbing their nose at orders to appear on the reservation. The Indians would rather die in such desolate surroundings than change their warrior life for the threadbare existence of meager handouts, starvation, and disease that were rife on the reservations.

Custer understood their risking everything to leave. He would have done the same, and yet he was tasked with bringing them back.

Traveling through those empty spaces, stopping only for food and rest at night, he found the most satisfying way of life imaginable. The Indian would not willingly give up

his ways any more than he, a cavalryman, would give up his. If either of them did, they would be much the poorer for it, their very heart eaten out of them.

He stared at his calendar, the grid of dates swimming meaningless before his eyes. These surroundings were beyond the reach of time or the commonplace rules of society. By his rusty calculation, he figured out it was his wedding anniversary.

To-day is our wedding anniversary. I am sorry we cannot spend it together, but I shall celebrate it in my breast.

With each passing mile the soldiers understood that they were attenuating their chance of rescue by supply train. Desperate, they decided to make contact. They galloped their horses into the Indian camp they had been trailing, taking possession of lodges, ponies, everything except for a single living Indian. The troops were mystified about how they had been discovered; it seemed an evil enchantment.

Then, a mile away, he spotted a party of Indians on horseback, heading straight at them at a full run. He called for a charge, and his men raced across the desertscape. When they were within a few hundred

yards, the Indians morphed into the decaying carcasses of half a dozen buffalo, given number and movement by the effect of the mirage. It was as if the land plucked the wants and fears from their minds and projected them out on the landscape.

No clue appeared on the ground to lead them forward, nothing except faith and hopelessness, which came close to being the same thing in such perilous times. Then an Osage guide espied the track of a lone travois pole scratching the earth like a plowshare. The man reluctantly offered the discovery, torn between duty and self-preservation.

They tracked as if they were following the ancient swish of a dinosaur tail. Many of the officers cursed that it was a wild-goose chase, the path figured to be a month old if not more. Custer knew the ways of the Indian, no one stayed alone for long in such country, solitariness equaling death. He took private council with Golden Buffalo, who agreed with his assessment. There was a chance that this lone straggler was hurrying to meet up with other members of his tribe. He browbeat the men into another few days of tracking before he would agree to turn back.

Sunset found the troop at a small stream.

There was evidence of the single trail being joined by two or three others. The dusted circles of lodges could be seen. The men became reenergized, their recent hardship forgotten, and looked more kindly on his demands.

He sent for Monahsetah to examine the remains of a campfire, which confirmed that the single hunting party had joined others like rivulets joining together and forming a stream, which itself would be traveling to join a greater river. She guessed the camp was at most two weeks old.

Studying the ground, she looked off into the distance, then followed a trail off into the desert. Behind a small swell lay the decayed body of a warrior.

— What did he die of? Custer asked.

Monahsetah dispassionately examined the body and at last seemed satisfied.

— Horse fall. He must have broke his neck. He died before he starved.

Custer nodded.

— Maybe the horse was crazy, she added.

— Crazy?

— When I was a girl, my best friend rode her brother's horse one day while we were on trail. Something spooked him, and he took off. She had not fastened her saddle tight enough. She slipped off but caught her

foot in the stirrup. He dragged her to her death. Her father was so angry when he heard his daughter was gone, he came with a gun to the herd, picked the horse out, and shot it.

— That must have scared you. A bad horse.

— The horse wasn't bad. He was crazy.

He wondered at Monahsetah's help — leading them to her people to convince them to go to the reservation. She said that it was better than to be made war on. She was a pragmatist, a trait he recognized in himself. That night they ate in his tent, and after he finished his reports and letters, they bedded down with just as much appetite. It was a delight to be with a woman who didn't need looking after. His Libbie quaked with every small scare. Not this girl. She rode as well as the men and was a better shot. When he looked down into her eyes he could not guess her thoughts but prepared to one night feel a blade lift his scalp from his head.

She lay on buffalo robes at night, lamplight gilding flesh, her voice a lullaby in his ears.

— You ride like a man. Who taught you? he asked.

— My father.

— Not husband?

She shook her head.

— You must learn to ride young to be comfortable on a horse.

— Why did you marry your husband if you didn't want him?

— He saved me.

— *Saved?*

She stretched and rolled like a cat. She loved to tell stories of her life, even if it was to him.

— I was a girl. Eight or so. The village was moving. It was a very hot day.

A group of five girls rode behind the travois, taking their time, when they saw the cool water of a stream beckon not far off. Time was short, the rest of the village was getting farther and farther away, yet they decided to plunge into the water so they could ride wet, cooled by the moving air. They led their horses into the water so they could drench themselves and water the horses at the same time to save precious minutes.

They were silly girls, always up to pranks, and Monahsetah dared her best friend to go underneath and see who could hold her breath the longest. The winner could pick anything of the loser's to use for a day.

Monahsetah recalled the dark and cold beneath the surface, and when a mysterious underwater woman appeared, she was not in the least surprised. Instead of being scared, the girl wanted to know who the water witch was, and why she had appeared. Suddenly there was pulling on her arms, the other girls dragging her to the riverbank, saying she had won long ago.

Her friend stood on the bank, laughing, water dripping off her.

— What do you want of mine? she asked.

— I wish to ride your horse the rest of the day.

The girls' mouths dropped open.

Monahsetah was the princess among them, already with an offer of marriage when she came of age. Her father had refused the warrior, saying the girl would decide for herself when she was old enough. Chief Little Rock doted on his daughter, giving her one of his best horses, a tall chestnut that ran like flame through dry grass. Her friend had an old, swaybacked white mare who moved slowly. Acts such as this were common from Monahsetah, though, used to deflect the envy she would have otherwise received. She did not have to ask twice. Her friend sprang up on her horse's back and left.

The afternoon was hot and the water so refreshing, Monahsetah sat in the water longer, laughing at her friend's haste. After the other girls left, she decided to use the occasion to bathe, and she pulled off her wet clothing and splashed herself. The water felt good on her bare skin. Such delay didn't worry her, as she was used to her own horse, who could catch up easily. Now, mounting the old mare, her miscalculation was obvious.

Her friends were far ahead of her when they all noticed a large herd of buffalo moving quickly up the valley, right in between the girls and their disappearing village.

The herd was shaped like a long anvil, narrow at the head and much wider farther on. The end could not be seen and probably stretched out a great distance. Her friends galloped for all they were worth to reach their families. Monahsetah put her heels to the horse, at once realizing her mistake. The mare's trot was as fast as a slow walk by any other animal, but still Monahsetah hoped she might catch up if the poor animal's heart didn't give out.

She whipped the horse, with the plan to get across the narrow tip before they got caught in the stampede. Something had spooked the herd into running — they were

moving as fast as she had ever seen — and nothing would stop it. If she and the mare got caught in the center and couldn't keep up, they would be trampled to death. This happened routinely to young and old buffs, but also to anything unlucky enough to get caught in the stampede's path.

Instead of speeding up with the abuse, the old mare gave up all effort and moved slower as the herd bore down on them.

Monahsetah lost sight of her friends, her retreating village, and even the sky and sun went dark. There was only the herd. A dark, overwhelming mass of power, and she was caught in the center of it. She couldn't focus because everything was in motion. The air was bitter and on fire, her breath tore from her lungs. Her nose filled with the oily reek of a thousand buffs close packed. Light-headed, she dropped the reins of the mare and felt herself slipping off. A buffalo pressed against the horse, and she pushed off its side to right herself. She was crying, the darkness blurred, and her ears deafened with awful roaring as if the earth were being ripped apart.

The mare turned to run along with the herd, at last understanding that otherwise she would be gored. Even at her utmost, she moved at half the speed of the animals

around her, continually hit and bounced from side to side. Soon the mare would drop in exhaustion, and they would both be trampled to pieces. Monahsetah did not expect to see her family again.

She did not know how long she clung on to the mare's mane, crouched over her neck, but her arms and legs ached. It was clear that they would go under long before the end of the herd was reached. Dizzy with fear, she closed her eyes and in that moment felt herself lifted off the mare's back. Was it the mysterious woman from underwater? More likely it was a buffalo. Perhaps even now the animal was preparing to gore her on one of its horns, but as Monahsetah went limp she felt something grab around her waist. She moved through the air slowly, legs behind her as if swimming. Opening her eyes, she saw the mare had stopped, legs buckling, but Monahsetah was no longer on her. Instead she was in the arms of the young warrior, sixteen years old, who had asked for her in marriage. Skillfully he moved them across the herd to its edge, and they broke free.

— After that, I agreed to marry him when I turned fifteen. He had proved himself a brave protector.

359

Custer ran a finger up and down her arm. The implication of the story was clear. Also the fact that when said husband later failed her, she did not hesitate to shoot him in the leg and leave.

Like a dog on the scent of a fox, the troops mounted with more eagerness the next morning, and within a few hours came upon another recently abandoned camp, this one increasing in size to twenty-five lodges. Monahsetah was pleased by her detective work. Feeling secure, the Indian hunting party moved leisurely in their progress, figuring no one was crazy enough to pursue them into such inhospitable terrain.

Coming off the alkali flats to a high, grassy plateau, the cavalry was within a day of the camp, which had swollen to three or four hundred lodges, the embers of fires still glowing. The men declared Custer a seer and cheered him with their cups.

The last night, he permitted only small supper fires to be lit, and once the food was cooked they were quickly smothered in damp earth to prevent smoke ascending.

The next day the guides found the expected Indian pony herd. Custer rode in advance with a small guard to alert the sentry wolves posted. Hoping that this

indeed was the Cheyenne camp with the captive women, he was at pains to call a parley before his troops caught up to him. The danger of a random shot from either side was too high. He had learned from Washita that it would lead to the captives' murder. To signal a truce he rode in a circle and then in a zigzag toward the bluffs on which the Indians waited. Soon a party of twenty warriors rode out to him.

His main body of troops still a mile away, he signed for a single one of the party to advance to meet him. The two exchanged handshakes, each taking the measure of the other. He requested an audience with the head chief, Medicine Arrows. As they waited, the party of twenty approached closer. He objected and they backed off. Finally Medicine Arrows arrived, his face wrinkled and worn as old shoe leather. They exchanged suspicious greetings.

The retired party used the distraction of the chief's arrival to press forward again. They now surrounded Custer as the chief demanded to know how many soldiers followed, the number clearly determining whether Custer would be quickly dispatched with a tomahawk or treated as an honored guest. As the number was enough — he doubled it for good measure — Medicine

Arrows requested him to follow to the village, assuring their peaceful intentions. The canny chieftain hid his displeasure at having been found in such desolated parts.

In the chief's lodge, a pipe was presented for him to smoke down. Much speechifying on their part followed, only partly understood because Golden Buffalo was back with the advancing troops. Custer omitted the rude observation that the tribe had clearly broken their pledge to move to the reservation, that their very presence was provocation. In friendship he requested to make suitable camp close to the village. The chief led him to a professed choice spot that yet was quite distant.

As his troops rode in to make camp, joined by the supply train, one hundred Indians chose that importune moment to pay a visit. All were armed with rifles, pistols, bows and arrows, as well as sturdy knives. They performed various feats of horsemanship, then went on to serenade with musical instruments and song.

While the entertainments dragged on, observers reported back what Custer expected — the village, in great calamity, was packing up. The pony herd had been drawn in, the lodges were in the process of being torn down, and women and children were

fleeing in haste. His command was ready to put a halt to the treachery and was surprised when he did not give the order to pursue.

Instead he instructed Tom with a contingent of soldiers to surround their circle of visitors in as unobtrusive a manner as possible, aware that any precipitate movement would result in bloodshed.

After the decoy show ended, he allowed the majority of the Indians to leave until only a few senior chiefs and warriors remained whom he had bribed to stay with the promise of a whiskey nightcap. These, he calmly informed, were now permanent guests of the U.S. Cavalry. In other words, they were under arrest. They would be treated well despite their attempted duplicity in trying to distract the soldiers while their village escaped. They would be held until the release of the two captives and the pledged return of the Cheyenne to their assigned reservation.

As expected, the reaction was much outrage and showboating, with a firm denial of the existence of any captives. The younger warriors called for bloodshed while the older men and chiefs urged patience. Custer wanted patience, too. He must be turning into an old man.

After Washita an equal number in the

press had disparaged as had praised him. He was long overdue a touch of the heroic, this time as peacemaker. The release of the captives would achieve that. He had his own hostage, one that was both held and not held. As she gave in willingly each night, she conquered him. He did not want to kill these people, but he could not stop history taking care of that, regardless of how he willed it.

That night, he decided to pen an article for a magazine clamoring for his writing about the frontier. It would not be what they expected.

The Indian warrior bids adieu — often a final one — to the dear ones of his tribe, and with his comrades-in-arms sets out, no matter how inclement the season, to seek what? Food, of course. Then the one hundred uses of the buffalo, from shelter and clothing, to household utensils, tools, weapons, decorative finery. They go, importantly, to make war on other tribes with the goal of increasing their own power and wealth, whether through territory, horses and women, or other stolen goods. What else do they seek? Because there never comes a prolonged time of peace for the Indian any more than for the white

race. As is common knowledge, it is the young bucks who urge this behavior. So what is it that they seek? They, like the young of all peoples, look to distinguish themselves for their bravery, for their horsemanship, for their ability as warriors, for counting coup on their enemy, for attaining glory and the possibility of becoming chieftain. It is almost the same, in fact it is precisely the same, as the life of our own soldier.

He looked at the page he had written for a long time. His thoughts recorded were always cathartic. This was a reverse on an earlier essay, but after rereading it, he crumpled the page into a ball and threw it into the fire. It was one thing to lose one's head, another to put it in the noose. There was a long line of officers who had taken up the Indian side and found themselves fast out of a job.

For days the hostage situation hung unmoving like a rain cloud overhead. When the four chiefs still being held were informed that they must disarm themselves while in custody, more enmity arose, and only with great difficulty was violence avoided.

One coolheaded chieftain calmly exam-

ined arrow after arrow, casting his eye along each shaft, separating the best out as if for a future confrontation. Custer admired the impossibility of admitting defeat. He recognized it in himself. Dying did not so much matter, the real disgrace was to be a coward.

At last on threat of force, arms were given over. As a concession, one chieftain was allowed to depart for the village as bearer of the army's demands. Upon leaving, this man was returned his weapons, as well as given gifts of coffee and sugar to be distributed as a sign of goodwill. Custer did not expect to see hide nor hair of the chief again, nor was he disappointed.

At nightfall one evening, a group of warriors called out from the darkness to check on the welfare of the remaining chiefs. They did not trust assurances that they could enter camp on safe passage, so Monahsetah volunteered to go out past the perimeter and escort them in. At the last minute, though, she claimed to be frightened at the prospect of being shot by the guards on her return, identified as the enemy, which in point of fact she was. Custer wondered that she did not worry about being killed as a traitor by her own people but admitted he did not understand the culture enough. He would accompany her. Surely, he joked, the

guards wouldn't shoot their own leader?

Inside camp, the night beyond was forbidding, but looking backward into camp — the lit fires, the glowing tents, the soldiers and weapons — he was surprised how it appeared equally threatening.

They walked together out into the forest, the darkness now opening up as their eyes adjusted, the privacy allowing him to cup a breast, push her against a tree trunk, lift her shift. He carried a revolver and saber, at her insistence adding quiver and bow. His technique under her tutelage had much improved, but he did not understand the need to bring these out in the night. In the starlight her face was an unknown constellation, only the dark, smoky taste of her familiar. She managed the top buttons of his shirt, and later he found a half moon of bloody teeth marks above his right breast.

She whispered into his ear to pull an arrow from the quiver and string it in the bow. When he did he immediately saw it was not the kind they usually practiced with but a stiffer one, painted a dark color. She stood in the darkness, her face lupine in concentration, and then pointed toward the north, directing his aim at the low stars on the horizon just above the trees.

— What is this?

— Medicine.

She ran her hand over his wrist, indicating pleasure at his increasing strength in holding the arrow steady. The arrow hissed through the air and was gone.

— I'll retrieve it for you, she said.

He grabbed her wrist hard and yanked her back.

— No!

A light fog had appeared through the trees, and as he held her he heard the hooting of an owl. A traditional Indian signal.

— Is this a trap?

She shook her head, dismissive, and faced in the opposite direction.

— Shoot another there.

He blinked in the fog, seeing the shadow of a cliff in the distance and aiming above it. His wrist, fatigued, shook now as he pulled the heavy arrow back, and she was next to him, stroking his back, her breath warm and damp on his neck as she urged him to release the arrow. For a brief moment he was afraid of her, but he pushed the thought away. The arrow flew off in the darkness. The fog had thickened, damp against his face as her breath, and again her voice was in his ear that she would go to retrieve the second arrow.

— Do you take me for a fool?

He pulled her to him, covered her mouth with his own. He felt light-headed and had lost his sense of direction. His body was on fire, his insides burning and molten. He worried she'd poisoned him.

A howl rose up so close that he felt it came from his own throat. He jumped as two shaggy shapes lumbered off into the trees — wolves. The beasts sat on their haunches and watched them. He should shoot but couldn't muster the energy to be frightened.

— It's good, Monahsetah said.

Not good at all. He wanted to return to camp, forget the whole undertaking, but his legs felt so heavy.

— Another arrow, she whispered.

— I can't.

— You must.

He directed it straight at the stars. He was shaking, chilled, drenched from the fog, and dead tired. His thinking came slowly. When the arrow left the bow, he felt the vibration through his whole body as if he had become the bow. The fog was so thick now, he couldn't see Monahsetah clearly. As if she had dissolved into fog herself. Blinded, he closed his eyes, felt himself moving along the trajectory of the arrow, wind rushing past his ears. He prepared for the impact of arrowhead plunging into its predestined

place, of which he had no knowledge. The night so black the stars were extinguished. Where had the wolves gone?

Her hands were on him, scratching, and he grabbed her and pushed her to the ground. He could not see. Breathing came with difficulty. He lay on top of her and felt the brush of the wolf's pelt against his coat, the stink of breath fetid with rotten meat. With one movement, he raised up on his knees, holding the last arrow in his fist, and smashed it into the wolf's head.

The fog disappeared. Stars shone and a crescent moon floated in the clear sky. Instead of a wolf, he'd smashed the arrow into the trunk of a tree and broken it in half, bloodying his hand in the process.

As if a fever spell had broken, Monahsetah pulled her clothing smooth and moved off to climb the bluffs and reassure the visitors. Custer returned to the protection of the picket post because even though he still had the scent of her in his nostrils, the slick of her on him, that did not mean revenge still might not be delivered. He would never be safe in her company. When the small group of warriors led by her came forward, he escorted them through the pickets to the guard post, where the chiefs were allowed a visit that lasted well into the night. He

bargained that this demonstration of good-will would help secure the release of the white captives. It did not.

Days passed.

More visits and offerings of food and gifts were followed by more unkept promises. The village envoys expressed the desire that the three hostages be released before the question of the captive white girls was even considered, an inadvertent admission that they existed. He refused. At last, in exasperation, he threatened to move the camp closer to the village than the distance that now delayed their parley. The implied threat was clear.

As expected, no reply came so the regiment pulled up and moved along the Sweetwater. Again Indian envoys came. They sat by the campfire and ate their fill. Again they requested the chiefs' release before discussing the issue of captives.

He was stuck.

Precedent was that the Indians receive ransom, which he was loath to do given the bad faith so far shown. It was a test of his will not only against the Cheyenne but also against his own men, who were crazed to avenge themselves. There was a growing likelihood of an accidental war being started. The Kansas Volunteers were specifi-

cally there to rescue those captives, and they longed for blood.

When he called for yet another parley, a mutinous grumble arose. Diplomacy was as trying as battle. He longed for the surety of a charge.

In his tent sat the three chiefs joined by a delegation from the village. In the oratory habit of these meetings, Custer reviewed aloud the steps that had already occurred, from their first meeting to the tribe's repeated attempts to escape, to the delay of the captives' return. A pause. He frowned. He had reached the end of his patience. If the girls were not returned by sunset of the following day, the chiefs would be killed. In addition the tribe would need to turn themselves in to the reservation. If they refused, the regiment would move on the village, which had no chance of fleeing given the burden of winter-weakened ponies and the numbers of women and children.

The delegation sullenly left.

Custer sat alone. Neither Monahsetah nor Golden Buffalo came to visit that night, a judgment. Tom avoided him also. For the first time he could remember, he felt weary. He missed Libbie's consolations. He was trying his best at playing diplomat but it brought no accolades, only suspicion and

discontent from all sides. No matter the effort, it always eventually came down to the necessity of brute force.

The next day passed slowly. The chiefs did not appear as confident as Custer would have hoped. One tried to negotiate his own release on the pretext of urging the village to move faster to save his fellow hostages. Custer dismissed the subterfuge. The troops scoured the hills in the direction of the village for an approaching party, but none came. Noon passed, then mid-afternoon, then late afternoon.

He did not want the chiefs' deaths on his head, but he couldn't back down on his threat without losing credibility.

An hour before dusk, a small party of warriors on horses could be seen approaching. Two riders sat on one of the ponies. A mile away, they dismounted and walked. Through field glasses, he saw they were the captive girls. One was short and stocky, the other tall and thin. They were clothed in Indian leggings and moccasins, the dresses over them fashioned out of flour sacks, the name of the mill stamped on each, indicating provisions supplied by the reservation. They had been ornamented with rings and necklaces to appear less abused, but later stories confirmed that both had suffered ravages

beyond enduring.

The soldiers, especially the volunteers, surrounded them, protecting what was already destroyed. Men who had stoically witnessed the most outrageous atrocities now swatted tears from their eyes, made shy before the women. They clasped the girls' hands yet would not hug them. It was discovered that both women were several months pregnant. Even the brother of one, who had spent the last two years tracking his sister, held himself aloof.

— Are we free? the sister asked.

In her early twenties, she had been married only a month when abducted.

— Yes, you are.

She proceeded to ask her brother about her husband and parents. He gave her satisfactory answer.

The shorter, younger one remained silent. She had seen with her own eyes that none of her kin survived.

Custer chastised himself for his discomfort around the victims. Once action was no longer called for, he felt superfluous in the face of their ruin. That night at retreat he had the band serenade them with "Home, Sweet Home."

Over the ensuing days, he observed that the girls lived at a remove among their own

people, ostracized into a permanent martyrdom. Did they sense the unconscious collective wish that they would have perished already and been ejected straight to sainthood?

The young women had been traded repeatedly from one tribe to another, finally arriving by chance in the same village and able to take comfort and strength from each other. Both had suffered repeated molestation, malnourishment, and forced labor. The captives had been planning an escape even though they did not know what part of the country they were in, nor in which direction rescue from settlements or military posts might be found. Their plan was to start walking into the desert plains until either safety or annihilation won.

As they marched to Camp Supply over the following week, almost perishing again from lack of food, many of the volunteers told Custer they were at first disappointed at his choosing diplomacy over attacking the village. They worried that he had lost his nerve to fight Indians, but now with the successful results they sheepishly commended him.

— Sir, no disrespect intended, but some were calling you a coward. A traitor to the regiment.

He swore by their faces they meant the exact opposite. They justified their doubts by explaining that such negotiations were simply not in keeping with his aggressive reputation, and it had taken them aback. To his ears their words sounded mostly like rebuke.

When the 7th Cavalry arrived at Fort Hays, the three chiefs were put in the stockade to join the women and children of the Washita campaign to await the return of the Cheyenne to their designated reservation.

Monahsetah visited her friends but preferred to stay in the comparative luxury and freedom of the 7th's camp. What did she think when she saw her "sisters" imprisoned in the stockade? Did she acknowledge she was simply in another type of jail? She was gifted a quantity of provisions — four boxes of biscuits, two pounds of coffee, one pound of sugar, a piece of salt pork, a bolt of calico, as well as a pair of bob earrings — for her part in the expedition.

The last night out, Custer sent her to Tom's tent as reward for his brother's superior actions during the campaign and for abstaining from alcohol since his last reprimand. It stung the slightest bit when she packed up her few belongings and left

without a backward look. He felt the part of sobbing debutante, but it was an opportune time for the separation. It pleased him to note that his brother's loyalty to Libbie did not prevent him from enjoying the girl's charms. When he later heard that Monahsetah had birthed a half-breed, he did not much concern himself with the possible paternity.

A peaceful outcome had been achieved.

All went well until a few weeks later when he learned of a new misfortune. Troops had determined to move the chiefs from tents to rooms in the guardhouse, not thinking it of enough import to inform him of the change. Without interpreter, the soldiers used rude sign language, coupled with the threat of rifles, to get their intention across. The chiefs, suspecting betrayal, refused to move and instead attacked with knives hidden in their blankets. Two died of wounds, the third was injured but survived.

In the spring, with the surrender of the last Cheyenne to the reservation, all that were still alive in the stockade, including Monahsetah and the one remaining chief, were at last given their liberty, if it could be called such.

Tom Custer

MY BROTHER'S WIFE

People teased that I was in love with Libbie but that was nonsense. My beloved fiancée, Lulie, was the ideal of womanhood to me, and if the fates had allowed I believe ours would have been as exemplary a union as Armstrong and Libbie's.

As it was, they were the envy of all social circles they passed through, whether it be the high society in New York or the most primitive outpost in the Territories. The type of love that turned a blind eye to a companion's faults. They found enjoyment in even the dullest moment if it was in each other's company. Although Armstrong found plenty of excuses to be separate, he lived each act through Libbie's eye, even bragging to her of his female admirers. She told me how it drove a knife in her heart, but she never let on to him. Jealousy was beneath them. Her

love was the not so secret source of his confidence. He, lucky man, knew he could rely on her loyalty no matter the ups and downs of the soldier's profession, or his philanderer's successes.

Lulie was the opposite of Libbie. She reminded me of a summer morning, how the sun heated the flowers to intoxication. Skin pale, eyes the color of the clearest lake, hair like corn silk, it was as if she were an angel unfit for the rough existence on this earth. When I first met her she wore a white dress, and I don't believe I ever saw her in any other color, but given her housebound, cloistered state, it well suited her other-worldliness. There was never a question that she could leave that house, much less Jersey City, much less the States, to live a frontier life such as Libbie had. She was much too rare.

Even as I held Lulie's hand I knew that she could never withstand the rigors of motherhood. The idea of a man lying atop her was unthinkable. She seemed so frail and delicate her bones might break under the weight of passion, but still I proposed and still she consented. It was our fairy tale. She knew that I could just as little give up the roaming, adventurous life of the army

George Armstrong Custer, Tom Custer, and Libbie Bacon Custer

to become her house companion, but our fanciful engagement fulfilled something in her girlish heart. The dream of a perfect union. Knowing it would be unrealized, it was never in danger of failing.

Comparison with Libbie was as inevitable as it was unfair. Libbie had as much beauty and refinement, but she also had fire in her heart. She was a Custer in her blood. The love between my brother and her was something to either admire, envy, or scorn, depending on your mood. I'll say no more than if Libbie had been mine, I would never have caused her such pain. When the consumption finally ended Lulie's too-short life, I mourned, and my beloved sister-in-law was there to dry my tears.

THE TENTH REMOVE

Buffalo work camp — Cavalry raid —
Massacre — Rescue

Another two years had passed when Anne
was again at a riverbank with her group of
fellow buffalo skinners. The village, several
miles away, was peaceful; the warriors
prepared for a hunt. Neha was large with
her first child. While Anne was unable to
escape the bondage of Snake Man, Running Bear had petitioned that she be allowed
to sew for all the members of the tribe.
Anne was now the master seamstress and
had apprenticed Neha so that she, too,
would have a degree of independence.

One of Running Bear's daughters would
soon marry a warrior she loved, and Anne
had agreed to make the bridal dress, one
that would be the finest thing she had ever
attempted. She wanted to specially prepare
the hide herself, lightening it to a pale cream

and making it as supple as heavy silk between the fingertips.

Although Neha and Anne could have forgone the butchering camp with their new status, they enjoyed their time away from their regular chores. The group of outcasts had found a camaraderie over the years.

It being the Moon of the Juneberries, Anne guessed it was close to her Christian birthday. She celebrated it by picking a large bag of berries to share with the other skinners. They all helped prepare a modest "feast" and then stayed up late into the night telling stories. Such times made Anne feel almost happy, and she only wished her children were there to complete it. They had stayed at Snake Man's teepee, now that they were old enough to be away from her for prolonged periods.

Knowing the white tradition, Neha presented her with a gift, in this case the Spanish icon of years before, its frame partly melted.

"Where did you find it?"

"Oldest wife bragged of pulling it from the fire. When I was cleaning her things I found it hidden away. It belongs to you."

"I found it the day Solace was born. It was a good birth. You have it now."

Neha looked at it skeptically. "White

man's medicine does not work for Indians."

It was more precious than anything Anne had ever owned. She would sew a special pocket, leather this time, which would hang around her neck, secreted away under her dress. It would never again be far from her.

After her escape to the fort had been foiled, something shifted within Anne. It seemed too exhausting to devise a new plot. She surrendered to her captivity, taking on faith that with the encroachment of settlers it would be only a matter of time before she would find a way out.

Since she was now given even more freedom and time alone with her children, she taught Solace her first English words in preparation for the future, swearing her to secrecy. The child was still young and could easily be tricked for information, but this was a risk Anne determined was worth taking. She scoured her memories for details of her growing up for her daughter's benefit, but found her recollections grown vague as if they were details in a book, the life she was now leading so far removed from the other as to not suggest the slightest kinship.

Neha had told of her own mother, taken from a town in Colorado Territory. Still in captivity seven years later, she had died of

cholera when Neha was a child. Secretly over the years her mother had taught her enough so that she knew it was not Indian blood alone that ran through her.

You have the streams of two warring peoples in your veins, her mother said. *It will give you double the strength.*

Her words empowered Neha.

If she perished, Anne wanted Solace and Thomas, young as they were, to have at least this much of their heritage. As they grew older, she would tell them more. The thought startled her that she was making accommodation for the possibility of spending her life in the tribe.

On the last afternoon of preparing the hides, the skinners loaded up the horses with bundled teepees, meat, and rolled skins for the trip back to the camp. Anne went off to pick the berries that were Solace's favorite, with which she would bribe her to learn her English numbers.

Suddenly, over the ridge, cavalry soldiers appeared riding full out. So loud and fast they appeared, Anne stopped, unable to react to what was happening before her. Her heart burst with joy even as her women friends ran in panic to the river while the old men mounted a feeble defense.

They are here to rescue us, Anne thought, yet even as she put up her hands to halt Neha's flight, the soldiers opened fire with their weapons, and two women on a fleeing horse were shot down. One was Hawk Woman, who the night before had given her a red-bead necklace for her birthday. The other was Adahy, the best dancer in the tribe, who taught the young people traditional steps. Four Bears, who was blind in one eye and talked to the horses, was stringing an arrow into his bow as he was sliced through with a saber. The realization came to Anne that to the soldiers they were *all* the enemy, including her, to be cut down. Instinct took over as she turned away and ran.

The smoke of guns, the dead bodies of her companions, the flying hooves of the horses, metal hammering the earth unlike the soft thud of unshod pony feet, the swinging blades of the sabers terrified Anne. She did not know where to find safety, following the old artist Yansa, who drew the history of the tribe on teepees, to a mesquite tree where he wrapped his thin arms around the trunk. It appeared as if he were asking the tree for protection. A soldier pursuing on foot shot a bullet into Yansa's head from behind. Anne put the trunk between the

soldier and herself, a false comfort as she felt the hot sting of a bullet penetrate her right arm. The soldier came around to get better aim at her body, and she sank to the ground.

"Don't shoot! American," she said. She pointed to her eyes with her left hand. "Blue eyes. American." She felt cowardly doing such a thing and yet continued when it had the desired effect.

The soldier, with effort, held still long enough to process her words, puzzled, then jerked his head back.

"Captain?" he yelled.

After the captain came and verified she might indeed be a captive, he held out a hand to help her up, but she refused it. Finally another soldier lifted her up by the waist. She smelled the burn of alcohol on his breath. All the soldiers reeked of it. When she struggled out of his grip, biting his hand, he shook her hard like a husk doll.

"Try that again, and you won't like what you get."

They walked her through the carnage, every tribe member who had not managed to run and hide under the riverbank's overhang now dead. Her soul sickened. The soldiers calmly and systematically moved from body to body, scalping them and at

the same time looking for souvenirs — pouches and sheaths that Anne had sewn — as the captain asked her questions and filled out his report.

"There won't be a record of your abduction. It will have been forgotten. We'll have to send for it to Washington."

He spoke so fast Anne could hardly understand him. It had been long since she'd conversed in her own tongue. It pained her, the stilted quality of her words. How could the words stick like paste in her mouth when they pertained to something as important as her own survival?

A woman's scream came from the riverbank. Neha. Two soldiers had her pinned down and were struggling with her skirt. Anne pulled away from her keeper and ran even as a bullet grazed just above her head. One of the soldiers had unbuckled his pants, showing the sickly white gleam of his thighs as he took a last swig out of an almost empty bottle. Anne charged into him, knocking him over despite the searing pain from her right arm. She stood over her friend, brandishing a buffalo scraper she'd grabbed. A circle of soldiers surrounded her, their attention piqued to give her a good drubbing.

"Captain," she screamed. "Bring the captain!"

When he came running, she again pointed to her eyes. "American." Then she pointed to Neha. "She is American, too."

The captain looked skeptical.

"Colorado mother," she insisted.

He shrugged, already worried at explaining away the killings.

"You two have been liberated and are now under the protection of the Seventh Cavalry, commanded by General Custer, courtesy of the United States government."

This would be the way Anne was at last rescued.

The soldiers tied their hands behind their backs so tightly the skin was raw. They put Neha and her on horses, for good measure tying them to the saddles. A soldier led the horses by the reins.

Custer of the long golden locks, her armored knight, had come too late.

Anne was humiliated to be made so helpless. Neha's face had become a mask, all expression drained. The two rode in silence. Although Anne's arm throbbed, no one offered to doctor it. It was bound in a dirty piece of cloth they offered her. Neha's shift was torn and filthy, and none offered to

replace it.

When they stopped for the night, they were laboriously untied from their mounts. Although separated from the men by a short distance, they were not given any other special privilege. Placed in front of a small campfire, they were under the watch of an armed guard who did not seem pleased by the duty. Plates of beans and hard bread were brought them from the mess, but they were not invited to sup with the men.

Later each was thrown a blanket, expected to sleep in the open on hard ground, something Anne knew they would never dare do to white women. When they had to go to the bathroom, they were directed to move a short distance away, and not even for modesty's sake were they allowed the privacy of a bush or boulder. In all respects, a new captivity.

The next morning as they were told to ready themselves for a long day's ride, Neha refused to get up. When prodded, she began to wail.

The captain came, outraged at the delay.

"She does not want to leave what she knows. Can she return to her people?" Anne asked.

"That would be us," he answered. "Unless you misled me."

"I told you her mother was white, but the Cheyenne raised her. She knows nothing else."

"I have much to ready for the march . . . We must leave immediately. Warriors will soon be after us. In case you need the reminding, the Indians are our enemy."

"Leave her behind," Anne said softly.

"Answer me one question, Miss Cummins. Are *you* friend or enemy?"

His address confused her for a moment, having not heard her surname in such a long while.

"Friend, I believe. I am white. Neha also. We are the same as you. Except that you treat us otherwise."

The captain's face went dark. He said nothing, making an effort to substitute each desired blow with a breath instead.

"From my experience, captives are grateful for their rescue. They do not threaten soldiers with teeth and knives. They most certainly do not wish to return to the brutes that savaged them."

"We cannot leave without my children."

"Your children are Indian, yes?"

"A girl, Solace, and a boy, Thomas."

"Regulations . . . unless they are white . . . it will risk us all. We must reach the fort as soon as possible for reinforcements. We shall

return later to avenge ourselves and remove them from harm."

Her words fell on deaf ears and so she quit trying. She walked away, and when she saw the armed guard was distracted she began to run. Quickly she was apprehended. This time ropes were applied with a vengeance.

"If you try again, next will be chains."

Anne felt empty. She did not mourn or feel sorrow or feel anything in particular. Picturing Thomas and Solace waiting for her return was like a knife driven in her side. Unfathomable that her family would be torn from her once more. She was all wisp, permeable, as if the wind might blow straight through her. Any resistance she offered was doomed.

The soldiers woke in the dark and were riding before dawn, covering large distances. Soon, Anne lost all compass of which direction her home could be found. At night when they rested, Anne squatted by the fire and sang the death song, even though she was not sure who she mourned. She was frightened for her children. If only they had been in Running Bear's care her heart would have rested more easily, but she did not trust Snake Man's wives to not take advantage and neglect them.

At suppertime she was apathetic over her

dinner, once even sweeping dirt into her mouth.

The soldier guarding them looked on in disgust. A report was made to the captain, and he came to chastise her.

"If you do not stop this behavior, we will stuff food down your throat like a goose."

Anne looked at the ground.

He raised his voice. "Do you understand me?"

She had turned into a ghost of herself. Her resistance, her defiance, her constant scheming to escape the Indians was over. The thing she had most desired had come, but she could not reconcile that these men were the rescuers she had so fervently prayed for. Even her father's hero, her own knight, the Boy General, was culpable in orphaning her children.

If possible Neha was even more despondent than she. Anne had not considered whether her friend chose to be rescued or not. But if the rescue was indeed a kind of grace, why were they being treated as prisoners? What had Anne done wrong, except to have been made captive against her will? She eyed the soldier who rode in front leading her horse, the selfsame one who had shot her, his gun now resting prominently in its holster around his mid-

dle. On his saddle was tied a pair of fresh scalps — long flowing black hair on curling hanks of skin. Did they belong to her fellow buffalo skinners, treated as sport and now trophied? She turned away, sickened.

When they reached the camp, Neha and she were escorted to a large tent at its center. A soldier came out. He was her own height and had long curling blond hair, his skin flushed to pinkness. He wore a leather-fringed coat over military pants and riding boots. He appeared rushed and thrown together, excitable. Only his eyes were steady, cold, and predatory as a hawk's. It was only by the deference of the other soldiers that she guessed this was General Custer.

"Welcome home," he said.

Anne nodded, unsure of what was expected of her, while Neha looked away.

"We have searched long and hard, and your rescue today —"

Another soldier stepped up and whispered to him. "Here comes the journalist, General."

"Damn, he should already have been here. Is the photographer here?"

"He's coming."

The general turned away as if he had forgotten them, and Anne made to move

off, when she was quickly stopped.

A heavyset man jogged to the scene, already scribbling in his notebook. After years spent with the Indians it was strange to see a man so overweight, so weak in physical shape, one who would not naturally withstand the rigors of the wilds. Sweat rolled down his face, and he mopped at it with a handkerchief, barely looking at the two women. Another man, the photographer, came wrestling a pile of equipment.

General Custer now turned around, filled with new life, his face a mask of kindness.

"As I was saying, it is my profoundest happiness to return you to your homes. We grieve for what you have suffered."

Anne did not know what to make of this change but knew it could disappear again as quickly as it had come.

"The soldiers came and killed us. We did not fight." English stuck in her throat, came out thick and sluggish, but it thinned and became pliable the more she spoke. "Please, General, we need to go back for my children."

General Custer's eyes gazed above her head and to the left so that she was tempted to turn to see what he looked at.

"The suffering that you endured and that we had the great fortune to rescue you

395

from . . ." His voice and attention trailed off.

"Ready for the picture," the photographer said.

A clumsy machine was set up in front of them. For the first time, General Custer stepped near her, and when the machine had been readied, he smiled and shook her hand, not letting go till the exposure was complete. Neha appeared as a blurred image in the background. It would be the only recorded image of her during her lifetime.

General Custer moved away as soon as the photo was taken.

"My children," Anne pleaded.

He squinted his eyes.

"You are overwrought. You must be patient with yourself."

"We must go back for them now!"

She grabbed his hand and pulled at him as if she intended to drag him back to the tribe herself. Quickly and with great force he swatted her off.

"We will do everything in our power," General Custer answered. "But it is in the Lord's hands."

With that he returned to his tent. He did not speak to her again until they reached the fort.

At the time of her rescue, Anne had been held in captivity six and a half years.

LIBBIE

During their separation, while Autie hunted the last of the Cheyenne, there was a long period of no correspondence, as if he had fallen off the edge of the earth. On his return, he dared to chide Libbie for her coldness. Their marriage had become so strained it hardly mattered if they were together or apart. Perceived inattention, jealousy over causes both real and imagined; more absences by his traveling back east, leaving her alone; rumors of women both while he was away and right under her nose at Leavenworth, one a married woman no less. Her one surety — their love — taken from her, making it less easy to endure other difficulties.

Then, suddenly, rescue came in the form of a new assignment.

The Plains tribes had been satisfactorily settled on their reservations, and the army was no longer needed. The happiest days of

their marriage began when Autie was assigned out of the States to Dakota Territory, one of the most severe, forbidding outposts that existed. None of that mattered to Libbie because it was just the two of them on a train, headed on a grand adventure like in the beginning. The War had formed in them an appetite for movement and activity despite its dangers. Open space was a lure they couldn't resist.

After Kansas they had been in Kentucky two years, Autie doing policing duties of breaking up the Klan and shutting down illegal distilleries. It was dull and grinding work, not what he had been trained for. The only salvation that they both indulged in was a love of horseracing; for a while they even considered becoming breeders.

Autie was elated to be returning to the wide-open spaces of the frontier as commander of the reconstituted 7th Cavalry, which had been spread across the South. They would guard the engineers of the Northern Pacific Railway as it surveyed routes to the Yellowstone. What might have made another man tremble — the fearsomeness of the warring Sioux — made him giddy.

It was Libbie's observation that great military leaders, from Napoleon down to

Sheridan, excelled in winning wars but were seldom interested in the monotony of keeping the ensuing peace. So it was with Autie. When the new orders came he ran crashing through the house, threw a chair, and broke it in his elation. He picked her up off her feet and swung her around to a lazy waltz rhythm of his own making. They played that day like children, giggling at meals, making faces at each other until finally Eliza complained.

"I've had enough of you two acting undignified."

Dakota Territory was home to the most rebellious of the remaining tribes, the Lakota Sioux. Subduing them would elevate Autie's status as nothing else had been capable of doing those last years since the Washita battle.

They would go off and leave the unsavory, less happy parts of their lives behind. If she had learned anything from Autie it was the possibility of constant reinvention. When Tom came to celebrate the news, she perched on the dining room table where Autie had lifted her to be out of harm's way while they played at "romps." The dogs joined in, yipping and running in wild circles from parlor to dining room to kitchen.

■ ■ ■ ■

On the train trip to Dakota, the whole regiment of nine hundred men, and as many accompanying horses, with matching provisions and luggage, weighed the train down so that they crawled slowly, heavily through the land. The leisurely pace was further compounded by long stops during which the horses were disembarked, watered, and exercised. Soldiers took advantage of the stops to walk and stretch, or if near a town, to forage for food.

At one such stop, they commandeered a diner, all at once filling the long communal tables and overwhelming the tiny kitchen. There was only a short time to eat and make it back to the train again. There being no separate table for servants, Autie, Eliza, and Libbie sat together, the seating arrangement more of happenstance than principle, and waited for their supper of chicken-fried steak and mashed potatoes.

When the owner of the establishment, a stout man in his middle years wearing greasy coveralls, came out, they paid little attention. The man portentously walked up to Eliza and told her to leave. The room quieted. Although the War had been won

years ago, people's attitudes, especially in the more provincial parts, had not.

Autie looked down hard at the table as if he were studying the wood grain.

"We are hungry and short of time. Be a gentleman and move off."

"I will not have colored eat at my tables. It's the law here."

"My observation is that you provide no table for servants. The girl has to eat."

"Not my problem."

"She is traveling with the military. She is my charge. She will dine with us, and only then will we leave."

Eliza had stopped breathing and looked ready to pass out. She began to rise.

"It's okay, General . . ." she whispered.

"Sit down!"

Autie grabbed her arm without gentleness and pulled her back down.

"You can all leave, far as I'm concerned. Suit yourself. Take the nigger with you," the owner said.

Eliza was up, ready to run from the establishment. Autie grabbed her and forced her back down in her seat. His face had gone dark red.

"You are talking to the brigadier general of the Seventh Cavalry, sir."

The owner grew rigid as a board.

"Get her up, or I will do it for you."

Libbie melted, petrified in her seat. She put her hand over Eliza's and felt both of their tremblings.

The owner made a move toward Eliza, and Autie leaped to his feet as if on a spring. His face was frozen in the most fearsome expression she had ever seen on him. Was this the side of Autie hidden from her, the part that existed in battle? The entire restaurant of soldiers sprang up with him, leaving only the two women seated. The owner stopped. Looking around, he made a quick calculation and without a word walked back to the kitchen. It was a miracle the man lived and his establishment wasn't razed.

"Good," Autie said, rubbing his hands together. "Now that bit of unpleasantness is behind us, let's eat."

After the food arrived, the incident entirely forgotten, Autie ate with relish, joking with the men while Eliza and Libbie sat stunned, not touching their food.

"Eat up, girls. It's a long afternoon ahead," he said.

The meat tasted like cardboard in Libbie's mouth, the potatoes like paste.

As they left the establishment, Autie shouted to the kitchen, where the owner

403

had sequestered himself.

"Two meals were unsatisfactory!" He grabbed a full cherry pie off the counter. "We are taking this in lieu."

After that day, Eliza would never allow a word to be spoken against Autie.

On the many train stops they used the opportunity to also take the dogs out to stretch their legs. Horses, dogs, men — the scene resembled nothing so much as a carnival in flight. People in the surrounding areas stopped and gawked at them, the passing of a train still novel, or came to find out their destination. The travelers represented the larger world to these people and stood for the benevolence of the faraway government in Washington, which had promised to make the land safe.

More often than not, they brought gifts of food, grateful for the army's protection and cognizant of the hardship of such a posting. When they realized Autie was on board, it became cause for outright celebration, as he was considered a hero for his actions on the plains. Sometimes as the train passed small towns, guns would be fired in the air, and crowds would cheer them on.

Many women set their hearts on an extrav-

agant gift for their birthday, but Libbie was never such a one. That particular year the day fell during their train trip so there was even less possible in the name of preparation. What did happen was that Eliza managed to use the engine's bed of coals to produce a dinner of steaks and potatoes out of thin air.

There she came, beaming at her cunning, carrying a board and tea towels. She ordered Autie and Libbie to sit on opposite benches facing each other, their knees forming the "legs" of the table. The rolling of the train, the pressure from cutting the meat, everything threatened to tip the table one way or another. When Autie reached for the breadbasket, the whole thing almost flipped over, water glasses sloshing big drops on the pats of butter, and then their laughter made it worse.

For dessert Eliza presented a large plate of macaroons, Libbie's favorite, and peppermint iceberg puffs, favored by Autie. She stood proudly while they ate them, describing how at a stop that morning Autie had hurried off the train and into the village investigating bakeries, sampling at each place until he found the very best ones.

By the time Eliza met him with her bag of groceries there was a long line of boys who

had heard the famous Boy General was in town and followed him, a little disappointed that he was simply a man in search of macaroons to please his wife, not the fierce Indian fighter of the newspapers, always mounted on a rearing stallion and flashing his saber.

LIBBIE

When the train finally stopped after days of traveling, they felt such relief. On an open plain outside Yankton, Dakota Territory, the train disgorged itself of its contents and went back the way it had come. They were at the end of the world. Yet ahead of them lay a five-hundred-mile trek to their destination of Fort Rice, which was as removed from the larger world as it was possible to be and still be of it.

Men, horses, crates, dogs, birds, sacks of food, barrels, personal furniture — a whole town deconstructed and in motion. The soldiers were to set up temporary camp out in the open, it being April, even though spring in such a northern clime was very different from the heat of Kentucky, where they had come from. The wives of the regiment went into town to be lodged in comfort at the sole hotel. In her vanity, Libbie, a stolid veteran of summer camp and its

discomforts, preferred to stay in camp because there she would avoid the biggest hardship — being separated from her Autie.

While waiting for the tents to be set up, she sat in an enclosure formed by their trunks and looked after the menagerie they had hauled with them — a litter of pups, full-grown dogs, a mockingbird, and a profusion of canaries in their cages. The animals felt as great a relief as she to be off the train and on firm earth again. The stillness and quiet were a great luxury.

She basked in the weak April sunshine, yet even as she sat there, eyes closed, her face tracking the light like a sunflower, she felt a puff of cold air so that she crossed her arms over her chest to ward off the temporary chill. To her astonishment clouds had appeared from nowhere. It felt like an unnatural enchantment. Little did she know it was only the beginning.

As the morning progressed the wind blew, first lightly, then with increasing force. Temperatures dropped so quickly, she hurriedly dug out her winter coat from a chest as goose flesh rose on her arms. Lucky that she did, because even as she buttoned it the winds assumed gale strength.

Libbie sat huddled in a blanket, using a chest as windbreak, jealously spying a

ramshackle wooden hut that looked as if it was uninhabited. She decided to make an effort to rent it while Autie was busy setting up the individual companies in their camps. She found the farmer who owned it, and he agreed to barter its use in return for supplies as raindrops began to spit down from the sky. While soldiers brought in her belongings, along with water and firewood, Eliza went to town to procure a stove, holding an old piece of canvas over her head for protection. Libbie congratulated herself on setting up a temporary little home. By afternoon Eliza had returned with food but no stove just as the first snowflakes fell. It was not just a flurry but an outright storm.

Autie returned exhausted, his hands and feet frozen. The change in climate in a few short days from the sweltering April heat of Memphis, where they had bivouacked while gathering men and supplies for the expedition, to the far-north freeze affected many of the men with illness. After tucking Autie under buffalo robes, Libbie sent for the doctor, who came and prescribed medicine that she was to give him every hour through the night.

Luckily the raging of the now blizzard precluded all thoughts of sleep. The cabin gave the lie to the label shelter, the only

thing worse being directly outside. Huge gaps between the logs had yet to be caulked and allowed the wind to blow in freely. Eliza went from gap to gap, plugging the most distressing of them with packed snow from the piles that had formed inside. They huddled at each side of Autie's bed while he plunged into a fevered delirium.

For the umpteenth time Libbie realized how even in their personal life his optimism kept her hopeful and of good cheer. The ability to make people feel safe and capable of the difficulties that arose was as rare as hen's teeth. In that hour, though, Libbie had no choice but to be in charge. She couldn't afford the panic and tears that threatened. It would not suffice to hide in the closet or under the bed from the world's dangers.

The thought that there was no closet or bed even if she wanted them made her smile, and the idea that she could find humor in these dire circumstances gave her courage. How disappointed Autie would be on his recovery to learn of her poor example, and so she set about playing the leader to their small group.

The first order of business was food. Eliza and she bundled up as best they could and stepped outside to light a tiny fire to cook a

hot meal. Libbie prided herself on having survived all types of harsh, inclement weather, but a Dakota blizzard was beyond anything she had encountered. The snow fell so fine and thick she could not see her hand in front of her. It whirled around her — one could not discern if it fell from the sky or rose up from the ground. The sun was just a pale memory hidden somewhere in all the blinding whiteness.

Eliza and she held each other's coattails in order not to get lost. Four steps away from the cabin, it had disappeared behind them. Eliza put her small bundle of kindling down while Libbie held on to her coat with one hand, the wall of the cabin with the other. If one played the child's game of blindman and spun around, one could easily go in the wrong direction and be lost altogether.

Tales were numerous of frozen bodies found mere feet from safety. Dakota storms were the reason barns were built close to houses. It was a commonplace that during a blizzard one did not dare cross even such a limited space in order to care for livestock without a rope strung from kitchen door to stable for safe passage.

It was the strangest feeling of suffocation, as if the snow were sand, and each breath

411

became a labor.

Libbie's face numbed; her eyelashes furred so she could only squint. Snow came at them from all angles. Her legs were frozen despite the wool blankets she wore, and she longed for Autie's heavy buffalo robes, impervious to weather, with which the Indians draped themselves.

Each time Eliza managed to nurse a small flame to life, the storm took a big huff and quickly extinguished it. After the fifth attempt, they realized the hopelessness of their cause. Eliza complained her fingers were frozen stiff, and she could no longer handle the matches. Resigned to a cold supper, they stumbled back in. Libbie's spirits were low. She longed to cower in the corner, and it took everything to resist that urge.

In camp the soldiers and horses suffered far worse. When the adjutant came for orders, Libbie marveled how he'd managed to find them. With difficulty Autie sat up. The decision was made to break camp and retreat to Yankton, requesting shelter from the townspeople. Since travel was too dangerous for Autie in his condition, they would stay put. Duty discharged, he slumped down and went back to sleep.

After Libbie heard the last of the horses pass the cabin on the road to town, there

followed the most forlorn silence, accompanied only by the howling wind. For a panicked moment she considered rushing outside and begging to be taken with them, but at mid-afternoon it was already dark, the soldiers must hurry, and in Autie's debilitated state they would be a fatal burden.

Autie burned like a coal with fever. Libbie examined the state of the shelter that she had chosen so casually but now depended on for their survival. Incredibly, the wind increased, its groans growing louder and more agonized, the entire structure leaning with each buffet of wind. It was not impossible that the roof might blow off, if the whole thing, built without a foundation, did not simply overturn like the child's playhouse it resembled. The building was like an old tugboat put out to sea past its prime, and they might just as surely perish in snow as at sea.

Fully dressed, Libbie remained under the blankets next to Autie to keep warm. He was burning up, his face red and damp with perspiration. He tossed the robes off as regularly as she put them back, tucking them under his chin. Each hour she warmed her icy fingers with her breath so that she could pour his medicine into a spoon

413

without spilling a precious drop. In this way they passed the night, the most isolated and frightful one she could remember, assuming an end to the storm with the coming morning.

Libbie had finally fallen into a light sleep when a heavy, thudding sound became part of her dream. She woke and saw Eliza frantically trying to open the door. For a moment, Libbie thought the girl had gone mad and jumped up to stop her until she realized the pounding was coming from the outside. Had rescue arrived? The door was frozen shut. After the two women finally managed to tug it open, they were met with a wall of snow that they had to dig through with their bare hands even as those on the outside dug in with shovels. At long last, six soldiers stumbled inside.

Poor men! They had lost their way on foot to Yankton. Disoriented, they retraced their steps even as those steps were being erased. Blindly they had passed the hut numerous times, locating it at last only by the faint glow of the oil lamp that Eliza had the foresight to put in the tiny window. As soon as the men came into the shelter, though, Libbie realized that their needs — fire, bedding, food, medicines — far outstripped her ability to aid. In desperation she remem-

bered the carpets packed for the new home at the garrison. Eliza and she broke open a chest and were able to wrap each man in a rug cocoon.

Only as they warmed did their real suffering begin. Frostbitten hands and feet pained them as if needles were being driven into their flesh. Their cries set the women on edge, making them feel helpless. Food that might have fed three for a week now was stretched between nine people. Eliza lamented that they had no liquor to warm the men and ease their discomfort. Something had to be done. The doctor who promised to check on Autie had not shown, stranded in town or, unthinkably, lost in the storm.

Eliza let out a small squeal and clapped her hands.

"I know just the thing!"

Her idea was the bottle of alcohol they had for the spirit lamps; not the most palatable, but it was a dire situation. Just a thimbleful each brought a small bit of relief to the men.

When morning appeared, their hopes of rescue were crushed again. The storm intensified its raging. What light came to them was dim twilight, drifts burying them alive. Ailing soldiers, her husband ill, Eliza and she without the means to prepare food

or give medicine — Libbie quaked inside but refused to show it.

There were many times during those years when she feared for her life, but that storm was something apart. She felt at the ebb of her existence and her equally doomed fellow creatures shared the bottom with her.

When night descended again, it seemed impossible but the storm increased in ferocity. It was unnatural, demonic. Libbie's resolve was abandoning her. It seemed more likely than not that as the shed grew colder despite the bodies inside they might perish. She hardly had the energy of despair.

Eliza, overwhelmed, collapsed from exhaustion in the corner. Hoarding the remaining food and alcohol, there was nothing for any of them to do but each nurse his or her own misery. Libbie kept vigil over Autie, feeling personally responsible for abating neither his fever nor the storm.

Periodically she went to the single window and with her hand melted a small view out the frozen pane. Solid white shifting walls. For moments the view would open and then just as suddenly slam shut. Drifts capriciously formed and were swept away. This seemed the normal state of things to Libbie's mind; sunshine and grass were just hearsay. The devouring wind had cleared

the front door but had packed snow to the roofline on the other three sides.

In the middle of the night came the sound of many hooves, and Libbie was giddy that at last the regiment had come to their rescue. Melting her view out the window, she saw a group of mules using the front wall as shelter. They jostled for warmth. Driven mad by the cold, they bit and kicked at one another before finally moving off into the storm again, disappearing behind white walls as if they were the last forlorn creatures on earth.

Libbie had entered the most terrible kind of dream, the kind that was real and was your life and you could not awake from. She longed to rouse Autie and take strength in his assurances, but he was too far lost in his delirium. Adding to her distress, his medicine bottle was almost empty.

The barking, whining sound of a dog woke her. Confused, she rushed to the window to see a trembling canine form, but by the time she managed to pry open the door it had disappeared back into the snowy murk. Eliza had collapsed and slept, and she let the girl rest.

The whole world consisted only of snow and cold and fear. Libbie grew so disoriented, time lost all meaning. Either minutes

or hours had passed when she awoke again, this time to the terrified squealing of a band of boars pushing against the rickety door so that it threatened to collapse inward. She screamed to Eliza, and they set their backs against the brittle boards, pummeled by each outraged thrust. Starving boars could easily attack and devour men.

Much later — it might have been morning or evening again — Libbie woke to the repeated neighing of a distressed horse. It went on for an hour, making sleep impossible, so that she hung on, waiting for the next sound, disturbed both to hear the animal again and then to not. When the horse seemed finally to stop for all time, Libbie was overcome with the most terrific remorse, imagining the sad beast had at last succumbed to the elements. She grabbed the sash of her coat and opened the door to see a cavalry bay looking at her with wild, crazed eyes. In his state, he could have trampled her, but Libbie could not bear passivity any longer, doing nothing for an ailing fellow creature. She must take charge or go mad.

The space between them had magically cleared for a moment like the eye of a hurricane so that Libbie, trudging out in Autie's boots, could walk the twenty feet to

the horse and slip the sash around his neck, the beast now steady as a docile house pet. She led him through the door. The minute she closed it behind them, the storm slammed down and obliterated the opening she had just walked through, packing it tightly shut. A moment sooner or later, the two might have perished.

The horse stood in the middle of the room like some phantasmagoria, as content as if the cabin were merely another barn stall, which it greatly resembled. The air turned feral and moist as the ice melted off the animal's coat, puddling on the ground where he sipped it. In her corner Eliza woke briefly, her eyes going wide, sure that either Libbie or she herself had gone lunatic. Sharing quarters with both the general and a horse, her world turned topsy-turvy. Her answer was to close her eyes and hope reality was a dream. The soldiers, either asleep or preoccupied with their pain, took no particular notice of the new guest. Libbie's heart jumped when Autie woke up once. He looked at the horse dreamily and seeming well satisfied went back to sleep.

Although the snow stopped the next morning, they discovered themselves to be buried within the cabin and seemingly forgotten to the outside world.

Hours later, digging could be heard, and there came a knock on the door.

They were delivered by a posse made up of town citizens and soldiers. Even in the town the streets had been so impassable that horses foundered and sank almost out of sight. The men had worked as a team to drag a cutter over the drifts for their recovery. Tom stood at the door with a big basket of food. For just the briefest moment Libbie saw what he had imagined — his closest family perished — and she shivered at how near it had come to that.

A true cavalryman, the sight of a horse standing in the room aroused no surprise.

"You've outdone us in pranks for a long while, I'm afraid," was all he said.

He picked her up in his arms and hugged till the breath left her body and she begged to be put back down.

For his part the horse stepped daintily between the men and trotted outside as if they were *his* strange dream.

Supplies! They feasted, ravenous. A stove had been brought which Eliza quickly put to use with kindling. Autie woke, weak but on the mend. Although he had looked straight at the animal, now he did not remember the horse and thought they were pulling his leg until Tom pointed out the

420

frozen pile of horse apples in the corner.

Libbie wandered away to an area roped off with blankets, and there burst out in hysterical sobs. When Autie found her he was astonished that she had decided to wait until danger was well past before showing fright. She reasoned that she had endured and now deserved her tears.

"Come on, Old Lady, don't make too much of it."

Libbie didn't care what the men thought. Although she would do anything to prevent such danger in the future, she also knew she was equal to the circumstances if it came to that. It was a good thing to know about oneself.

The men who had sheltered with them ended up losing fingers, toes, and even ears to frostbite. In camp an unlucky few had whole feet and legs amputated, but all lived. It was a miracle that no soldiers had frozen to death, although many had suffered a variety of calamities from the storm. The soldier guarding the horses had tried his best to shelter Autie and Libbie's puppies by holding them against himself and sharing his blankets, but despite his efforts the entire litter had frozen to death, one by one. The only ray of light came on receiving the news that a laundress stranded in a tent on

the far side of camp had safely given birth
to one hardy little soul.

My Rosebud,

The worst thing I can imagine in this life would be feeling that the love of the one person whose love was desirable was surely but slowly departing from them. From my unique position in society I have the opportunity to examine the marriages of many and can tell you that ours is one most rare. I have yet to find husband and wife here who enjoy life as we do. Regardless of the rumors you have heard of that other woman, you alone matter to me. I realize that I alone am responsible for that spark of distrust . . . in your mind but which others have fanned into a flame . . .

My love for you is as unquenchable as my life and if my belief in a future state is true, my love will survive my life and accompany me to that future. You may doubt my love but that does not disprove its existence. I love you purely and simply, no woman has nor ever can share my love with you.

Your faithful boy,
Autie

THE ELEVENTH REMOVE

The return — Life at the fort — Tintypes

After the story and tintype were taken, General Custer went back in his tent, handing off Neha and Anne to his next in command for transport. Anne would not be given the opportunity to speak with him again. Later she learned that her rescue had made him a national hero.

When the soldiers reached the fort — a haphazard collection of log cabins and huts surrounded by a stockade fence — Anne and Neha were turned over to the commander's custody. Colonel Montrose was a mustachioed senior officer running down his last years of service, and the prospect of announcing the rescue of two long-captive women would be a fitting highlight to his career. He was less enthused once he learned that Custer had already "scooped" the story, having two newspapermen es-

corted overnight to base camp, bypassing the fort entirely. He became reconciled to the loss because the two women — one full white, one half-breed — did not fit his idea of Christian virtue. Or so Anne came to believe during the period of her confinement.

The two huddled together in the stone guardhouse in their filthy blankets against the chill and refused the baths offered by the fort's army wives. The returning captain had advised that by their rebelliousness the women might as easily be considered hostiles as liberated captives. Under no circumstances should they be allowed any freedom as they might well use it to escape, giving the lie to the story that the buffalo-skinner massacre had been a battle to free the women.

During interrogation, the two captives were sullen, refusing to sit in chairs but instead insisting on unladylike squatting on their haunches, as if chairs, questions, food, shelter, and rescue were all part of an elaborate deceit against them.

Montrose had read of such cases of delusion in those suffering from long captivity, and he prayed for these lost souls while trying not to show his justifiable vexation.

"I must go find my children," Anne in-

sisted. "I told General Custer."

"Then it is being undertaken, I'm sure. Custer, Custer . . . You are now under *my* hospitality."

"Yes, sir."

He was embarrassed by his outburst of peeve. He'd long ago given up the idea of outstripping Custer, but the man still got under his skin. He forced himself to focus on the captives. In Christian humility, he tried to imagine the same happening to his wife, his daughter. Unbearable. He tried for a conciliatory tone.

"Soldiers will be riding out against the camp shortly."

"No soldiers!"

"Certainly soldiers. Your children will be liberated and returned to you. The perpetrators punished."

"My family is killed," Anne said, meaning her Indian one.

The buffalo skinners had been friends, as close to her in their way as Running Bear's family. The pain in one limb of the tribe hurt the entire body.

"Your immediate family were massacred, yes, but we have contacted an uncle who has been searching tirelessly for you. Your return will be his crowning jewel."

"Let me go with the soldiers to get my

children."

He sniffed.

"Certainly not. Much too dangerous an undertaking for a woman. It is a tragedy what you have already been made to endure."

His comments were ridiculous considering her hardship these last years, although once upon a time before her captivity she would have wholeheartedly agreed with him.

Neha looked and acted too much like an Indian to garner his sympathy, but Colonel Montrose looked slyly at the curve of Anne's nose, which was delicate, the line of her chin, the straightness of her back, the deep indentation of her waist, and thought what an abomination that a paragon of womanhood be ruined in such fashion, virtue stripped from her as she was made to bear half-breed brats. What a dismal future awaited such a woman with no possible prospects of domestic happiness. Let the children survive with their own as best they might.

Anne and Neha listened to the jangling sounds of weaponry being loaded on wagons. The soldiers, tripled in number, planned to ride out against the main camp at dawn. Anne imagined her Solace and

Thomas's terror at the sound of cannon, their fear of soldiers, who they had been told were devils. There had not been time enough to make them understand otherwise. Who would look after them now? Even if one of the chief's wives took charge of their care, wouldn't they surely be mistaken for Indian children and thus doomed to an Indian fate? Anne was the only one who could act as a bridge for them to cross from one world to the other, the divide as deep and treacherous as a forbidding canyon. Instead, she was locked behind a fence like an animal.

"What will happen to my children?" Anne whispered.

"They will be hunted with the rest of the tribe," Neha said. "They will suffer like Indians. You must forget them."

The two women made keening cries — mourning, loss, and prayer all mixed together — until the soldiers, unnerved at how they sounded like wolves, bade them be quiet with the point of a gun. Anne pressed her hand over the icon that had represented all she so pined for, but now instead it recalled the beauty of its lack. The return to civilization had not provided succor.

After the soldiers departed on their campaign, the fort calmed. Anne was informed

that her uncle was on his way to claim her. In the meantime, it was suggested she re-acquaint herself with civilization by way of a comb and a looking glass. At first she had refused to talk or to eat, but eventually could not overcome the protests of her stomach. Each piece of delicious bread, each morsel of meat, seemed a betrayal of her children, who might at that very moment be suffering unknown privations.

She watched the white children of the soldiers be coddled and dandled much as she herself had been as a young child. They were given no experience of life outside the confines of their windows, unlike the upbringing of an Indian child reared in self-sufficiency from the earliest years. Her dear Elizabeth, unmindful of the meaning of a snake's rattle.

Simple woman that she might be, Anne knew more than the commander — there was no justice in the worth accorded the two sets of children, one Indian, one white. It angered her, the varying treatment they received. They had no differing worth in God's eye, only in man's jaundiced one.

Also disturbing, a group of visitors had arrived, and Anne found she had been sold as a sort of public spectacle: the white savage. Nearby settlers came to gawk, and a

man who took tintypes set up his equipment. They were allowed to observe Anne and Neha from an elevated platform on the other side of the fence, and comment on them as if they were exotic specimens in a menagerie garden.

One woman, who wore a pink silk dress, her blond hair rolled in oiled curls, said to a companion, "She looks hard-used, doesn't she?"

Anne looked down at her deerskin shift, which she had so proudly stitched together herself, and at her dirty, callused hands, widened from hard labor. Her hair was ratted and unkempt. The experience of self-consciousness was strange after so many years. She hated the pink-dress woman for making her feel shamed at what she considered a hard-won victory. Doubtful the pink-dress woman would have survived the things she had, but that victory now meant nothing. Defiant, Anne stood with arms folded across her chest and cast a burning glare at the woman, who finally realized the captive did indeed understand English. She blushed and hurried away with her friend.

The man with the tintypes came into the stockade and asked respectfully if he could take their image.

"For the history books, you know."

Neha refused to sit for him, but Anne agreed. The softness of his voice made her amenable; he did not bark orders at her as the soldiers did. He tried to get Anne into poses he imagined were those typical of an Indian, but at this she refused. There was, after all, an avarice in his eye that she had not noticed. She sat in the chair and looked straight at the lens, her commanding gaze frozen as he exposed the negative. All she could think was that it would be a good thing to have a likeness in case her children ever wanted to know of her.

Years later when she saw the image for the first time on an exhibition wall, she hardly recognized the wild self she had become.

The Twelfth Remove

Repatriation — A bath — Tea

After several more days had passed, Anne's rebellion in the stockade was becoming more pose than reflection of her true state of mind. Much time had passed in her former captivity, but she still understood the rules of white society — the sooner she acquiesced to outward appearances, the sooner she might gain her liberty. Each meal with its piece of milled bread flooded her with memories of home, memories she had not allowed herself to indulge because of their mournfulness. When after two weeks the troops returned empty-handed — the Cheyenne camp had disappeared, Solace and Thomas along with them — it was clear that she would have to journey alone to find them or risk losing them forever. A plan solidified in her mind when she overheard gossip of General Custer's wife paying a

visit to the commander's wife that day. She would beg her to help get her children back.

She requested an audience with Colonel Montrose and apologized at her folly in refusing his wife's offer of refreshment. That afternoon, a contingent of women invited her into the colonel's quarters. Notably, Neha was not included in the invitation, nor would she have obliged. Anne knew it was on her shoulders to purchase freedom for them both.

Before she was allowed to sit in the parlor, or enjoy a cup of coffee, or eat a single bite of food, a black servant girl took her to the back of the house. In a shed she found a zinc tub of hot water and a bar of home-made soap. The servant seemed frightened of her and kept her distance. Anne guessed that outlandish stories of barbaric ways were being circulated through the fort at her expense.

She declined the offer of help and turned modestly away to undress. As she stepped into the tub, lost in memories of her mother washing her hair, the servant girl gathered her discarded clothes, including the pocket that held her prized icon, and hurried out of the room.

Anne yelled after her. When the girl did not return, she jumped out of the tub and

ran naked outside chasing her. In the court-yard, the girl plopped the pile of clothing into a brick fire. She shrank back as Anne screamed at the loss of her clothes and burned her hand trying to retrieve the icon from the obliterating flames.

The colonel's wife, russet curls and dump-ling face, stood in the doorway, horrified. The other women crowded in behind her to gape, including a striking brunette in a military-style riding habit whom Anne guessed to be the famous Mrs. General Custer. She was the only one who seemed genuinely stricken by the captive's distress.

Anne had no choice but turn and go back, sink into the tub, put on another's clothes, sit in the salon, butter her bread and drink her coffee, and tell stories of her abduction for the afternoon entertainment, all to survive. Mrs. Custer had to leave early before the tea started, and they never did meet that day.

LIBBIE

Trees. Fort Lincoln was distinctly without them. West of the fort lay country that stretched out seemingly for thousands of miles without a single tree, hardly any bushes, the only growth being along the river. Soldiers would ride in blinded, their eyes scorched by the alkali reflection from the hardpan earth. Horses that would allow it were blindfolded and led by feel.

Wind. The land was plague to constant, sand-laden wind that wore out the features of both land and people. Domesticity was doomed by great clouds of dust that dimmed the sun, shortened the horizon, and eddied in great sheets of tan, adhering to doors and windows, dusting furniture and floors, so thoroughly coating them that even the hue of their clothes took on the tint of sepia. Libbie did not like to think it, but she was sure it formed a portion of their diet, between breathing it in, eating it in

their food, and drinking it in the sulfurous-tasting water.

Libbie loved it.

With no summer campaign planned, she happily watched the spring grass grow without its usual association with an approaching campaign. The only trick was to get Autie actively involved in projects and hobbies to avoid boredom. As soon as the snow melted, he went off hunting, cataloging a whole zoo of conquests. Libbie's great project, in which she enlisted him, was to soften the harshness of their surroundings with trees. When the first grass began to come up, indicating thaw, soldiers equipped with shovels marched down to the riverbank and dug up hardy young cottonwoods, the only tree that survived in that climate, to transplant around the buildings. Libbie joyfully watched the progress of her nursery, and if there was grumbling about turning the men into private gardeners for the commander's wife, she steadfastly ignored it.

She had heady visions of tree-shaded windows, treed bowers forming a small park for picnics and outdoor concerts, a cottonwood grand allée to be used for special occasions so that crowds might be shaded during parades or even the occasional wedding. If she had used logic, she would acknowl-

edge that in all likelihood they would be transferred within years if not months, but no woman planning a home could think like that. She was no longer the young innocent from Monroe. She planted with no hope of seeing her efforts come to fruition. Such detachment was an acquired ability. She wondered if this was how God felt, content to trust in the goodness of his creation to survive on without him.

This forced domesticity met with resistance. Autie feigned interest in the forestation of their area, but he frequently was subject to black moods where he sat in his study all day, talking to no one. He grappled with demons he did not share with her.

His new passion was buffalo hunts. Regularly he was requested by Sheridan to lead them for visiting celebrities. The ensuing stories and pictures in newspapers gave the army necessary goodwill from the public. Libbie went out and entertained in camp, setting table with candelabra and crystal in the wilderness to the great astonishment and delight of the guests. She was fast becoming a legendary hostess of the West. Theirs was an envied matrimony; no one guessed their recent discord.

One day when a group was out riding, a party of warriors appeared over a hill.

Gunshots were exchanged, and Custer and a few of his officers spurred their animals to drive them off. He gave orders to the man left to guard the women.

"Whatever happens to us, make sure the women are safe. Especially my Libbie!"

Minutes passed. The officer waiting with Libbie and the other ladies had his gun ready.

Libbie began to tremble and cry.

"Autie will be killed!"

Suddenly over the hill Custer and the officers came galloping back, surrounded by the Indians. As they came closer, the women realized with astonishment the men were laughing.

"You didn't even realize they were the guides, Old Lady! Not even Golden Buffalo! You should have seen your face."

Libbie turned away, her face hard.

"You are cruel," she said.

During their separations he had written to her feverishly every day, but now that they were in daily proximity they sometimes hardly talked.

All that hot summer it was the duty of the men to pour barrels of water around the trees to ensure that they took root and survived. Many of the soldiers came from

farming backgrounds and knew the methods of horticulture. Unable to make a living thus they had joined the army for little more than room and board. Libbie spent long hours outside discussing strategies to create verdancy in a place hostile to it. When a number of the trees, only as high as her waist, sported new green leaves, they cheered.

Autie received orders to escort the Northern Pacific Railway through Wyoming and Montana, in an action that would come to be called the Yellowstone expedition.

He wrote to her of coming across a most lovely red-tailed deer, rosy as a sunset, the first of its kind he'd seen. He was too far away to get a good shot at it. Each day he felled at least two antelope, growing acquainted with a new Springfield that he bought himself, the army being too parsimonious to supply its soldiers with them. He wrote that he was the envy of all the officers for having it. Tom even vowed to abstain from alcohol and gambling until he had saved enough to buy his own. In his letter to Libbie, Autie congratulated himself that he had thus turned a soul away from vice. He did not mention Tom's failure, that his drinking had worsened, that he'd had to

reprimand him several times more.

When confronted with a Sioux ambush, a reporter along on the expedition wrote that fear was not an element in Autie's nature; he exposed himself freely and recklessly.

I don't believe I've ever witnessed a human being so alive, so absolutely suited to his purpose. He is one of the finest specimens of soldier to ever grace the ranks of the US cavalry.

Autie returned safely, a hero, with no mention of his skirmish with the Sioux, or the fact that he'd neatly upstaged his commander, Colonel Stanley. He only told her of having come across three head of army cattle lost during Stanley's failed attempts of the summer before. It was a small lesson in miracles that the beasts had somehow survived the twin dangers of wilderness and Indians, but they did not survive the danger of hungry cavalrymen's bellies.

In the fall, the trees began to wither. No one had told her that their earlier behavior was a false health, that their seeming vitality was a variety of death throe. She should have remembered the logs cut for their buildings, how the walls sprouted tender

shoots of green months after being built. Instead, excited as children, they took delight in the small, hand-sized patches of shade, watching their dogs and the native birds take shelter underneath them.

After the trees revealed their true state, Autie ordered them cut down for kindling. A few hung on in a stunted, enfeebled state, a reminder of great expectations come to naught.

Many, many years later, as a widow living in New York City, she received a letter from people stationed at Fort Lincoln. They enclosed a leaf — the size of a man's outspread hand and healthy! — from the tree in front of their former quarters. It was tall and spread out to provide welcome shade on the yard and porch. By then she had forgotten the cottonwoods, but they had survived, even thrived, despite her neglect. She looked at that leaf for hours, shocked at its defiant, glorious existence when so much else had long disappeared.

There was one tree that belied all her efforts to pretend that their only enemy was the climate. The tallest object for many miles around on the eastern side of the fort, it had a thick trunk, and when the wind blew a perfect snowfall of seedpods flew in

all directions. It was truly a magnificent specimen, and when Autie and she first spotted it, they rode full speed to explore its possibilities for shade. It was one of the good days when Autie was his old self. As they rode closer, they saw its strange burden — Indians used it as a scaffold for remains. Corpses, wrapped and bound in blankets, were tied to its main branches. The tree was laden — they counted eight bodies — and their anticipation of relaxation soured. They left the shade chastened and returned to their sun-baked purgatory.

Their time at Fort Lincoln was the longest period of uninterrupted domesticity they would ever have. It was Libbie's only glimpse of what life might have been like if Autie had found other occupation in business or politics.

He never talked of it, but in the end none of his various and prolonged visits back east led to any solid offers of employment. Powerful men were only too glad to share their table and their company with a celebrity, a war hero and Indian fighter, but they did not take seriously his occupying any other role.

These failures made Autie explore ever more questionable ventures. He agreed to

be a spokesman for the railroad, then the representative of a mining concern, neither position leading to any income. Many officers languished professionally in the drought after the War, and Autie joined these. He had gone long in being distinctly unpromoted, so long the possibility diminished as quickly as the Dakota precipitation. Thunderheads and slanted rays in the distance indicated rain sublimed before reaching the ground. Autie's financial fortunes proved just as fickle.

In truth Libbie did not believe him suited to these other pursuits. Every time he went before Congress, he got tangled in the deep ruts of partisanship. He always left with more enemies than when he came, including no less a personage than President Grant himself, who almost prevented him leading the expedition against the Sioux at the Little Bighorn.

During one of his trips to Washington, Libbie went back to Monroe to visit family and friends, doing an accounting of her own. Her life was so unlike the civilian existence of her friends. Life in the army was about constant motion. When one was stationary it was harder to see the inevitable changes in life, they happened so subtly. By the time one did notice, all one could do

was mourn what was already past.

Motion put one on the same rhythm as life itself. It became an addiction, one that Autie had in large measure, one that he shared with the Indians, an austere nomadic life that did not allow for attachment toward hearth and home, but one that he deeply admired. Against her natural tendencies, Libbie grew to share that love, albeit in smaller measure. She felt sorry for her peers that had stayed behind, confined to the town's small possibilities. It came as a rude shock when some of those same matrons exhibited a condescending attitude toward her life.

"Poor Libbie," they said. "Blowing like a leaf in the wind, no permanent home. Stranded in those forsaken outposts. How we admire your endurance."

Libbie resolved that her next visit would be long in coming. Although packing a large quantity of cologne and face cream for her return to the Territories, she did not regret her choices.

During the Fort Lincoln period, Autie as fort commander served as a kind of Great Father, and the tribes came in regularly with their complaints and troubles. Although he would gladly have given them their provi-

sions upfront and seen them on their way, their code frowned upon charity. They insisted on the formality of pipe smoking and long recitations of their plight. In their abacus, the destruction of the buffalo, the incursions on their lands, the partial and shoddy level of "payments" on the reservation justified their grievances. The unspoken was that it also justified the vengeance certain elements took.

The dignity of the Indians impressed Libbie, especially one chief who in lieu of jeremiad removed his blanket and shirt in silence, revealing a body damningly reduced to skin and bones. Libbie had Eliza send him a heaping plate of dinner to eat in Autie's study, but even as she did it she understood what a paltry and inadequate gesture it was.

Not only did Indians ask for an audience but also settlers living outside the fort, few and far between as they were. After a year of drought and two years of devastation by grasshoppers, the military was assigned to distribute rations to carry civilians through to the next growing season.

The year before, Autie had met a grizzled old character, a hermit of sorts, who lived on the same side of the river as the fort, among hostile Indians and too far away

from neighboring whites for help. One could not begin to guess his age — his skin had weathered to a wooden texture, his hair was white and bristling from his own barbering, and many of his teeth were missing. To his credit, he seemed unaffected by these afflictions. His blue eyes were happy; he smiled and laughed as often as he talked. His words faltered, then came in spurts, the habit of solitude making his conversation rusty in company. He claimed kin in Tennessee, toward whom he harbored a great "despise," and so although he was already old and feeble, he nonetheless set out for a place of his own. He preferred his barren spot rather than treat their mendacious ways.

Shyly he would question Autie about the great cities of the east — Washington and New York — as if they were as out of reach as the moon or ancient Constantinople.

"Cities, no, cities do not sit well with my nature. Years ago I set out to live in St. Louis because of a female."

Here, Autie, pretending to be scandalized, winked at the man.

"You know how it is. The crowding! Houses piled one atop another so that you can hear what your neighbor talks of at breakfast. Streets so crowded that you can get run over by a carriage or a horse if you

aren't careful. The howls of dogs and babies day and night. Bars! Whorehouses!"

Here the old man remembered Libbie's presence in the room and shushed himself.

"Sorry for my filthy tongue, ma'am."

For a moment he sat blinking but then started right back up.

"Drinking! Fighting! Fornicating! My head hurt every day for two months until I took my permanent leave. I never did return, never will. Said goodbye to the idea of a wife."

"Aren't you lonely, though?" Libbie interjected.

She found the old man's ideas subversive and joked that her Autie might empathize too much.

"No, can't say I am, missus. None but an Indian woman would live out here anyways. Present company excepted. I think God has created the goose, and he has created the wolf. Each has his right way to live. I have found mine."

"Which are you? The goose or wolf?"

She knew Autie would be amused by her engaging the man thus, but he took the question seriously and thought hard on it.

"Neither, ma'am. I believe I take after the rhinoceros."

Dead silence in the room as Autie and

Libbie swallowed the laughs that threatened to erupt.

"A fearsome animal that commands respect, yet I believe feels quite differently about himself from his own vantage."

"I see."

"I have been on the prairie long years, and she has taken good care of me. I shall die here."

Libbie gave a small shudder that the man could speak of his fate so lightly.

The hermit bowed and held Autie's hand in both of his roughened ones, thanking him for the previous year's supplies, which, meager as they seemed, kept him going the whole winter long.

Autie bit his lip. "I'll have my men come around and check on you weekly. Let them know if you are in need of anything."

"You are too kind to me, General."

The hermit never left his little ranch except to bring in pelts and crops, afraid to leave the place vulnerable to destruction from the warring tribes. During the long winters, he left his house only by laundry line, back and forth to the barn. A sad way to end a long life, but the man seemed to have made the best of it. He had brought a few undersized molty coyote pelts in gratitude.

"To put around the lady's neck," he said.

"I'm sure she would much love that. Wouldn't you, old girl?"

Libbie smiled and remained silent. Sometimes female decorum was a welcome thing to hide behind.

Autie gave the old man his allotment of rations and then threw in some extras from his private supplies. The hardship of the ancient pained him as if the man were his own father.

Months later, Golden Buffalo, along with two other scouts, reported riding by the ranch on their way back to the fort, and it appearing deserted. Worried, Autie sent a search party to ride out and check on the man. On approach it was clear the place had been defiled. Household items lay strewn on the path leading to the house. Livestock had vanished. The place had the desolate feel of being abandoned. Getting closer, they could see the house was charred although still standing, an effigy of itself, the inside empty and in ruin. One of the troopers went to the barn and there found the old man lying in a halo of his own blood, his skull bashed in.

When word of his demise reached them, both Autie and Libbie were brought low. The unfairness of it, having someone so

harmless come to such a violent end, made them feel keenly the precariousness of their existence in such a place. But as singular and exceptional as the old man was in his situation, he was not unique. That was the great privilege of their days living on the frontier — regularly they met extraordinary individuals who were heroically brave, generous, and kind. It took a special sort to make it out there, and they inspired Libbie.

In this relatively fallow period, Autie in frustration turned to hunting with a vengeance, planning it almost as carefully as he would a military campaign. In one letter during the Yellowstone expedition, he cataloged his kills: 41 antelope, 4 buffalo, 4 elk, 7 deer (4 of them blacktails), 2 white wolves, and a red fox. Geese, ducks, prairie chickens, and sage hens without number.

They had constant company between regular faces at the fort and outside visitors drawn for a variety of reasons to the frontier. To each, Autie sat in his chair very elder-statesman-like to regale them with hunting stories, anecdotes in which he always starred, and outright brags of his accomplishments large and small, including full lists of his recent kills.

Tom would roll his eyes and take a bottle

away for company.

In the past Libbie had worried of Autie appearing less than humble, but he had always ignored her warnings. Now she saw the frozen looks of their guests, either blank or appalled. Her beloved husband was turning into an outright bore.

She could imagine a time in the future when he, silver-haired, would recount his military feats of prowess in their entirety at the drop of a hat, something he would have been unwilling to do only a few short years before. It felt disloyal to have such ungenerous thoughts about her husband. She tried to believe he simply wanted to relive the high points of his career, to not be forgotten, as if he were already forgetting himself. His existence on the plains was performing a kind of erasure of his former self. Would they someday totter down the streets of Monroe in their dotage while acquaintances crossed to the other side to avoid yet another lecture on his accomplishments?

When orders came for him to go on a reconnaissance expedition to the Black Hills, Libbie was as overjoyed as he at the prospect.

We are goading the Indians to madness by invading their hallowed grounds, and throwing open to them the avenues leading to a terrible revenge whose cost would far outweigh any scientific or political benefit possible to be extracted from such an expedition under the most favorable circumstances.

— WILLIAM CURTIS, *NEW YORK WORLD*

Black Hills, Dakota Territory, July 1874

Every man who lacked fortune, and who would rather by scalped than remain poor, saw in the vision of the Black Hills, El Dorado.

— John Finerty,
Chicago Times

For days they rode through the Badlands, poisoned by alkaline water at each stop, until they began the ascent into the Paha Sapa, the sacred Black Hills, promised to the Sioux in perpetuity, in this case defined as until the government had other ideas for its use. They were not allowed to be there. Custer felt the thrill of the explorer. He had been given sole command of an expedition explicitly in violation of the Fort Laramie Treaty.

This was the territory of the fiercest Sioux tribe, the Lakota, a group composed of seven tribes — Hunkpapa, Oglala, Brulé, Miniconjou, Two Kettles, Sans Arc, and Si-

453

hasapa — that shared not only geography but language and customs, often intermarrying, so war on one was war on all. Golden Buffalo explained that "Lakota" was their self-given name, meaning friend or ally. The army always used "Sioux," which meant enemy.

The official object was to find a passage from the Missouri River agencies to the Yellowstone River and to locate a site for a possible fort between them. They also were looking for minerals, timber, or arable land, and found all three in abundance. The unofficial expectation was of course centered on gold. It was the magic word, which once unleashed would bring a flood of prospectors. Although illegal they would be protected by the military, thus breaking yet another treaty.

The mob was waiting with pick, axe, and shovel, eager for the next gold rush and its promise of quick wealth. The government, worried about the faltering economy, did not want to say no to this spoiled child. The newspapers were impatient for a yea. Only a figurehead was needed, and Custer had been chosen for the dubious honor, his likeness in the newspapers promising riches in the wilderness. If not him, it would be someone else. More and more, he felt a

puppet to the machinations of Washington.

The expedition included twelve companies of cavalry and infantry, guides, scouts, interpreters, teamsters, a cannon, three Gatling guns (which regularly delayed even such a leisured march), and more than a hundred wagons. There was a scattering of scientists, geologists, miners, and journalists. An epic journey that would be recorded as it unfolded, an exploration with a foregone conclusion.

The journey itself was everything he desired. Sacred, edenic country. He wrote to a friend that such a trip "would do more to strengthen your energies physical and mental than anything you might do." It did such for him, and except for missing Libbie he would gladly have it go on for twice as long.

They rode through a petrified forest, traversing the ruin of a long-vanished nature, trunks and branches preserved as in their living prime. It was an eerie, sublime sight, and he longed to stay to view it in the moonlight. What, he wondered, would the wind sound like strung through such stony harps?

When they first entered the hills, Custer watched as Golden Buffalo dismounted and kneeled. He burned a bundle of herbs, wav-

ing it back and forth while chanting. His face was so serious, Custer couldn't help but tease him.

— Didn't know you went in for this hocus-pocus.

Golden Buffalo looked up at him.

— These hills are the spirit of the Lakota soul. They will destroy nonbelievers who enter them.

— We'll see about that.

They entered lush valleys, meadow grass so high one had to stand in the stirrups to see beyond the end of a horse's head. A great white crane glided down from the hills over the green-treed canopy like a feathered angel, its wingspan as wide as a man's arms outstretched. Custer stopped the column and signaled for quiet as he went forward stealthily through the tall grasses. In awe of its beauty, he shot the bird as it stood in the river's streambed searching for breakfast.

Each night they camped along rivers as fresh and crystalline as the ones in the badlands had been stagnant and clouded. Flowing freely over rocks, the water was so pure and delicious he had barrels of it stored to bring back to Libbie. They rode through fields carpeted by flowers that gave off intoxicating perfumes as they were crushed under the horses' hooves. Each trooper

leaned down and plucked his own bouquet, and looking back Custer saw an endless May Day line of cavaliers. Men had woven flowers into their horses' manes as they rode along. Some had tucked blossoms in their hatbands or in the buttonholes of their uniforms. Luckily, the more scientifically minded pressed specimens between pages of books to later prove that the place was not a delusion but indeed an enchantment.

Custer would make this an enjoyable ride if he could help it. Since he did not believe in the aim of the expedition, he chose to ignore it, instead trying to re-create the feeling of the picnics with Libbie in Kansas. He commissioned a sixteen-piece brass band, the impressions of each day heightened by musical accompaniment: a serenade to rise in the morning, and a lullaby to send one off to sleep at night. The column was so long as it wound about switchbacks in the Black Hills that the head came across its tail at various turnabouts. The soldiers would huzzah across the chasm to one another. The sound of the band, which periodically fired up, was diminished in the grand space, sounding small and tinny, a whistling into the void.

Golden Buffalo and he sat their horses and looked over the valleys and hills, some

so steep they admitted little sunlight.

— What else can one do with such wilderness but conquer its riches?

— Revere it, pray to it.

Custer shook his head.

— That's not our way. Many years from now there will be towns and cities, ranches and farms here. There will be no room for either you or me.

The boundaries between the two men had so dissolved that they could speak honestly of their own demise.

A frisson to their pleasure was the knowledge that they were being closely followed in their movements by the outraged Sioux. Golden Buffalo pointed out the wolves stationed on overhead peaks.

— They call you *wasichus*. Like flies or ants. Things you cannot rid yourself of.

No white man had ever penetrated those hills, or rather none had ever lived long enough to come out and tell of it. At the first word of the discovery of riches to be unearthed, an unstoppable deluge of opportunists would break the law to come. The Sioux would murder, and the army would retaliate. A simple equation: gold equaled war. It was not a question of if, but when.

The army kept climbing higher, the air

growing cooler and more healthful, passing from one virginal valley to another of even more surpassing beauty. One was thick with wild berries, and the men glutted themselves on choke cherries, blackberries, raspberries, wild strawberries, and wild plums until they appeared intoxicated. Custer found Tom sleeping in the grass, his mouth and cheeks stained purple as when he was a boy. He, too, felt like a boy in this Eden. How tired he had become, mired in routine, until he felt ancient.

He could not help the desire to keep these riches to himself; it would be better not to share it with those who would despoil it. He did not fault the Indians their fierce attachment.

As they climbed an especially steep hillside the column stopped. Custer rode up to find the cause and saw the lead wagon stuck at a high switchback, hemmed in by trees on the narrow path so that it couldn't be turned. His favorite, Bloody Knife, and another scout had been directing it.

—Whose fault is this? he demanded.

The scout pointed at Bloody Knife, figuring he would more easily be forgiven.

Custer's anger flared, sure the two had been drinking, telling tall tales and not paying attention to driving the mules. Favorite

459

or not, Bloody Knife regularly got out of hand. Custer drew out his pistol and shot at them both as they jumped off their horses, ran, and ducked behind trees.

When he'd emptied both his gun and his temper, Bloody Knife walked up to him, grabbing his horse's reins so that he couldn't maneuver his crop for a lash.

— You have the madness of a bull buffalo. If I were to act as you do, you would not see another day, Bloody Knife said.

— Then you are lucky I am such a poor shot.

Bloody Knife looked away, not amused.

— Forgive me, my friend. It will not happen again.

— It is forgotten, and we both know it will happen again. As a token, I will accept you speeding my ask of a new saddle.

Meek, Custer nodded and shook hands.

The Sioux wolves did not move closer, and Custer wondered at their restraint. Throughout the journey his guides would spot silhouettes on the faraway hills watching the army's progress. When they stumbled on a recently vacated village, he worried it was an ambuscade. He sent Bloody Knife and the Arikara scouts to reconnaissance. They returned in double time, reporting the loca-

tion of the Lakota and asking permission to attack their traditional enemy.

Custer shook his head.

— This is an exploratory mission. We aren't here to kill if we can help it.

— Let us go alone. It is our right.

— I will not start a war to please you.

— We will go without the army.

— No! That is an order. Stand down. You are a soldier first, an Indian second, understand?

Bloody Knife stalked away and refused to speak with him.

Custer had to beg Golden Buffalo to come with him to approach the camp with a white flag. He wasn't entirely pacifist, though, grabbing the Lakota chief One Stab as guide and hostage, ensuring safe passage until they left the hills. Bloody Knife and the Arikaras were forced to guard him. It was putting the foxes in charge of the henhouse.

— If anything happens, it will be *your* scalps, Custer told them.

A scout led them to a cave known to be a place of powerful medicine to the Sioux. Offerings were laid outside the entrance in the dirt: bracelets, beads, pipes, flints, as well as scalps, knife blades, pistols, and a human skull. The cave was rumored to wind

for miles inside the hill. Strange, unearthly noises could be heard echoing deep inside its belly.

As the men walked in, their way lit by oil-rag torches, the noise of their voices and feet set off a cacophony of echoing sound. The walls showed drawings of animals, reptiles, and fish. Deeper in the cave the floor was crusted in guano, and the men ducked at the fluttering terror of bats loosing themselves from the ceiling to escape. Custer took a sideways glance at a spooked Tom, then snuck up behind his brother and grabbed his head in a lock. The two were immediately scuffling along the floor, their laughter gruesomely amplified through the deeper caverns. The other soldiers were annoyed at their hijinks.

The drinking started that night and continued till dawn. The absence of danger from the Sioux relaxed the men too much. If they were attacked the next morning, they likely would be slaughtered one and all in their stupor. It had been long since Custer had challenged the insubordination of drinking, instead choosing to turn a blind eye to win his men's goodwill. He himself abstained, it being the easier of his sins to banish.

Unknown to him, a young private was suf-

fering from diarrhea and pleurisy, but the doctors, too deep in their cups, overlooked treatment for two days until on the third a grave had to be dug instead. This was the freedom and lack of discipline that the men had been so bitter at being denied. Custer wrote to Libbie about the grizzly he killed, listening to band concerts, and playing the first baseball game ever in the Black Hills, but omitted mention of the private who had perished.

I am coming to the cross;
I am poor and weak and blind;
I am counting all but dross;
I shall full salvation find.

One afternoon he was distracted while writing by the sound of church hymns being sung, only to discover it was from a group of Indian scouts who had sung in choir on the reservation and had taken a liking to the music. For the length of the song Custer's heart was at peace, which showed how much it was otherwise most times. He prayed for the first time in his life sincerely that maybe, just maybe, this glimpse of assimilation could be the answer to the Indians' dilemma.

Golden Buffalo looked into his tent and

463

saw him in prayer.

— *Hi'es'tzie* is okay?

— 'Course I am. Doing God's work.

At night he begged off joining the men in their revelries with the excuse of writing his reports and letters home. It was past time sending the fateful report of gold. If not him, others would announce it, but if he refused at least that particular sin wouldn't land on his conscience. He delayed.

Instead he climbed away from camp, scaling a large rock to enjoy a quiet place to see the stars. A large comet scraped the bottom of the sky and cheers came from the camp below, guns fired into the air — lucky he wasn't accidentally shot by his own. The Indian scouts declared it was either a good omen or a bad one, which seemed to cover just about every eventuality.

To the extent that anyone chose to set store on such nonsense, the comet put him in mind of the sighting of the morning star before the battle on the Washita, so he chose to find in it a prophecy of success. Thirty-three was a ripe old age in the cavalry; not promoted, it wore even more roughly. This band of Sioux was among the last rebellious, and then what? The old girl would not be able to pretend cheerfulness many

years longer at staying a military wife. Resounding success must come and come soon to land them a comfortable civilian existence. He had been rebuffed soundly at every business venture. The truth was he couldn't imagine a life he wanted to live outside the army, but soon he would have no choice. Domestic life had always felt like a coffin being built around him one board at a time.

His first sighting of a comet, he had been but a boy, out with Tom and a group of other scoundrels on a hunting trip. A bobcat had come at him and Tom, scaring his young brother so much that he had peed his pants. Custer shot the cat and then ordered Tom to grab it and dunk himself in the river. When the other boys came at the sound of gunfire, he claimed that Tom had stolen up on the cat, grabbed it, and jumped in the river to drown it, otherwise it would have torn Custer in half. The boys had hoisted Tom on their shoulders and paraded him around the campfire, much to his mortification. He looked young and afraid up on those shoulders, and Custer sensed his brother did not belong there above other men.

That night, the boys had all been mesmer-

ized by the shooting fireball of a comet. They hooted and shouted much like the men below Custer now.

— What does it mean? Tom had whispered all those years ago.

— It means I will always be there to protect you.

Now Tom sat below in camp, his head probably doused in a bucket of whiskey. Chasing after whores and cowed by Libbie, he was a brave, fearless soldier who was yet afraid to be a husband.

When the brothers had dinner privately in his tent the night before, Custer had egged his brother for losing the hand of yet another pretty girl who had come visiting at Fort Lincoln, and was set to marry one of the officers on their return. Libbie was deep in preparations for the celebration.

— So how'd you manage to bungle that one?

— Didn't want her.

— She was good-looking. Practically threw herself at you. *Tom, teach me to ride. Tom, teach me to shoot.* Lots of opportunities to steal a kiss.

Tom said nothing.

— Are you stewed?

— Nope.

— Lulie would have never come out here.

You know that?

— I figured.

Custer slammed his cup down. Tom had been this way since boyhood, so silent and self-effacing he melted into the rug.

— Damn it, man! It's good to grow old with someone.

Tom nodded.

— I have you and Libbie.

If Custer was honest, he himself did not understand much except war. The Custers were not what one would call well rounded. He did not understand the passing of time, did not know why his loved ones, even while underfoot, grew distant and changed. He did not understand why he ended up spending the least amount of time with those he loved the most, and despite his best intentions he also ended up hurting those very same ones. In his mind he had prepared long ago to die among strangers on a battlefield, but why should he also live as among strangers? He had a gift for making friends yet still felt alone most of the time. During the War he could have just as well fought for the Confederate cause; he had as many friends on both sides. Now he did not know why he fought the Indians, some of whom he also counted as friends, except

that he was told to do so.

The hills, so vast, so lovely, made him melancholy. Around him on the rock came his usual spectral companions, grown in number, the Indians fair equaling the Confederates now. If only Libbie was at his side. She could make sense of everything, give him confidence in his endeavor. Only she had the power to make the ghosts go away.

Procrastination was fruitless. He would write the report that was expected of him, sending it post-haste by courier.

As he noted, almost every corner of the earth yielded gold if enough effort was used in its extraction. It was simply a determination of whether the effort was worth the gain. Insisting on invading sacred land and igniting a war was a steep price.

He would not much exaggerate the small find, but anything would be enough to ignite the next rush.

The newspapers would make him famous again, waxing on about the riches to be found, even though the geologist on the trip said he said seen gold in only the smallest amounts; that man was reviled in the papers, declared unpatriotic.

Unlike the previous Yellowstone expedition, here in the Black Hills Custer felt keenly the violation of expansion. He sym-

pathized against the duplicity of the government. It stung when he later found that the Sioux named the route he took back to Fort Lincoln "Thieves' Road."

TOM CUSTER

MY BROTHER'S HORSE

Horses were part of our life from the time we could walk, companions in work and play, but in the cavalry the relationship deepened to one of life and death. Picking the right horse took on the utmost urgency. During the War both Armstrong and myself had numerous horses shot out from under us, so it was from plain practical experience that we could spot a good horse a hundred yards off.

In fall 1868 while in Kansas, we had been sent five hundred additional mounts for the upcoming winter campaign in Indian Territory, the number of horses telling us both that we were valued and that the upcoming expedition would be a potentially deadly one. Armstrong, as was his prerogative, had the horses first pass by his tent while he made note of them and pulled out the

470

choicest for his personal use. Much as he chose brave soldiers for his company or, I'm sorry to say, fine women for his bed. When a bay Morgan paraded by, Armstrong's eyes narrowed, noting the springing gait, the impression of caged energy despite the slightness of size. The animal stood only 15 1/2 hands high, his face animated by a white nose and elongated star on his forehead that gave him a mischievous expression. After putting the horse through his paces, he was bought, and Dandy became part of the family.

Vic, a thoroughbred, was the horse Armstrong used for speed in battle, but Dandy could outthink him by a prairie mile. Besides being indefatigable, he could navigate obstacles while his rider was otherwise occupied, either hunting or defending himself against Indians. I've never seen a horse who could leap sideways like a cat as he did, in and out of buffalo wallows that would break the leg of a less nimble mount. He could pick his way through a prairie dog village at full run, miraculously avoiding all holes.

During that first winter I observed first-hand how Dandy supplemented his meager grain rations by foraging through the snow, pawing it away with a hoof to reach the desirable dried grasses below. Within a few

Captain Custer (left) with General Alfred Pleasonton on horseback in Falmouth, Virginia

days, the other horses had learned the maneuver, and it made a comical sight to see them plow up a field thus.

One would think that Armstrong's commandeering of the horse would have caused resentment, but Dandy shared his owner's peculiarities, and he was not coveted. Both horse and owner were an equal bundle of vices and virtues that were impossible to separate. Dandy always insisted on leading any expedition, and lucky for him, the commander that sat on his back agreed. His gait was a short, rough one; even on a long journey, he would curvet instead of walk, exhausting his rider, whose back would pay the price for such bouncing energy.

In the course of things while in Kansas after the Washita campaign, Armstrong happened across the farmer who sold Dandy to the army. Confirming his good bloodlines, the farmer expressed distress at having had to part with such a fine animal at a fraction of his true worth. Due to financial hardship, he had had no choice and would be grateful to have him back at double the price he'd sold him for. Armstrong smiled thoughtfully but turned a deaf ear. I believe he would have sooner returned Libbie to her father's house.

Eight years of devoted service later, we

were ready for our summer campaign against the Sioux in Dakota and Montana Territories. Dandy had at last begun to slow down, and Armstrong requested an extra horse for the battle just in case. Dandy would be used only for the less rigorous parts; the rest of the time he was kept back with the led horses.

THE THIRTEENTH REMOVE

Uncle Josiah — Returning home —
Neha's escape and capture — Burial

Her immediate family members perished,
the only one able to come for Anne was her
distant uncle Josiah. She had only the vagu-
est memory of him, he being the eldest child
by a decade from the youngest, her father.
He was a man driven to the Bible, embrac-
ing ordination after the travails of the farming life and sales at a general store proved
failures. Josiah was searching for a position
in government to preach on the reservations, this considered an easy employment.
He spoke openly that bringing his niece
back to the fold would give him credentials
for the conversion of the heathen.

When he bounded into the colonel's
parlor with his arms spread wide, Anne
rushed to him, hoping for the long-sought
embrace of family and release from her cur-

rent unnatural confinement. Josiah stopped her short, an arm outstretched, and bade her fall on her knees alongside him while they gave thanks to the Almighty.

"Thank you, O Lord, for rescuing this child from her degradation and delivering her back to the loving care of her family."

It was agreed that Neha would accompany them to be taken back to her kin, distant cousins who had never known her mother before her abduction, much less of Neha's existence until the previous week.

Josiah was preoccupied with the details of what Anne would find on arrival.

"Your parents' homestead was left unattended and would have been claimed by strangers. A few of us took turns working the crops. Then my eldest son generously set up his household there. Of course the land rightfully belongs to you."

"I only ask that you allow me to work there for my keep."

His face relaxed into a broad smile.

"I am happy to see that you've remained a Christian woman through your ordeal."

"My faith is strong, Uncle."

"Then your rescue indeed deserves the name miracle."

Readying for the trip home, it was noticeable that her uncle had not come provi-

476

sioned. He blamed this on his elation and the haste with which he had left on hearing of her delivery. He borrowed horses and food from the army in order to accommodate the women, especially Neha in her condition. The army willingly did this rather than having to sacrifice a contingent of soldiers as escort.

Once they left the fort, their days consisted of long, grueling miles of riding, unalloyed by either conversation or stops for rest. The only exception to this was when Josiah chose to talk about himself, which he characterized as "sermonizing." Each morning and each evening he forced the two women to bend their knees and pray with him. The prayers were harsh and scalded like being dipped in lye and the hottest water. Anne rose from them feverish and troubled rather than at peace.

The first night when they stopped for sleep, Anne was made to understand that they were to have nothing more than an army-issued woolen blanket for a bed. It was not a blanket meant for soldiers but one reserved for annuities to reservation Indians. This was obvious on inspection, as it was rotting apart and useless as cover.

Josiah set out the donated provisions of beans and meal, laid out an iron pan, and

sat back, expecting the women to prepare his meal, which they did. When he tasted his first spoonful, he spat it out.

"What is this slop?"

He dumped the pan out in the dirt and proceeded to show Anne how to prepare food properly, seasoning it with lard and salt. After he fell asleep, Neha crawled to the pile of discarded beans on the ground and ate the whole of it.

Anne lay awake when she came back.

"I do not care for him," Neha whispered.

Anne looked out into the night. They had come to a more arid part of the prairie that resembled high desert, with scrub brush, sage, and cactus. Dryness stuck in her throat.

"I don't much like him, either."

"He tries to get near me. Out of your sight."

"You're mistaken. He's a man of God."

"He's a man."

Anne paused.

"Whenever he comes near you, say out loud your prayers."

The truth was he seemed nothing like family and nothing like a religious man either. Anne took on faith both claims. She didn't like how he ordered them about. He was as bad as Snake Man, making them do

all the labor of setting up camp each night, packing up each morning, while he supped a large share of each meal, not caring if he left enough for them. After several days' riding, they were down to biscuits and hardtack, as he was a poor shot and had killed nothing fresh to supplement their dinner.

After a week they came off the high plateau over which they had been traveling. Grass covered the ground again, and with the grass came plentiful game.

"Uncle, would you lend me a shotgun?"

"What for?" he asked.

She guessed he worried about the bullets spent.

"Please."

"Women have no need —"

"I'm familiar with guns. I would like to try my hand for our dinner."

Within an hour, Anne had downed a buck, and the two women jumped off their horses to dress the animal. Josiah sat his mount and watched in quiet astonishment. When Neha, who had waned on their poor diet, lobbed a bloody piece of flesh into her mouth, he grew red in the face.

"We do not eat like savages," he yelled.

"Uncle, it is the way she was raised."

But Josiah dismounted and pushed past Anne, grabbed Neha by the neck, forcing

her to spit the meat out or risk choking.

"That is a sin. It is filthy. An abomination."

She lay blue-faced on the ground before he let go. Anne went to her, but Neha pushed her away.

"You had the gun. You could have killed him."

"Listen to me. If you do not bend, they will destroy you. You must not insist on the old ways."

"Escape. While there is only one to chase after us. Each day we move farther away from our tribe."

Her words were like balm to Anne's heart. In all her imagining of returning home, she had never pictured it would be like this. Time had stopped for her years before when her family was still alive, and it was only to that family she longed to return. These people were strangers and would not love her children even if she managed to recover them. That was the real problem — she could not be without Solace and Thomas. The hardships of native life had been made endurable because of them.

The women would not get far without horses and provisions. In her condition, Neha was not able to endure much privation at all. Anne decided the only step

would be to convince Josiah of the logic of allowing them to leave. Surely he would see the folly of an undesired deliverance?

She sought him out and began her speech but immediately sensed his dissatisfaction. He sucked on his front teeth as if something pained him and there was no quick prospect of relief.

"So the time and effort I've spent on your rescue is not appreciated? Not to mention the ransom paid?"

"It's most appreciated, Uncle. But I've left my children behind, consigned to grow up in darkness without me. Perhaps I can return to you . . ."

"You believe the Indians will let you come and go as you please?"

Anne remained silent.

"I am a pillar of the community. A leader of the church. Like Moses I risked going out into the wilderness to save you. You speak foolishness."

"My children —"

"Are a sin. A blasphemy. A most unnatural union. For your sake we will speak of them no more."

"I cannot do that."

"You will. I risk much bringing you back into the family. With your contagion. Your sin. I will not have you sully the minds of

the womenfolk."

Shaken, Anne did not know what else to do. She reconciled herself to continuing on, with the hope that her other relatives would not be as hard-hearted and difficult to persuade as he. Neha was not as equanimous. She had grown frantic. She feared an even greater imprisonment than a rival tribe would threaten. She resolved to run away alone, even if death be the likely outcome.

Anne could not argue her out of her decision but would not stand in her way. Straight after supper, she pleaded exhaustion and rolled up in her blanket and feigned sleep to conceal Neha's activity. Hours later she was wakened from real sleep by Josiah's curses when he discovered the girl missing. He loaded his gun and jumped on his horse.

"You stay here. If there is any bloodshed, know it will be on your head."

For over an hour Anne shivered by the campfire, paralyzed by indecision. She could run off, but felt responsible for Neha, especially since their tormentor was her kin. For years she had given herself purpose by imagining this very rescue, the joy of being reunited with her friends and family. Without her accounting it, time had eroded that possibility. When the long-withheld rescue finally became reality, her family consisted

of her children, Neha, Running Bear's family, the buffalo skinners, and sundry other tribe members. Affection built by proximity, the habits of daily life, the sharing of both triumphs and vicissitudes, and not only restricted to blood ties.

When Josiah finally rode in, he trailed a rope with the end looped around Neha's neck. Her arms were bound behind her so that when she stumbled during the night march back to camp she was unable to break her fall but landed on her belly. One of her eyes was swollen shut, her lip split open, and blood trailed from an ear.

"She bleeds!" Anne accused him.

"I beat the devil from her. I believe the work is well done."

Josiah sat his horse, staring into the fire. He sucked his teeth in deep contemplation as Anne untied Neha, and she collapsed on the ground. Josiah seemed to have reached some satisfactory conclusion and nodded his head as he dismounted.

That night Neha's labor began. Before dawn the child had already passed from the world. Despite Anne's best efforts, the infant never drew a single, mewling breath. Neha wrapped the girl child in a blanket but took no further interest in her.

"It is a mercy," Anne whispered.

The next morning Josiah announced a change of plans. They would make an early start to arrive at Neha's homestead that day instead of stopping at his home, which lay closer. When Anne saw he intended merely to pack their provisions and leave, she protested.

"We must give the baby a Christian burial."

"Get on those horses and follow. There is nothing — nothing — here worth burying."

Neha studied the ground. She seemed to sleep while awake, and Anne feared for her. She had seen this state in the tribe's captives when they removed themselves mentally from whatever tortures lay in wait for their physical being. They became like husk dolls with nothing inside.

Anne put her arms around her and whispered in her ear.

"You are Mary now. Do you hear? Mary. Say it."

Neha nodded but remained silent.

Anne squeezed her shoulders till she winced.

"Do not let him triumph. Protect your spirit. Hide under the skin of their false name. Keep Neha safe and warm until you become strong enough to escape."

Neha looked up at her, doubting.

"Me?"

"Mary. Not until you are returned to the tribe do you again become Neha."

LIBBIE

The summer of 1874, the women waited.

Each time Autie left on campaign felt like a small death. Libbie called it her black hour, when she lay in bed unable to talk, eat, drink, or even think clearly. Eventually by sheer strength of will she would rouse herself and go about the routine of her day in a kind of fugue state.

Due to the high threat of attack in the Black Hills, she was not allowed to accompany him. She and the other wives held vigil at Fort Lincoln as if they were on an island stranded on the vast sea. Their sea, though, was a parched one. The sun beat down but gave no life. It was the year of the great drought on the northern plains, and the landscape dried from brown to gray. There was never enough water at the best of times, and now they had to make do with even less.

Libbie learned to sponge bathe in a tea-

cup's worth, and not drink more than half a cup a day. Each morning they woke to a crackling heat and stayed inside, the shutters drawn in semidarkness until evening.

A great plague of grasshoppers descended, which seemed entirely unfair given their other numerous trials, and she wondered how the pests managed to survive the drought. Survive, though, they did. Thrive, even.

The sky would be without a wisp of vapor, a hard mineral bowl set down on the land, and then without warning a scrim would descend between sun and earth. Thinking it was a cloud, one looked up to see a brown mass of flying insects. They fell to the earth, destroying everything in their path.

The women screamed and ran inside. Soldiers stabled the horses, who otherwise went mad as insects covered and bit them, crawled in to invade eyes, ears, and mouth. The only thing in which they were lucky was that the land was too barren to tempt the insects for a long stay, and after their devastation they flew off in one day. Their damage, on the other hand, lasted.

Libbie's vegetable garden was only a memory, as were the gardens of the other families. The newly planted cottonwoods were stripped not only of leaves but also

bark, the denuded remains resembled tooth-
picks. She found holes in her clothing.
Whole pages had been eaten out of books.

The Black Hills Expedition was to be gone
two months, with regular mail drops during
that time. The arrival of the mailbags was
akin to Christmas, Thanksgiving, and the
Fourth of July rolled together. The wives
tittered in anticipation like children and
went off separately to each savor her "treasure." In the evening a group made the
ascent of the hill behind the fort and stood
guard with the sentries, squinting into the
far distance, hoping to conjure scouts carrying messages from their loved ones. If they
could not have that, they gladly would have
settled for an approaching rainstorm, but
most days they received neither.

Libbie was going stir-crazy at the small
circumference of her world, warned off going outside the limits of the fort and hill. It
was then she began to ride the surrounding
prairie in her sleep. Over many nights her
dreams changed from riding over dull
prairie to traveling through lush meadows
filled with flowers. She imagined stuffing
her mouth full to choking on luscious berries and letting icy mountain water cascade
down her throat. When she woke she re-

alized Autie's letters from the expedition had quite invaded her imagination.

A small black speck, a high whine, and then the sting. Libbie swatted and found a small spat of blood on her arm. With an almost biblical vengeance, the grasshoppers made way for the mosquitoes. Instead of staying just one day, though, the mosquitoes took up permanent residence. She had considered the Red River in the South the ultimate in mosquito persecution, but Fort Lincoln put the Southern mosquitoes to shame. The wind blew and the insects hitched a ride, arriving to torment them.

In the heat of the day, the women escaped inside, but in the evening they longed for fresh air and any bit of coolness they could find. At Libbie's suggestion, therefore, the ladies concocted the most outrageous uniforms against the scourge. They wore overcoats on top of dresses, scarves around their necks, hats and gloves to cover any exposed flesh. Libbie took honors for a device made out of reeds covered with netting that fit over the head, resembling a kind of demented beekeeper's bonnet. Another lady discovered that if they wrapped their legs, ankles, and feet in newspaper, then put on stockings, they were well protected down to

their shoes. They shuffled along in these uncomfortable costumes, fanning the air clear around themselves. It did not pay to examine oneself in the mirror, nor to look too closely at one's neighbor. Their lives took on a dream-like unreality. In this way they sat on their porches and held vigil.

She did not know what to make of Autie's first mail delivery, in which he went on at great length about the sublime beauty of the virgin territory they were reconnoitering: the pine forests, cold rushing streams, lush meadows of flowers and fruit that informed Libbie's dreams. In that same mail delivery, another wife had a letter from her husband describing the unbearable hardship during the first two hundred miles of the trek before they reached the Black Hills: blistering heat, brackish and undrinkable water, a dust storm that almost overwhelmed them. Why did Autie omit all these details? What other unpleasant realities did he hide from her?

Since their marriage she had been aware of his purposeful shielding of her from the harsher facts of the soldiering life. He had not shared the horrors of the War nor later of the Indian battles; he did not admit to the myriad dangers he encountered on each

campaign. She learned more about the Washita battle from the newspapers than from his lips, and yet she did not fault him the omission. Whenever possible she tried to ferret out the gory details he was exposed to, and yet she would never concede to the knowing. It was part of the myth of their marriage, their unspoken vow to each other to deny hardship.

She knew the dust storm was true, because it had reached the fort, too.

Libbie, unable to enlist any of the other women, had made the walk up to the sentry post alone. Alongside the guard, she squinted out in the direction from which the scouts would appear, realizing perfectly well that the last post had occurred scant days before. It would be a week or more before she again heard from Autie, but she needed to have a concrete task so she chose that. The horizon glowed like a penny. She called to the sentry, fearful of irritating him with her woman's anxiety. He studied it for a few moments with his field glasses, and his face paled.

"Get the women inside," he said.

Indian raids often made their appearance this way, the dust kicked up from the running ponies creating a voluminous cloud that heralded their warpath. The sentry

checked for bullets in the chamber of his pistol, his hand shaking, then handed it to her with a gruff nod.

"Use it if you need."

The penny cloud on the horizon was moving too fast and growing too large for Libbie to make it back to her house in time. It moved at an impossible speed for men on even the fleetest of horses. She stumbled on the loose gravel on her descent, scuffing her palms, kneeing a hole in her skirt. By the time she reached the house, her hand holding the pistol trembled. The usual blue-marbled sky overhead had turned the rust of dried blood. The door handle sparked to the touch, hot as an iron. Eliza opened the door from inside, using a kitchen towel to grip the metal.

Not Indians, but an attack nonetheless. A sirocco, one that turned air to metal. Libbie looked back, and it seemed the end-times. Her eyes felt abraded by sand as if she hadn't slept in days. Skin became leathered. Whatever had somehow escaped the calamity of the insects earlier that summer was now incinerated. Green became a memory. Plant life petrified in the dry heat. The earth rang hard like an anvil.

An irrational anger took hold of Libbie. The poor souls of the fort had struggled in

that purgatory for so long, this last blight seemed cruel and purposeful. A punishment. It would have been the greatest relief to her to fire the pistol at the sky, but the price in tarnished reputation was too steep. A few hours later both the storm and her fit of pique passed.

There was a code among the wives. They cheerfully accepted the hardships of the frontier, and it was a sign of dishonor to complain of the life to the outside world. They considered their own roles as important in their way as the men's: they brought civilization, which would be the lasting victory, not the brute force being used at the moment.

Even among themselves there was rarely any admission of flaws in their spouses. Drunkenness, profligacy, gambling, these were part and parcel of outpost life. There were darker defects that only showed themselves as bruises on the women's faces and arms, on parts hidden under clothing. A few suicides occurred over the years by soldiers and one by a laundress whose husband abandoned her. They could only pray that those despairing souls found a kinder life in the next world.

In subsequent mail deliveries, Autie wrote of finding a large hidden cave with the

skeleton of a white man outside it. Among his belongings were initialed buttons that matched the letters of an old beau of Libbie's. Autie, prankster, wrote that said beau must have escaped into the wilderness in order to avoid marrying her.

Autie went on to assure her that the regiment was maintaining healthful routines, no drinking or gambling permitted. Other wives received letters describing the exact opposite condition — considerable drinking and gaming. These were trifling disparities, though, when the main news was that Autie was safe. He wrote that there had been no fighting with Indians. Only later did she learn that it was because they were holding a Sioux chief hostage.

LIBBIE

Although mail deliveries from the Black Hills were infrequent, the fort had regular contact with the outside world through Bismarck. One of the wives received a letter from her sister, also a military wife, about a captive settler woman recently returned to her community. The woman was quite out of her mind, having suffered a year's captivity by the Comanche before her rescue. Her husband, overjoyed on her return, had after a few months moved out to a brother's house. All the women took a morbid interest in this dark tale of an unknown woman's demise. The fear of becoming just such a victim circumscribed their lives each and every day.

Libbie could only add her small knowledge of the return of the two captives that Autie had effected years before.

The famous incident occurred in Texas while Autie tried to bring the last of the

tribes off the Llano Estacado. During their short stay at Camp Supply the two women lived in a kind of isolation within the larger population, which would have been cruel punishment in any other circumstance. Autie noticed they only took council and comfort from each other. The soldiers, so zealous in their rescue, had become uncomfortable with the results because although the two women lived and breathed, ate and talked, they had lost what was most precious to their being and to their families.

After hugs, kisses, and tears, the brother of one of the women captives insisted his sister take off the native garb she had been dressed in, which she quickly did, borrowing an old tattered dress from the cook. Libbie did not add that Autie, too, seemed ambivalent about the outcome of the rescue after he was heralded in the newspapers for it. He did not keep in correspondence with the women, which was uncharacteristic on his part.

Without a doubt Autie would have shot Libbie rather than let her endure any such suffering in captivity. She, on the contrary, would want him back at any cost, even if he were missing limbs or was otherwise disabled. Would he really rather her dead than returned under such deleterious circum-

stances? She knew, without question, that Tom would never have shot her. Despite being so frightened of the stories of depredations, Libbie may or may not have found the strength to shoot herself. One could never know how one would act in extremity.

Stories like those took on a life of their own, engendering others.

One of the wives told of a young girl she knew in her hometown who had swallowed kerosene on her return when the magnitude of her ruination for marriage became apparent.

Another chimed in that a young bride captured after being married only a single month, once rescued from captivity and finding herself a widow, never spoke a word of her ordeal. In a short time she had gone off to another state where she was unknown. There she remarried and had five children. The wives marveled at the woman's strength and prepossession. The room was quiet for a moment while each of them explored within themselves if they would be strong enough to act thus, and of course they prayed, asking for deliverance from such a fate, hoping they would never be required to face such trials.

The society of the fort became an ex-

tended family of sorts, with all the expected rivalries but also loyalty against the outside world. None of the women mentioned the infamous and less known incident of which they were all surely thinking.

The 7th had been patrolling an area rife with rebellious Cheyenne and Sioux when a hunting detachment by pure chance came across a small group of buffalo skinners, including a captive that had been long assumed dead, along with her half-breed family member.

Although surprised by the Indians, once attacked, the soldiers defended themselves honorably. In the course of the conflict, due to quick reconnaissance they realized the presence of captives. Imagine with what renewed ferocity they fought once they understood the life of two white womenfolk hung in the balance. Once they had subdued the aggressors, the two women were delivered into their protection and in due course brought to Autie. He was overjoyed and allowed reporters to document the story of the brave rescue.

When some of those same newspapers started to call the incident a massacre of Indian women and old men, he fell into a dark mood and withdrew. He refused to see one of them when she requested an audi-

ence to discuss a search for her children, still being held captive.

A year later while Autie was back east, Libbie was paid a visit by the woman, along with her uncle, a preacher. She had glimpsed the girl through a doorway when she was first rescued, and had been quite haunted by her distress. Libbie was curious how she had settled and what was her true nature, removed from the traumatic terms of her captivity.

The uncle was personally affronted by the fact that Autie wasn't sitting at the fort waiting for just such a visit although no advance request had been made by letter. The acting commander thought perhaps an audience with Libbie would mollify him.

Both claimed to have sent voluminous correspondence to the fort, which had gone unanswered, and had finally decided to risk coming in person. Libbie at first thought they lied, as Autie was usually meticulous in answering all mail, considering it his public duty. But there was his strange coldness on the matter, the fact that the rescue was tarnished. Libbie suspected they might be telling the truth.

She had made sure she was well dressed and had Eliza put out a nice assortment of teas and cakes. Libbie entered the room

late, in a flutter of silk and scent, speaking to them like long-known acquaintances, a trick she had learned in the parlors of Washington and New York.

"Reverend, I hope I haven't kept you waiting."

Josiah Cummins stood tall, imposing, in his ill-fitting homespun. His features were large and unfinished as if he were a sketch the artist had been overwhelmed by and abandoned. When he came to shake her hand she smelled the odor of cellars and root vegetables. There was something subterranean about him, which was odd since by vocation he should have been closer to the heavens. His impression compared unfavorably with the average eccentric she encountered on the frontier, and her heart sank at having allowed herself to be bullied into accepting the visit.

"Mrs. General Custer . . ."

"Libbie, please. Shall we sit down and enjoy some tea?"

"Perhaps I should say a quick prayer of thanks?"

"That would be lovely. We don't receive —"

"O Almighty God, the Sovereign Commander of all the World, we bless and magnify Thy great . . ."

The prayer was neither quick nor particularly thankful, but it gave Libbie an opportunity to observe the girl.

She stood in the corner by the door, ill at ease, as if the surroundings might gobble her up. Libbie was used to such behavior from the various Indians who came to petition Autie, but had never seen it in a white person. The truth was that Libbie had accepted the visit partly motivated by prurience in meeting a former captive. In person, the girl broke Libbie's heart, and she immediately wanted to mother her.

"Come, dear. Sit by me."

The girl didn't move, hardly seemed to understand the words directed at her, but she flinched when Josiah spoke.

"Go, Anne! Say hello to Mrs. Custer."

She came carefully, wearing slippers that were unsuited for use outside or for traveling. They were now threadbare and filthy. She wore the plainest of clothes, with no feminine corset to tie in her waist. Libbie regretted putting her own on, uncomfortable as always with the unnatural constriction.

The girl had a striking face and form, or she formerly had. Now her skin was sun darkened, her limbs hard and sinewy like twisted rope. But the unnerving thing was

her gaze, the eyes furtive and darting. Libbie would describe it in no other way than it was like having a doe trapped in her parlor. She'd seen deer so frantic that they'd risk broken limbs to escape enclosure.

"What was your name again, sweetheart?"

Libbie held the girl's hand in her own as she sat on the edge of the settee, ready to spring at the least provocation. The hand was shockingly hard and callused.

"Anne."

The word came out so softly it was as though the girl regretted revealing it to the room.

"What a beautiful name. It means full of grace. Anne was the mother of the Virgin Mary."

No one spoke, so Libbie plowed on. She had learned her role of hostess well.

"A lovely name to go with a lovely face. General Custer will be so sorry to have missed your visit."

"I am equally sorry," her uncle said. "We are here on the urgent matter of reparations."

"Oh, yes," Libbie said, distracted as she stirred a lump of sugar, rare luxury, in her tea. The girl was looking at the china teacup as if it were a puzzle to pick up.

"Come, dear, it won't bite."

Libbie took a small, dainty plate and placed a few tidbits on it, setting it on the girl's lap.

"You simply must try one of Eliza's apple fritters. I've been told they are the best in the territory. Eliza is from the South, and they know their cooking down there . . ."

Neither Anne nor the uncle paid the smallest notice to her words.

"Reverend, please have some tea."

"The Lord does not encourage the drinking of stimulants."

"Yes, I'm sure, but then . . ."

Libbie was already tiring of the visit and thinking how to bring it to a graceful conclusion.

"General Custer's word would go a long way in Congress to get my niece's application for reparations accepted. We are hoping for land and a monthly stipend. Perhaps you would put in a word?"

"Oh," Libbie stalled. "I don't get involved in the general's official matters. I'm sure Autie . . ."

The girl plopped the entire fritter in her mouth and then, cheeks bulging, stood so that the china plate slid off and fell to the floor, shattering.

"Look what you've done!" Josiah yelled.

He jumped up from his seat, treating the

accident as a major maliciousness on her part, but Anne had already moved across the room, oblivious, and now stood at the window.

"Oh, it's nothing at all," Libbie said.

It was one of the precious plates from her bridal trousseau. She cursed her foolishness in using her fine china.

"I'll just call Eliza to sweep it up."

Now Libbie stood, watching Anne's rigid back as she pressed herself to the window. What could she be looking at? Was the girl unwell?

Josiah, his breath rancid, came close to whisper in Libbie's ear.

"Now you understand what I've been given back. She's no longer right in the head. I hope you see the duty in getting her compensation."

Libbie moved away on the guise of giving Eliza instruction.

On her hands and knees, Eliza swept up the shards. She resented Libbie entertaining such poor folk and causing her the extra work.

Josiah didn't bother to move his feet from her sweeping.

"When you're done," he said to her, "bring me a bottle of your master's whiskey." He no longer felt the need for pretense.

Eliza stood upright, shoulders stiff with dislike, her dustpan filled with the general's precious china.

"Liquor is not served in this house," she said.

Anne had a hand on each side of the window frame, and Libbie worried she might plunge herself straight through the glass. The girl was fixated on the scout camp in the distance where a few of the Arikara were cooking dinner outside.

Josiah now moved so close to Libbie that she was again immersed in his unwashed, ferine smell.

"They took her when she was a maiden of fifteen."

He moved even closer, and Libbie's heart beat wildly. He only slightly lowered his voice.

"She was violated over and over. Ruined. She even bore a few bastards."

The blood rushed to Libbie's face and she perspired heavily despite the chill room. She could not believe this man was whispering such obscenities in her ear.

"Her life is worthless. Better if she had died out there. But now . . . I'm not a wealthy man to take care of her needs."

Anne whirled away from the window and looked at Libbie as if for the first time.

"My children!"

Libbie had been wrong about the girl. Her face was filled with a surfeit of emotion, her eyes a kaleidoscope of excruciating feeling, a molten sorrow.

"Will you get General Custer to rescue my Solace? My Thomas?"

"Does the general know about your children?"

"Never mind that," Josiah said.

Anne now rushed at Libbie and went down on her knees, wrapping her arms around Libbie's legs so tightly it almost unbalanced her.

"I beg you. I want nothing except to have my children returned."

Libbie trembled. She patted the girl's head, the hair stiff from being long unwashed. She had never imagined such maternal anxiety in one so removed from the influences of civilization.

"Go wait outside," Josiah said, his voice low and threatening.

Libbie would not want to be under such a man's thumb.

The girl slipped out of the room without a word, grateful at the release.

"Damaged beyond return. No one will marry her. Reparations will be all she has to sustain her in this world."

"I hope that isn't true."

"As her relative I'm under obligation to do my best for her. I would hate to think of her ending in a home for the indigent. Or an asylum for the hysteric."

Libbie shook her head and moved away from him. She could not breathe. Out the window the girl was moving briskly toward the scout camp.

"I will certainly let the general know of your visit," she said, and walked him to the door.

Sensing a dismissal, his expression became even more dour.

They walked outside, a cool wind blowing, and saw Anne across the distance, sitting crossed-legged by the campfire. She was speaking to one of the Arikara. In her lap was a small boy of three, one of the scout's children. Libbie did not know the child's name.

It was strange to see a white woman in a housedress squatting down by the fire as natural as could be, but the girl was more relaxed and animated than she had been the whole time inside with them. The scouts stood around, bemused. Libbie bet that the girl was trying to finagle information as to her tribe's whereabouts.

When Josiah signaled to Anne to come to

the horses, she feigned not to see him. He stalked over the field toward her, his steps stiff, his hands balled into fists. Libbie, feeling protective toward the girl, ran after him.

"She can stay a while longer if it pleases her," Libbie offered.

Josiah shook his head. "She will come now with me. Where she belongs. She needs to be in the bosom of her family to be right."

The girl watched his progress toward her and let go of the child, readying herself in a crouch, the fire between them the only barrier.

"I cannot tell you the trial she's been. Quite demented," he spat out.

Libbie was sure the same could be said from the girl's side.

When Josiah ordered her to come, Anne shook her head.

Libbie did not understand the import of what was happening but sensed it was dire.

He lunged at the girl, but she easily dodged him, to the laughter of the scouts.

Libbie was stricken, feeling the animal terror inside the girl, not wanting him to catch her.

"Reverend Josiah!"

Now he leaped over the fire, singeing a pant leg, and caught at the girl's dress, tearing the hem. She twisted away from him,

picking up a sharp stick of kindling, and thrust it in his thigh. He stopped, purple-faced, and looked down as blood saturated the cloth of his pants.

Libbie let out a scream, and now the scouts realized the fun was up, and they easily caught the girl between them, pinning her arms against her like a bird's banded wings so that she was helpless.

Josiah walked up to her, saying something Libbie could not make out. As if possessed, the girl pitched forward with all her might, even though Arikaras held each arm, and bit his cheek as if it were a ripe apple. More blood, and Libbie was quite sure she would faint.

She could have nothing to do with the girl as much as she sympathized with her plight. The poor child had indeed gone mad.

Josiah smiled as he touched his cheek, blood trickling down his chin and onto his shirt. He now seemed more composed, even pleased at the outcome, as if vindicated. He slapped Anne so hard across her face her whole head was jerked back.

"Sir!" Libbie yelled. "I will not stand for this!"

These were the wages of the brutal life many lived on the frontier, a reality from which Libbie deliberately kept herself aloof.

Something terrible, irreparable, had been done to the child. Libbie only wished she knew who was to blame but assumed it went back to a whole line of men who had wronged the girl, possibly up to and even including her Autie in his neglect.

After they left, Libbie never spoke of the girl. When Autie finally did return, she told him nothing of the visit.

The day of homecoming arrived. The men rode in, tanned and bearded from their long summer outdoors. Faded and patched uniforms, boots worn out at the toes, even the overloaded wagons looked spent.

Overcome, Libbie hid inside behind the door, her happiness so intense it was akin to pain. Her heart was like to explode. When she heard the band start a tolerable "Garry Owen," she could contain herself no longer. She ran outside crying and in front of all hugged Autie. Tom stood behind, patiently waiting his turn for a sisterly hug. The men set up a great cheer. Reunions made a moment of unalloyed joy for all there. After the unsettling feeling of the captive's visit, Libbie was trebly grateful for the life they had together.

The wagons bristled with elk horns strapped to their exterior, giving them the

appearance of a strange breed of beetle. Autie would have a magnificent chandelier constructed from a number of them to illuminate their parties and dances in the great room. He gave away the surplus horns as presents. The wagon beds groaned under loads of specimens from scientific investigations as well as the gold exploration. Crowded together were mineral specimens of mica, quartz; petrified specimens of marine shells and wood; pressed flowers; snake rattles; skins of numerous animals; and a menagerie of live animals. Tom had collected an assortment of snakes, which he kept in boxes. The academic nature of the "souvenirs," rather than the usual gruesome ones of war, pleased her.

As she had doubted the veracity of the brothers' story, they produced artifacts of the "beau" skeleton found at the cave entrance. Her eyes went wide to see a brass button engraved with the initials of her long-lost admirer although it most certainly did not belong to him.

After all had been unloaded, a lone keg was brought off Autie's personal wagon. It contained the most heavenly water from a mountain stream. Libbie had Eliza go fetch glasses. After the water was poured, she held hers up to the sunlight, marveling at its clar-

ity as much as its taste. Clear water was only a memory during those years at the fort. It was amazing how deprivation made that first taste gloriously memorable for decades afterward. They had become so habituated to the murky, sediment-filled kind from the muddy Missouri they hardly knew what to make of such a luxury and doled it out in their finest glasses as if it were champagne.

New York City, Winter 1876

They had gone on leave to the states in late autumn. Although Custer savored his trips alone to New York City, it was worth much to watch Libbie take delight in the civilization long denied her. They dined at Delmonico's. He took her to clever dinner parties where as usual he was expected to sing for his supper with Indian tales, although these had lost the sheen of the novel for him years ago. At thirty-six, he was not a young pup anymore. The wealthy and important flattered him as extravagantly as ever, but he began to suspect it was because it cost them so little.

For the first time he took careful inventory of the houses, better furnished than any he could provide for Libbie. Too, he noticed the fineness of the men's suits, the stylish French cuts of the women's silk dresses compared with Libbie's homespun frocks, although in his biased opinion she

still outshone them by her natural beauty unadorned. Although she was too tactful to ever admit thinking this, he felt a deep dissatisfaction in their station.

His tactic was to adopt an attitude of swagger. He wore his most threadbare uniform, his most worn-out boots, his military ulster for overcoat as badge of authenticity. He would play the part of hero, Indian fighter, he need not dress the dandy. High society lapped it up. He was as unreal to them as a character out of a vaudeville show. He rented rooms far above his means on Fifth Avenue because he believed their workaday hardship merited it. Libbie would soon enough return to their clapboard home at Fort Lincoln, and he would again be making the hard ground his bed. He would not admit it to the old lady, but he had accumulated gambling debts and had speculated on a mining concern with borrowed money. The interest rates charged him were usurious. Anxiety now ate at him.

As they strolled a fashionable street of women's stores, Libbie's glance stopped on a beautiful baby-seal muffler, the kind all the women wore that season. He marched in and purchased it, not asking the price, knowing that buying it would mean having to go home earlier. Her delicate hands,

though, would be as stylishly toasty as those of the highest society lady.

He could not put his finger on it — the season was as spectacular as any previous one — but his enjoyment was forced, his gaiety strained. It was akin to alcohol on one unused to it. The first few times the effect was divine, but that initial euphoria was not to be repeated, no matter how much one imbibed later. All drunks could attest this truth. In his experience only battle never diminished in its power to intoxicate.

Custer had been waiting for something to happen in his life that was too long in coming, a victory impressive enough to take care of his whole extended family. He was their rock, not only for Libbie and Tom, but the rest of the Custers, too. At the least he needed to be named field commander for the next, possibly last, Sioux campaign.

Even when Tom joined them in the city it did little to lift his mood. His brother, too, had gone through a rough patch. His fiancée, Lulie, had passed away finally from the consumption that had plagued her for years. Custer had considered the relationship fanciful at best. Lulie was a delicate flower who never strayed far from Jersey City. For his part, there had never been a shadow of possibility that Tom would resign his com-

mission. The interesting question was why his brother bothered with the charade of an engagement at all. Why not find someone suitable?

Tom had fallen into his usual vices when away from Libbie's influence, but now he showed new confidence after the Rain-in-the-Face capture. The Indian warrior had been heard bragging of the killing of two soldiers during the Yellowstone campaign. Tom had laid a trap and captured him at a trading post. At last he was coming into his own. Perhaps Tom was ready to spread his wings.

That winter Custer ran into an old friend from West Point, a man who he once had considered a rival. Grosnor had left the service years ago to pursue business interests, but the new life had been difficult for him. Custer was surprised by how he had aged, his body gone soft down to the pot-belly. How he longed, he claimed, for the simple choices of the battlefield. Bravery or cowardice, victory or defeat, life or death. Civilian life by comparison was murky, unfathomable. Grosnor's eyes moistened, and he wiped at his lips. He whispered into Custer's face, his breath heavy with whiskey.

— This life is a slow death. How I envy that you stayed.

As the season wore on, Custer realized he was not at his best in the city. He was a man of the country, he belonged to the empty spaces where he had spent the greater part of his life. He understood Grosnor only too well.

Nightly he woke up with dreams of the men who had died fighting either for or against him. They had grown to a large, unwieldy crowd, an assorted group of men in uniform, Indians, women and children, horses, dogs, buffalo, antelope, deer, bears, birds without count. They crowded the hallways and jostled one another in the empty midnight street below. They clamored for his presence, but he knew better than to give it. One night it got so bad he woke up Libbie, and she asked him why he was pointing out the window.

How had it come to pass that a man could feel more at ease in the wilderness than in civilization? But so it was for him. He understood hardship, had even come close to understanding death, at least in terms of the battlefield. Still, if a soldier fought bravely there was honor in that. What he didn't understand, what he couldn't tell Libbie, was the sickening disorientation he felt in the cities.

Society had a stench. Although the stakes

were less than in battle (no one died of a snub), the loss was more insidious. People, wealthy people especially — Astors, Vanderbilts — ate at table with him, hungering for his entertainment. He was their trained pet, his act to bring them in contact with the real. He was a war hero. He had killed men. The rich, old men thrilled at that. The scantily clad women clamored for stories of Indians lusting for white women, the bloodier the depredations, the better. No one who had experienced the reality would consider it entertainment fodder.

He refused to trade on the deaths of his men so made up tall tales instead. He understood he was there to play a part. He, not those on the stage, was the consummate actor. Yet his part in history was ending, and he needed to reinvent himself. The sum total of all the dinners ended up in not enough opportunities to quit the army. Frankly he did not much have the stomach for quitting it either. Sitting in those drawing rooms, he felt as much a curiosity as the Indians themselves.

If he could have chosen his talent and vocation other than soldiering, he might have chosen to be an actor. Always when they visited the States, the first order of business was to get tickets to any available

plays. Other than the battlefield the theater was the one place he felt himself totally present. Those big, clear-cut choices Grosnor lamented not finding in everyday life were skillfully laid bare in a play.

Years before, he had become good friends with the actor Lawrence Barrett, and that winter Lawrence played Cassius in *Julius Caesar*. Custer sat on the edge of his seat for every performance, sometimes going backstage to sit with his friend while he waited to be called back on. It was very much like waiting out the lulls of a battle. The old lady counted and claimed he sat through forty performances that winter. It was as thrilling in its way as battle, the knowing of the outcome in advance in no way diminishing the excitement. This play in particular seemed torn from Custer's life, it rolled around in his head during the day much as it must have for Barrett before each night's performance. It seemed to be speaking directly to him, but he knew this was the trick of all great art — it spoke to all men and addressed each one at a time, in the solitude of his own mind and heart.

He smiled as he walked down the street to lunch, changing the words he knew by heart.

Danger knows full well
That Custer is more dangerous than he.

No one ever listened to a story except to find a clue to his own fate within its progress. When they left to go back to Fort Lincoln in late winter rather than waiting for spring, their friends asked why they had to depart so soon. Jaws dropped when Custer announced that they had simply run out of money. It was somehow in bad taste in society to mention the truth. None offered to part with theirs to lengthen their stay.

He did not despair, as he felt he had firm prospects. Literary men had praised his articles, and there was talk of money to be had on the lecture circuit that fall. Who would have thought it possible to earn one's living by the pen of all things? If the summer campaign delivered his grand victory perhaps he could aim higher than a scribbler.

That spring began with the winter's unraveling. Events occurred whose full import would not make themselves known until the fateful summer. He passed through those months with the play's counsel still in his ears. Like in a play, the various strands began tightening: two thieves accused of

stealing grain from the army shared imprisonment, and in the case of one, chains, with Rain-in-the-Face, the warrior accused of the murders during the Yellowstone expedition. One spring night that April, they escaped. Once safe, they sawed off the shackles binding them and separated.

Another version of the story was that the two grain thieves had arranged the escape and paid off the guards to effect it. Worried that Rain-in-the-Face might sound the alarm, they invited him to join. Since the escapees were not pursued, nor the guard on duty punished for dereliction, Custer feared that the latter was the likely truth.

Tom raged that his glorious capture should come to naught. In actuality Rain-in-the-Face was still only accused, although he had been heard bragging of the murders on the reservation and had confessed before officers. According to the Indian, the two men — one a veterinarian, the other a sutler — were unarmed when attacked. Rain had first shot the old man, who did not die immediately but fell off his horse a short ride away. Quickly Rain went to him and smashed his skull with a stone mallet, then shot his body with arrows for coup. The younger man sat shaking in the bushes, making clear signs of surrender and peace,

going as far as handing over his hat as a gift. Disgusted by such cowardice, Rain shot him with a gun, then finished with arrows. Neither man was scalped for the simple reason that one was bald, the other wore closely cropped hair, a fact of which the white listeners took careful note.

Rain was known to be a big talker. He raged on about revenge against his captor. He bragged that he had drawn a bloody heart on a piece of buffalo skin and sent it to Tom as bad medicine, yet the latter never received it. It was at this point that Custer started to have doubts about the earlier confession. Both brothers guessed that if Rain's braggadocio extended to claiming the two deaths, perhaps his escape was the best justice for all.

Knowing that returning to the Standing Rock agency would mean certain recapture, Rain went to join the fierce Chief Sitting Bull. After performing a Sun Dance, the whole tribe moved to their ultimate destination in the valley of the Little Bighorn. Both brothers contemplated this news in silence.

When Custer left New York that February it was with a sense of finality. The city's lures had proven illusory, and he was ready to embrace the only life that had always

been true to him. He longed for the familiarity of the frontier.

The Fourteenth Remove

Neha's return — The voyage home

Josiah's decision to push straight to Neha's homestead without stopping meant two days of grueling travel crushed into one. The two women were in mourning, numbed by the previous night's ordeal. They rode meekly in single file, with little talk. When prodded to eat, Neha mumbled, "I am Mary." She moved as if everything around her was a dream she hoped to wake from soon.

As they came close to her kin's homestead, Anne was shocked when Josiah stopped and offered to make coffee for them. Previously he had treated them as less than human.

"Perhaps you should make her more presentable? For her relatives' sake," he said.

Neha was far past the state of being able to be cleaned up. The gash along her ear had crusted black, while the rest of her face

purpled as bruises formed. One eye was almost closed shut.

"Maybe we'll explain she fell off her horse," he suggested.

"I will not," Anne answered.

His face loosened with the return of his habitual temper.

"Do you insist on revealing her shame first? Before there is a chance for a slip of affection to be formed?"

He taunted Anne with his wrongdoing.

"Perhaps you should have considered that last night," she said.

"Ungrateful girl."

When they arrived at the homestead, a crowd of relatives and neighbors formed. A great-uncle, who only remembered Neha's mother from childhood, had agreed to take her in, and he greeted her like a long-lost daughter. As he opened his arms, Anne recalled her own father and felt the bitterest of tears. She could not recall the feeling of happy innocence she'd had in her own family. Such emotions had withered away. For the first time she felt the size of her loss.

Neha resisted the man's embrace, believing this was her new chief until Anne explained the family relation. When the uncle's wife came out and wrapped a shawl

around Neha's shoulders, she clung to the woman, sure that the crowd of onlookers intended her harm. Anne had to patiently explain that these were kindly, Christian people, who treated their own well.

"But I am an Indian," Neha wailed, and Anne could only give thanks that her words were not spoken in English so they could be understood.

They were invited to spend the night. Anne greatly desired to stay and help settle Neha in her new surroundings. A loving family, which this one appeared to be, was a gift after all these years. She wished time to savor it. Josiah, however, frowned. He insisted loudly to onlookers that they must press on, that he had been away from his parish and his fields far too long and would be sorely missed.

It did not escape Anne's attention that before they left he transacted business with Neha's uncle. Money passed hands. As they said their goodbyes, the realization came to Neha that she would be left with these strangers, and she clung to Anne. At last two male cousins were forced to restrain her. Josiah hastily mounted and bade Anne do the same, as if the relatives might change their minds at the worth of their transaction and refuse the girl.

"Take care, Mary," Anne said. "I will come to visit soon."

After they had ridden a distance, Anne could stay quiet no longer.

"We were not ransomed. You paid out no monies."

"Time and effort are not without their value," he answered.

"That is the reason you would not allow her to escape?"

"You are a bright girl. It must run in the family."

"Honesty was supposed to be a prime virtue in our family also."

"Speaking of. You will say nothing of the existence of your children when we reach home. You will deny your ruination. We will say that you are untouched, unsullied."

Anne rode in silence, his ploy of shaming her effective.

Josiah studied her as he sucked his teeth. "You are a sly boots. In case any bright ideas are forming, don't even think of attempting to flee. In your case it's the family honor that is at stake. *My* honor. You have been rescued from the heathen inferno. You are saved, your soul redeemed. Rejoice, child!"

He laughed to himself as at a great joke, never sharing the cause of his hilarity.

THE FIFTEENTH REMOVE

Return home — Recuperation —
Heartsickness

Josiah's wife, Lydia, was so unlike her husband it was hard to see how they had become a couple. Kind and long-suffering, she undoubtedly had been tempered by her long years of marriage to him. On their arrival, she put her arms around Anne as tenderly as a mother.

The members of the family, Anne's extended kinship of cousins and friends, were as solicitous of her as she could have hoped. Josiah faded into the background of daily life, and after a time it was hard to recall his harsh treatment in light of the Christian charity and goodwill she now enjoyed.

She was treated as a prodigal who had come from far away, and whose rest and recuperation were of utmost concern. After a few days, it began to resemble the treat-

ment enforced on an invalid. Anne was allowed to do nothing but sit in the house all day. Suggested pastimes beyond prayer included reading, sewing, and playing music, for none of which she had the slightest inclination.

The younger girls brought their castoffs, it being decided that those best suited Anne's extreme thinness as opposed to the fuller dresses more appropriate to a women her age. A mother of two, Anne felt foolish in the virginal, bright-colored calicos and florals, yet a part of her coveted this part of her youth that had been stolen. She felt keenly how great chunks of her life had been torn away, never to be recovered.

For the first time in over six years she had leisure to contemplate what had happened to her. She spent long hours in a rocking chair by the window with the decoy of needlepoint to keep busy, her idleness otherwise arousing worry. She longed to take strenuous walks outside, but her time out of doors was curtailed until it became hardly any at all. Her skin again paled, the calluses on her hands softened, but what should have been a time of healing became instead a time of fretting.

Although Anne could not experience it viscerally as when living outdoors, she felt

the waning of summer by the changing slant of light, the sun setting sooner, the coolness creeping into the late afternoon air. It was a time of harvest. The tribe would be busy drying berries and meat for the long months of lack that lay ahead. How did Solace and Thomas fare? Had the tribe escaped the harsh punishment of the army? If so, where were they now? Did they miss her or was she already in the process of being forgotten? How could she enter this white world again when they had been left behind in that other one?

Uncle Josiah kept a hawkish watch over her. It was as if he were privy to her innermost thoughts. She had the uncanny feeling he read hers. Although he had suggested it, she was loath to keep a journal, knowing he would scour her writings for hidden meaning. The only way to gain her freedom was to lull her uncle into a belief that the Indian influence on her had been exorcized, that she had indeed put the desire for her children in the past.

Shyly she asked Lydia if she could begin helping with chores, as her unproductive hands were a curse to her. Soon she was cooking in the kitchen, bringing in the milk and eggs from the barn, sandwashing the floors, and sewing — in all ways making

herself of service. Artfully she let slip that she wished to progress with her life, to marry and start a family. A parade of young men began to appear at the dinner table.

When any of the grown daughters came with their own young children, Anne insisted on playing aunt with the little ones, dandling them on her lap, feeding them sweets. It took only a small kiss to remind her of her own babies surviving in privation.

Lydia noticed her downturned mouth.

"Are you sad?"

"I think of my little ones," Anne whispered.

Lydia's face tightened at the unwanted revelation, but she did not seem greatly surprised. Either Josiah had divulged it, or she had guessed her husband's lie.

"They are passed?"

Anne bit her lip.

"Solace. Thomas. They are unclaimed. Abandoned by their mother. With all my heart I long only to retrieve them."

She cursed herself for confessing her longing, undoing months of the careful planting of lies.

"I suspected."

"Forget I said anything," Anne said.

Lydia folded her hands in her lap. She

bowed her head. The toll of long years as Josiah's obedient wife made her hesitate, weighing her words carefully.

"Your uncle explains to me that they are a sin . . . I do not agree. In my eye every child born is blessed. Truly, my heart bleeds for you."

Her words loosed a flood of tears from Anne. She unraveled.

Lydia continued, "I could never have the strength to shun my own blood. You have been chosen for a grave trial. Josiah says so. The Lord must have determined you strong enough to bear it."

"I am the weakest of women."

"After all, they *are* Indians. Perhaps they could not adapt happily to our life? Could it be God's wisdom that they are better left to their lot?"

"I do not believe so," Anne answered, too sharply for politeness. "If your babes were torn from your arms, would you say it was for the better for them to be without you? To live in such harsh circumstances, in such heathen ways? Children thrive on happiness, goodness, all of which you have shown me in abundance."

For several moments neither woman spoke.

"Would you tell me something?" Lydia

whispered, leaning closer.

"Surely, Aunt."

"During your time there, did they ever force you to scalp a man?"

THE SIXTEENTH REMOVE

Rejoining the fold — Josiah's sermonizing
—
Letters of Neha

It was spring. All in the town spoke of Anne's remarkable transformation from gloomy and brooding victim into the energetic woman they assumed she would have been, minus her captivity. They congratulated themselves on having erased the effects of the previous seven years as if they had never been.

Her baking and her embroidery became famous. Every local celebration brought a request for her cakes and pies. Her vanity was kindled by the attention she received from the eligible young men in the area. For the first time in years, she took an interest in her appearance and put on weight, nicely filling out the stylish dresses she now sewed herself. At social gatherings, she

became a great favorite, singing and dancing with more grace than any girl there,
arousing considerable enviousness.

The jealousy thus engendered kept alive
conjecture over her time in captivity, how
she had bartered with an Indian chief to
retain her purity. They gossiped that she had
dressed as an Indian woman and partici-
pated in massacres of white people. One
homely girl went so far as to claim that in
her room she kept scalps hidden in the bottom drawer of her dresser that she intended
to sew into a dress.

Anne docilely turned her cheek to such
maliciousness. She attended each and every
church service, sometimes twice a day, and
sat in the front pew with her attention
riveted on Josiah's words, so much so that
he found it unnerving. Often he would lose
his train of thought until he stood dumb on
the podium, conscious only of the blinding
sun streaming through the windows, and
the expectant, upturned faces of the congre-
gation, most especially Anne's steady blue
gaze, which made a mockery of his shep-
herding.

He sensed a dark, cold spine of rebelliousness in her that needed to be broken. It
could almost be described as diabolical, how
even as he complained of her recalcitrance

to his wife and others, they protested that she was the very embodiment of an angel.

The town was aflutter with gossip of two cowboys who ran a ranch outside the settlement coming across an Indian boy wandering the plains. Horseless, dehydrated, he did not seem to know where he was. They hailed him and asked him his purpose in crossing such a desolate area as they grazed their herd on. He glanced at them and without reply continued on his way. Outraged, the men lassoed him and dragged him behind their horses for sport till he died. Only a few days later did his mother and brothers appear, claiming him deaf and mute.

Anne betrayed no emotion on hearing the story, although Josiah studied to find out her sympathies. When Lydia later found her crying, she attributed the tears to the girl's natural softheartedness, never guessing it was due to horror at such barbarity.

Her latest outrage was to resist his plan to take her to the state legislature to seek restitution after being ignored by General Custer. He had read in the papers how other captives had grown prosperous in such manner, yet she showed no interest in pursuing this, somehow feeling superior to it and him.

"You can't expect to rely on my charity forever," he said.

"I work for my keep," she said quietly. "If it is not enough, let me go elsewhere."

There it was. Tacit acknowledgment that the desire to remove herself from the homestead lingered still. The capricious child wished to return to her savage state.

"Your mind has been so defiled you do not know what you say."

Josiah closed his eyes and began to pray. Unable to hold his tongue, he blurted out his provocation.

"You are blind. Your Mary is on her way to be turned out into the wilderness to fend for herself."

He would not tell her the details and give her satisfaction. During the last months he had exchanged letters with the uncle of the half-breed Neha/Mary. Mostly they were letters of pleading that Josiah take the girl and allow her to live with Anne.

Dear Pastor Josiah,

. . . She is impossible. We believe she is quite out of her mind. Whenever she is loose, she attempts to run away. It is so bad we have resorted to the un-Christian act of tying her to a tree. And she much prefers it! She begs to be left outside the

entire night. Cooks her bit of meat herself over a small twig fire. She then smudges soot on her face till it is black. She sings and chants, yells in her unintelligible tongue. My wife fears that she is possessed by the devil.

More practically, do you know the meaning of her tribe's customs? We gave her a knife to cut her meat, but when we turned away she cut off half her hair with it before she could be stopped. The other night, her face blackened, she plunged the sharp end of a stick into her breast and allowed the blood to drip into the flames. Regularly she eats dirt. She repeats a dirge that depresses us all. Simply put, we are afraid. Do you think these satanic rituals or merely the expression of aboriginal sorrow?

When I was a young boy I was a great collector of wild animals and brought all manner of birds and varmints home: swallows, quail, frogs, turtles, field mice, and prairie dogs. I was quite the trial to my parents. A young boy does not understand the concepts of life and death, suffering and imprisonment. The outcome was always the same. The animals fought for their freedom for a long while until they finally resigned themselves to their

confinement and then inevitably death quickly followed. My father, our Mary's grandfather, told me it is in the nature of a wild thing to remain free. Take away that nature, and you have taken away their very being. Could it be the same for our Mary? We could not bear her death on our conscience. I have prayed fervently and come to entertain the unthinkable. Should we give the girl her heart's pleading and release her to return whence she had come? The very idea saddens us, and yet we must trust the Lord to guide us to the right decision. We anxiously await your council on these matters.

Sincerely,
Edward Mulford

LIBBIE

The last summer could only be described as a darkening.

It began with another planned winter campaign to attack the Indian when he was snowbound and his horses depleted. Finances depleted, Autie and Libbie ended their leave of absence in New York and headed back to Dakota Territory, running straight into yet another blizzard. The Northern Pacific, grateful to the army, had outfitted a special train with a plow to get them back to Fort Lincoln despite the heavy snows that had immobilized the plains all winter.

Drifts stranded them in a gully outside Bismarck for a week. Marooned in boxcars, they shared their rations with a small group of soldiers traveling with them, but the cold had to be endured singly. Autie bundled her up in blankets and buffalo robes, and she lay bound like a papoose all the miserable

long day.

By the end of the week they were reduced to dried biscuits and hardtack carried in the soldiers' rations, washed down with melted snow. With Autie in charge, Libbie did not exhibit the same stamina to go through a blizzard again, happy to let him shoulder the burden. She made peace with the idea that this absurd predicament might be their end, but at least they would be together.

In desperation, a fellow soldier fashioned a crude telegraph key, connected it to the wire running alongside the track, and sent out a message for help. Tom came to their rescue once again.

"This is getting to be a regular habit with the two of you," he said, nonchalant, as if he had only come to fetch them from the neighbors'.

In retrospect it seemed fate toyed with them. No sooner did they arrive than Autie was called back to Washington to testify against the Indian ring, retracing the treacherous journey they had only just completed. He cited the dangerous traveling and their lack of funds to shut down the possibility of her accompanying him.

Libbie worked hard to hide her jealousy. She did not mind sharing danger if she also partook of the joy. Always the worst thing

was being left behind. He preened as he packed, and she noted him being sure to include his best shirts. From Washington Autie wrote that spring had already arrived back east with green grass, flowers, and lightly clad women. *What a good thing it is,* he wrote, *to be out of the cold.*

President Grant was angered by Autie's testimony concerning the administration's corruption. In revenge, he delayed Autie's return so that he could not go out with the 7th on the campaign, which had been now delayed into April. Libbie was secretly pleased with the result if not the cause.

Autie could easily have slipped his destiny, but instead he was frantic to embrace it. He begged General Terry to intercede, which he did. This was not altruistic — Terry needed a decisive victory and did not have the stomach to fight. Autie would go wrest victory for him. Newspapers got hold of the machinations in Washington — Libbie suspected with some nudging of Autie's journalist friends — and wrote that Grant was punishing him for testifying. With the public outcry, he got his heart's desire.

Even at the time everyone sensed that it would be a fearful campaign compared with more recent ones. The Sioux had been

driven to the edge. The unsubdued were angered over the violations in the Black Hills. Enough time had elapsed so that they knew from their brethren on the reservation that the promises of plenty by the Great Father in Washington were false. Anger was rampant over poor rations, and many young warriors left to go hunting in order to save their families from starvation. Once they left the boundaries of the reservation, they were declared hostile. They had been put in a position from which they had nothing to lose.

When General Crook set out in June, he was attacked by a joint Sioux and Cheyenne war party. He held his ground but did not gain victory. A shift in balance occurred. The Indians gained confidence and would make the summer a violent one. The army needed someone bold and fearless to combat them.

Libbie wished that Autie had hesitated, or that he was forced to go and had been reluctant, but that would be false. He went above and beyond to make sure he was part of the campaign. He loved war and thirsted for victory.

When the column finally set off from Fort Lincoln, they rode one last time circling the parade ground to take leave of their families.

The departures always tore a hole in Libbie's heart. The regiment consisted of the 7th Cavalry, two companies of the 17th Infantry, four of the 6th Infantry, Arikara scouts, a Gatling gun detachment, teamsters, and civilian employees. Usually such a sight of strength reassured, but somehow it failed that morning. She searched and searched the cause but could find nothing out of the ordinary. The melancholy mood was not helped by the fort being enveloped in a thick fog, which made the review spectral and anonymous, contributing to the poor impression.

The expressions of grief from the various women also dampened spirits, and Libbie marveled that such a universal feeling could be expressed so differently. The Arikara scouts, as was their custom when going to war, chanted and made fighting sounds. Their women lay prostrate on the ground and gave heartrending wails, shedding tears that threatened to make all of them lose their composure. She could only imagine the terror of such a sight to their children.

Golden Buffalo and the other "bachelors" seemed not as well loved in comparison. Once they proved themselves, maybe in this very battle, they would also be entitled to marry. Although such open display of grief

scandalized Autie, at the moment Libbie wished to join the keening women. Instead, she stood silent, stoic, dry-eyed, in anguish.

Farther up the troops passed "soap suds row," and the laundresses, too, were extravagant in their sadness, crying loudly and calling names, running up to their men for a last kiss. The somber officers' wives stood each before her own quarters or in small groups. They bit their lips, at most pressing a kerchief to an eye, no more. Their husbands would have chastised any outsized display of emotion. Strength was expected. Many rushed inside afterward to cry alone. Libbie did not pretend to understand the difference in accepted behavior.

Tom stopped his horse in front of their quarters, dismounted, and ran to his room. He claimed to have forgotten a favorite shirt. Libbie followed and saw him pause at the single cot he used as a bed. His eyes were damp, and she put her hand on his shoulder.

"Is something wrong?"

He shrugged her hand away. "Just thinking I wished there was someone to miss me while I was gone. Cry tears."

"You're still a young man. You'll find her."

She had noticed Golden Buffalo's loneliness but had been oblivious to her own fam-

ily member. Tom seemed as above human frailty as his brother.

Libbie handed him a kerchief from her pocket.

"Will you keep this for me? And bring it back with you?"

He nodded and brought it to his nose. It held her cologne. He began to say something but then thought better of it.

As the column wound its way up a bluff, the sun at last began to burn through the fog, creating a halo around the men. As they climbed, it appeared as if the cavalry rode from earth to sky and trod on the clouds. Ever hopeful, Libbie took it as an omen of success. It was not.

As usual she camped out with the regiment that first night, riding in the paymaster's wagon. The custom was for the men to receive their wages while out in the field so as not to splurge on alcohol and other vices. After the battle, witnesses said paper money blew across the hills, as useless to its owners as the army intended it to be.

Over the years she had become every bit the army wife, the camp follower, as at home in a tent as in the grandest house.

That night the couple ate early, and instead of socializing with the men, Autie

went to bed. They lay side by side, the cicadas loud in the breeze, the stars floating lazily in the summer night. They held each other in the dark but did not speak. After all their years of marriage, nothing more needed to be said. She squeezed his hand as she began to fall asleep and then he spoke.

The next morning the paymaster hitched his mules for the return trip to the fort. It was as bright and sunny as the previous day had been glum. Libbie lingered at the campfire, a blanket over her shoulders, and drank her coffee. How she wished the moment might never end.

Finally the column was ready and moved off. She felt reassured. The day before had been simply a case of jitters. If all went well, they planned that she would rejoin Autie by supply steamboat in a few weeks.

Riding away in the wagon, she turned for a last glance. No one watching her would have ever guessed her heart quaked, that like the other women she wanted to scream and protest to the heavens at the separation. No, she appeared as cool and composed as if going on a picnic. A worthy wife to the last.

Autie had just reached the top of a promontory and turned around. Thankfully, even

if he suspected it, he was too far away to see her façade was already cracking, tears appearing unbidden. He took off his hat and gave a casual wave. She could not reconcile the man on the horse, riding away to battle, with her husband. But it had always been so.

She no longer believed in the mission, only in him, and so now she feared.

The previous night in the tent he had curled against her and kissed her ear.

"I am afraid," he whispered.

The culmination of their marriage, when he finally reached out to her for comfort, and she had failed him. The admission, so unlike him, had petrified her. She pretended she had not heard. Instead, she kissed his cheek, rolled on her side, and feigned sleep.

The column moved on up the hill, moved on and went down the other side, went down the other side to disappear forever from her life. She never saw her husband again.

THE SEVENTEENTH REMOVE

Preparation — The dance — A farewell

Anne had stored away a sack of medicines and foodstuffs to last a week if she was sparing in her portions. Her plan was to go fetch Neha, and together they would find their way back to the tribe. To the whites the Indians were nomads, impossible to locate, but within the tribe there were well-known paths north and south along valleys and rivers that varied depending on the season and the migration of the buffalo. Since it was spring, the season of young green grass, within a month the ponies would have fed enough to regain their strength for the long trip north.

The memory brought a catch to Anne's throat. She did not remember ever not being hungry and in pain during those trips, exhausted by the arduous travel, sure that with the very next step she would expire.

Just as vividly she recalled the sting of icy, sweet air in her nostrils, the lifesaving warmth of the weak spring sun on her numbed limbs, the comfort of a buffalo robe to sleep in by the fire. These impressions created an indefinable longing for a life that only now did she choose to claim as hers. Migration had lodged in her blood as it did in a bird's.

Before her captivity she had always lived protected in houses, inside walls, under roofs. Caged. Even when traveling, she had been hidden away under the canvas canopy of wagons. She had not experienced the immensity of the land around her but rather had lived in fear of it. Did her people hate nature that they were so determined to tame it? The warming prairie in various shades of gold and green appeared to her eyes every bit as beautiful as the prophecy in church, an embodiment of the land of milk and honey if looked at from the right vantage. The pulchritude of nature, its attendant liberty, had been revealed to her in her captivity.

She chided herself for her schoolgirl nostalgia for a life in which she had endured such brutal hardship. Sentimentalizing it was to delude herself, but to deny its isolated joys was equally wrong. The only

overwhelming certainty was her continuous ache for her missing children. She could not fathom the advice she received, not only from Lydia and Josiah, but Neha as well, to forget them, pretend they did not exist. Such thinking convinced her more than anything else that she did not belong in her old world.

She did not pretend to herself that she would be welcomed back to the tribe. As likely as not, she might be considered a bad omen. Even if accepted, the life was a brutish one and became more precarious with each passing year, yet she was convinced it would be the only possible existence for her children. She had witnessed the cruelty meted out to Neha by Josiah, and even to herself, a feeling that she had been tainted by her contact with the Indians. Returning was a choice fraught with risk, but the only one that held any hope for a life lived on her own terms.

A new moon graced the night of the dance, which Anne considered an auspicious sign. It would make tracking her more difficult. She had learned to compass herself by the stars alone. The hop was the largest social gathering of the spring, people coming from far away, and it was easy to lose oneself in

the milling crowds. Two fiddlers had been brought in, and their playing exhilarated the dancers. A great storming of heels on the wooden floorboards pounded through the bodies like an extra heartbeat, laughter like an extra bellows of lungs. The music pulsed through Anne's blood, making her feel as if drunk on spirits. She stood in the middle of it all, letting it pour over her, knowing it would likely be her last such event. She accepted every invitation she received, danced with a joy and abandon she could not have mustered if she were not leaving. Her behavior risked censure.

Josiah sat against the wall throwing disapproving looks. The other young ladies, scandalized their partners were queuing to dance with Anne, tittered about her licentiousness and vowed future snubs. There was one particular boy, Jeremy, to whom she had taken a liking. A farm boy who reminded her of her old beau Michael. She had purposely cultivated the relationship, but even as she did it toward her own ends, it was clear she could not possibly settle for such a life any longer. Perhaps Josiah was correct — she was indeed ruined, tainted in some irretrievable manner.

At the height of the evening when the dance hall was most full, Anne accepted

Jeremy's suggestion that they go for air. Outside, she realized how hot and breathless she had been, dancing as if possessed, unable to take sufficient deep breaths due to the confines of a corset she found repellant. The icy spring night chilled her burning flesh, the perspiration making her shiver. Jeremy took off his jacket and wrapped it around her shoulders.

"You are much the gentleman," she said.

"I would rather not be and kiss you."

"Shhh," she said, and placed her finger on his lips.

"I'd like to talk with your uncle Josiah, with your permission," he said.

"Maybe tomorrow, but tonight I ask you for one thing."

"Anything."

"Go home straightaway. Do not ask why. Tell everyone who asks that I was overtaxed and stayed at your home till morning."

"But you can't —"

"Your mother and sister will chaperone."

She leaned up against him, and he placed his arms around her. She swooned.

"I want my children," she whispered.

"Yes, I want a family, too. We will, I promise. Strapping boys."

She is not with the boy in front of her but transported seven years back, a young girl

at her family's house, her mother and father in the kitchen. Michael and she are outside, under the trees. He kisses her for the very first time. That kiss promises a life that will roll out before them like a beautiful golden carpet. Although she did not intend it, she kisses Jeremy, whom she has wronged with her deceitful intentions. The kiss is long and perfect and then she is gone.

Gen. George A. Custer, dressed in a dashing suit of buckskin, is prominent everywhere. Here, there, flitting to and fro, in his quick eager way, taking in everything connected with his command, as well as generally, with the keen, incisive manner for which he is so well known. The General is full of perfect readiness for a fray with the hostile red devils, and woe to the body of scalp-lifters that comes within reach of himself and brave companions in arms.

The Badlands, June 1876

Truly hell with the fires burned out.
— Brig. Gen. Alfred Sully,
describing the Badlands

The regiment rode for weeks, the only sign of a white presence a railroad peg left by surveyors back in '73. Plenty of signs of the enemy visible. They passed a pole from which a strip of red cloth and several hanks of hair trailed, a clear warning of the dangers of trespassing into Lakota territory. They gave it a wide berth but still they pressed on.

After Custer's announcement of gold the government demanded a purchase of the Black Hills be negotiated with the Sioux. The tribes were given an impossible deadline to come in to the reservation or war would be declared on them. As expected, they refused, thus supplying a justification.

Custer took a small party to find a path

through the Badlands by which the larger column could follow to reach the river. The land grew greasewood, sage, saltbrush, cactus, and not much else. Crow scouts were assigned for their greater knowledge of the contours of that forbidding land, as he had been favorably impressed by their superb tracking ability.

Easterners didn't understand Indian scouts, why they worked for the army or how they could be trusted, but the tribes were used to making alliances between themselves, some of them unholy. The more prescient saw the inevitable and were seeking the most advantageous accommodation. The ones that acted on their outrage were doomed.

That first night Custer came to the campfire to compliment the scouts. He was amused that they took it as their due. They in turn said they were proud to be under his command as it was said that he never abandoned a trail; when food gave out he ate mule. That was the kind of man they wanted to fight under. They were willing to eat mule, too.

When they reached base camp, all were gathered there — cavalry, scouts, infantry, band, packers with wagons of provisions, excess horses, mules, and herd of beef. He

made sure his brothers Tom and Bos, his nephew Autie Reed, and his brother-in-law Jimmi were near. He felt in need of family.

This being the last opportunity for inspection, Custer demanded to see each man's mount to determine if it was fit for battle. Turkey Feather, one of the Crow scouts, appeared horseless.

— Where is it? Custer asked impatiently.

— He is already across the river, resting for battle.

Custer's face went dark.

— Bring him now and quit this nonsense, or I'll shoot him dead.

The horse was produced. Predictably Custer discovered a sore on his back.

— Is this why you hid him?

Turkey Feather stood expressionless.

— You're staying, Custer said, moving on.

— This horse born this way. This horse runs as swiftly as the river and stops as little. This horse will outrun your horse.

Custer stopped and turned back.

— Is that so?

— If he stops, I will run to keep up with you.

Custer burst out laughing.

— Since you are named after a bird that does not fly, I'd better give you a ridable horse. Go tell the lieutenant to let you pick

one from the cavalry horses.

Thinking he had gotten a too-good offer, Turkey Feather took off before Custer could change his mind.

The Missouri in that part of the territory was winding, the riverbeds filled with quicksand, bogging the horses, who pitched the soldiers into the water when they attempted to ford it. To the great hilarity of the entire regiment, Tom was among the first to receive such baptism. Cliffs rose up on each side of them; nightmarish, dead-end ravines spread below. They got lost with disturbing frequency.

The crow scouts talked about the verities of life on the high plains — how the sun and the grass and the wind and the buffalo would be there for all time. Custer held his tongue. The holy emptiness, the star-glutted night sky, the brittle air were experiences soon to be gone. Life for the Indian would be made impossible, between the railroads and the encroachment of settlers. The cavalry, too, would soon be endangered. Without the tribes, they were unneeded, reduced to a police force, something he could not accept. This freedom would soon be a thing of memory.

The frontier was closing. This was his last

big chance. Crook got himself promoted to brigadier general in the regular army with his successes fighting the Apache. Mackenzie, too, amassed citations in this netherworld. So did Miles. So would he. It seemed possible that the Indians might elude them once again on this expedition as they had on past ones, but his melancholy was not based on that possibility. Whether they succumbed this time or another, their end and his own were already written in the stars.

He'd been quite sanguine at West Point about the Indian's right to exist in his traditional way of life on the land of his birth, but it was always easy for people far away to dismiss the fates of those whom they will never meet face to face. Let them come and look, travel, eat and sleep in their company, endure hardship together. He was being too optimistic by half. Studying the histories of the world, not even brotherhood was enough to safeguard people who had what others coveted. Custer considered quite a few Indians as friends, and he had trusted many more with his life. They had no chance.

The scouts camped near Custer's tent. Regularly he visited at suppertime when they would cook the meat they had hunted that day. He let Golden Buffalo pick his

favorite cut and prepare it. He enjoyed eating and talking to the scouts, took pleasure in the pranks between the warriors that reminded him of his brothers. Like a mother hen, he urged them to eat.

— If you are full, you will be strong for the fight.

He would stay by the fire peacefully until he fell asleep then get up to stumble back to his lodge.

One night well into the expedition a young man came to Custer's tent to carry away papers. The youth hesitated.

— That will be all.

When the young man remained, Custer turned to study his face: high-slatted cheeks, a common mien. He flushed.

— You were the boy at the Washita. You'd taken an arrow to the face.

— Was, sir. I've been away a bit but rejoined the Seventh to serve under you again.

— The bugler . . .

— Thank you for remembering.

Custer felt the blood in his veins run cold. Hadn't the boy joined the legions of specters haunting him? How could he have died and be in the flesh now?

— Good night, boy.

His concentration fled him. Custer had lost track of time. Eight years had passed, time enough for boys to grow into men. What had he grown into?

The rest of the night was spent sleepless. Never had he heard of a ghost returning to the land of the living. Surely it portended ill.

He kept Terry's orders in his jacket pocket, having read them over so many times he could recite them.

It is, of course, impossible to give any definite instructions in regard to this movement, and were it not impossible to do so, the Department Commander places too much confidence in your zeal, energy and ability to wish to impose upon you precise orders which might hamper your action when nearly in contact with the enemy.
— GENERAL TERRY, JUNE 1876, INSTRUCTIONS TO GENERAL G. A. CUSTER

Everyone in the military, and especially the cavalry, knew such orders meant do anything you will but make sure you win.

He bid Terry and Gibbon goodbye and headed out to scout the Rosebud and meet them at the Little Bighorn. His objective was to find Indian camps and drive them

into Gibbon's forces. Gibbon and everyone else believed Custer would attack on his own to win all the accolades for himself.

— Now Custer, don't be greedy, but wait for us, Gibbon chided.

— No, I will not.

With that, Custer rode away laughing.

At the mouth of the Tongue River, a skull nested in the campfire's charred remains. Nearby they found part of a cavalryman's uniform. Custer picked up the stiffened fabric, noted the yellow piping on the tunic and the "C" on the overcoat buttons. Sticks lay nearby stained with brownish blood.

He stared into the ashes without a word. At least for this one, life's troubles were over. What had this poor soul found on the other side? Even if it was cherubs and harps, did it make what happened to him on this side more bearable? Custer shook himself, tried to knock the nonsense from his head. The trembling in his hand had stopped. The stopping scared him more than the quaking flesh that he'd endured all these years. He had the sensation of riding a great swell that he had no ability to control. He had been riding it his whole life. What had changed was that now he feared where it would land him.

The weight of this nameless soldier would join the others who haunted him. *Not fair. I had nothing to do with this one.* Custer was a soldier, and it would be an untruth that he had not thought of his own death in the intervening years since West Point. Any soldier who denied doing such was either fool or liar. But the long line of attendant ghost men for whose death he was responsible had become familiars and made him a kind of philosopher: . . . *Death, necessary end / Will come when it will come.*

All his philosophizing ended when Reno's scouts going up the Rosebud reported the remains of a month-old deserted village of 380 lodges. If the end was indeed written, why should he not be its author?

They came to a deserted campground, the scouts reporting signs of it having been the site of a Sun Dance circle. Golden Buffalo showed Custer evidence of the Sioux medicine — sand arranged and smoothed, pictures drawn on it. The Dakota scouts studied the pictures for long minutes and spoke among themselves.

— What? What do you see?

— The Lakota know the army is coming. They are prepared.

Custer refused to believe this superstition, but knew the scouts were telling the truth

in their roundabout manner: the Sioux had been warned somehow.

— The Lakota believe it is better to die on the battlefield than live to be old.

— We can help them with that.

The camp had been abandoned hastily. In one of the sweat lodges still standing there was a long ridge of sand. On it were figures indicated by hoofprints, army on one side, Sioux on the other. Between were stick figures depicting dead white men lying with their heads toward the Sioux.

— Their medicine is too strong. We will be defeated by them.

— Ridiculous, Custer said, but he feared the opposite.

On nearby sandstone they found a drawing of two buffalo fighting.

— This means the Great Spirit has given the Sioux victory. The scouts are afraid. They say it means do not follow the Lakota into the Bighorn country, or they will destroy you.

Custer chewed his lip.

— I'll pass that on to General Terry. See how that fares.

A few days later where the Tongue joined the Yellowstone River, they came across an Indian burial ground. Mummy-like wrapped

corpses lay on scaffolds. It gave the men the shivers for a minute until Custer, Tom, and some officers decided to go on a macabre treasure hunt, collecting beaded moccasins, rawhide bags, horn spoons, shields, bows, and arrows.

If the Lakota medicine was strong he would create some of his own. It turned into a ghoulish party, the men unwinding the blankets to look at the corpses — an infant with his limbs folded like a furled flower, his face painted red for the afterworld; a warrior's scaffold painted red and black, denoting he had been especially brave. Custer thought it not a bad way to honor the dead but then allowed his men to pull down the body and help themselves to the funeral trousseau. So weighed down were they with "loot" that from a distance one couldn't distinguish them from Indians. Afterward they dumped the corpse in the river, but not before nicking off some flesh for baiting fishhooks.

The men's mood had turned savage. Custer noticed that Tom was especially brutal, the lines of his once boyish face turned hard and without mercy. The scar on his chin that had been an anomaly had now become an essential marker of character. What had become of the shy farm boy

who gleefully captured enemy flags? What had happened to them both?

Some of the older officers moved off, disgusted by their hijinx. Benteen even complained that they had cursed themselves and the whole mission. Ninnies, one and all, as far as Custer was concerned. The scouts, though, moved off, mumbling of bad medicine.

The curse took effect immediately.

A mood, unspeakable, hovered over the expedition, and a sense of gloom pervaded the men. They mumbled of bad dreams and made out wills. Base alliances were struck to avoid torture by the enemy. None smelled victory, they stank of fear, yet Custer refused to bow to it. How could he? He went out ahead of the cavalry with Tom and Bos to let off steam.

When Bos stopped to fix his horse's foot, Tom and he decided to play a prank. They disappeared behind a bluff. As they waited, Tom took up a piece of long grass and chewed it.

— It's been a good run, brother.

Custer bowed his head.

— It has.

They waited companionably until Bos had the horse's hoof on his knee then shot off their guns right over his head. Boston's face!

567

Eyes bulging, his skin aflame, he leaped on his horse and took off at a gallop. They had to hurry, spurring their horses to catch him up before he falsely alerted the whole column and stirred panic. The troops were mystified by the Custers' unseemly high spirits. For days after, each time either Tom or he looked at Bos they burst out laughing.

A fresh Sioux trail was found. It bore the feeling of the inevitable.

The leader of the scouts talked to his men, and Golden Buffalo listened and knew this was the beginning of his prophecy.

— Men, ride fast and hard into their camp. Take their horses to make them weak. Boys, I will not lie to you. It will be a day of hard fighting, but if you live through it you will emerge as men, as warriors. Keep your courage.

Custer went to the scouts and wanted them to sing the death song for the coming battle. When they skipped over any particular of the ritual, he reminded them and waited until they had done it complete. When it was over, he was well satisfied.

Afterward they sat around the fire to eat.

—What do you think of the report of large camps of Sioux?

Golden Buffalo sprang to his feet and did a dance as if possessed around the fire, his

568

feet quick and dodging, his head and body twisting and turning as if against the blows of an enemy.

— This is how the Indian will fight. They will not stand still in lines to shoot. The Sioux brag hunting soldiers is as easy as hunting buffalo calves when they do this.

Custer nodded, amused.

— It is not how the white man has learned to fight. I know the Indian way. Your people are like the coyote, you know how to hide, to creep up and take by surprise. You are born part horse.

The scouts were well pleased at the compliment.

Now the officers joined them by the fire.

— I have orders for you scouts. I say it in front of my men so no one can say they misunderstood. You have done well finding the Lakota for me. All that is left is for you to take away their horses. Then your job is done. I want you scouts to be careful. In the heat of battle, soldiers might mistake you for the enemy. When I win victory, you will be well taken care of by me.

Everyone was silent around the fire. Custer looked up again as if from a painful thought. He spread out his arms to everyone.

— Many of the faces here are known and

loved by me. We have traveled together on other expeditions over the years. Seeing you again makes my heart glad.

Ghosts gathered around Custer, including the last ones from the recent burial ground. The warrior from the red-and-black scaffold joined. The red-painted infant. *This cannot be blamed on me.* Yet he saw how that could be argued. A kind of reversal was happening — instead of death growing less powerful, it had outgrown the living. The dead men, far from being anonymous, grew more demanding each time they presented themselves, and Custer grew more deferential. He was being pressed into responsibility for each life cut short. Would his own life be asked for as final payment? If so, would it be enough? He felt himself already consigned to the past.

He bowed his head.

The world as far as he could see was mainly faithless and unjust. If it had been in his power to change it, he gladly would have. It was all he could do to try and not be at its mercy.

Bloody Knife was mounted next to him as they surveyed the valley below, the silvered windings of the Tongue and Bighorn rivers.

— We will win. It will be victory enough

to last both of us our lifetimes, Custer said.

Bloody Knife did not look him in the face but instead pointed.

— See that sun in the sky? If you say it will not move, I cannot dispute you.

Bloody Knife slapped his hand down hard on his thigh and rode away.

—You will see, Custer called to his retreating back.

All eyes, of both the dead and the living, were now upon him, expecting . . . demanding . . . victory, which if achieved would be begrudged. If he was unsuccessful, the papers would crow that he'd grown soft. Even his favorite scouts had lost the stomach for the coming confrontation, and they were right more often than not. A bad omen. Some made to turn around, their job to find the camp done. Others, who insisted on staying by his side, in unfathomable loyalty, said if they followed him into the Bighorn Valley, they would not return alive . . . *Death, necessary end / Will come when it will come.*

As he walked through camp he saw Golden Buffalo standing alone and went to him.

—What do you think of the coming battle, my friend?

— It is a fool's errand.

Golden Buffalo met Custer's eyes, knowing the disrespect of his words. The general chuckled.

— No doubt. And I am just that fool.

He walked back through the crowded darkness to his tent. He was bone tired. Instead of dinner he ate only a piece of bread dipped in honey. It tasted as sweet as a woman's lips.

GOLDEN BUFFALO

When *Hi'es'tzie* walked away, Golden Buffalo saw in his steps a defeated man although he himself did not yet know it. He would lead the blue soldiers to their death. The prophecy now revealed the last bit of itself. With the buffalo gone, his people were conquered and would not be able to rise up again. He, Golden Buffalo, had named himself after something that no longer existed.

After this nothing more would happen.

He wished to be like the old men riding off to final battle. *Hi'es'tzie* was no worse than another, and so Golden Buffalo would follow him down into the valley from which there was no return. There would be no one to shout his feats of bravery, no seed to carry his name. He did not belong to the world of the future.

LIBBIE

The days before official word was received passed as if in a dream. The atmosphere was like in a hospital where things are going badly for the patient. People avoided Libbie's eye. Dispatches had come in and Indian scouts had taken off like lightning to reach the expedition. After they left, the women were told for the first time about Crook's defeat and how those same victorious warriors had gone on to join Sitting Bull against the army in the valley of the Little Bighorn. Their troops, it was feared, would be overwhelmed by numbers if not warned. The scouts arrived too late.

Each day the fort was subjected to attacks by hostiles, which the guards repulsed. The women were made hostages in their house. They banded together and tried to take comfort in one another's company, but there was a feeling of dread over the whole place.

575

Without telegraph lines or steamboats, the Indians had a far more supple, organic way of obtaining information of events, and knew about the massacre long before official word came. Days before the news, an Indian scout had come and talked of Autie being dead, along with his whole company, but these words struck them as fantastical. Libbie watched the scout, saw his extreme grief in describing the rout, and knew it was true.

Then on July 5 the steamer *Far West* came, bearing the wounded and the terrible, terrible news.

It was the middle of a very hot summer night. The moon pooled like mercury over the land, beautiful and menacing. Knocking could be heard at the back door and then loud voices, the clap of boots along the thin wooden boards. Libbie's first, sleep-filled thought was that Autie must have come home early. Drowsy, she heard the front door open, admitting more people. Then she knew.

Her hands shook as she fumbled with buttons until finally Eliza had to dress her as if she were a small, distraught child. In the parlor men as pale as wax read the words aloud. She wept, knowing that this was simply the beginning of endless tears,

unending grief. The real pain would start soon, but she reminded herself she was Mrs. General Custer. As post commander's wife, her last duty now was to go with the men and inform the other widows. Despite the heat she wrapped a shawl around herself to stop her shaking.

It was not until she was outside that she realized her feet were bare.

The whole country as one focused on the national tragedy. The telegraph labored between Bismarck and Fargo and St. Paul and then on eastward: ALL THE CUSTERS KILLED. Not only her Autie, but his brothers Tom and Boston, his nephew Autie Reed, his brother-in-law Jimmi Calhoun. Not a single survivor in his force, 260 killed. It was a disaster hard to comprehend. Headlines ran in *The New York Herald, The New York Times,* and the Philadelphia papers. No one could believe the truth. At first rumor, even Sherman and Sheridan had insisted it must be false. The entire country was stunned. Her own shock was so great it seemed entirely natural that the world shared her state of mourning. But the sanctity of her bereavement did not last long. Criticism started almost as soon as the condolences had ended. She had to

become a fighter to defend Autie even after he was gone. Although in life he had not held a grudge, she would not forgive his enemies now.

My soul is too small to forgive.

Afterward there were rumors.

Scurrilous things such as *Custer shot himself.* That Indian women drove sewing needles into his ears, shattering the delicate incus bone so that he would hear better in the afterlife. Darker rumors of disfigurements not fit to be told. Articles quoted Reno and Benteen as they lied to cover their misdeeds. Their jealousy translated his bravery into recklessness. She gave the last word on the matter to General Nelson Miles, who wrote: *It is easy to kill a dead lion.*

Benteen, whose bile did not subside even when his rival was long buried, said that Autie was not among the dead, but that like at the Washita, he had gone off to graze his horse. Seeing the tide of evil, he had escaped.

Another rumor, more painful, was that the Crow scout Curly, realizing the battle was futile, begged Autie to escape with him. Autie dropped his head on his breast in silence for a moment — a gesture Libbie had seen him do hundreds of times before — then

waved Curly away and rode back to his men. How could he not choose her?

His men were up against a force far greater than they. The scouts, when they found the fresh Indian trail, estimated from the width and size of the grazing area that the population of the camp was 1,200. They knew that the camp was ahead in the Bighorn Valley but had not yet seen it. History had taught that it was impossible to surprise such a large camp, with its lookouts and signal fires on each hill. If they discovered a large approaching army they would flee. So Terry had the generals divide, each taking a smaller force that the Indians would stand against. Of course Autie felt that the 7th with 600 men was an easy match for 1,200 Indians. What he had no way of knowing was that a greater number of Indian bands had come in from the north. Instead of 1,200, the village was more than 5,000 strong. An unfathomable number, a number never seen before or since.

The Arikara and Crow scouts, having led the 7th to the camp, were allowed to make their exit, although some stayed on to fight. Whether that was due to their fellow feeling for the doomed or if it was an opportunity to fight their traditional enemy remained unclear. Most took off their army uniforms

in order to fight as Crow, as Arikara, and give honor for the killing where it was due.

Another wicked rumor was the one that ironically most comforted Libbie over the years, and it came from the Indians themselves. Autie had been wounded at the beginning of the battle, and the soldiers pulled him to safety while they fought on to their death. The actual last stand took only half an hour by all accounts. When the women moved in to do their work — murder the wounded, mutilate the dead — a group of Cheyenne women recognized Autie as the white husband of Monahsetah. Therefore he was family and sacrosanct. He was carried away and nursed back to health, on condition that he live out the rest of his days with them. Did the idea of his being alive, husband to Monahsetah, pain her? Beyond anything except for his being dead.

Sometimes she pretended he was out there, aware of her efforts to preserve his legacy. Perhaps Autie lived in the nature he so loved. Anonymous, immune to fame, he could at last rest. Perhaps he had the sons she could not give him. If only he was alive, she could bear it all.

At the battle the only man who acted on his conscience was Captain Weir, who never

recovered from his guilt in not disobeying the cowards Benteen and Reno. By nightfall Weir could stand their inaction no more and made the attempt to break through, but it was too late. He died only a few months later, Libbie believed of a broken heart.

When Terry finally arrived the next day, Reno and Benteen reported a force on horseback riding up to them, clothed in the jackets and hats of the cavalry. They expected it was Custer's column riding back in victory. Instead, as it got closer, they saw it was warriors wearing the 7th uniform jackets, riding their cavalry horses, bearing the 7th's flags and arms. Minus only the pants. A great joke that would have made Autie roll in laughter, something that he might have done himself.

The only living being found on Last Stand Hill was the badly wounded horse Comanche. He was nursed back to health and lived out his days in honor. Libbie wondered at the scenes of carnage the animal had been witness to. Did he have equine nightmares as she had human ones? He survived his wounds because his rider, Myles Keogh, died holding his reins, and the Indians were superstitious about taking a horse from a dead man.

Weeks later Dandy was delivered back to

her. It was hard to describe the sight of Autie's beloved horse alive while his owner had perished. Libbie went under the covers of her bed with no intention to rise again. Of course she was not in a position to give the animal a home, and made arrangements for him to go to Father Custer. A collection was taken up among the soldiers to pay the travel fare. The horse gave the old man great comfort, a link to his three deceased sons. In such grief one clings to whatever can sustain one. The two were inseparable companions for the next thirteen years till Dandy passed from old age. He was buried under an apple tree on the farm.

Libbie did not visit the farm, could not bear this link to Autie, but was told that it was a beautiful sight in summer when the blossoms fell to the ground, a fitting tribute to a brave, loyal steed.

A black-draped train waited in Bismarck to take Autie and her away a final time. It stopped at each town as if grief weighed it down, and crowds stood in silence to see the car pass. Sad bouquets of flowers were laid along the tracks, wilting in the hot sun.

Never did she regret marrying a soldier. People asked how she managed to survive the heartache, but Libbie had been prepar-

ing for the possibility since her wedding day. Each step one took in life, from what one ate for breakfast in the morning to whom one married, involved regret for the choices not taken. Each decision involved a narrowing of the experiences possible. In an honest accounting, the end of the happiest existence still contained a mountain of regrets that were part of being alive. Maybe, just maybe, it was finally the regrets that defined one.

Autie's mystery was the mystery of them all. Once he was there and then he was not.

At the bidding of men in Washington, whom he would never know, he had been sent out into the wilderness to subdue the Indian, a decision based on avarice and dishonesty, squeezed in between afternoon paperwork and a cocktail party that evening. Autie ended up having more respect for those he fought than for those who sent him. Sometimes bigger events set in motion lifted an individual to fame, and sometimes they dashed him on the rocks. Autie experienced both.

History betrayed him as well as the Indian. The great, fearsome Sitting Bull afterward traveled in a Wild West show. Autie complained often of how he was expected to perform when he was back east in the

Custer's scouts at the site of Custer's death. From left: Goes Ahead, Hairy Moccasin, Curly, and White Man Runs Him

States. A few decades more of fighting and then the frontier closed.

It had been another world. The land and the freedom that went with it seemed without limit. They had simply glutted themselves.

After the railroads were built shooting parties could be easily brought out to the plains. Rich men rode in private cars for their "frontier" experience, complete with shooting buffalo from the windows of the train. Almost eight million buffalo were killed in the space of three short years for their hides or simply for sport. They, too, seemed as plentiful as the grass or wind, without end. Herds that stretched five miles wide and twelve miles long disappeared. It was almost as unthinkable to the Indians as the oceans being sucked dry or the sun extinguished.

There was a story that by the beginning of the twentieth century the appearance of one lone buffalo wandering the hills near a small town in Wyoming was a major occurrence. It generated a holiday atmosphere, with families hitching up wagons and riding out to see the novel sight. Children were told to look carefully and commit the display to memory — the thin, shaggy beast, knock-kneed, bleating, standing in confu-

sion before them — because he might be the last specimen of his kind to be seen in their lifetime. The people filled their eyes, their imaginations, with the vision of this forlorn creature, who stood in for the mighty millions he had descended from, birthing the very land they stood on. Then, not sure what else to do, they shot him dead. That was the frontier.

The bible exhorted one to love the eternal over the transient, an impossible command. The immortality Autie was so enamoured by was dead and faraway, trapped in history books. For decades Libbie niggled over the prosaic in her quest to restore Autie's memory to its rightful place. How much more she would have preferred to simply grow old with him. The heart was fugitive, it reached out to its own. Hers had reached out to him. Love, fleeting, was all that mortals could hope to know.

Libbie's consolation came mostly in sleep because in dreams Autie and she were always together. More often than not, she dreamed of their early days in Kansas, racing along the plains. She felt the thundering speed of the horses as the earth sped under their hooves. Although she never saw his face, she knew it was Autie beside her, their

horses running shoulder to shoulder. Strong arms reached around her waist and before she knew it she was airborne, suspended between heaven and earth. Safe. The world had been so big then. So unutterably alive. It was the purest freedom. So perfect she knew she could bear whatever followed. When she woke, tears were in her eyes because for a time she had been so very, very happy.

THE EIGHTEENTH REMOVE

Escape — Recapture — Punishment —
Neha

The night is ink under the faint scrawl of stars. Although Anne clearly reads the direction to Neha's homestead by it, she cannot see the few feet of ground in front of her. She compares the night's journey with providence — the riddling, unfathomable events of her own life. Her sack of essentials is found in the hollow of the tree where she left it, yet she realizes she has forgotten to include the most basic item: suitable walking shoes. Her thin-soled dancing slippers allow every sharp rock to pain her. She has planned poorly. It seems her fate to remain badly provisioned for each journey in her life. She longs for her thick moccasins that offered surprising protection and comfort, besides leaving no trail, but Josiah has long since destroyed them.

For the first hour she stumbles down every small wash, brushes against each barbed bush that tears at the delicate fabric of her dancing dress. She has prepared all wrong. In her imagination there was only the end of her journey, being united with her children, rather than the arduous trip and necessities needed to get there. Just as she looks up to the sky for direction, she steps on a low-lying prickly-pear cactus and hisses as the thorns bite into the flesh of her foot. She sits on the ground to examine the abraded skin, but it is too dark to pull out the spines.

When she comes to a river, she is confused. She has no recollection of the terrain between the two homesteads because Josiah forbade her visits. Perhaps she can follow it down and find a crossing at daybreak? It will make her rescue of Neha more perilous once others are awake.

She walks along the river, careful to avoid the sandy, crumbling banks and scratching willow lining its sides when she hears the expected sound of hoofbeats from the posse. She should hide herself but already her legs have turned to rubber. Her months of confinement, not being allowed to roam outdoors, have made her as weak as before her captivity. In the fiery judgment of the

pine-knot torches, she sees horses speeding toward her. The swiftness of the discovery leads her to guess that it is due to Jeremy's treachery. Perhaps he chose not to endanger his own standing in the community for an outcast, especially in going up against the formidable influence of Josiah.

However it came about, she has lost. Instead of the indignity of hiding, she chooses to stand still and let the men find her. If she attempts to scurry under a bush or along the bank, it will only prolong the inevitable. The whole town will soon be out looking for her. Josiah has seen through her deceit of the last months. A lookout will be watching Neha's homestead, and regardless, Anne would be afraid to attempt the voyage back to the tribe alone. Likely she would wander the prairie until she perished, either from the elements or other malevolent forces. She is all resignation and surrender and meekness when at last they ride up. As she suspected, Jeremy rides at the side of her uncle and will not meet her eyes.

Josiah sits atop his horse and looks down at her in undisguised delight, the illumination from the torches coloring his face a virulent rust against the surrounding shadows.

"A grave disappointment," he says, for his

audience rather than her. "It is clear that your morals have been destroyed. The devil resides within you."

Jeremy looks ill with remorse. It gives her a small comfort that perhaps he, too, feels duped.

"Tie her up and put her on a horse," Josiah instructs, then turns his horse around for the short ride back home. Anne discovers she had made even less progress than she had first assumed.

At the dance hall there is a hitching post for the horses. With great care Josiah instructs the men to bind each of Anne's wrists to the horizontal rail so her arms are outstretched. Because he is a man of God and because she is his niece, he allows her blouse to remain on to deny any lascivious interest that might distract from her punishment. The large crowd of revelers mills about, scandalized and titillated in equal measure. A carnival atmosphere pervades. Although the dance allowed only lemonade to be served, men have secreted away small flasks of spirits that they are now passing around. The crowd grows boisterous, unsure of the proceedings. The women stand mesmerized, not knowing the cause of the lashing. Josiah understands that he must hurry, that his brand of justice might look more

591

dubious in the light of day.

He takes out a long bullwhip. It cracks through the air and leaves a slash of bright red blood along the cloth of Anne's back. She moans, her whole will concentrated on not giving him the satisfaction of crying out. Her broken flesh excites Josiah, and in his mind proves her putrescence. For that alone he will punish her. The paradox is that the bruising of her further inflames him. He does not lust after her, no. He punishes her for giving herself to the heathen rather than martyring herself to retain her purity. *His* purity. Her very abasement arouses him, and he fears the taint of her flesh. Eventually she collapses against the post. Josiah is engorged with rage at this stripling girl who has been nothing but a thorn to him since he retrieved her. He brings back his arm for yet another stroke. He does not know when he will stop, how many lashings will lance the poison from the girl, or indeed if he will stop. Perhaps he will keep on until the girl is only a memory, but as he winds his arm back, it is grabbed painfully.

Lydia buries her nails into his skin. The expression on her face will remain with him always.

"That is enough!" she says. "You have gone too far this time. Your righteousness

has corrupted you."

Trembling, she takes the whip, stumbles for a moment in her anger, and walks off.

Anne wakes to the sweet smell of alfalfa and hay, the green, muddy scent of horse manure. She has been put in the barn. When she tries the doors, they are of course bolted shut from the outside. She stands, her head spinning, legs shaky, when the sound that woke her comes again — wolves howling far away. She tries to look out but can only see the dove gray of dawn through the high window. With the last bit of her strength she drags a bale of hay over, feeling the sear of her back as the cloth stuck by blood to her wounds rips away. She is beyond pain as she unsteadily climbs up. The bloodline of the horizon to the east pulses with its promise of day and warmth. It seems the profoundest miracle that the world goes on, that there is something beyond her pain, her confusion, her despair.

When the howling comes again, her heart skips then rushes against her ribs. Not wolves, but the cries and chants of Indians. Signaling one another for a raid. She prays for it.

It has always been thus in her life. Never imagining the waves about to engulf her.

Even now, she can with no certainty decry her future — if she will ever again be reunited with her daughter and son, or if instead she will be made prisoner to a stunted, irreconcilable town life. This was her last attempt at escape. Josiah has broken her so that she will never have strength enough again to attempt it. Each human is capable of only one such effort in a lifetime, but for a magical moment as she stands on tiptoe, clinging to the window frame, she has a vision as clear as the growing, bleeding horizon.

Painted warriors burst through the flimsy door of the house. Their faces are brilliant in stripes of red, yellow, and white. They pull the covers off Mary curled in her pitiable slumber. Indian women strip her of the foreign cotton nightgown and over her head slip a deerskin chemise that is like a second skin. They pull beaded leggings over her legs, thread bone through her earlobes. Piece by piece they transform her back into Neha. She will grip the pony beneath her as surely and easily as taking a breath. In the toughness required to gain freedom, she does not give Anne a second thought. As swift as the wind, the band of Indians will travel north following the great herds, all the way to the valleys of the greasy grass,

fields filled with wildflowers resembling the pastures of heaven. As always Anne has been too dull and slow to understand. She has mistaken a treacherous gift for an unalloyed curse. The raid will right things. For however long it lasts, the land will again be Neha's birthright. The land, forgiving and without limit, will be the last true freedom.

AUTHOR'S NOTE

As a European come early to the United States (read: age five), I have long had a fascination with the American West, both as myth and as reality. I believe it is as much a state of mind as a physical place. My mother told me that as a young girl she devoured the pulp fictions of Karl May, a German writer who never ventured outside of Europe but wrote adventure novels about the Old American West, featuring the characters Winnetou and Old Shatterhand. Although our current understanding of the time is more nuanced and sophisticated, it is still in many ways as romanticized and unrealistic. I can attest that on a recent visit to Colorado, I saw many galleries featuring depictions of a West that exists no longer. In rural areas wooden wagons were staged in open fields, and I even passed a teepee in a pasture that I used as a landmark to find my way home. The frontier was formative

to our national character, and although it disappeared physically as a place with no boundaries, it is very much alive in our national psyche.

What I find even more interesting is the pendulum swing from the simplistic depictions of Indian warfare in the old Hollywood westerns to the opposite but equally false ones in more current books and films. I have to thank the balanced historical writings of both S. C. Gwynne and Peter Cozzens for this insight. We honor the past most when we depict it as accurately as possible without contorting it to contemporary mores. By doing this we allow ourselves to better understand our present.

This is a work of imagination, using as a starting point the life of General G. A. Custer and his wife, Libbie Bacon Custer, from the Civil War till the Battle of the Little Bighorn, or the Battle of the Greasy Grass. The writer Tim O'Brien says "stories are for joining the past to the future," and that was very much my motivation for writing about this defining moment in our history. While trying to adhere to the historical facts of the period, I have given myself the fiction writer's liberty of blending and mixing fact and fiction in order to serve the greater story truth. For instance, Libbie Custer was

not present at Camp Supply to watch the parade of captives from the Battle of the Washita, or the Washita Massacre, but for my purposes her presence there was essential to the ongoing story of the Custer marriage. Golden Buffalo and Anne Cummins are imagined characters who are based on myriad sources: Lakota and Arikara narratives of the Little Bighorn for Golden Buffalo; captivity narratives for Anne's story. The use of the numbered Removes as chapter headings comes from the *Narrative of the Captivity and Restoration of Mrs. Mary Rowlandson.* I borrowed from many sources but particularly the story of getting caught in a buffalo stampede from the oral narrative in *Pretty-shield* by Frank Linderman. De Trobriand's *Military Life in Dakota* colored forever my idea of being caught in a blizzard. Following are some of the sources that were instrumental in my research, not only for facts, but for immersion in time and place. For those looking for further reading on the history the book depicts, this may provide a beginning reading list. Although I believe literature by its nature is political in that it gives us empathy for those unlike ourselves, this is a novel and I do not pretend to be a historian. In trying to balance current sensibilities with historical

realities, I have found wisdom in the following quote by Kate Atkinson: "Hindsight is indeed a wonderful thing but unfortunately it is unavailable to view in the midst of battle."

It goes without saying that all mistakes, intentional or not, are mine.

BIBLIOGRAPHY

Barnett, Louise, *Touched by Fire* (Bison Books, Oct. 2006)

Brown, Dee, *Bury My Heart at Wounded Knee* (Henry Holt, Jan. 1971)

Connell, Evan S., *Son of the Morning Star* (North Point Press, Oct. 1997)

Cozzens, Peter, *The Earth Is Weeping* (Knopf, Oct. 2016)

Custer, Elizabeth B., *Boots and Saddles* (Digital Scanning Inc., Dec. 1999)

———, *Following the Guidon* (University of Oklahoma Press, July 1976)

———, *Tenting on the Plains* (Palala Press, May 2016)

Custer, General George Armstrong, *My Life on the Plains* (University of Oklahoma Press, July 1976)

Day, Carl F., *Tom Custer: Ride to Glory* (University of Oklahoma Press, Feb. 2005)

De Trobriand, Philippe Régis, *Military Life in*

Dakota, translated by Lucile M. Kane (University of Nebraska, May 1982)

Elliott, Michael, *Custerology* (University of Chicago Press, Oct. 2008)

Frankel, Glenn, *The Searchers* (Bloomsbury, Feb. 2014)

Greene, Jerome A., *Washita* (University of Oklahoma Press, Nov. 2014)

Gwynne, S. C., *Empire of the Summer Moon* (Scribner, May 2011)

Hardorff, Richard G., *Washita Memories* (University of Oklahoma Press, Oct. 2008)

———, editor, *Lakota Recollections of the Custer Fight* (University of Nebraska Press, March 1997)

Hoig, Stanley, *The Battle of the Washita* (Bison Books, Nov. 1979)

Jackson, Helen Hunt, *A Century of Dishonor* (Dover Publications, June 2003)

Kelly, Fanny, *Narrative of My Captivity Among the Sioux Indians* (Pomona Press, Jan. 2006)

Kelman, Ari, *A Misplaced Massacre* (Harvard University Press, Feb. 2013)

Leckie, Shirley A., *Elizabeth Bacon Custer and the Making of a Myth* (University of Oklahoma Press, Sept. 1998)

Libby, Orin G., *The Arikara Narrative of Custer's Campaign and the Battle of the*

Little Bighorn (University of Oklahoma Press, Sept. 1998)

Linderman, Frank B., *Pretty-Shield: Medicine Woman of the Crows* (Bison Books, Oct. 2003)

McLaughlin, James, *My Friend the Indian* (Wentworth Press, Aug. 2016)

Merington, Marguerite, *The Custer Story* (University of Nebraska Press, Sept. 1987)

Philbrick, Nathaniel, *The Last Stand* (Penguin Books, April 2011)

Rowlandson, Mary, *Narrative of the Captivity and Restoration of Mrs. Mary Rowlandson* (Hard Press, Nov. 2006)

Silko, Leslie Marmon, *Ceremony* (Penguin Books, Dec. 2006)

Stiles, T. J., *Custer's Trials* (Vintage, Oct. 2016)

Utley, Robert M., *Cavalier in Buckskin* (University of Oklahoma Press, 2001)

Wert, Jeffry D., *Custer* (Simon & Schuster, May 2015)

ACKNOWLEDGMENTS

The Little Bighorn battlefield National Monument is a wonderful place for anyone interested in the time explored in this book. Simply walking the fields, scanning the horizon that still remains mostly empty, and coming across the stone markers where fallen soldiers and warriors were found is a powerful experience. The rangers' talks made history come alive, and I sat through three of them in one day. As well, the Crow reenactment of the battle was an amazing experience of horsemanship.

Much gratitude to Henry Dunow, without whom this book would not have come into being. Thank you, Sarah Crichton, for being brilliant and a perfectionist. I appreciate all the efforts from everyone at FSG, especially Lottchen Shivers. A special thank you to Peter Cozzens for answering my endless questions, and to Kevin McIlvoy for asking the right questions at the right time.

I owe a big debt to Adrienne Brodeur, Aspen Words, and the Catto Shaw Foundation for giving me a "room of my own" at a critical juncture.

To my personal posse of family and friends, you keep me going with constant reasons to be inspired.

ILLUSTRATION CREDITS

Frontmatter illustration: "Red Horse pictographic account of the Battle of the Little Bighorn, 1881." National Anthropological Archives, Smithsonian Institution, manuscript 2367A, image 08569600.

49 "Portrait of Maj. Gen. (as of Apr. 15, 1865) George A. Custer, officer of the Federal Army." January 4, 1865. Civil War Glass Negatives and Related Prints collection, Prints & Photographs Division, Library of Congress, reproduction number LC-DIG-cwpb-05341.

78 Libbie Bacon Custer (detail), from "Gen. and Mrs. George A. Custer," ca. 1860–ca. 1865. Photographs Relating to the Civil War, 1921–1921 series, Records of the Office of the Chief Signal Officer, 1860–1985, National Archives and Records Administration, 530596 111-BZ-102.

152 "Typical surface of the country underlain by the Ogallala formation of the High

Plains of western Kansas. Buffalo wallow, shallow circular depression in the level surface, in foreground." Haskell County, Kansas, 1897. U.S. Geological Survey/ photograph by Willard Drake Johnson.

220 "Rath & Wright's buffalo hide yard in 1878, showing 40,000 buffalo hides, Dodge City, Kansas." Miscellaneous Photographs 1937–1940 series, Records of the National Park Service, National Archives and Records Administration, 520093 79-M-1B-3.

380 "George Armstrong Custer, in uniform, seated with his wife, Elizabeth 'Libbie' Bacon Custer, and his brother, Thomas W. Custer, standing." ca. January 3, 1865. Miscellaneous Items in High Demand collection, Prints & Photographs Division, Library of Congress, reproduction number LC-USZ62-114798.

472 O'Sullivan, Timothy H. "Falmouth, Va. Capt. George A. Custer and Gen. Alfred Pleasonton on horseback." April 1863. Civil War Glass Negatives and Related Prints collection, Prints & Photographs Division, Library of Congress, reproduction number LC-DIG-cwpb-04041.

575 By Gaylord Soli.

584 "Here Custer Fell." Rodman Wanamaker photograph collection relating to

American Indians, 1908–1909 (NAA Photo Lot 64), National Anthropological Archives, Smithsonian Institution, INV 02510500.

ABOUT THE AUTHOR

Tatjana Soli is the bestselling author of *The Lotus Eaters, The Forgetting Tree,* and *The Last Good Paradise.* Her work has been awarded the UK's James Tait Black Prize and been a finalist for the *Los Angeles Times* Book Award. Her books have also been twice listed as a *New York Times* Notable Book. She lives on the Monterey Peninsula of California.

Tatjana Soli is the bestselling author of
The Lotus Eaters, The Forgetting Tree, and
The Last Good Paradise. Her work has been
awarded the UK's James Tait Black Prize
and been a finalist for the Los Angeles Times
Book Award. Her books have also been
once listed as a New York Times Notable
Book. She lives on the Monterey Peninsula
of California.

The employees of Thorndike Press hope you have enjoyed this Large Print book. All our Thorndike, Wheeler, and Kennebec Large Print titles are designed for easy reading, and all our books are made to last. Other Thorndike Press Large Print books are available at your library, through selected bookstores, or directly from us.

For information about titles, please call:
    (800) 223-1244

or visit our website at:
    gale.com/thorndike

To share your comments, please write:
    Publisher
    Thorndike Press
    10 Water St., Suite 310
    Waterville, ME 04901

That *Druid's claw* at the threshold's center —
F. The *pentagram* can make you wince?
Confide to me, Gehenna's prince,
If that confines you, how then did you enter?
How was a mind like yours betrayed?
M. Look at it closely: it is not well made;
One of the corners of it, as you see,
That faces outward, is a little split.
F. Then I have chance to thank for it!
So, you are now a prisoner to me?
That was a windfall, quite unearned!
M. The poodle scampered in quite unconcerned;
The Devil can't get back.)[3]

Is the use of the terms "Pentagramma" and "Drudenfuß" in close proximity both in Wieland's note and Goethe's drama a chance similarity, or did Goethe find in Wieland's note a diagram and terms which he could use as raw material for an incident in the Faust drama?

This specific question leads to a general inquiry into the larger contribution which the Greek satirist Lucian and his German translator Wieland may have made to Goethe's *Faust*. Is it possible that the apparent echo described above is only one small part of more general borrowing? If a fundamental relationship between Lucian and *Faust* can be demonstrated, what contribution to our understanding of the drama does it make? The following chapters will be devoted to exploring these questions and their broader ramifications.

I.

Coincidence of Time and Place

MANY WORKS OF literature have been enriched by the fortuitous meeting of a significant influence with a mind ready to receive it. One such coincidence, whose results have not yet received scholarly attention, is the publication of Christoph Martin Wieland's translation into German of the works of the second century Greek satirist Lucian and the return of Johann Wolfgang von Goethe from two years in Italy, ready to resume work on his drama *Faust*.

Wieland's translation was not Goethe's first opportunity to know Lucian. His earlier impressions were, however, colored by the schoolboy's mocking rejection of the predilections of his teachers. As reported in *Dichtung und Wahrheit,* Dr. Albrecht, Rektor of the Frankfurt Gymnasium and Goethe's tutor in Hebrew, always carried a well-worn copy of Lucian and, as a result, "würzte er alles, was er sagte und schrieb, mit beizenden Ingredienzen."[1] (he spiced everything that he said and wrote with corrosive ingredients)

Such a first encounter with Lucian would not have inspired young Goethe to seek a closer acquaintance with that Greek author. Goethe's mastery of the Greek language was never sufficient to enable him to read and sample Greek authors casually, and when he later attempted to read the great writers of tragedy in the original Greek, he always did so with the aid of a translation.[2] A further deterrent to Goethe's acquaintance with Lucian was the direction taken by the German classical revival inspired by Winckelmann's vision of Greece. In Winckelmann's world of "edle Einfalt und stille Größe" (noble simplicity and quiet grandeur) there was no place for the irreverent satire of Aristophanes or of his admirer Lucian.

The Goethe who left Weimar in 1786 for a vacation in Italy had been prematurely aged by the heavy load of his official duties at the Weimar court. In Italy the onerous responsibilities were sloughed off and the ebullient spirits of youth returned. From the Italian sojourn Goethe brought back in 1788 a lusty enjoyment of life and a glowing enthusiasm for all things classical. He was ripe for a meeting with the works of Lucian in a linguistic form which made their wit and grace available to him.

It is a curious fact that Goethe never mentions Wieland's translation in journals or letters, especially since it appeared in 1788–1789, immediately after his homecoming. This omission may be a consequence of the sometimes cool relationship between the two Weimar poets. Wieland's biographer Sengle reports, however, that after Goethe's return, and before the formation of Goethe's close association with Schiller, Goethe and Wieland had a true poets' friendship based on their mutual interest in "humorous classicism."[3]

The concrete evidence that Goethe knew Wieland's Lucian is of two kinds. The first comes from two lists of books: the catalogue of works in Goethe's personal library and the record of books borrowed from the Weimar library. From the former we know that Wieland's translation of Lucian was in Goethe's own collection, and from the latter that he also borrowed Lucian's works from the Weimar library in 1812, and again in 1826.[4] Another indication that Goethe read Lucian, presumably in Wieland's translation, comes from his employment of Lucianic material in his own writings after 1789, in works as diverse as *Wilhelm Meisters Lehrjahre,*[5] the poem "Der Zauberlehrling,"[6] *Dichtung und Wahrheit,*[7] and *Faust.* Scholars have identified themes from Lucian's works in the first three of these, but there is almost no mention in critical studies of any material taken from Lucian into *Faust,* a lacuna which reflects Goethe's own silence about this source.[8]

An extensive search has discovered only three critics who have linked Lucian with *Faust,* one Germanist and two Classicists. Stuart Atkins appears to be alone among scholars in noting Lucianic elements in *Faust II.* He characterizes the whole Classical Walpurgis Night as "an episode whose tone of sophisticated humor recalls Lucian's late-Greek *Dialogues of the Dead.*"[9] More specifically, he mentions the "implausible,

Lucianic tale of Hermes' miraculous infancy," which is told by the chorus in lines 9629 ff.[10]

The other scholarly observations of Lucianic echoes in *Faust* come from the classical scholars John Jay Chapman and Francis G. Allinson. The focus of their interest was on Lucian as a source of motifs in later literature. In Chapman's book, *Lucian, Plato, and Greek Morals* (1931), we find the following passage about Lucian's dialogue between Lycinus and Hermotimus:

> The substance of Lucian's argument is well known to us and almost commonplace. We know both the personages of the dialogue well: the sceptic and the enthusiast. Goethe, for instance, has given them to us. The first is Faust, the overshadowing, superior spirit, who perceives that philosophy is a will-o'-the-wisp, and that all the great questions remain forever unanswered. The second is Wagner, the self-complacent, ambitious scholar with his cry 'Zwar weiss ich viel, doch möcht ich alles wissen.' It is such familiar and modern ghosts as Wagner and Faust that haunt Lucian's pages. One wonders how many of them were first flung into modern literature by this magician.[11]

Allison, five years earlier, had noted that "we catch in Faust's pessimistic monologue the despair of the disillusioned Stoic neophyte, Hermotimus."[12]

There is one more piece of circumstantial external evidence

which links Lucian with Goethe's *Faust.* In a letter of June 22, 1797, Goethe wrote to Schiller that he had decided to return to work on his Faust drama, which had been laid aside for some time. To explain this decision, Goethe added: "Unser Balladenstudium hat mich wieder auf diesen Dunst- und Nebelweg gebracht."[13] (Our ballad study has brought me again onto this mist- and fog-enshrouded path.) The significance of this remark for the present study lies in the source of one of the ballads written by Goethe in this period. "Der Zauberlehrling" (The Sorceror's Apprentice) is an adaptation of a legend told by Lucian in "The Syrian Goddess."[14] Goethe's epistolary comment thus leads to speculation that ideas generated by reading Lucian may have been among the influences which led to renewed work on *Faust.*

II.
Wieland's Translation of Lucian

WIELAND WAS NOT the first to translate Lucian into German. Heinrich Waser, a cleric of Zürich (1714–1777), had published a German version of Lucian's works in 1769–1777, and Gottsched had also made a German translation of several of Lucian's writings. Wieland scorned Gottsched's translation, but he welcomed Waser's with enthusiasm, used it in his own works, and read aloud from it to the duchess Anna Amalie in Weimar.[1]

Extended acquaintance with Waser's Lucian, however, made Wieland increasingly dissatisfied with its "Helvetismen" and its "Mangel an Lucianischen Grazie" (lack of Lucianic grace).[2] Finally Wieland decided to undertake a translation of his own, a task he carried out during the years 1786–1788, while Goethe was in Italy. In the introduction to this translation, Wieland freely acknowledges his debt to his predecessors, the translators of Lucian into various European languages.

For Wieland, the most important of these translators was the humanist Erasmus of Rotterdam (1466–1536), who had made a Latin version of Lucian's works and adapted many of the Greek author's themes to his own writings. Wieland admired Erasmus' impartiality, his graceful wit, and his all-embracing intellectual activity, and would have liked to be for his own time what the Dutch scholar had been for his, a mediator between the literature of antiquity and that of his own day. In the essay, "Ein Fragment über den Charakter des Erasmus von Rotterdam," Wieland called Erasmus "vortrefflich" (outstanding) and "Lucianisch" (Lucianic).[3] It is interesting to note that Martin Luther also employed the same word "Lucianisch" to describe Erasmus, but as a term of opprobrium rather than praise, because Erasmus' impartiality had led him to remain aloof from the controversies of the Reformation.

In Germany Wieland was singularly qualified to be a successful translator of Lucian, for he comprehended in himself the aims and the literary means of the Greek satirist.[4] Wieland's own writings exhibit a thorough knowledge of classical literature and are characterized by sophisticated irony, graceful wit, and stylistic polish. In a memorial address in 1813, after Wieland's death, Goethe praised Wieland for his translation of Lucian, "der uns den griechischen um desto lebhafter darstellen mußte, als Verfasser und Ubersetzer für wahrhafte Geistesverwandte gelten konnten"[5] (which was able to present the Greek

the more vividly, since author and translator could stand as
veritable intellectual cousins).

In "Das Urteil des Paris," Wieland characterized Lucian in
these lines:

> *Daß niemand feiner scherzen kann,*
> *Daß er ein schöner Geist, ein Kenner,*
> *Ein Weltmann war, gesteht ihm jeder ein;* . . .
> *Was uns betrifft, die gern sokratisch lachen,*
> *Uns dient er oft zum wahren Aesculap;*
> *Er treibt uns manchen Wind und manche Grillen ab,*
> *Und weiß die Kunst, mit Lächeln oder Lachen*
> *Uns klüger oft, vergnügter stets zu machen.*[6]

(That no one can joke more elegantly,/ That he was a wit,
a connoisseur,/ a man of the world, these all admit;/ . . .
For us, who like to laugh socratically,/ For us he often is a
true Aesculapius;/ He gently cures distentions of the body
and soul/ And knows the art, with smile or laugh/ To
make us often wiser, always more content.)

Of this Lucian, whom Wieland characterizes as "ein schöner
Geist," "ein Kenner," "ein Weltmann," and an "Aeskupap,"
little historical information has survived. The meager amount
which has been preserved, however, reveals a man of unusual
literary and critical gifts.

The extant works of Lucian are in Greek, so pure that it can stand as a model for study of the language, yet this was not his native tongue. He was born about 120 A.D. in Samosata on the Euphrates River, just within the eastern borders of the Roman Empire, then at the height of its territorial expansion. His language environment there was Syrian, and his family of tradespeople expected him to become a stonecutter or mason. He managed, however, to frustrate their plans, left Samosata for Ionia on the coast, somehow supported himself while he learned Greek, and pursued careers first in law and later in public-speaking. He immersed himself in the best literature of Greece, that of the classical age of six centuries earlier, and used quotations from the great dramatists and philosophers freely in his works. After becoming wealthy as a traveling lecturer, Lucian returned to his Syrian home to gather family members and move them to Athens. There he turned from speaking to writing and produced the satirical works for which he is best known today.

In two ways Lucian was an important path breaker and forerunner of later writers. The first is his emphasis on literary style, with the corollary expressed by his literary descendant Boccaccio "that there is nothing so unchaste but may be said chastely if modest words are used."[7] A second significant aspect of Lucian's works is that he stands early in a long procession of writers whose works used, and thus revived interest in the literature of classical Greece. Lucian's stylistic virtuosity and his classical allusions particularly endeared him to Wieland. These were qualities which the polished German stylist and Hellenist could well appreciate. Other readers might be more impressed with Lucian's clever wit and his sharp attacks on human failings. Wieland, however, recognized Lucian as an idealistic reformer in whose hand the pen was a tool and a weapon for good. Disagreeing with those who regarded Lucian's wit as destructive, and maintaining that Lucian was instead making positive use of his peculiar gifts, Wieland wrote:

> *Ein Mann von wahrem Genius unterscheidet sich haupt-sächlich durch diese zwey Puncte; erstens, daß er in Zeiten das Maas seiner Kräfte und diejenige Anwendung und Richtung deselben kennen lernt, wodurch er mit dem besten Erfolg auf die Menschen, besonders auf seine Zeit-genossen wirken kann; und dann, daß er sich eigene Werkzeuge, womit er diesen Zweck bearbeitet, zu bilden weiß, denen ein Anderer, der sie zu gleicher Absicht brauchen will, doch nie das ausrichten wird was er.[8] (I[1], XXV)*

(A man of true genius is distinguished primarily by these two points: first, that he surveys at times the extent of his capabilities and that direction and use to which he can turn them to produce the greatest benefit for mankind, especially for his contemporaries; and then, that he knows how to develop his own tools for achieving this goal, tools with which another, who has similar aims, will never achieve what he will.)

In translating Lucian, Wieland was particularly concerned

to preserve those qualities of language and style which he felt
had suffered at the hands of other translators. In this connection
he wrote:

> *Mein angelegenstes Bestreben war, daß ich ihm kein*
> *Unrecht thun, und daß er von den Schönheiten, welche die*
> *Kenner der Griechischen Sprache an ihm bewundern, so*
> *wenig als möglich unter meinen Händen verlieren möchte.*
> *Ich habe mich seines Geistes, seiner Laune, seiner Genial-*
> *ität zu bemächtigen, und, soviel es die Natur unsrer von*
> *der seinigen so sehr verschiedenen Sprache, die Deutlich-*
> *keit, und andere Rücksichten nur immer erlauben wollten,*
> *auch seine Wendungen und das Colorit seiner Schreibart*
> *nachzuahmen gesucht. (I[1], XLIV)*

(My greatest concern was to do him no injustice, and that
he should lose as little as possible under my hands the
beauties which those familiar with the Greek language
admire in him. I have sought to acquire his spirit, his
humor, his originality, and to imitate his idiom and the
coloring of his language, as far as the nature of our
language, so different from his, clarity, and other considerations permitted.)

The translation which Wieland produces is a richly anno-
tated one. It is introduced by a long essay "Ueber Lucians
Lebensumstände, Charakter und Schriften" (On the Circumstances, character, and Writings of Lucian). Accompanying the

text itself are detailed footnotes explaining the references to matters that might not be familiar to contemporary readers. These include historical events, philosophical and political controversies of Lucian's time, and Greek religion and mythology. To augment further the reader's background in the last category, Wieland began the second of the six parts of the translation with a "Vorrede zu den Göttergesprächen" (Preface to the Dialogues of the Gods), followed by a "Kurzes Schema der Verwandtschaft der Griechischen Götter und des alten und neuen Götterhofes zum Behuf der Lucianischen Göttergespräche" (Short Outline of the Relationship of the Greek Gods and of the old and new temples as they appear in the Lucianic Dialogues of the Gods). In the footnotes Wieland exhibited his extensive knowledge of classical literature and philosophy, frequently quoting from the works of other well known classical authors.

By including this critical apparatus, Wieland provided his contemporaries with an excellent introduction to a much wider range of classical literature than the translation of one author could contain, but also with a delightful mine of classical trivia. Goethe, who was at best only a casual scholar, always enjoyed new and stimulating ideas. These were amply available to him in Wieland's translation and the notes accompanying it.

Wieland also used his introduction as a platform to refute the French philosopher Pierre Bayle's negative evaluation of Lucian. Wieland cited Bayle's opinion that the Greek satirist wrote "bloß seinem natürlichen Muthwillen und Spottgeist ein Feld aufzuthun, wo er sich nach Herzenslust herumtummeln könne" (merely to open a field for his natural mischievousness and mocking wit, where he might romp to his heart's content). He replied to Bayle's criticism by asking

> *Warum sollen wir, bloß darum weil er Witz und Laune zum Vehikel seiner Arzney macht, ihm die Absicht zu heilen absprechen? Was berechtigt uns, einen Schriftsteller, bloß weil er die Wahrheit scherzend und lachend sagt, zum Scurra zu machen? und mußten wir nicht, aus gleichem Grunde, einem Horaz, Juvenal, Chaucer, Rabelais, Cervantes, Swift, Sterne, und allen komischen und satyrischen Dichtern überhaupt, das gleiche Urtheil sprechen? (I[1], XXXVII-XXXVIII)*

(Why should we, merely because he makes wit and humor the vehicle for his medicine, deny him the intent of healing? What right have we to turn an author, only because he jocosely and laughingly speaks the truth, into a farce; and would we not be forced for the same reason to pronounce the same judgment on Horace, Juvenal, Chaucer, Rabelais, Cervantes, Swift, Sterne, and all comic and satirical poets in general?)

Wieland was not the first or only reader of Lucian to recognize the positive value of the satirist's attacks on negative human traits and practices. As early as the fourth century, Lucian was dubbed "earnest in his laughter" by the historian Eunapius.[9] It was, however, Wieland who made the idea of the serious potential of humor available to the creative mind of his contemporary Goethe, where it could bear fruit of particular consequence.

III.
Goethe's *Faust* Before and After 1788

ECHOES OF WIELAND'S Lucian in Goethe's *Faust* must be sought in those parts of the drama which were added or revised after the publication of the translation in 1788–1789, i.e. after Goethe's return from Italy in June 1788. The Faust manuscript which Goethe took to Italy in 1786 has not been preserved. The only version that may be close to it is the Göchhausen manuscript, generally called the *Urfaust,* which contains scenes read by Goethe to the Weimar court and copied off from his papers by Luise Göchhausen. It is not even certain that this version contains all the scenes of *Faust* which Goethe had composed by that time, for he may have made a selection of those he felt were the best suited for reading aloud.[1] Since the *Urfaust* is, however, the only extant manuscript from the period before Goethe's trip to Italy, it is useful as a point of reference.

Between the *Urfaust* and *Faust, ein Fragment,* which was published in 1790, there are a number of additions and changes. These include, for the first scenes, the additions of lines 1770–1867 and 2051–72, and major revision of lines 2051–2072. Lines 1770-1850 contain the dialogue between Faust and Mephistopheles in which Faust describes his ambitions to experience the entirety of human life. Lines 1851–2050 present the scene between Mephistopheles and the student, revised and expanded. Lines 2051–2972 describe the departure of Faust and Mephistopheles to see the world.

Also between the *Urfaust* and the *Fragment* the prose of the Auerbach's Cellar scene was recast into verse, with some accompanying changes in content. Significant among these is the shifting of the role of magician from Faust to Mephistopheles. The Witch's Kitchen scene was also added to the *Urfaust* material before the publication of the *Fragment,* but since this scene is known to have been written during Goethe's stay in Italy, it belongs to the pre-Lucian version. The other changes made in this period involve principally a re-ordering of material and the omission of part of the scene with Gretchen's brother Valentine.

The additions made between the *Fragment* (1790) and *Faust I* (1808) are much more extensive, more than doubling the length of the text. Of these the first major change is the addition of three sections preceding the drama itself: the "Zueignung" (Dedication), the "Vorspiel auf dem Theater" (Prelude in the Theater), and the "Prolog im Himmel" (Prologue in Heaven).

Within the main part of the drama, the first large addition is the filling in of what Goethe called "die große Lücke"[2] (the great gap) of lines 605–1770. The added passages include the scene in which Faust is deterred from drinking poison by the sound of the Easter chorus, Faust's walk with Wagner outside the city gate on Easter morning, and the subsequent two scenes in Faust's study, where the pact with Mephistopheles is made. The other large addition consists in the entire Walpurgisnacht scene, including the dream sequence. In addition there are revisions of the Valentine and final prison scenes.

In the same period when these additions were being made to *Faust I,* parts of *Faust II* which depended on them were also being planned, and some lines were written. The sections that come from this time include parts of the action at the Emperor's court, the Helena episode, and the final conclusion of *Faust II.* The writing of the remainder of *Faust II* belongs to the last decade of Goethe's life.

In sum, the manuscript of *Faust* which predates the publication of Wieland's translation of Lucian centered about the Gretchen tragedy, and contained beyond this only the opening soliloquy, the scenes with the macrocosm and Earth Spirit, the dialogues between Faust and Wagner and between Mephistopheles and the student, and the scenes in Auerbach's Cellar and the Witch's Kitchen.

The additions which were made after 1788 contain some of the most significant and characteristic parts of Goethe's Faust tragedy. Among these are the wager between Faust and Mephistopheles and its basis in the conversation between Mephistopheles and God, the development of Mephistopheles as rogue and cynic, the sharp social criticism contained in the "Walpurgisnacht" of *Faust I* and the Emperor's Court of *Faust II*, and the evocation of classical Greece in the Helena episode. The presence of social criticism and Hellenic material in the post-Italian additions to *Faust* would justify a search of the works of Lucian, the greatest Greek satirist and social critic, for possible sources of influence, even without the external connections cited in Chapter I. When the dates of publication of Wieland's translation and Goethe's use of Lucianic materials in other works of this period are also taken into consideration, a search for internal evidence of Lucian's influence on the creation of *Faust* is mandated.

IV.

The Hermotimus Dialogue

LUCIAN'S CHARACTERISTIC MODE of narration was the dialogue, a conversation between two persons, one of whom generally serves as interlocutor, and the other as respondent. The first dialogue in the third volume of Wieland's translation, opening the fifth part, takes place between Lycinus (a transparent representation of Lucian himself) and his friend Hermotimus, a student of Stoic philosophy. Hermotimus is on the way to a session with his philosopher mentor when he is hailed by Lycinus. In the course of their ensuing discussion, Lycinus employs Socratic techniques to uncover the weaknesses in his friend's philosophic pursuits.

A long footnote commentary by Wieland at the beginning of this dialogue evaluates it as among the best, if not the very best of the dialogues of Lucian in terms of "Absicht des lehrreichen

Inhalts, als was die Kunst der Composition, die Schönheit der Sprache, die Klarheit und Nettigkeit des Styls, die Urbanität des Tons, und das ächte attische Salz des Dialogs betrifft." (intention of the informative contents, as well as what pertains to the art of composition, beauty of language, clarity and precision of style, urbanity of tone, and genuine Attic salt of the dialogue)[1] (III[5], 3)

Lycinus is here the devious tormentor of his more simple minded friend, and he employs the Socratic method with diabolical skill. Wieland comments editorially on this process:

> *Es scheint Lucian habe in diesem Dialog eine Probe machen wollen, was er in der dem Sokrates ehmals eigenen Manier zu disputieren vermöge, die, indem sie unter dem angenommenen Schein der Unwissenheit, den durch verstelltes Nachgeben sicher gemachten Gegner mit treuherzigen Fragen und einfältig scheinenden Einwendungen nach und nach in die Enge treibt, ihn zuletzt unvermerkt in seinem eigenen Netze fängt, und ihn dahin bringt, daß er selbst das Gegenteil dessen wovon er sich anfangs überzeugt hielt, behauptet, oder wenigstens eingestehen muß. (III[5], 3–4)*

(It appears that Lucian wanted to make a test in this dialogue of what he could do with the Socratic manner of disputation which, while assuming the appearance of uncertainty, drives the opponent, who has been made confident by feigned yielding, little by little into a corner by using apparently naive questions and simple-minded objections, until at last he is caught unsuspecting in his own net, so that he asserts or at least admits just the opposite of his original position.)

Hermotimus has wide Faustian goals in prospect with his philosophical studies. He asserts:

Es kommt hier auf nichts kleines dabei auf dem Spiele; es kommt hier auf nichts geringeres an, als entweder elendiglich mit dem Auskehricht des menschlichen Geschlechts, dem großen Hauffen der Unwissenden, zu grunde zu gehen, oder durch die Philosophie glücklich wie ein Gott zu werden. (III[5], 5)

(What is at stake here is nothing small; it is nothing less than either to perish miserably with the dregs of the human race, the great crowd of the ignorant, or to become divinely happy through philosophy.)

To this proud aim, Lycinus answers sympathetically, "Das ist freylich keine Kleinigkeit, mein guter Hermotimus, so ein Preis ist schon werth daß man um ihn ringe!" (That is indeed no small matter, my good Hermotimus. Such a prize is well worth pursuing!) (III[5], 5) Then he goes on to raise a question of the time involved in reaching such a goal, citing the twenty years his friend has already invested in the pursuit of perfection, a number with Faustian overtones for the modern reader:

"Denn, wofern mich mein Gedächtnis nicht betrügt, sind es beynahe zwanzig volle Jahre, seitdem ich dich nichts anders thun sehe, als die Schulen der Philosophen besuchen, über Bücher gebückt sitzen, und, alles was du bey deinen Lehrern gehört hast, in große Hefte zusammenschreiben." (For, if my memory does not deceive me, for almost twenty long years now I have seen you do nothing but go to the philosophers' schools, sit bent over books, and write all that you have heard from your teachers in large notebooks.) (III[5], 6)

Turning to one of the scenes added to *Faust* after Goethe's return from Italy, we find echoes of the above dialogue where Faust says to Mephistopheles:

Und was der ganzen Menschheit zugeteilt ist,
Will ich in meinem innern Selbst genießen,
Mit meinem Geist das Höchst' und Tiefste greifen,
Ihr Wohl und Weh auf meinen Busen häufen,
Und so mein eigen Selbst zu ihrem Selbst erweitern.
(1770–1775)[2]

(And what to all mankind is apportioned
I mean to savor in my own self's core,
Grasp with my mind both highest and most low,
Weigh down my spirit with their weal and woe,
And thus my selfhood to their own distend,
And be, as they are, shattered in the end.)

A skeptical Mephistopheles raises objections worthy of a Lycinus to dampen the enthusiasm of the striver Faust:

> *O glaube mir, der manche tausend Jahre*
> *An dieser harten Speise kaut,*
> *Daß von der Wiege bis zur Bahre*
> *Kein Mensch den alten Sauerteig verdaut!*
> *Glaub' unser einem, dieses Ganze*
> *Ist nur für einen Gott gemacht!*
> *Er findet sich in einem ew'gen Glanze,*
> *Uns hat er in die Finsterniß gebracht,*
> *Und euch taugt einzig Tag und Nacht. (1776–1784)*

Oh, take my word, who for millenia past
Has had this rocky fare to chomp,
That from his first breath to his last
No man digests that ancient sourdough lump!
Believe the likes of us: the whole
Is made but for a god's delight!
He dwells in an eternal aureole,
Us he committed to the depth of night,
And you make do with dark and light.)

To Faust's further assertion, "Allein ich will!" (1785) (And yet I choose it!), Mephistopheles like Lycinus raises the question of time:

Das läßt sich hören!
Doch nur vor Einem ist mir bang;
Die Zeit ist kurz, die Kunst ist lang. (1785–1787)

(Worthily decided!
I fear just one thing, for my part:
Short is the time, and long is art.)

This last sentiment, which Goethe had earlier assigned to Wagner (lines 358–359), is an aphorism usually attributed to Hippocrates. Hermotimus, who seems to be the same type of pedantic, plodding student as the later Wagner, also uses the Hippocratic aphorism to describe his studies to Lycinus:

Ich wiederhohlte die gestrige Lection, und suchte mir, soviel möglich, alles was er vorgetragen hatte, von Wort zu Wort wieder gegenwärtig zu machen. Unser einer kann, denke ich, nicht wirthschaftlich genug mit seiner Zeit umgehen. Denn das Leben ist kurz und die Kunst lang, wie der berühmte Arzt von Kos mit Wahrheit sagt. (III[5], 4–5)

(I repeated the lesson from yesterday and tried, as well as I could, to bring to mind again word for word, what he had said in his lecture. People like us cannot be too careful in our use of time. For life is short and art is long, as the famous Coan doctor said with truth.)

Lycinus requires many more words to undermine the ambition of his victim Hermotimus than Mephistopheles uses to bring Faust to a state of deep discouragement. It is not until almost the end of the lengthy dialogue that Hermotimus breaks down and bemoans the time that he has lost in pursuing false goals, saying:

> *Was kann ich dir antworten? Ich möchte lieber weinen, so tief fühle ich, wie wahr und vernünftig das alles ist, was du mir gesagt hast. Ist es nicht erbärmlich, daß ich unglückseliger Mensch einen so großen Theil meines Lebens verlohren, und für alle die Mühe die ich mir gegeben, noch so viel Geld bezahlt habe; und nun ist mir als ob ich aus einem derben Rausch erwache, und sehe, an was für einen unwürdigen Gegenstand ich meine Liebe verschwendet und wie viel Leides ich mir selbst dadurch gethan habe! (III[5], 101–102)*

(What can I say? I would rather weep, so deeply do I feel how true and reasonable everything you say to me is. Is it not pitiable that I, a miserable wretch, have wasted such a large part of my life, and in addition to all the trouble I have given myself have paid out so much money! And now I feel as if I were coming out of a period of drunkenness and see what an unworthy object I have squandered my love on and how I have injured myself in doing so.)

Only a score of lines intervene between Mephistopheles' elabo-

rations on the limitations of man and Faust's expression of
regret:

> *Ich fühl's, vergebens hab' ich alle Schätze*
> *Des Menschengeists auf mich herbeigerafft,*
> *Und wenn ich mich am Ende niedersetze,*
> *Quillt innerlich doch keine neue Kraft;*
> *Ich bin nicht um ein Haar breit höher,*
> *Bin dem Unendlichen nicht näher. (1810–1815)*

> (In vain all treasures of the human mind,
> I feel it, have I raked to me; at length,
> When I sit down to marshall them, I find
> There wells within no fresh resource of strength;
> Not by a hairsbreadth am I grown,
> No nearer to the limitless unknown.)

The comfort offered to their suffering companions by Lycinus
and Mephistopheles is strikingly similar. To Faust, Mephistopheles says:

> *Mein guter Herr, ihr seht die Sachen,*
> *Wie man die Sachen eben sieht;*
> *Wir müssen das gescheidter machen,*
> *Eh' uns des Lebens Freude flieht.*
> *Was Henker! freilich Händ' und Füße*
> *Und Kopf und H— — die sind dein;*
> *Doch alles, was ich frisch genieße,*

Ist das drum weniger mein?
Wenn ich sechs Hengste zahlen kann,
Sind ihre Kräfte nicht die meine?
Ich renne zu und bin ein rechter Mann,
Als Hätt' ich vier und zwanzig Beine.
Drum frisch! Laß alles Sinnen sein,
Und g'rad' mit in die Welt hinein!
Ich sag' es dir: ein Kerl, der speculirt.
Ist wie ein Thier, auf dürrer Heide
Von einem bösen Geist im Kreis herum geführt,
Und rings umher liegt schöne grüne Weide. (1816–1833)

(Dear Sir, you look on things as crudely
As men are apt to do; instead,
We must conduct ourselves more shrewdly,
Before the joys of life have fled.
Bah! Hands and feet belong to you,
And head and arse too, if you please,
But what I freely taste and view,
Is that less mine than these?
If I can pay for half-a-dozen horse,
have I not bought their sixfold thew?
I run and show off with the force
Of four-and-twenty legs, not two.
Cheer up! Throw over all reflection,
And off into the world post-haste!
Take it from me: the slave of introspection
Is like a beast on arid waste

By some foul fiend led round and round,
While, all about, green meadowlands abound.)

In the above passage there is an echo of the more discursive
advice which Lycinus gives Hermotimus. However, while both
mentors recommend realistic activity in place of philosophic
speculation, the direction of the action proposed by Lycinus is
social usefulness, that suggested by Mephistopheles personal
gratification. Lycinus says:

Was könnte dir's helfen, mein Bester, die bittersten
Thränen über eine Sache, die nun einmal nicht mehr zu
ändern ist, zu weinen? Mich dünkt es sey ein sehr verstän-
diger Rath, den uns Aesop in einer seiner Fabeln giebt. Ein
Mensch, sagt er, saß am Ufer des Meeres, und zählt die
Wellen; da er sich nun verzählt hatte, betrübte er sich und
wurde ganz ärgerlich darüber; endlich sagte ein Fuchs,
der dabey stand: was kümmerst du dich so um die Wellen
die schon vorbey sind? fange lieber wieder an, und zähle
die, die jetzt entstehen, du wirst immer noch genug zu thun
finden. So, mein Freund, dächte ich solltest du es auch
machen; Laß was vorüber ist, gut seyn, und lebe dafür was
du noch zu leben hast wie andere ehrliche Leute; gehe
deinen bürgerlichen Geschäften und Verhältnissen nach,
laß die ungereimten schwülstigen Hoffnungen fahren, und
schäme dich nicht, wiewohl du schon auf diesen Jahren
bist, denen Sinn zu ändern und den bessern Weg einzu-
schlagen. (III[5], 102)

(How could it help you, my friend, to shed the bitterest tears over something which cannot be changed? It seems to me that it is very good advice that Aesop gives us in one of his fables. A man, he says, was sitting on the seashore and counting the waves, and when he made a mistake he became very angry about it. Finally a fox, who was there with him, said, Why do you worry so much about the waves that are past? Rather start again and count the ones that are coming; you will still find enough to do. Thus, my friend, I think that you should also let bygones be bygones, and live the rest of your life like other honest men. Pursue your daily business and activities and leave behind your preposterous high-flown fantasies. Do not be ashamed, though you are advanced in years, to change and take a better path.)

The immediate reactions of both Hermotimus and Faust to the advice they receive is to worry about their personal appearance. To Lycinus' advice, Hermotimus answers:

Gut! Ich gehe mit diesem Schritte, um meine neue Lebensart gleich damit anzufangen, daß ich mein äußerliches umgestalte. Du sollst diesen langen Zottelbart gar bald verschwunden, und die traurige Lebensart, die ich bisher geführt habe, mit einer behäglichern und freyern vertauscht sehen. Ich will sogar nächstens einen rothen Rock anziehen, damit jedermann sehe, daß ich mit jenen Thorheiten nichts mehr zu schaffen habe. (III[5], 103)

(Good! I'll start my new way of life right away by changing my appearance. You will soon see this long shaggy
beard gone, and the sad life that I have been leading
exchanged for a more comfortable and freer one. First I'll
put on a red cloak so that everyone may see that I am done
with all that foolishness.)

Faust, too, is worried about his beard, a concern he voices in
answer to Mephistopheles' invitation to see "die Kleine, dann
die groß Welt" (2052) (the small world, then the great)

> *Allein bei meinem langen Bart*
> *Fehlt mir die leichte Lebensart. (2055–2056)*

(My long gray beard, though, spoils my chance,
It cramps the proper nonchalance.)

The real rejuvenation of the aging Faust must wait, however,
for a visit to the witch's kitchen.

V.

The Pact

IT WAS NOT until about 1800 that Goethe wrote the pact scene in its final form and at the same time added the two parts of the drama which form an introduction and final result of the wager, the Prologue in Heaven and the concluding scenes of *Faust II*. In these three sections of the drama, the kernel of the action is predicted, defined, and concluded. Herman Meyer has suggested that this sequence may be one of Goethe's "serious jests."[1] This opinion is corroborated by the presence of a number of echoes of the earlier serious jester Lucian.

Turning first to the Prologue in Heaven, which sets the tone and limits of the Mephistopheles-Faust relationship, we find Mephistopheles expounding his view of man to the Lord in entymological terms:

Er scheint mir, mit Verlaub von Ew. Gnaden,
Wie eine der langbeinigen Cicaden,
Die immer fliegt und fliegend springt
Und gleich im Gras ihr altes Liedchen singt. (287–290)

(He seems to me, begging your Honor's pardon,
Like one of those grasshoppers in the garden
That leg it skip-a-skimming all day long
And in the grass chirp out the same old song.)

The Lord suggests that his servant Faust is an exception to this
denigrating description, but Mephistopheles objects:

Fürwahr, er dient Euch auf besondre Weise!
Nicht irdisch ist des Toren Trank noch Speise!
Ihn treibt die Gärung in die Ferne,
Er ist sich seiner Tollheit halb bewußt;
Vom Himmel fordert er die schönsten Sterne
Und von der Erde jede Höchste Lust,
Und alle Näh und alle Ferne
Befriedigt nicht die tiefbewegte Brust. (300–307)

(Forsooth! He serves you in a curious fashion.
Not of this earth the madman's drink or ration,
He's driven far afield by some strange leaven,
He's half aware of his demented quest,
He claims the most resplendent stars from heaven,

And from the earth each pleasure's highest zest,
Yet near or far, he finds no haven
Of solace for his deeply troubled breast.)

Mephistopheles' cynical observations and the Lord's reiterated
expressions of confidence in Faust's eventual salvation culmi-
nate in Mephistopheles' bold challenge:

> *Was wettet ihr? den sollt ihr noch verlieren,*
> *Wenn ihr mir die Erlaubniß gebt*
> *Ihn meine Straße sacht zu führen! (312–314)*

(You'll lose him yet! I offer bet and tally,
Provided that your Honor gives
Me leave to lead him gently up my alley!)

The permission is given, with a subsequent justification:

> *So lang er auf der Erde lebt,*
> *So lange sei dir's nicht verboten.*
> ....
> *Des Menschen Thätigkeit kann allzuleicht erschlaffen,*
> *Er liebt sich bald die unbedingte Ruh;*
> *Drum geb' ich gern ihm den Gesellen zu,*
> *Der reizt und wirkt und muß als Teufel schaffen.*
> *(315–316, 340–343)*

(As long as on the earth he lives,
So long it shall not be forbidden.

. . . .

Man all too easily grows lax and mellow,
He soon elects repose at any price;
And so I like to pair him with a fellow
To play the deuce, to stir, and to entice.)

While the debts of the Prologue in Heaven to the biblical book of Job are clear, especially in line 229 (Kennst du den Faust? — Do you know Faust?) and in the above-quoted lines 315–316, other aspects echo Lucian's Hermotimus. The first of these is the comparison of man to an insect. In the dialogue with Lycinus, Hermotimus describes the course of his philosophical studies in terms of the ascent of a steep mountain. When the peak has been attained, the successful climber can look down on the men he left behind, who now appear like ants:

> *Die hingegen bis zum Ende ausdauern . . . sehen von der Höhe wo sie sich befinden, die übrigen Menschen für eben so viele Ameisen an. (III[5], 9)*

At this pejorative view Lycinus takes offense:

> *Behüte Gott! zu was für winzigen Thierchen machst du uns, Hermotimus! Ich wollte es gelten lassen, wenn du uns noch für Pygmäen angesehen hättest; aber uns so am Boden, so ganz und gar auf der bloßen Haut der Mutter*

Erde herumkriechen zu machen, ist auch gar zu arg!
(III[5], 9)

(God forbid! What tiny creatures you make us, Hermotimus! I could allow it if you had seen us as pygmies, but to have us crawling around on the ground, on the naked skin of Mother Earth, is really too disgusting!)

In both this passage and the remarks of Mephistopheles to the Lord, the familiar optical impression of the small size of distant objects is extended to a reduction of man's intrinsic worth. Goethe's comparison of man to crickets in Mephistopheles' comments has the same evaluative effect as Lucian's view through Hermotimus of man as an ant.

A further echo of Lucian in the Prologue in Heaven may be found in the idea that man falls back when he attempts to reach heights, though this idea is presented in different images by the two authors. Lucian has Hermotimus describe the struggle to scale philosophical heights in the following terms:

Freylich giebt es ihrer nicht wenige, die einen herzhaften Anlauf nehmen; sie gehen auch wohl eine Strecke weiter fort, einige weniger andere mehr: aber wenn sie ungefähr bis zur Hälfte gekommen sind, und sehen daß der Weg immer schwieriger und mühsamer wird, lassen sie sich abschrecken, und kehren keuchend und von Schweiße triefend wieder um, weil sie es nicht länger auschalten können. (III[5], 9)

(Of course there are not a few who make a sincere beginning. They even go a way, some less, others more, but when they have come about halfway and see that the path is becoming more and more difficult and burdensome, they let themselves be frightened off and turn around panting and dripping with sweat because they cannot endure it any longer.)

The similes of Lucian appear to have been transformed in what Harold Jantz has called Goethe's process of "symbolic extension."[2] For Lucian's two separate pictures of the industrious and the ineffectual human mountain climber, Goethe has given a single image of the vain struggles of the grasshopper. The entymological view of man, which reduces his importance to that of an insect, is entirely appropriate to the cynical Mephistopheles. Man's lifelong struggle toward a lofty goal, which forms the basis for the argument between Mephistopheles and the Lord, and subsequently an underlying theme of the whole Faust drama, is also the substance of Lucian's dialogue between Hermotimus and Lycinus.

The central pact scene, where Faust concludes his agreement with Mephistopheles, contains further echoes of Lucian. In the Hermotimus dialogue Lycinus questions whether his friend's struggles are worthwhile. A lengthy discussion of the philosophical path and its rewards brings the following exchange:

Hermotimus. Ich wünsche mir so lange zu leben bis ich zur Weisheit gelangt seyn werde, und wenn ich auch nur einen

einzigen Tag in ihrem Besitz glücklich seyn sollte.
Lycinus. Wie? Du würdest für so viele Mühe und Arbeit
mit einem einzigen Tage vorlieb nehmen?
Hermotimus. Ich wollte mit noch weit wenigerem zu-
frieden seyn. (III[5], 11)

(Hermotimus. I wish to live until I have achieved wisdom,
even if I enjoy its possession for only a single day.
Lycinus. Really? You would put up with so much work
and trouble for a single day?
Hermotimus. I would even be satisfied with much less.)[3]

For Faust the matter to be traded for a single moment of
highest contentment is not earthly struggle, but his eternal soul,
as he states in his well-known proposal to Mephistopheles:

Wenn ich zum Augenblicke sage:
Verweile doch! du bist so schön!
Dann magst du mich in Fesseln schlagen, . . .
(1699–1701)

(If the swift moment I entreat:
Tarry a while! you are so fair
Then forge the shackles to my feet, . . .)

Goethe's Faust has made a number of attempts to lift the veil
of mystery that covers the real essence of things before he
makes his wager with Mephistopheles. However, his experi-

ments with the formulas of Nostradamus, the appearance of the
Earth Spirit, and the temptation to suicide by poison have all
ended in inaction. Mephistopheles, the abrasive element who
can stir Faust to active participation in his own development,
appears in human form only after Faust finds in the opening
words of the Gospel of John the active meaning, "Am Anfang
war die Tat! (1237) (In the beginning was the Deed!) From this
point on, Faust is continually in motion, and his life of purposeful activity contributes to his final salvation.[4]

The important place assigned by Faust to action also contains an echo of the Hermotimus dialogue, where near the
conclusion of an attack on the life of philosophy, Lycinus says:

> *Aber ausser dem allen kommt noch etwas in Betrachtung,*
> *woran du noch nie gedacht zu haben scheinst, und das ist:*
> *daß die Tugend im Wirken besteht, nehmlich gerechte,*
> *weise und tapfre Handlungen wirklich zu thun. (III[5],*
> *96)*

(But beyond all this there is something else to consider,
about which you do not appear to have thought, and that
is that virtue lies in action, namely in actually doing just,
wise, and brave deeds.)

As Lycinus leads Hermotimus toward a clearer perception of
the realities of his present position and future goals, the gradual
revision in Hermotimus' thinking has a strong resemblance to
the basic course of Faust's development. In the following

excerpts from the conversation between Hermotimus and Lycinus, the passages of particular import for their relationship to *Faust* are underlined. Early in the dialogue, Lycinus asks:

> *Wie sagt er [der Lehrer] denn daß es droben aussehe und worin Glückseligkeit, in deren Besitz man da gesetzt wird, eigentlich bestehe? Ist es in baarem Gelde, oder in Ruhm und Ansehen, oder in überschwänglichen Wollüsten?* (III[5], 11–12)

> (What does he [the teacher] say then about how it looks up there and what are the elements of the happiness you will possess? Do they consist in money, in fame and recognition, or in volluptuous pleasures?)

To this apparently innocent question, Hermotimus reacts indignantly:

> *Behüte Gott! rede nicht so ungebührlich, lieber Freund! Das alles hat ja mit der Tugend und der Glückseligkeit, die aus ihr entspringt, nichts gemein.* (III[5], 12)

> (God forbid! do not talk so improperly, my friend. All those things have nothing to do with virtue and the happiness that comes from it.)

Lycinus then pursues the matter further:

Was für Güter sagt er denn daß man am Ende der Lauf-
bahn davontragen werde, wenn es diese nicht sind? (III[5],
12)

(What kind of rewards does he say then that one will carry
away at the end of the course, if not these?)

The list that Hermotimus enumerates is totally in the realm of
the ideal, separate from earthly things:

Die Weisheit und die Stärke des Gemüths, und das was in
sich selbst schön und recht ist, und mit der festesten
Ueberzeugung zu wissen was es mit allen Dingen für eine
Beschaffenheit hat. Reichtum und Wollüste, und alles was
unsern thierischen Theil angeht, oder bloß durch den
Wahn der Menschen zu einem Gut gestempelt wird, das
alles hat er unten gelassen, es wie ein beschwerliches
Gewand von sich geworfen, um desto freyer und leichter
emporzusteigen. (III[5], 12)

(Wisdom and strength of character and what is in itself
beautiful and right, and certain knowledge of the nature of
things. He has left behind riches and lusts of the flesh and
everything that concerns our lower nature, as well as those
things that deluded men see as good, discarding them as a
burdensome garment in order to climb more freely and
easily.)

The method Lycinus uses to turn Hermotimus away from his fruitless philosophical studies is first to destroy the credibility of the teacher and then to replace unattainable, dream goals with nobler and more achievable ambitions. During the course of the discussion, Lycinus comforts Hermotimus with the assertion that he is not alone in his delusions:

> *Es geht dir wie den wackern Leutchen, die sich in einem wachenden Traum irgend ein Luftschloß gebaut, oder sich in das berühmte Schlaraffenland hineingeträumt haben, wo alles, was man sich wünscht, gleich auf der Stelle da ist. Wenn ihnen dann, während sie steinreiche Leute sind, <u>einen unterirdischen Schatz gefunden haben, oder die</u> <u>Welt regieren, alles Vollauf haben und in Wohlleben und</u> <u>Vergnügen schwimmen</u>—Dinge, die jener allmächtigen und höchst freygebigen Göttin der Wünsche (die uns nie widerspricht, und wenn einer auch Flügel haben, so groß wie der Koloß zu Rhodus seyn, oder ganze Berge von gediegenem Golde finden wollte) nur Kleinigkeiten sind —wenn, sage ich, während sie solchen Einbildungen nachhängen, der Bediente kommt und fragt, wo er Brod kauffen, oder was er dem Hausherrn, der den Miethzinß fodert, antworten solle? so erboßen sie sich... (III[5], 87)*

(You have the same problem as the good people who have built a castle in the air during a waking dream, or have dreamt themselves into a life of idleness and riches where everything one wishes is immediately provided. If then, while they imagine themselves to be very wealthy, to have dug up buried treasure, or to rule the world, and with abundance to swim in luxury and pleasure—things which are only trifles to that all-powerful and most generous goddess of wishes (who never denies us, even when someone asks for wings as large as the colossus of Rhodes, or wants to find entire mountains of solid gold—if, I say, while they are wrapped in such visions, the servant comes and asks where he should buy bread, or what he should say to the landlord who is asking for the rent, then they get angry . . .)

The positive intention behind Lucian's writing becomes evident in Lycinus' next words:

Aber das sey ferne von dir, mein alter Freund, über mich ungehalten zu werden, daß ich, da du dich mit Schatz graben oder fliegen oder andern solchen ausschweifenden Einbildungen und Hoffnungen unterhieltest, als dein Freund nicht zugeben konnte, daß du dein ganzes Leben in diesem freylich angenehmen Traum, aber doch immer in einem Traum zubringen solltest, sondern dich aufgeweckt habe, und dir rathe dich um nöthigere Dinge zu bekümmern, und wobey du für dein übriges Leben mit dem gemeinen Menschenverstande auslangen könnest. (III[5], 88)

(But do not become angry with me, old friend, because I, as your friend, could not let you entertain yourself with digging treasure, or with flying, or with other such escapist fantasies and hopes, so that you would spend your whole life in this admittedly pleasant dream, but always a dream, but have waked you up and advise you to devote yourself to more necessary things, whereby for the rest of your life you can get along with common sense.)

In place of the imaginary vision of Hermotimus, Lycinus has suggested an earthly incorporation of "Tugend" (virtue) into communal life:

Ich will mir also einbilden, die Tugend sey eine Stadt, deren Einwohner . . . sammt und sonders die seligsten Menschen in der Welt, weise im höchsten Grade, tapfer, gerecht, mäßig, kurz, nur nicht gar Götter sind. Von allen den Lastern und Unthaten, die bey uns so häuffig vorkommen, von gewaltsamen Beleidigungen und Anmaßungen, von rauben, wuchern und betrügen, ist da keine Spur zu sehen: so etwas kommt den Leuten dort gar nicht in den Sinn, sondern sie leben in Frieden und Eintracht wie eine einzige vom Geist der Liebe beseelte Familie beysammen. Und wie sollten sie das nicht, da alles was in andern Städten der ewige Zunder zu Unruhen, Partheyen und Streitigkeiten ist, und weßwegen die Menschen einander nachstellen und auflauern, aus dieser glücklichen Stadt gänzlich verbannt ist? Denn da ist nichts zu sehen, was dem Geiz, der Wollust, oder der Eitelkeit und Ehrsucht Nahrung geben und dadurch Streit unter Ihnen veranlassen könnte; sie haben alle diese Dinge als unnützes unbrauchbares Zeug schon längst aus ihrer Stadt hinausgeschafft, und leben also, wie gesagt, in schönster Ordnung, Gleichheit und Freyheit, und im Genuß alles andern Guten, das heiterste und seligste Leben, daß man sich nur denken kann. (III[5], 31)

(It seems to me that virtue is like a city, whose inhabitants are all the happiest people in the world, outstanding in wisdom, brave, just, moderate, in short almost gods. Among them there is no trace of all the vices and crimes which are so common with us, of violent insults and arrogance, of robbing, profiteering, and cheating. Such matters do not even occur to the people; instead they live in peace and concord like a single family inspired with the spirit of love. And why should they not, since everything which serves in other communities as a constant source of unrest, divisions and conflicts, and causes men to pursue and lie in wait for each other is entirely removed from this happy city. For there is nothing there which could support greed, lust, or vanity and ambition, and so give rise to dissension. They have long ago removed all these things from their city as vain and useless nonsense and therefore live the most cheerful and blessed lives that one can imagine in perfect order, equality and freedom, and in the enjoyment of every other good thing.)

In Faust's development Mephistopheles plays a role somewhat different from that of Lycinus for Hemotimus. Mephistopheles is not the well-intentioned mentor, but a gadfly who
drives Faust along various false trails. Faust, like Hermotimus,
is filled with all-encompassing ambition, and he challenges the
joys offered by Mephistopheles in words that seem to echo
Lycinus' scepticism about Hermotimus' goals. Where Lycinus
asks, "Ist es in baarem Gelde, oder in Ruhm und Ansehen, oder
in überschwenglichen Wollüsten," (Do they consist in money,
in fame and recognition, or in volluptuous pleasures?", Faust
says:

> *Was willst du armer Teufel geben?*
> . . .   *hast*
> *Du rothes Gold, das ohne Rast,*
> *Quecksilber gleich, dir in der Hand zerrinnt,*
> *Ein Spiel, bei dem man nie gewinnt,*
> *Ein Mädchen, das an meiner Brust*
> *Mit Äugeln schon dem Nachbar sich verbindet,*
> *Der Ehre schöne Götterlust,*
> *Die, wie ein Meteor, verschwindet? (1675-1685)*

> (What is, poor devil, in your giving?
> . . .   the red hue
> of gold which, shifting and untrue,
> Quicksilverlike will through the fingers run,
> A game which always stays unwon,
> A girl who at my very breast

Trades winks already with another's eyes,
But honor's fair and godly zest
Which like a meteor flares and dies?)

The reply of Hermotimus to Lycinus' mocking challenges, the assertion that he wishes to know the nature of all things and to leave physical pleasures behind (pp. 47–48 above), again seems to find an echo in lines spoken by Faust:

Du hörest ja, von Freud' ist nicht die Rede.
. . . was der ganzen Menschheit zugetheilt ist,
Will ich in meinem innern Selbst genießen. (1765–1771)

(You heard me, there can be no thought of joy.
. . . what to all of mankind is apportioned
I mean to savor in my own self's core.)

The dreams of finding buried treasure, ruling the world, and living in luxury, with which Lycinus taunts Hermotimus (pp. 49–50 above) find an echo in the scene at the Emperor's court, and particularly in the discussion between the emperor and Mephistopheles about digging up treasure:

Kaiser
Die Töpfe drunten, voll von Goldgewicht,
Zieh deinen Pflug, und ackre sie an's Licht.

Mephistopheles
Nimm Hack' und Spaten, grabe selber,
Die Bauernarbeit macht dich groß,
Und eine Heerde goldner Kälber
Sie reißen sich vom Boden los. (5037–5042)

(Emperor. Those hoards of gold below ground, coin
and cup,
Go pull your plough and pry them up.
Mephistopheles. Seize pick and spade yourself and
battle.
Your peasant labor reaps great spoil.
You'll see a flock of golden cattle
Be wrested from the harrowed soil.)

A second mention of digging up treasure by Lycinus in his
dialogue with Hermotimus is coupled with the magical experience of flying (pp. 50–51 above), and we are reminded that
the departure of Mephistopheles and Faust from Faust's study
is through the air. As they leave, Mephistopheles says:

Wir breiten nur den Mantel aus,
Der soll uns durch die Lüfte tragen. (2065–2066)

(We simply spread my mantle wide,
It shall convey us on our airy courses.)

One of the most striking similarities between Lucian's Hermotimus dialogue and Goethe's Faust drama lies in the description of the ideal city by Lycinus and in Faust's vision of a utopian society. Lycinus' description (pp. 51–52 above) is lengthier and more detailed, but the essential elements of harmonious activity in equality and freedom are common to both. A juxtaposition of Lycinus' summary with Faust's words shows some of the common features:

> *Lycinus. . . . und leben also, wie gesagt, in schönster Ordnung, Gleichheit und Freyheit, und im Genuß alles andern Guten, das heiterste und seligste Leben, daß man sich denken kann. (III[5], 31)*
> *Faust. Eröffne' ich Räume vielen Millionen,*
> *Nicht sicher zwar, doch thätig-frei zu wohnen.*
> *Grün das Gefilde, fruchtbar; Mensch und Heerde*
> *Sogleich behaglich auf der neusten Erde,*
> *Gleich angesiedelt an des Hügels Kraft,*
> *Den aufgewälzt kühn-emsige Völkerschaft.*
> *Im Innern hier ein paradiesisch Land. (11563–11569)*

(Lycinus. . . . and therefore live the most cheerful and blessed life that one can imagine in perfect order, quality and freedom, and in the enjoyment of every other good thing.

Faust. I'd open room to live for millions
Not safely, but in free resilience.

Lush fallow then to man and cattle yields
Swift crops and comforts from the maiden fields,
New homesteads near the trusty buttress-face
Walled by a bold and horny-handed race.
A land of Eden sheltered here within.)

This vision brings Faust to the fateful moment when he speaks the aforedetermined words of contentment.

The conclusion of Faust's long and active life is played in a setting which includes the gates of Hell and the doors of Paradise. With its strongly Christian symbolism, this passage seems a most unlikely vehicle for echoes of a Greek satirist. However, the comparison of a few lines from this part of *Faust* with a passage from Lucian's Hermotimus dialogue indicates that impressions from Lucian's work may have contributed even to these scenes.

During their descent to rescue Faust's soul from the jaws of Hell, the chorus of angels sings:

Wendet zur Klarheit
Euch, liebende Flammen!
Die sich verdammen
Heile die Wahrheit;
Daß sie vom Bösen
Froh sich erlösen,
Um in dem Allverein
Selig zu sein. (11801–11808)

(On to the light,
Loving flames, stream,
May Truth redeem
Self-damned from blight,
That, gladly weaned
From evil and cleaned,
In the All-Unity
Blessed they be.)

As the angels take Faust's immortal part and ascend with it to
Heaven, they sing:

> *Heilige Gluthen!*
> *Wen sie umschweben*
> *Fühlt sich im Leben*
> *Selig mit Guten.*
> *Alle vereinigt*
> *Hebt euch und preis't,*
> *Luft is gereinigt,*
> *Atme der Geist! (11817–11824)*

(Sheltered by glows
All-holiest, mightiest,
Bliss with the righteous,
Living, he knows.
In unison fair
Soar now and quire,

In purified air
May the spirit respire.)

Waiting to receive Faust's soul in Heaven are Gretchen and the
Mater Gloriosa.

Next to this magnificent vision let us set the picture painted
in the words of Hermotimus, where he describes the bliss he
hopes to achieve on his philosophical mountain in terms of
Hercules' sacrifice and entry into the company of the gods:

*Die Weisheit und die Stärke des Gemüths, und das was in
sich selbst schön und recht ist, und mit der festesten
Ueberzeugung zu wissen was es mit allen Dingen für eine
Beschaffenheit hat. Reichthum, und Wollüste, und alles
was unsern thierischen Theil angeht, oder bloß durch den
Wahn der Menschen zu einem Gut gestempelt wird, das
alles hat er unten gelassen, es wie ein beschwerliches
Gewand von sich geworfen, um desto freyer und leichter
emporzusteigen, auf eben dieselbe Weise, wie man uns
sagt, daß Herkules, da er sich auf dem Oeta verbrannte,
ein Gott geworden sey: denn sobald er alles, was er von
seiner Mutter empfangen, abgeworfen hatte, und das Gött-
liche an ihm durchs Feuer gereinigt und von allen
Schlacken abgeschieden war, flog er zu den Göttern auf.
(III[5], 12)*

(Wisdom and strength of spirit and that which is intrinsi-
cally beautiful and right, and the full knowledge of the

nature of all things. He has left behind riches and passions and all those things which pertain to our lower nature or have been labeled good by the error of men, has thrown them off like a burdensome garment in order to climb more freely and easily, just as we have been told that Hercules became a god when he immolated himself on Mount Oeta; for, as soon as he had discarded everything which he had received from his mother and had purified his immortal part through fire and had left behind all dross, he flew up to the gods.)

Because of the visionary quality of the ascension of Faust into Heaven, critics have sought Goethe's inspiration in paintings, notably Lasinio's reproduction of the Campo Santo frescoes at Pisa. There is of course no reason why the scene could not as well have received inspiration from a picture painted with words.

Several aspects of the above story of Hercules' ascension suggest that it was another contributor to the dramatic picture of Faust's salvation. The traditional medieval division of Faust's personality into soul and body is prefigured in the dichotomy of the nature of Hercules, who had one mortal and one divine parent. It was thus necessary for Hercules to be purified by the removal of his maternal inheritance before he could join the gods on Mount Olympus, a purification effected by fire. Similarly, in accordance with Christian theological teachings, Faust is shown at his death in need of purification from his earthly part (body) so that his immortal part (soul) can be transported up to Heaven, and again fire plays a role in this purification. In both visions the purified immortal part of man is seen ascending into a region where known associates are waiting for him. Hercules goes to his father Zeus and the other gods on Olympus; Faust rises to rejoin the waiting Gretchen. Both leave behind earthly aspects of their personalities, and these are consumed by fire.

VI.

The Student Scene and the
New Mephistopheles

THE DIALOGUE BETWEEN Mephistopheles and the Student, which immediately follows the pact scene in *Faust,* was revised before the publication of *Faust, ein Fragment,* by both the omission and addition of lines. Those omitted contain the student's worries about encounters with evil and Mephistopheles' advice to him about girls, gaming and places of residence, omissions that have been attributed to Goethe's loss of youthful interest in such matters, but beyond the autobiographical reasons for leaving these lines out are deeper bases in the reshaping of the whole plan of *Faust* at this time. Central to the changes in the drama lie the new character and role of Mephistopheles.

Goethe's final version of the drama presents a devil figure very different from the embodiment of evil in the old chapbook version of the Faust story. One of the first to notice this difference was Goethe's contemporary, Mme. de Staël, who wrote in 1810:

> The Mephistopheles of Goethe is a civilized Devil. He handles with dexterity that ridicule, so trifling in appearance, which is nevertheless often found to consist with a profundity of malice; he treats all sensibility as silliness or affectation.[1]

Even earlier, in 1797, Mephistopheles' character had been discussed in correspondence between Goethe and Schiller. On July 22 of that year, Goethe wrote to Schiller that he had decided to try to bring together the printed version of *Faust* (i.e. the *Fragment* of 1790) and other materials he had collected or invented in order to carry out a larger plan, "der eigentlich nur eine Idee ist"[2] (which is still only a concept). In this attempt to realize his new idea of the drama, Goethe asked for Schiller's assistance:

> *Nun wünschte ich aber, daß Sie die Güte hätten, die Sache einmal, in schlafloser Nacht, durchzudenken, mir die Forderungen, die Sie an das Ganze machen würden, vorzulegen, und so mir meine eignen Träume, als ein wahrer Prophet, zu erzählen und zu deuten.*[3]

(Now I could wish that you would be so kind as to think over the matter during a sleepless night and to tell me the

demands you would make on the whole work, and thus,
as a true prophet, recount and interpret my dreams to me.)

Only four days later, Schiller sent back a reply in which he
commented on a confusion he sensed in the roles of Mephistopheles and Faust. This overlapping raised the question, Schiller
said, of whether the course of events in the drama should be
taken in jest or in earnest:

> *In Rücksicht auf die Behandlung finde ich die große
> Schwierigkeit, zwischen dem Spaß und dem Ernst glück-
> lich durchzukommen, Verstand und Vernunft scheinen
> mir in diesem Stoff auf Tod und Leben miteinander zu
> ringen. Bei der jetzigen fragmentarischen Gestalt des
> Fausts fühlt man dieses sehr, aber man verweist die Erwar-
> tung auf das entwickelte Ganze. Der Teufel behält durch
> seinen Realismus vor dem Verstand, und der Faust vor
> dem Herzen recht. Zuweilen aber scheinen sie ihre Rollen
> zu tauschen. Eine Schwierigkeit finde ich auch darin, daß
> der Teufel durch seinen Charakter, der realistisch ist,
> seine Existenz, die idealistisch ist, aufhebt. Die Vernunft
> nur kann ihn glauben, und der Verstand nur kann ihn so,
> wie er da ist, gelten lassen und begreifen.*[4]

(In reference to the treatment, I have great difficulty
finding myself between jest and seriousness. It seems to
me that common sense and reason are in a life and death
struggle in this material. One feels this strongly in the

present fragmentary figure of Faust, but postpones judgment until having the fully developed character. The devil is intellectually acceptable by his realism, and Faust appeals to the heart. Sometimes, however, they seem to exchange places. I have difficulty when the devil justifies his existence, which is idealistic, by his character, which is realistic. Only reason can believe him, and only common sense can validate and understand him the way he is.)

Schiller's arguments do not appear to have troubled Goethe at this time, though they may form an early basis for Goethe's later characterization of the play as "diese sehr ernsten Scherze"[5] (these very serious jests). His answer to Schiller's comments was:

Ihre Bemerkungen zu Faust waren mir sehr erfreulich. Sie treffen, wie es natürlich war, mit meinen Vorsätzen und Planen recht gut zusammen, nur daß ich mirs bei dieser barbariscen Komposition bequemer mache und die höchsten mehr zu berühren als zu erfüllen denke. So werden wohl Verstand und Vernunft, wie zwei Klopffechter, sich grimmig herumschlagen, um abends zusammen freundschaftlich auszuruhen. Ich werde sorgen, daß die Teile anmutig und unterhaltend sind und etwas denken lassen.[6]

(Your comments on Faust pleased me very much. They correspond very well, as was natural, with my intentions and plans, only that I am not so worried about this barbaric composition and expect to touch rather than to fulfill the highest expectations. So good sense and reason will probably fight furiously like rowdies, only to rest together afterwards as friends. I shall take care that the parts are charming and entertaining and provide food for thought.)

The Mephistopheles that gradually emerged from Goethe's amalgam of old and new elements is far more worldly and less metaphysical than his chapbook ancestor. He also has a striking resemblance, especially in the student scene, to Lucian's interlocutor Lycinus in the Hermotimus dialogue. A few comparative references illustrate the similarity.

In the remarks of Hermotimus which immediately follow the quoting of the Hippocratic aphorism, he cites his teacher's comparison of the fields of medicine and philosophy:

> *Und doch sagte ers nur von der Arzneykunst, einer Sache,*
> *die denn doch am Ende so schwer nicht zu erlernen ist. Mit*
> *der Philosophie hat es eine ganz andere Bewandtniß: da*
> *kann einer viele Jahre aufgewandt haben, und dennoch*
> *nicht weit gekommen seyn, wenn er die Augen nicht Tag*
> *und Nacht unverwandt und mit stierem Blick auf sie*
> *geheftet hat. (III[5], 5)*

(And yet he said it only of medicine, a field that is on the whole not so difficult to master. Philosophy is another matter; a person can have spent many years and still not have made much progress, unless he has kept his eyes on it day and night with unwavering gaze.)

During the ensuing discussion, Lycinus leads Hermotimus to describe the blessedness he expects to achieve through his studies. In an ecstasy of anticipation, Hermotimus envisions the final goal of his efforts:

> *Die hingegen bis zum Ende ausdauern, gelangen endlich bis auf den Gipfel, und von diesem Augenblick an sind sie den Göttern an Seligkeit gleich, genießen ihr ganzes übriges Leben durch einer wundervollen Ruhe und Heiterkeit. (III[5], 9)*

(Those, on the other hand, who persist to the end finally reach the peak, and from this moment on they are like the gods in happiness and enjoy for the rest of their lives a wonderful peace and joy.)

When Lycinus questions this vision, Hermotimus refers to the authority of his teacher:

> *Lycinus. Aber woher kannst du wissen, es gehe so herrlich und selig da oben zu, daß es sich der Mühe verlohne soviel deßwegen auszustehen, da du doch selbst noch nicht droben gewesen bist?*
> *Hermotimus. Natürlicher Weise glaube ich das auf das Wort meines Lehrers; denn er muß es notwendig wissen, da er schon lange auf dem höchsten Gipfel ist. (III[5], 11)*

(Lycinus. But how can you know that it is so splendid and happy up there that it is worth enduring so much for it, since you have never been there?

Hermotimus. Naturally I believe it on the testimony of my teacher; he must necessarily know because he has been long on the highest point.)

With such innocent sounding questions and simple-minded replies the dialogue continues until Lycinus has shown Hermotimus that his teacher is a charlatan whose words are without firm basis.

As the modern reader watches Lycinus gradually lead Hermotimus into a carefully prepared trap, he is tempted to call the process of argument with anachronistic irony "Mephistophelian," for it is with just that same apparent air of helpfulness that Mephistopheles gives the new student at the university an analysis of the social and intellectual conditions there. Using proper chronology, however, Mephistopheles' words should be called "Lycinian" or "Lucianic" in passages like the following one, added after the composition of the *Urfaust,* but before the publication of the *Fragment*:

> *Ich wünschte nicht euch irre zu führen.*
> *Was diese Wissenschaft betrifft,*
> *Es ist so schwer den falschen Weg zu meiden,*
> *Es liegt in ihr so viel verborgnes Gift,*
> *Und von der Arzenei ist's kaum zu unterscheiden.*
> *Am besten ist's auch hier, wenn ihr nur Einen hört,*
> *Und auf des Meisters Worte schwört.*

Im ganzen—haltet euch am Worte!
Dann geht ihr durch die sichre Pforte
Zum Tempel der Gewißheit ein. (1983–1992)

(I would not give the wrong impression
As it concerns this discipline.
It's all too easy to get sidetracked in,
So much of poison lies concealed within
That's scarce distinguishable from the medicine.
Here too the risk is least when just one voice is heard;
Swear only by the master's word.
In sum—have words to lean upon,
And through that trusty gateway, lexicon,
You pass into the shrine of certainty.)

These words of Mephistopheles directed toward the study of theology carry an echo of Lycinus' indictment of Hermotimus' philosophical studies. Haggling over verbal details is a focus of both Mephistopheles' indirect and Lycinus' direct attack.

Hermotimus supplies the initial point of departure in the report of his study methods:

> *Ich wiederholte die gestrige Lection, und suchte mir, soviel*
> *möglich, alles was er vorgetragen hatte, von Wort zu Wort*
> *wieder gegenwärtig zu machen. (III[5], 5)*

(I was repeating yesterday's lesson and trying as well as I could to recall what he had said word for word.)

The method which Lycinus employs to destroy Hermotimus' study of philosophy is, first, to discredit his teacher as a man, and then to suggest that a philosophical system can only be known by its practical fruits. The only way that a sensible person could remain with one philosophy, he says, is by listening to only one teacher and believing all that he hears from him. After developing this argument over some seventy pages of the Wieland translation, Lycinus gives a final assessment of the danger which lies in too much philosophical hair-splitting.

Aber ausser dem allen kommt noch etwas in Betrachtung,
... daß die Tugend im Wirken besteht; ... ihr hingegen
(und wenn ich ihr *sage, so meyne ich eure bereühmtesten*
Philosophen) laßt das eine geringste Sorge seyn, und
bringt dafür eure meiste Lebenszeit mit streiten über
unverständliche Wörter, Syllogismen und spitzfündigen
Fragen hin, und wer darin dem andern überlegen ist, der
scheint euch der große Mann zu seyn. Dieß ists denn auch,
soviel ich sehen kann, was ihr an eurem alten Professor
bewundert; oder was fändet ihr am Ende mehr an ihm,
als daß er eine große Fertigkeit besitzt, diejenige die sich
mit ihm einlassen durch unerwartete Fragen in Verlegen-
heit zu setzen, und daß er besser als andere weiß, wie man
es machen muß um jemanden durch Sophismen und Sub-
tilitäten dahin zu bringen daß er sich nicht mehr zu helfen
weiß? (III[5], 96)

(But beyond all that there is something else to consider, . . .

and that is that virtue consists in activity. . . . On the other hand, you (and when I say "you" I mean your famous philosophers) have that as your least concern, and instead spend most of your life in conflict about obscure words, syllogisms and subtle questions, and whoever can best the others in these seems to you to be the leader. For it is this, as far as I can see, that you admire about your old professor; or what is it that you ultimately find in him except that he has great skill in embarrassing those who have dealings with him, and that he knows better than others how to reduce someone to helplessness through sophistries and subtleties.)

This long attack by Lycinus is direct, while Mephistopheles takes the more subtle and devious route of irony. Lycinus' lengthy exhortation to Hermotimus is nevertheless consonant in spirit with Mephistopheles' briefer ironic mandate to the student, "Haltet euch am Worte!" (Have words to lean upon!)

As was noted earlier (cf. p. 10 above), John Jay Chapman saw an echo of Lucian in the relationship of Faust with his assistant Wagner. It seems to me, however, that the echo is much stronger in the scene between Mephistopheles and the student. The Goethe who speaks through Faust in his conversations with Wagner is the Storm and Stress poet of the *Urfaust,* impatient with pedestrian scholarship. Faust lacks the intention to satirize academic pedantry common to Lycinus and Mephistopheles. The mocking voice of Mephistopheles as he speaks with the student is, however, reminiscent of the Lucianic Lycinus.

The most important difference between Mephistopheles and Lycinus is, finally, not the difference in their methods but in their ultimate goals. Both mock fields of study, but Lycinus seeks to destroy only that which is hypocritical and socially unproductive. Mephistopheles, on the other hand, purposes to lead Faust to eternal damnation, but is constantly thwarted and forced to produce good results despite his evil intentions. Hence Faust, goaded toward the positive by Mephistopheles' negations, finally achieves a productive social role and attains salvation for his soul.

VII.
Echoes of Lucian's Saturnalia and Epigrams

THE WALPURGISNACHT CELEBRATION on the Blocksberg in *Faust I* is an essentially Germanic revel. In the parallel "Classische Walpurgisnacht" of *Faust II,* surrounded by creatures of the classical world, Mephistopheles himself affirms the Germanic nature of the Blocksberg gathering in this complaint:

> *Auf meinem Harz der harzige Dunst*
> *Hat was von Pech und das hat meine Gunst;*
> *Zunächst der Schwefel. . . . Hier, bei diesen Griechen*
> *Ist von dergleichen kaum die Spur zu riechen.*
> *(7953–7956)*

(Upon my homely Harz, the whiff of resin
Is redolent of pitch, which I find pleasant;

Second to sulphur. . . . Here, among these Greeks,
You hardly sense a trace of suchlike reeks.)

With this satanic authority for the Germanic character of the
Blocksberg scenes, one would scarcely expect to find in them
echoes of a Greek writer.[1] There are, however, some Lucianic
elements in the Walpurgisnacht revels, though they are primarily echoes of concept and technique, rather than of content.
Wieland added a footnote to his translation of the first of
Lucian's "Saturnalische Verhandlungen" (Saturnalian Discussions), in which he commented on the use of these festivals as a
vehicle for a particular type of social criticism:

Unter diesem allgemeinen Titel sind verschiedene sinn-
reiche Aufsätze begriffen, wozu die Saturnalien unserm
Autor Anlaß und Stoff gegeben, und worin er seine seltene
Gabe, scherzend zu philosophiren, und eine eben so feine
als freymüthige Kritik der Sitten seiner Zeit in das leichte
Gewand der Grazien zu kleiden mit allem Witz und aller
Urbanität, die seine besten Werke auszeichnen, spielen
läßt. (II[3], 3)

(Under this general title are included various clever essays,
to which the Saturnalia provided our author occasion and
material, and in which he could give rein to his rare gift for
philosophizing in a jesting manner, and for clothing criticism of the customs of his time, as fine as it was candid, in

the light garment of the graces, with all the wit and all the urbanity that distinguishes his best works.)

Wieland's remarks about Lucian's use of the carnival atmosphere of the Saturnalian revels for criticism of the contemporary scene could be transferred to the Walpurgisnacht scenes of *Faust.* On the Blocksberg, as in the Saturnalian celebration, the unrestrained mythical setting provides a vehicle for the author's comments on living persons and existing problems. However, it is doubtful that Lucian's text without Wieland's footnote would have given the later author any impression he could have used in the Walpurgisnacht.

Lucian's "Saturnalische Verhandlungen" follow a very discursive pattern. They begin with a dialogue between Saturn and his priests, followed by an enumeration of the laws of the Saturnalia, and conclude with a set of Saturnalian letters: "I to Saturn," "Saturn to Me," "Saturn to the Rich Men," and "The Rich Men to Saturn." Lucian thus used the theme of the Saturnalian revels, rather than their enactment, as a basis for his social commentary.

Goethe, on the other hand, employed the revel setting directly for attacks on his critics. During the journey of Mephistopheles and Faust up the Blocksberg, they encounter unflattering representations of persons and groups whom Goethe wished to attack, but this is the extent of the direct similarity to Lucian. If Goethe took anything for *Faust* from Lucian's Saturnalian discussions, it must have been the idea outlined in Wieland's footnote, rather than material from the text itself.

Goethe's use of a moving protagonist who meets strange creatures in a mythical setting has many forerunners in earlier literature. Among these are several narratives by Lucian, in particular the tale of a voyage into space, "A True Story," the report of a visit to the underworld, "A Downward Journey," and the many dialogues of the dead.

The "Walpurgisnachtstraum" (Walpurgis Night Dream) provides a different and more direct example of Lucianic influence. The writing of this scene belongs to the time of the close friendship and literary collaboration between Goethe and Schiller, when they developed theories of literature and stood together against contemporary literary trends.

Their opposition to tendencies current in German literature and their outspoken criticism of the works of others earned them in return the hostility of many of their contemporaries. At the height of the literary controversy, Goethe and Schiller co-authored a little group of aphoristic verses with the apparently harmless, but in reality sharply ironic title "Xenien," or gifts of hospitality. These verses, some written by Goethe, some by Schiller, but all worked over by both, contain observations on life and literature combined with attacks on some of their critics.

Counter-attacks were not slow in coming, and Goethe joined battle again with a second poetical attack, a collection of verses with the title "Oberons und Titanias goldne Hochzeit" (Oberon and Titania's Golden Wedding). When Schiller refused to publish these verses in his *Almanach,* Goethe wrote to him (December 20, 1797):

Oberons goldne Hochzeit haben Sie mit gutem Bedachte weggelassen, sie ist die Zeit über nur um das Doppelte an Versen gewachsen, und ich sollte meinen, im Faust mußte sie am besten ihren Platz finden.[2]

(You have left out "Oberon's Golden Wedding" for good reasons, only meanwhile it has grown to twice as many verses, and I should think it might best find a place in *Faust.*)

The collection of "Xenien" assembled by Goethe and Schiller took its name from the collection entitled "Xenia" which was one of the fourteen volumes of epigrams written by the Roman author Martial. Almost all of Martial's "Xenia" carry the names of the gifts they accompanied. The German "Xenien" are, however, not at all the same type of verses as those in that "book of serviceable, catch-penny couplets to accompany Saturnalian gifts and dinner party souvenirs."[3] They are rather distinguished by personal attacks on contemporary literary figures and by general comments of a literary and philosophical nature. As Paul Carus has evaluated the Goethe-Schiller verses,

The first Xenions were very aggressive, but by and by they became more general and lost their personal character. There are among them many which are lofty and full of deep thought, . . . gems of permanent value, reflecting in a few words flashes of the deepest wisdom.[4]

These German "Xenien" have a close resemblance to the epigrams of Lucian which Wieland included at the end of the last volume of his translation. Wieland had found these brief verses in various sources, "theils in den Ausgaben derselben, theils in den griechischen Anthologien unter seinem Nahmen" (III[6], 454) (part in editions of his works, part in Greek anthologies under his name). Included are verses with titles such as "Auf einen Schlemmer" (to a Glutton), "Das menschliche Leben" (Human Life), "Amor," "Die Schmeichler" (The Flatterers), "Auf eine große Nase" (To a Large Nose), and "Die Macht des Glücks" (The Power of Good Fortune). The last of the group, entitled "Auf Lucians Werke" (To Lucian's Works), begins:

> *Dieß schrieb einst Lucian, der keiner Thorheit schonte,*
> *Wie alt sie war, wie hoch wie thronte,*
> *wie unverschämt sie sich der Weisheit Miene gab! (III[6],*
> *454)*

(This Lucian wrote, one who spared no folly,
No matter how old it was, or how highly enthroned,
nor how shamelessly it wore the manner of wisdom.)

To this description may be compared the verse in the German "Xenien" entitled "Vorsatz" (Purpose):

> *Den Philister verdriesse,*
> *den Schwärmer necke, den Heuchler*

Quäle der fröhliche Vers,
    der nur das Gute verehrt.[5]

(May the merry verse,
    which pays honor only to the good,
Annoy the philistine,
    tease the fanatic, and torment the hypocrite.)

Among the Goethe-Schiller "Xenien" are three epigrams
that refer directly to Lucian and his works. The first, "Peregrinus Proteus," concerns Wieland's narrative of that name written in answer to Lucian's story, "The Passing of Peregrinus:"

Siehest du Wieland, so sag ihm: ich lasse mich
    schönstens bedanken,
Aber er that mir zuviel Ehr' an, ich war doch
    ein Lump.[6]

(If you see Wieland, say to him: I send him my
    best thanks,
But he has done me too much honor; I was still
    a rascal.)

The second, "Lucian von Samosata," reads:

Nun, Freund, bist du versöhnt mit den Philosophen?
    Du hast sie
Oben im Leben, das weiß Jupiter! tüchtig geneckt.[7]

(Well, Friend, are you reconciled with the philosophers?
  You have
Thoroughly plagued them up there in life, Jupiter
  knows!)

The third, which follows immediately, gives Lucian's answer under the title "Geständniß" (Confession):

Rede leiser, mein Freund. Zwar hab ich die Narren
  gezüchtigt,
Aber mit vielem Geschwätz oft auch die Klugen
  geplagt.[8]

(Speak more softly, my friend. Indeed I have disciplined
  fools,
But, in my extended chatter, I have often plagued
  wise men as well.)

The presence of these three verses in the "Xenien" gives further evidence of Goethe's acquaintance with both Lucian's and Wieland's literary work, and of his active concern with Lucian and Wieland at the time of the writing of *Faust.*

In summary, echoes of Lucian can be found in both the Walpurgisnacht and Walpurgisnachtstraum scenes of *Faust,* but they lie not so much in individual images or lines as in creative patterns. From the Lucianic "Saturnalische Verhand-lungen" Goethe may have taken the idea that such a festival could be used as a vehicle for criticism. Also Lucian's epigrams could well have been the models for the aphoristic "Xenien" published by Goethe and Schiller, and subsequently for the verses of the "Walpurgisnachtstraum."

VIII.
Dialogues in Other Worlds

WHEN STUART ATKINS noted that characters and events of the Classical Walpurgisnacht have a Lucianic tone of sophisticated humor, he was referring to the best known of Lucian's literary vehicles, the dialogue (see pages 9–10 above). Lucian employed the dialogue in preference to other literary forms, and his imaginary conversations are often set outside the temporal world. Also in *Faust* the classical underworld is the setting for Lucianic discourse.

The first strange creature met by Mephistopheles in Hades is a Griffin, who takes offense at the use of the word "Greis" (gray, old) to describe him:

Nicht Greisen! Greifen—Niemand hört es gern
Daß man ihn Greis nennt. Jedem Worte klingt

Der Ursprung nach wo es sich her bedingt:
Grau, grämlich, griesgram, greulich, Gräber, grimmig,
Etymologisch gleicherweise stimmig,
Verstimmen uns. (7093-7098)

(Not grizzling! Griffin! No one likes to be
Addressed as grizzled. Words still bear within
Echoing traces of their origin:
Grey, grumbling, gruesome, graveyard, grimly, grunted,
Alike etymologically fronted,
Affront us.)

Mephistopheles counters this objection:

Und doch, nicht abzuschweifen,
Gefällt das Grei im Ehrentitel Greifen. (7098-7099)

(Take this point: while "grizzled" teases,
The "grip" in the proud name of griffin pleases.)

The play with double meanings of words is very much in
keeping with Lucianic wit, and the mythical Griffin also
appears in one of Lucian's dialogues (I[2], 112).

Faust encounters a very different character in Hades, Chiron,
the restless centaur:

Ein Reiter kommt herangetrabt,
Er scheint von Geist und Muth begabt,

Von blendend-weißem Pferd getragen. . . .
Ich irre nicht, ich kenn' ihn schon,
Der Philyra berühmter Sohn!—
Halt, Chiron! halt! Ich habe dir zu sagen . . . *(7325–7330)*

(A horseman cantering ahead
He seems highminded, spirited,
And of a dazzling white his mount . . .
No doubt! I know him from afar,
The famous son of Philyra!
Halt, Chiron! Halt! I would request account . . .)

The chief characteristic of Chiron in Goethe's portrayal is the restlessness of a creature who asserts that "zu kreisen mich erfreut" (7480) (I delight in circulating.).

The restlessness of Chiron is also the subject of one of Lucian's "Dialogues of the Dead." In this dialogue the cynical philosopher Menippus questions Chiron about how he happens to be in Hades with mortals, when he should have been immortal, since he is the son of Saturn and Philyra. Chiron replies that he sought death because he was so bored with the world of the living where he perceived everything as repetitive and lacking variation:

Für mich ist nichts Angenehmes ohne Mannichfaltigkeit;
immer einerley Vergnügen, ist meiner Meinung nach kein
Vergnügen. Also immer zu leben, wie mein Fall war, und
immer dieselbe Sonne zu sehen, und mich immer auf

dieselbe Weise zu nähren, und zu sehen wie die Jahres-
zeiten, und alles was sie mit sich bringen, immer sich
selbst ähnlich in derselben Ordnung, eines hinter dem
andern, in einer ewigen Reyhe folgt, und immer heute
voraus zu wissen daß es morgen eben so seyn wird—das
machte mir endlich lange Weile, und ich wurd' es schlech-
terdings überdrüßig; denn, noch einmal, das Vergnügen
liegt nicht im Genusse der nehmlichen Sache, wie ange-
nehm sie auch seyn mag, sondern entspringt aus der steten
Abwechslung neuer Gegenstände. (I[2], 283–284)

(For me nothing is pleasant without variety; monotonous
enjoyment is in my opinion no enjoyment. Thus to live as
I did, and always to see the same sun, to nourish myself in
the same way, to see how the seasons and all that they
bring occurs similarly in the same order, one after the
other in an eternal progression, and to know that it will be
the same tomorrow—all that finally made me bored and
became too much for me. To repeat, pleasure is not in the
enjoyment of a familiar thing, no matter how pleasant, but
comes from the constant change to new things.)

Chiron is known throughout classical literature as the
teacher of many of the ancient Greek heroes, including Helen's
brothers Castor and Pollux, but his frenetic restlessness, as
recorded above by Lucian, is the characteristic which was most
useful to Goethe, since he wished to have Faust traverse the
entire area of Hades in search of Helen.

After following Faust and Chiron to Manto, the daughter of
Aesculapius, Goethe takes the action back to the upper
Peneios, where a discussion is taking place among a number of
mythological creatures. The actions of Seismos, who is earthquake personified, have revealed gold in cracks of a new-
formed mountain, and the Griffins send their servants, the ants,
to collect it:

Greife
Gold in Blättchen, Gold in Flittern
Durch die Ritzen seh' ich zittern.
Laßt euch solchen Schatz nicht rauben;
Imsen auf! es auszuklauben.
Chor der Ameisen.
Wie ihn die Riesigen
Empor geschoben,
Ihr Zappelfüßigen
Geschwind nach oben!
Behendest aus und ein!
In solchen Ritzen
Ist jedes Bröselein
Werth zu besitzen.
. . . .
Nur mit dem Gold herein!
Den Berg laßt fahren.
Greife. Herein! Herein! Nur Gold zu Hauf,
Wir legen unsre Klauen drauf. (7582-7603)

(Griffin. Gold in slices, gold in slivers
In the cracks and crannies quivers.
Such a hoard, let no one snatch it;
Up, you emmets, pick and catch it!
Chorus of Ants. As giant thew
Labored to lift it,
Scrabble-feet you,
Scurry to sift it!
In and out nimbly!
In every cleaving
There is a crumblet
Worth the retrieving.
. . . .
Hurry in the gold,
Let go the rock.
Griffins. Come up! Come up! bring gold in heaps,
We lay our claws on it for keeps.)

Gold-digging ants may also be found in one of the oddest of
Lucian's dialogues, the conversation of Mycellus with his rooster, who has awakened him out of a dream of riches. In the
course of the dialogue, the rooster claims to be a reincarnation
of the philosopher Pythagoros. His master Mycellus was, the
rooster says, in an earlier incarnation a gold-digging ant:

> *Mycellus. Was war ich denn? Kannst du mirs sagen?*
> *Der Hahn. Eine indianische Ameise von einer gewissen*

Gattung,, deren Geschäfte ist Gold aus der Erde zu graben. (I[1], 126)

(Mycellus. What was I then? Can you tell me?
The Rooster. An Indian ant of a particular sort, whose business is digging Gold out of the earth.)

As Wieland observes in a footnote to this passage, such ants are mentioned by ancient writers, including Strabo, Aelian, Plinius, Mela, and others, but are here brought into the story to emphasize the greed of Mycellus. A similar comment could be made about the ants in *Faust.*

The activity of the gold-digging ants in *Faust* is interrupted by the arrival of a variety of natural and mythological creatures, Dactyls, Pygmies, Herons, and Cranes. The Pygmies supplant the Griffins in directing the work of the Ants and Dactyls and initiate a war against the Herons. The Cranes hear the cries of their allies the Herons and swoop down to annihilate the ranks of their attackers.

In these attempts at colonization and war among partly real and partly imaginary creatures can be found an echo of another situation in one of Lucian's narratives. It is the fantastic tale, deceptively titled *A True Story,* where a battle takes place between the inhabitants of the moon and those of the sun. The king of the moon asks Lucian and his shipmates to help him in an imminent encounter with forces from Phaeton, ruler of the sun, and explains the background of the hostilities in the following terms:

Die Veranlassung dazu war diese. Ich hatte den Entschluß gefaßt, die ärmsten Leute in meinem Reiche als eine Colonie in den Morgenstern zu schicken, der damals noch öde und unbewohnt war. Dieses wollte nun Phaeton aus Mißgunst nicht zugeben, und stellte sich meinen Colonisten mit einem Hauffen Pferdameisen in den Weg. Da wir uns dieses Angriffs nicht versehen hatten und also zur Gegenwehre nicht gefaßt waren, so zogen wir damals den kürzern. Nun aber bin ich entschlossen, noch einen Gang mit ihnen zu thun und die Colonie an Ort und Stelle zu bringen, es koste was es wolle. (II[4], 154–155)

(The cause of it was this. I had made the decision to send the poorest people in my land as colonists to the morning star, which was at that time still empty and uninhabited. This Phaeton malevolently opposed, and blocked the way for my colonists with a troop of ant cavalry. Since we had not anticipated this attack and were therefore not prepared to defend ourselves, we were the losers. Now, however, I am determined to make another attempt with them, and to establish a colony at all costs.)

The ensuing conflict ends first with victory for the forces of the Moon, in part because some of the Sun's allies arrive late or not at all. Among the absent are the "Pferdekraniche" (II[4], 156) (crane cavalry). As in *Faust,* however, the final outcome is changed by the appearance of new forces, in Lucian's tale a battallion of "Wolken-Centauren" (II[4], 160) (cloud centaurs), who rally Phaeton's forces and chase the soldiers of the Moon from the field, in *Faust* the cranes.

In the sequel to this tale, Lucian tells of a stop at the "Insel der Seligen" (Isle of the Blessed), where he encounters the heroes of the Trojan War. They are gathered around a banquet table, where their festivities are accompanied by a series of adjudications by their ruler Rhadamanthus. Among his cases are a controversy between Theseus and Menelaus for possession of Helen (II[2], 193), a reference to the seduction of Helen by Theseus, which is also mentioned in *Faust* (II, lines 8848 ff.). In Lucian's story, Helen is awarded to Menelaus on the grounds that Theseus has other wives. Her openness to seduction is emphasized, however, by her departure from the Isle of the Blessed with a young man described as "ein gewisser Cinyrus, Scinthars Sohn, ein großer schöner junger Bursche" (II[2], 206) (a certain Cinyrus, son of Scinthar, a large, handsome, young fellow). The Helen of Lucian's tale is evidently the same susceptible character as the Helen who was open to seduction by Faust.

Another clear echo of Lucian is the debate of the two philosophers, Thales and Anaxagoras. Much in the way developed by Lucian in his "Dialogues of the Dead," Goethe uses a discussion between two Greek philosophers now residing in Hades to present opposing sides of a current intellectual controversy.

In Goethe's time, discussions about the origin of life on earth centered about two theories, the catastrophic earthquake theory and the theory that man had evolved from beginnings in the sea. Goethe favored the Neptunist, or evolutionary, view, rather than the Plutonist, or earthquake, idea. In *Faust II,* as the two philosophers look at the newly formed mountain, Anaxagoras the Plutonist asserts: "Durch Feuerdunst ist dieser Fels zu Handen" (7855) (That cliff exists by dint of swathes of flame.). In answer, Thales the Neptunist replies, "Im Feuchten ist Lebendiges erstanden" (7856) (It is in moisture, though, that life became.). Homunculus, whose interest is in the creation of life rather than in that of rocks, fastens himself to Thales as the dispute continues.

Thales leads Homunculus to a water festival, which has been called "the boldest and most obscure poetic sequence in the entire *Faust* drama."[1] The descriptions of the Nereids and Tritons, the Sirens, Telchines, sea monsters and dolphins that make up the magnificent procession which accompanies Galatea on her shell, are so vivid that they are thought to be inspired by some painting. Among the pictures which have been mentioned as possible sources for the scene are the Galatea frescoes of Raphael and the Caraccis, of which Goethe had engravings in his personal collection. The scene also recalls Goethe's translation of a description by Philostratus of a picture of Galatea and Cyclops.[2]

There is in Lucian's "Dialogues of the Sea-Gods" a description of a similar pageant, which took place when Zeus abducted Europa. The description is found in a conversation between two winds, Notus and Zephyrus, which Zephyr begins with the words, "Nein, keinen prächtigern Aufzug hab' ich auf dem Meere nie gesehen, seitdem ich wehe!" (I[2], 109) (No, since I have been blowing I have never seen a more splendid procession on the sea!) She goes on to give a full account of the events, and includes the following description:

> *Vor ihnen her flogen eine Menge Liebesgötter, so nah über dem Meere daß ihre Fußspitzen zuweilen am Wasser hinstreiften, mit brennenden Fackeln in der Hand und das Brautlied singend; die Nereiden tauchten aus dem Wasser auf, und ritten, meist halbnackend, auf Delphinen zu beyden Seiten neben her und klatschten vor Freuden in die Hände. Auch die Tritonen, und alle andere Meerbewohnern deren Anblick nichts grausenhaftes hat, tanzten in Reigen um das Mädchen herum; ja Neptun selbst hatte seinen Wagen bestiegen und fuhr, mit Amphitriten an seiner Seite, fröhlich vor ihnen her, um seinem schwimmenden Bruder gleichsam den Weg zu bahnen. Und damit nichts fehle, trugen noch ein paar nervigte Tritonen die Liebesgöttin, auf einer großen Muschel liegend, die alle Arten von Blumen auf die Braut herabstreute. (I[2], 110-111)*

(Before them flew a crowd of cupids, so close to the sea that their toes brushed the water from time to time, carrying burning torches and singing the wedding song. The Nereids emerged from the water and rode, mostly half-naked, on dolphins on both sides and clapped their hands for joy. The Tritons too and all the other inhabitants of the sea who were not frightening to look at, danced

around the maiden in circles. Neptune himself had
mounted his carriage and rode joyfully ahead of them
with Amphitrite at his side as if to clear a path for his
swimming brother. And to omit nothing, a pair of muscular Tritons bore the goddess of love, reclining on a shell,
who scattered all sorts of flowers on the bride.)

To Zephyr's description Wieland wrote the following
footnote:

*Auch dieser Dialog hat keine andere Absicht, als einem
Mahler die Idee zu einer sehr reichen und glänzenden
Composition zu geben, wofern das Lucianische Gemählde
nicht vielmehr, wie ich vermuthe, die Copie irgend eines
damals berühmten Kunstwerkes ist, wodurch Lucian dem
Meister oder dem Besitzer desselben seine Cour machen
wollte. (I[2], 109)*

(This dialogue too has no other purpose than to provide a
painter an idea for a very rich and sparkling composition,
unless it is rather, as I suspect, a description of some work
of art which was famous at that time by which Lucian
wanted to pay his respects to the artist or the owner.)

Returning to *Faust,* we find a scene which is strikingly
similar to the description of the abduction of Europa, as told by
Lucian. In the search for an opportunity to begin his evolution-

ary process, Homunculus is carried over the sea by Proteus, who has assumed the form of a dolphin. Sirens on rocks above the sea describe the action below:

> *Was sehen wir von weiten*
> *Das Wellenreich durchgleiten?*
> *Als wie nach Windes Regel*
> *Anzögen weiße Segel,*
> *So hell sind sie zu schauen,*
> *Verklärte Meeresfrauen. (8160–8165)*

> (What from afar comes gliding,
> The realm of billows riding?
> As if by Aeol's choosing
> Some snowy sails were cruising,
> So bright they are with radiance,
> Transfigured ocean-maidens.)

The observations of the sirens are augmented by those of Thales and Nereus, who watch the progress of Homunculus in the pageant accompanying Nereus' daughter Galatea. Nereus says:

> *Tauben sind es, die begleiten*
> *Meiner Tochter Muschelfahrt,*
> *Wunderflugs besondrer Art,*
> *Angelernt vor alten Zeiten. (8351–8354)*

(Doves they are, my daughter's pages,
Which her roving shell escort,
Flight of rare and wondrous sort,
Learnt from immemorial ages.)

The observers continue to watch the procession, as the partici-
pants in turn sing choral passages describing themselves and
their mission. From the edge of the sea the sirens observe:

Leicht bewegt, in mäßiger Eile,
Um den Wagen, Kreis um Kreis,
Bald verschlungen Zeil' an Zeile
Schlangenartig reihenweis,
Naht euch, rüstige Nereiden,
Derbe Fraun, gefällig wild,
Bringet, zärtliche Doriden,
Galateen, der Mutter Bild:
Ernst, den Göttern gleich zu schauen,
Würdiger Unsterblichkeit,
Doch wie holde Menschenfrauen
Lockender Anmuthigkeit. (8379–8390)

(Softly gliding, gently pacing,
Round the chariot, ring on ring,
File on file now interlacing,
Serpentine meandering,
Buxom Nereids, come near,
Pleasing-wild unto the sight,

Bring, sweet Dorids, Galatea,
Her high mother's image quite.
Grave she seems like godly faces,
Shares immortals' earnest worth,
Yet with all the luring graces
Of the loveliest maid of earth.)

The difficult description of the final dissolution of Homunculus, as he breaks his vial on the shell of Galatea and merges with the sea, is accomplished by Goethe in questions and answers between Nereus and Thales, who can only surmise the action, since it takes place at the limit of visibility. Nereus asks:

Welch neues Geheimniß in Mitte der Schaaren
Will unseren Augen sich offengebahren?
Was flammt um die Muschel, um Galatee's Füße?
Bald lodert es mächtig, bald lieblich, bald süße,
Als wär' es von Pulsen der Liebe gerührt. (8464–8468)

(Amid the attendants, what secret untested
Would now be to wondering eyes manifested?
What glares at the shell, by Galatea's feet,
Now mightily glowing, now gracious, now sweet,
As though by the pulses of love it were stirred?)

To this question Thales gives an answer that is both suggestive to the visual imagination and essential for the plot, since it describes the final, supreme, sacrificial moment of the magical creature Homunculus:

> *Homunculus ist es, von Proteus verführt . . .*
> *Es sind die Symptome des herrischen Sehnens,*
> *Mir ahnet das Ächzen beängsteten Dröhnens;*
> *Es wird sich zerschellen am glänzenden Thron;*
> *Jetzt flammt es, nun blitzt es, ergießet sich schon.*
> *(8469–8473)*

(Homunculus is it, by Proteus ensnared . . .
These symptoms betoken imperious craving,
The clamorous drone of an agonized raving;
He'll crash at her glittering throne and be shattered;
It's flaming, now flashes, already is scattered.)

The picture is completed by the sirens:

> *Welch feuriges Wunder verklärt uns die Wellen,*
> *Die gegen einander sich funkelnd zerschellen?*
> *So leuchtet's und schwanket und hellet hinan:*
> *Die Körper sie glühen auf nächtlicher Bahn,*
> *Und ringsum ist alles vom Feuer umronnen;*
> *So hersche denn Eros der alles begonnen! (8474–8479)*

(What lights us the billows, what fiery wonder
Sets blazing their clashes and sparkling asunder?
It lightens and wavers and brightens the height:

The bodies, they glow on the courses of night,
And ringed is the whole by the luminous wall;
May Eros then reign who engendered it all!)

A comparison of these passages with Lucian's reveals similarities in the procession, though Goethe has, in addition to the water creatures mentioned by Lucian, Sirens Tritons, Telchines, Psylli, and Marsi; their steeds also are not only dolphins, but also hippocampi, sea-bulls, sea-calves and sea-rams. In Lucian's procession, Aphrodite is seen reclining on a large shell; in Goethe's it is Galatea. In both pageants love plays an essential role, personified as Aphrodite in Lucian's description, as Eros in Goethe's.

It is interesting to set beside Lucian's Europa and Goethe's Homunculus pageants, the description by Philostratus of a painting of Galatea:

> The nymph sports on the peaceful sea, driving a team of four dolphins yoked together and working in harmony; and maiden-daughters of Triton, Galatea's servants, guide them, curbing them in if they try to do anything mischievous or contrary to the rein. She holds over her head against the wind a light scarf of sea-purple to provide a shade for herself and a sail for her chariot, and from it a kind of radiance falls upon her forehead and her head, though no whit more charming than the bloom on her cheek; her hair is not tossed by the breeze, for it is so moist that it is proof against the wind. And lo, her right elbow

stands out and her white forearm is bent back, while she rests her fingers on her delicate shoulder, and her arms are gently rounded, and her breasts project, nor yet is beauty lacking in her thigh. Her foot, with the graceful part above the foot, is painted as on the sea, my boy, and it lightly touches the water as if it were the rudder guiding her chariot. Her eyes are wonderful, for they have a kind of distant look that travels as far as the sea extends.[3]

Since Lucian and Philostratus were near contemporaries and both lived for part of their lives in Athens, there is an interesting possibility that Lucian's Europa scene in the "Dialogues of the Sea-Gods" and Philostratus' description of Galatea are based on the same work of art. If Goethe was, in turn, influenced by the description of Philostratus and by the dialogue of Lucian in writing the final Homunculus episode, his two sources might ultimately reflect the same, now lost, picture.[4]

IX.
Perspectives

ON MAY 6, 1827, Goethe remarked to his amanuensis Peter Eckermann that it had never been his artistic practice to work from an abstract principle, but rather from gathered impressions:

Ich empfing in meinem Innern Eindrücke, und zwar Eindrücke sinnlicher, lebensvoller, lieblicher, bunter, hundertfältiger Art, wie eine rege Einbildungskraft es mir darbot; und ich hatte als Poet weiter nichts zu thun, als solche Anschauungen und Eindrücke in mir künstlerisch zu runden und auszubilden und durch eine lebendige Darstellung so zum Vorschein zu bringen, daß andere dieselbigen Eindrücke erhielten, wenn sie mein Dargestelltes hörten oder lasen.[1]

103

(I received in my mind impressions, and those of a sensuous, animated, charming, varied, hundred-fold kind—just
as a lively imagination presented them; and I had, as a
poet, nothing more to do than to round off and elaborate
artistically such views and impressions, and by means of a
lively representation so to bring them forward that others
might receive the same impression in hearing or reading
my representation of them.)[2]

In the foregoing chapters we have given evidence that some
of the impressions which Goethe wove into the rich fabric of
the Faust drama were taken from the works of the second
century Greek satirist Lucian, as translated by Christoph Martin Wieland. The question may now be asked: What is the
significance of such echoes of Lucian for our understanding of
Faust? A second question may be added: Does the adaptation
of material from this particular Greek author add to or change
the traditional perception of the influences of the literature of
ancient Greece on German Classicism?

Twice in his last year Goethe referred to the second part of
Faust as "serious jests." The first time was on November 24,
1831, in a letter to Sulpiz Boisserée, where he apologized for
sealing the manuscript of the second part of the Faust drama
and thus postponing the pleasure his friends might find in
"diesen ernst gemeinten Scherzen"[3] (these seriously intended
jests). Again, on March 17, 1832, in the last letter of Goethe
which has been preserved, he mentioned the sealed manuscript

to Wilhelm von Humboldt and referred to it as "diese sehr ernsten Scherze"[4] (these very serious jests).

On the whole, however, Goethe scholarship has regarded *Faust* as "a work of the highest poetic stature and the deepest seriousness,"[5] i.e. not "jest" in any real sense. The apparent paradox in the oxymoron "serious jests" must then be resolved, and this can happen only in a context where poetry, serious purpose, and jest are not mutually exclusive.

The tradition of serious humor begins in western literature with Aristophanes, whose works contain both passages of lyric beauty and situations of broad comedy, but whose underlying purpose is social and political reform. Aristophanes is recognized today as a dramatist who was the equal of the great writers of tragedy, but even by his contemporaries he was often misunderstood. His dramas appear, from the fragmentary evidence still extant, to have stood alone in his times between bawdy buffoonery on the one hand and light situation comedy on the other. Many then and later saw only these popular aspects, which are undeniably present in his works, but give only a partial understanding of his art. An essential feature of the plays of Aristophanes is their verbal virtuosity, a clever witty humor replete with puns and ironic plays on words.[6]

Six centuries later Lucian, who greatly admired Aristophanes, adopted the Aristophanic spirit for his satirical dialogues, which again frequently used humor as a tool for achieving serious goals. Thus serious humor became in western literature a subdivision of satire, a genre which is often but not always amusing. Lucian, like Aristophanes, has been frequently misunderstood (cf. pp. 19–20 above), and the serious purpose of his satirical humor overlooked.

In the preceding chapters, it has been seen that most of the echoes of Lucian in Goethe's *Faust* center about the demonic Mephistopheles. Goethe's version of this satanic figure is far more complex than his medieval ancestor, and with his unhappy admission that he "stets das Böse will und stets das Gute schafft" (1335) (would do ever evil, and does ever good), the Goethean Mephistopheles embodies in his basic disposition the paradoxical contrast essential to satire.[7]

There are two curious gaps in the scholarly treatment of Mephistopheles. The first concerns his origins. As recently as 1951 and 1967, Harold Jantz and Valters Nollendorfs commented on the absence of genealogical studies of this interesting character.[8] Goethe himself mentioned his friend Merck as a model, and traits of other friends, in particular Behrisch and Herder, have been noted.[9] Jantz suggests that the Italian Renaissance poet Pulci may have more than an accidental similarity to Faust's companion.[10] Beyond these specific suggestions, however, there is a paucity of more general research into Mephistopheles' background.

The studies of Mephistopheles which have been made[11] show another surprising omission. They treat Goethe's Mephistopheles as a single fixed character and do not distinguish between the Mephistopheles of the *Urfaust* and that of later versions, though these are not at all the same. The earlier Mephistopheles is a true descendant of his medieval chapbook ancestor, a devil whose primary business is the gathering in of sinful human souls. This purpose is conspicuously present as he leads Faust into actions which will bring with them a burden of guilt.

The Mephistopheles of the *Fragment* of 1790, of *Faust I* of 1808, and particularly of the posthumously published *Faust II*, is a very different character from that sketched in the *Urfaust*. As was noted in Chapter VI, Schiller commented in 1797 on the confusion between the satanic emissary, who was the historic Mephistopheles, and the worldly character that was already emerging in the *Fragment*. One might draw the analogy that if an acquaintance in the real world were to undergo a personality change as profound as that exhibited by Mephistopheles between the *Urfaust* and the *Fragment*, we should seek a cause in surrounding events. For a fictional character, the causes of change must be sought in the influences encountered by his author.

The Mephistopheles of the *Urfaust* is an only slightly modernized version of the sixteenth century chapbook devil; his orientation is metaphysical, his evil purposes appropriately demonic. The later Mephistopheles is, on the other hand, a classical type, Greek in the spirit of Aristophanes. He is worldly, sophisticated, witty, and sometimes bawdy. He brings to the drama comic relief, both in intentionally humorous actions and comments, and in unintentional frustrations of his evil designs. When we investigate the influences that could have produced such a striking change in Goethe's concept of the Mephistophelian personality, the publication of Wieland's translation of Lucian in 1788 and 1789 assumes special significance. The many echoes of Lucianic elements enumerated in the earlier chapters of this study bear out this premise.

It is generally accepted that Goethe intended from the very first to let his hero Faust be saved. As Valters Nollendorfs has observed, however, this salvation was impossible without a fundamental change in his tempter.[12] The alterations which Goethe introduced turned Mephistopheles into an essentially classical character. They also brought into a major work of German literature an inheritance from Greek culture that has generally been overlooked.

Greek influence on German literature is traditionally divided according to Nietzsche's dichotomy into "Apollonian" and "Dionysian" or, as he further defined the terms, "Bild" (picture) and "Musik" (music).[13] This division omits, however, another important aspect of the Greek literary scene, Aristophanic comedy, with its exploitation of verbal effects. The amalgamation of seriousness and humor, which Schiller noted in the early revisions of *Faust,* and Goethe reiterated in the phrase "ernste Scherze" as he concluded the work, is essentially an inheritance from Aristophanes. The Mephistopheles of the revised Auerbach's Cellar scene, of the Walpurgisnacht revels, and of the bemused encounters with the classical underworld would have been entirely at home on the Aristophanic stage. Even the discussions in the Prologue in Heaven and in the pact scene have in their particular ironic tone a classical echo.

Another less familiar Aristophanic characteristic of Mephistopheles is his ability to assume a purely lyric mode. One such occasion occurs in *Faust II,* where Mephistopheles, disguised as Phorkyas, speaks lines beginning "Höret allerliebste Klänge" (9679 ff.) (Listen, strings in sweet collusion!) which are reminiscent of the choral passage in Aristophanes *Clouds* that commences "Rise and soar Eternal Clouds!"[14]

In literary as in human inheritance, resemblances may be found to a distant ancestor, while specific traits are taken from a more recent progenitor. In this way aspects of the character of Mephistopheles and of events surrounding him can be truly Aristophanic, while specific elements come more directly from Lucian.

The employment of serious humor in *Faust,* centered as it is about the later Goethean interpretation of Mephistopheles, thus brings to the classical period of German literature the missing element of the inheritance from Greece. To the already acknowledged visual "Bild" and emotional "Musik" is now added the witty "Wort." The echoes of Lucian in *Faust* carry a re-echoing of the Aristophanic, and so complete the basis on which the age of Goethe is called "German Classicism," and is correctly seen as a modern European revival of the essential aspects of the culture of classical antiquity.

Notes

Prologue

1. Lucian von Samosata, *Sämtliche Werke,* translated by Christoph Martin Wieland (Darmstadt: Wissenschaftliche Buchgesellschaft, 1971), (III[5], 236). This is a photographic copy of the original edition and preserves the original spelling and punctuation. Subsequent references to this work will be given parenthetically within the text (volume [part], page).

2. *Goethes Werke,* Sophien-Ausgabe (Weimar: Hermann Böhlau, 1889), v. 14–15. All references to *Faust* will be given by line numbers parenthetically within the text.

3. Johann Wolfgang von Goethe, *Faust, A Tragedy,* translated by Walter Arndt (New York: W. W. Norton & Company, 1976). Translations of passages from *Faust* will be taken from this edition.

I. Coincidence of Time and Place

1. *Goethes Werke,* Sophien-Ausgabe, v. 26, 199. The translation of this and other German passages (except those from *Faust*) is mine, unless otherwise noted.
2. Humphrey Trevelyan, *Goethe and the Greeks* (Cambridge: Cambridge University Press, 1942), 60 ff.
3. Friedrich Sengle, *Wieland* (Stuttgart: J. B. Metzlersche Verlagsbuchhandlung, 1949), 460–461.
4. Elise von Keudell, *Goethe als Benutzer der Weimarer Bibliothek* (Weimar: Hermann Böhlaus Nachfolger, 1931), 125, 271.
5. *Goethes Werke,* Sophien-Ausgabe, v. 21, 41.
6. See James Boyd, *Notes to Goethe's Poems,* II (1786-1832), (Oxford: Basil Blackwell, 1949), 98–103, for a summary of the source research on "Der Zauberlehrling."
7. *Goethes Werke,* Sophien-Ausgabe, v. 26, 331.
8. Ernst Grumach, *Goethe und die Antike* (Berlin: Walter de Gruyter & Co., 1949), 314–315.
9. Stuart Atkins, *Goethe's Faust, A Literary Analysis* (Cambridge: Harvard University Press, 1958), 171.
10. Atkins, 221.
11. John Jay Chapman, *Lucian, Plato and Greek Morals* (Boston: Houghton Mifflin, 1931), 82.
12. Francis G. Allison, *Lucian, Satirist and Artist* (Boston: Marshall Jones Company, 1926), 177.
13. *Goethes Briefe,* Hamburger-Ausgabe (Hamburg: Christian Wegner Verlag, 1964), II, 280.
14. See Note 5 above.

II. Wieland's Translation of Lucian

1. Julius Steinberger, *Lucians Einfluss auf Wieland* (Göttingen: W. Fr. Kaestner, 1902, 4–11. See also P. Geigenmüller, "Lucian und Wieland," *Neue Jahrbücher für Wissenschaft und Jugendbildung,* 3 [1927]), 35 ff., for other aspects of Wieland's interest in Lucian.

2. Steinberger, 4.

3. Christoph Martin Wieland, *Werke* (München: Carl Hanser Verlag, 1965), III, 350–358.

4. See Allinson, *op. cit.,* 175–176; also Charlotte Craig, *Christoph Martin Wieland As the Originator of the Modern Travesty in German Literature* (Chapel Hill: University of North Carolina Press, 1970), 3.

5. "Zum Andenken des edlen Dichters, Bruders und Freundes, Wieland," *Goethes Werke,* ed. Karl Heinemann (Leipzig und Wien: Bibliographisches Institut, 1891), 331.

6. Wieland, *Werke,* IV, 76–77.

7. Giovanni Boccaccio, *The Decameron,* translated by Richard Aldington (New York: Dell, 1970), 637.

8. See Note 1 under Prologue above.

9. John Higginbotham, *Greek and Latin Literature, A Comparative Study* (London: Methuen, 1969), 225.

III. Goethe's Faust Before and After 1788

1. Calvin Thomas, in his Introduction to *Goethe's Faust—Part I* (Boston: D. C. Heath & Co., 1904), xxxix ff., has an interesting discussion of this matter.

2. Letter to Schiller, April 3, 1801, *Goethes Briefe,* II, 416.

Emil Staiger, *Goethe* (Zürich und Freiburg: Atlantis Verlag, 1956), II, 334–356, discusses some of the problems posed by the filling of this lacuna.

IV.   The Hermotimus Dialogue
1. See Note 1 under Prologue above.
2. See Notes 2 and 3 under Prologue above.

V.   The Pact
1. Herman Meyer, *Diese sehr ernsten Scherze* (Heidelberg: Lothar Stiehm Verlag, 1970), especially 38–39.
2. Harold Jantz, *The Form of Faust* (Baltimore: The Johns Hopkins University Press, 1978), 135 ff.
3. The translation into English of Hermotimus' assertion in the Loeb Classical Library edition, "For me even a moment is enough," is closer to *Faust,* but not as close to the original Greek as Wieland's version. *Lucian,* with an English Translation by K. Kilburn (Cambridge: Harvard University Press, 1959), VI, 270–271.
4. An amusing summary of the critical opinions of Faust's salvation can be found in Meyer, *op. cit.,* 36–37.

VI.   The Student Scene and the New Mephistopheles
1. Mme. de Staël, *On Germany* (London: John Murray, 1814), II, 181–185.
2. *Der Briefwechsel zwischen Schiller und Goethe* (Frankfurt am Main: Insel Verlag, 1966), 404.
3. *Ibid.*

4. *Briefwechsel zwischen Schiller und Goethe,* 408.
5. *Goethes Briefe,* IV, 481.
6. *Briefwechsel zwischen Schiller und Goethe,* 409.

VII. Echoes of Lucian's Saturnalia and Epigrams

1. For a study of the sources of the Walpurgisnacht material, see Georg Witkowski, *Die Walpurgisnacht* (Leipzig: F. W. von Biedermann, 1894).
2. *Briefwechsel zwischen Schiller und Goethe,* 516.
3. Paul Nixon, *Martial and the Modern Epigram* (New York: Longmans, Green and Co., 1927), 38.
4. Paul Carus, *Goethe and Schiller's Xenions* (Chicago and London: The Open Court Publishing Company, 1915), 8–11.

VIII. Dialogues in Other Worlds

1. Cyrus Hamlin, ed. *Faust* by Johann Wolfgang von Goethe (New York: W. W. Norton & Company, 1976), 333.
2. *Goethes Werke,* ed. Heinemann, XXIII, 257–258.
3. Philostratus, *Imagines*; Calistratus, *Descriptions,* translated by Arthur Fairbanks (London: William Heinemann, 1931), 215. This is an English translation of the same passage translated by Goethe. See Note 2 above.
4. Another possible source for Goethe's vision is a sketch made by Dürer on the basis of Lucian's description of the seduction of Europa. See Paul Schultze, *Lucian in der Literatur und Kunst der Renaissance* (Dessau: Hofbuchdruckerei C. Dünnhaupt, 1906), 17.

IX. Perspectives

1. Johann Peter Eckermann, *Gespräche mit Goethe in den letzen Jahren seines Lebens* (Leipzig: F. A. Brockhaus, 1868), III, 118–119.

2. Translation by John Oxenford, in Hamlin edition of *Faust*. See Note VIII, 1 above.

3. *Goethes Briefe,* IV, 461.

4. *Goethes Briefe,* IV, 481.

5. Herman Meyer, *Diese sehr ernsten Scherze,* 7, translated by Dolores Signori and Cyrus Hamlin in Hamlin edition of *Faust,* 603.

6. Otto Seel, *Aristophanes oder Versuch über Komödie* (Stuttgart: Ernst Klett Verlag, 1960), 18. Further relevant evaluations are found in Gilbert Murray, *Aristophanes* (New York: Oxford University Press, 1933); Cedric H. Whitman, *Aristophanes and the Comic Hero* (Cambridge: Harvard University Press, 1964); and K. J. Dover, *Aristophanic Comedy* (Berkeley and Los Angeles: University of California Press, 1972). Edith Hamilton, *The Greek Way* (New York: W. W. Norton & Company, 1942), 137–157, finds an amusing but apt resemblance between the operettas of Gilbert and Sullivan and the dramas of Aristophanes.

7. Cf. Alvin B. Kernan, *Modern Satire* (New York: Harcourt, Brace and World, 1962), especially 167–177.

8. Harold Jantz, *Goethe's Faust As a Renaissance Man* (Princeton: Princeton University Press, 1951), 23; Valters Nollendorfs, *Der Streit um den Urfaust* (The Hague and Paris: Mouton & Co., 1967), 186.

9. Calvin Thomas, *op. cit.,* lxxvi-lxxviii.

10. Harold Jantz, *Goethe's Faust As a Renaissance Man,* 23 ff.

11. Ada M. Klett, *Die Streit am Faust II seit 1900* (Jena: Verlag der Frommanschen Buchhandlung [Walter Biedermann], 1939), 109–111.

12. Valters Nollendorfs, *op. cit.,* 186.

13. Friedrich Nietzsche, "Die Geburt der Tragödie aus dem Geiste der Musik," *Werke,* Bd. 1 (Leipzig: Alfred Kröner Verlag, 1917), 93.

14. Translation by William Arrowsmith in Aristophanes, *Three Comedies* (Ann Arbor: University of Michigan Press, 1969), 28.

Index